HOME TRADE NAVIGATION GUIDE
FOR HOME TRADE, FISHING AND COASTAL YACHTMASTER EXAMINATIONS

HOME TRADE
NAVIGATION GUIDE

FOR HOME TRADE, FISHING AND COASTAL
YACHTMASTER EXAMINATIONS

BY

CAPTAIN WILLIAM MACFARLANE, F.R.A.S.

Author of
"Nautical Knowledge for Fishermen's Examinations."

GLASGOW
BROWN, SON & FERGUSON, Ltd., Nautical Publishers
52 Darnley Street

First Edition	–	–	1941
Second Edition	–	–	1952
Third Edition	–	–	1956
Fourth Edition	–	–	1963

Printed and Made in Great Britain

© 1963. BROWN, SON & FERGUSON, LTD., GLASGOW, S.1

PREFACE TO FOURTH EDITION

NEW syllabuses in the examination for all grades of Fishing Certificates; the adoption in examination rooms of the 1958 edition of the *Abridged Nautical Almanac*; a new lay-out in the *Admiralty Tide Tables*; and the re-introduction of examinations for the Coastal Yachtmaster Certificate have combined to make necessary a new and somewhat enlarged edition of this book.

Much of the subject matter has been rearranged to make step-by-step progress more smooth and easy for students, and many new exercises have been included to familiarise users with each individual problem they can expect to encounter not only in the examination rooms, but also at sea.

While the syllabuses do not specifically call for a knowledge of the Marcq St. Hilaire (Intercept) method of position-finding, this method has been included for the benefit of students who prefer to use it.

Permission to include relevant extracts from the 1958 *Abridged Nautical Almanac* has been received from the Controller of H.M. Stationery Office, and permission has also been obtained from the Curator of Liverpool Observatory and Tidal Institute to reproduce an extract from Part I of the 1959 *Admiralty Tide Tables*. I wish to acknowledge my indebtedness to both sources for the courtesy and help I have received. I wish also to thank Messrs. Brown, Son & Ferguson, Ltd., for their continued permission to use extracts from their publication, *Burdwood's Completed Azimuth Tables*.

Examination papers at the end of the book include papers for Home Trade and Fishing candidates, and also for candidates for Coastal Yachtmasters' Certificates.

The following Table enumerates the chapters in which will be found the requirements for each grade of Certificate.

HOME TRADE

MATE

Part   I. All.

Part II. All. (Chapter 7 to elementary Day's Work only.)

Part III.   Chapters 16 to first part of 23.

Part IV.   Chapter 34, so far as it alludes to the Sun.

MASTER

In addition to the requirements for MATE, Home Trade,

Part IV.   Chapters 29 to 35.

Part   V.   Chapter 38. (Lattice Charts.)

v

FISHING.

SECOND HAND (LIMITED)

Part   I.   Chapters 1 and 2.
Part   II.   Chapters 5 to 14, excluding Chaps. 7 and 13.
Part III.   Chapters 16 to 21, excluding Chapter 18.
Part   V.   Chapter 37.

SECOND HAND (SPECIAL)

Part   I.   Chapters 1 and 2.
Part   II.   Chapters 5 to 12, excluding Chapter 7.
Part III.   Chapters 16, 17, 19 (last part), 20 (first part) and 21.

SECOND HAND (FULL).

Part   I.   All.
Part   II.   All except Chapter 15.
Part III.   Chapters 16 to 25, excluding Chapter 18. (Chapters 26, 27, 28 are optional).
Part   V.   Chapter 37.

SKIPPER (LIMITED)

In addition to the requirements for Second Hand Limited.
Part   I.   All.
Part   II.   Chapter 7, to Day's Work.
Part III.   Chapters 16 to 25, excluding Chapter 18.
Part   V.   Chapters 37 and 38.

SKIPPER (FULL)

In addition to the requirements for Second Hand Full.
Part   II.   Chapters 13 to 15.
Part   IV.   Chapters 29 to 33, and Chapter 35. (Chapter 36 optional)
Part   V.   Chapter 38.

COASTAL YACHTMASTER.

Part   I.   As necessary for revision.
Part   II.   All except Chapter 7.
Part III.   Chapters 16 to 20.
Part   V.   Chapter 38 so far as it relates to Consol stations.

I shall be glad if any errors, clerical or otherwise, which may inadvertently have been overlooked, are brought to the notice of the publishers.

W. M. F. MACFARLANE.

CONTENTS

PART I.

CONTENTS

CONTENTS

x CONTENTS

MINISTRY OF TRANSPORT EXAMINATION REGULATIONS

EXAMINATION IN PRACTICAL NAVIGATION
MATE (HOME TRADE).

Qualifications.—A candidate must be not less than twenty years of age, and have served four years at sea in a deck capacity.

SYLLABUS.

Paper 1. (Written).　　**Chartwork and Pilotage.**　　　　(2 hours.)

(a) Given the Variation and a Table of Deviations to convert True Courses into Magnetic and Compass Courses and vice versa. To find the compass course and distance between two positions. The effect of current on speed. Allowance for leeway. To find the compass course to steer allowing for a current. Given compass course steered, the speed of the ship and the direction and rate of the current, to find the true course made good.

(b) To fix the ship's position on a chart by simultaneous cross bearings, applying the necessary corrections. To fix the ship's position on a chart by bearing and range or by wireless cross bearings. To fix the ship's position by bearings of one or more objects with the run between, allowing for a current and to find the distance at which the ship will pass a given point. The construction of a line of soundings. The use of a single position line approaching the coast.

(c) The use of clearing marks and horizontal and vertical danger angles.

(d) To find the time and height of high and low water at a Standard Port (Admiralty Tide Tables). The use of tables or diagram to find the height of tide at any given time and thence the approximate correction to soundings or to the charted heights of shore objects.

(e) Candidates will be examined orally on the information given on a chart or plan, particularly about buoys, lights, depths and nature of bottom, contour lines, tides and tidal streams. Recognition of the coast. The intelligent use of Sailing Directions. Chart correction.

Paper 2. (Written).　　**Practical Navigation.**　　　　(3 hours).

(a) To find the True Bearing of the Sun and the deviation of the compass for the direction of the ship's head.

(b) To find the latitude by meridian altitude of the Sun.

(c) From an observation of the Sun near the meridian to find the position line and the latitude through which it passes corresponding to a given longitude.

(d) To determine the position line and a position through which it passes from an observation of the Sun out of the meridian.

MASTER (HOME TRADE).

Qualifications.—A candidate must be not less than twenty-three years of age, and have served five years at sea of which:—

(a) One year must have been in a capacity not lower than that of First Mate of a home trade or coasting vessel, whilst holding a Mate's Certificate for Home Trade passenger ships, or a Second Mate's certificate for foreign-going vessels;

(b) 1½ years must have been in a capacity not lower than Second Mate of a home trade or coasting vessel in charge of a watch, whilst holding a Mate's certificate for home trade passenger ships, or a Second Mate's certificate for foreign-going vessels;

(c)   1½ years must have been in a capacity not lower than Third Mate in charge of a watch on a foreign-going vessel whilst holding a Mate's certificate for home trade passenger ships, or a Second Mate's certificate for foreign-going ships; or

(d)   2½ years must have been in a capacity not lower than Third Mate in charge of a watch in a home trade or coasting ship whilst holding a Mate's certificate for home trade passenger ships or a Second Mate's certificate for foreign-going ships.

SYLLABUS.

Paper 1.   (Written).   **Chartwork and Pilotage.**   (2 hours).

In addition to the syllabus for Mate (home trade) questions on the following may be asked either in the written or oral parts of this paper.

(a)   Distance of sighting lights.   Distance of a point of land of known height.

(b)   The use of bearings obtained by ship's Wireless Direction Finder and bearings given from a Shore Station.   The use of Wireless Beacons.

(c)   Candidates will be examined orally on the selection of suitable points or bearings, approaching an anchorage and entering narrow waters.   The reliability of charts.   The use of Lattice Charts.

Paper 2.   (Written).   **Practical Navigation.**   (2 hours).

This paper may include questions in the syllabus for Mate (home trade).

(a)   To find the true bearing of any heavenly body and the deviation for the direction of the ship's head.

(b)   To find the approximate time (to the nearest minute) of the meridian passage of a star.   To find the latitude by meridian altitude of a star.   Latitude by an observation of Polaris.

(c)   From an observation of a star near the meridian to find the position line and the latitude through which it passes corresponding to a given longitude.

(d)   To determine the position line and a position through which it passes from an observation of a star out of the meridian.

(e)   Recognition of stars of the 1st Magnitude by reference to the principal constellations.

FISHING CERTIFICATES.
SECOND HAND (LIMITED).

Qualifications.—A Candidate must

(a)   be not less than 19 years of age; and either

(b)   have served four years at sea (in a deck capacity) of which at least two years must have been on board deep sea fishing boats; or

(c)   have served four years as an indentured apprentice to the sea fishing industry, of which at least two-thirds must have been actually served at sea fishing, provided that his indentures are endorsed by the owner to the effect that he has performed his service faithfully during the time that he remained an apprentice.

SYLLABUS.
Chartwork and Pilotage.

(1)   To use a chart or plan and understand the meaning of all the marks, signs and abbreviations thereon.   (Candidates will be examined orally on this part).

(2)   To find the compass course (or courses) and distance (or distances) between two positions on the chart.

(3)   To find the ship's position by cross bearings of two objects, and the set and drift experienced.

(4)   To find the ship's position from two bearings of the same object, the course and distance run between taking the bearings being given, making

due allowance for a given tide or current, and the distance of the ship from any given position at the time of taking the second bearing.

(5) To find on a chart or plan the course to steer by compass in order to counteract the effect of a given tide or current and find the distance the vessel will make good towards a given position in a given time.

Practical Navigation.

(1) To find the latitude by meridian altitude of the sun.

(2) To find the deviation of the compass by time azimuth of the sun by means of tables, diagrams or any other method the candidate may select.

(3) To answer elementary questions in nautical astronomy dealing with solar meridional observations. Definitions of latitude, longitude, mean and apparent time, equation of time, dip and refraction, semi-diameter, true altitude, zenith distance, declination and polar distance.

SECOND HAND (FULL).

Qualifications.—Same as for Second Hand (Limited).

SYLLABUS.

The syllabus for a 'Full' certificate is always to be regarded as including the syllabus for a 'Limited' certificate of the same grade, and the 'Full' certificate of a lower grade (if any).

Chartwork and Pilotage.

(1) To use a chart or plan and understand the meaning of all the marks, signs and abbreviations thereon. (Candidates will be examined orally on this part.)

(2) To find the compass course (or courses) and distance (or distances) between two points on the chart.

(3) To find the ship's position from two bearings of the same object, the course and distance run between taking the bearings being given, making due allowance for a given tide or current, and to find the distance of the ship from any given position at the time of taking the second bearing.

(4) To find on a chart or plan the course to steer by compass in order to counteract the effect of a given tide or current and find the distance the ship will make good towards a given position in a given time.

(5) To fix the ship's position by horizontal sextant angles.

(6) To obtain the compass error by transit bearings; selection of suitable objects.

(7) To find the ship's position by cross bearings of two objects and the set and drift experienced.

Practical Navigation I.

(1) By the use of the Traverse Table to obtain the D.R. position of a ship at any time, given compass courses, variation and deviation and the run recorded by log or calculated by estimated speed and time. The candidate may be asked to allow for the effects of current and winds. A departure position may be given as a bearing and distance from a point of land.

(2) To find the deviation of the compass by time azimuth of the sun by means of tables, diagrams or any other method the candidate may select.

Practical Navigation II.

(1) To find the latitude by an observation of the sun on the meridian.

(2) From an observation of the sun out of the meridian to find the direction of the position line and a position through which it passes.

(3) To find the ship's position at the time of the second observation by the use of position lines obtained from two different observations with a run between. The two observations may both be of the sun or a solar observation together with a terrestrial position line.

Principles of Navigation.

(1) To understand the terms: Geographical position of the sun, Greenwich Hour Angle, local hour angle, celestial meridian and prime vertical, azimuth.

(2) To understand the use of position lines both celestial and terrestrial.

(3) To obtain the course and distance from one position to another by means of Plane and Mercator Sailing.

(4) To obtain the clock or chronometer time of the sun's meridian passage.

(5) Use of a pelorus to obtain compass bearings and to put the ship on a pre-determined true course from a known position.

(6) To draw a figure showing the celestial sphere on the plane of either the observer's meridian or the rational horizon naming some required parts.

SECOND HAND (SPECIAL).

Qualifications.—A candidate must

(a)   be not less than 21 years of age;

(b)   have served four years at sea (in a deck capacity) of which at least two years must have been served on board fishing vessels.

> (NOTE: The *total* period of service required by all Second Hands—but not the minimum period required to be served in fishing boats—may be reduced, subject to a maximum reduction of twelve months, by satisfactory attendance at a recognised training establishment).

SYLLABUS.
Navigation.

(1) To use an Admiralty chart or plan and have a sound knowledge of the information to be derived from it, e.g., abbreviations, depth of water, nature of bottom, navigation lights and marks, variation, etc.; to set a course to steer from a position to any harbour or other position, being given the set and drift of the tide or current, the first position being fixed either by cross bearings or by plotting the courses and distances run from a previous position making due allowance for a given tide or current; to take a bearing by compass and by using a card of deviations, convert it to a magnetic and thence to a true direction to lay off on the chart.

(2) To find the latitude from an observation of the sun when on the meridian; to understand the difference between compass direction, magnetic direction and true direction and to find the deviation of the compass by the following methods:—

(a)   Transit bearings.

(b)   Bearing of the sun at noon and on rising or setting.

(c)   Approximately by bearing of Pole Star.

SKIPPER (LIMITED).

Qualifications.—A candidate must

(a)   Be not less than 21 years of age; and

(b)   Have served five years at sea (in a deck capacity) of which one year must have been as a Second Hand on board fishing boats of 25 tons gross tonnage or upwards whilst holding a Second Hand (Full) or (Limited) Certificate, and produce satisfactory evidence of his twelve months' service such as Discharge Book S.I.A., Discharge Certificate S.I., etc.

Providing a candidate produces evidence of having served for at least two years on deep sea fishing boats, service as Skipper of a fishing boat on which possession of a Second Hand (Special) Certificate is required will be accepted as qualifying service towards the required period of twelve months' service as certificated Second Hand.

SYLLABUS.
Chartwork and Pilotage.

As for Second Hand (Limited) and in addition:—

The use of Decca and Consol Lattice Charts.

Practical Navigation I.

(1) By the use of the Traverse Table to obtain the D.R. position of a ship at any time, given the compass courses, variation and deviation and the run recorded by log or calculated by estimated speed and time. The candidate may be asked to allow for the effects of current and winds. A departure position may be given as a bearing and distance from a point of land.

(2) To find the deviation of the compass by time azimuth of the sun by means of tables, diagrams or any other method the candidate may select.

Practical Navigation II.

(1) To find the latitude by an observation of the sun on the meridian.

(2) From an observation of the sun out of the meridian to find the direction of the position line and a position through which it passes.

(3) To find the ship's position at the time of the second observation by the use of position lines obtained from two different observations with a run between. The two observations may both be of the sun, or a solar observation together with a terrestrial position line.

(4) To answer elementary questions on nautical astronomy dealing with solar observation. To understand the terms:—geographical position of the sun, Greenwich hour angle, local hour angle, celestial meridian, prime vertical, azimuth.

SKIPPER (FULL).

Qualifications.—A candidate must

(*a*) Be not less than 21 years of age;

(*b*) Have served five years at sea (in a deck capacity) of which one year must have been as a certificated Second Hand on board fishing boats of 25 tons gross tonnage or upwards whilst holding one of the Certificates listed in (*c*) below, and produce satisfactory evidence of his twelve months' service as Second Hand such as Discharge Book S.I.A., Discharge Certificates S.I., etc., and

(*c*) Hold a Second Hand's Certificate issued before 1st July, 1937, or a Second Hand (Full) Certificate or a Skipper (Limited) Certificate.

SYLLABUS.
Practical Navigation I.

(1) To find the latitude by observation of the Pole Star.

(2) To determine the direction of the position line and a position through which it passes from an observation of a star out of the meridian.

(3) To determine the position of the ship from two simultaneous observations of stars, or by observation of a star and the sun with a run between, or a star and the bearing of a terrestrial object.

Practical Navigation II.

(1) To find the deviation of the compass by time azimuth of a star (use of tables or diagram will be accepted).

(2) To recognise the following stars by their positions relative to the constellations:—Polaris, Dubhe, Arcturus, Aldebaran, Rigel, Bellatrix, Betelgeuse, Sirius, Castor, Pollux, Capella, Regulus, Altair, Vega, Deneb.

(3) Definition of a great circle, rhumb line, first point of Aries, and sidereal hour angle of a star.

Chartwork and Pilotage.

As for Second Hand (full) and in addition:—

(1)   Use of a line of soundings.
(2)   Use of a gnomonic chart.
(3)   Use of Decca, Consol and Loran Lattice charts.
(4)   To find the time and height of high and low water at a Standard Port (Admiralty Tide Tables). The use of tables or diagram to find the height of tide at any given time and thence the approximate correction to soundings, or to find the time at which there would be a specified depth of water over a rock or shoal.

Navigational Aids (including electronic aids).

(1)   Elementary questions on compass deviation.
To find the Magnetic bearing of a distant object taken on equidistant points and to construct a table of deviations.

(2)   Care and maintenance of magnetic compasses. Siting of compasses with particular reference to proximity of magnetic material and electrical appliances.

(3)   Principle of the echo sounder and its practical use: false echoes, fish echoes.

(4)   The practical use of Radar and its limitations as a navigational aid, abnormal propagation, multiple trace echoes, effect of high land inshore.

(5)   The use of Decca Navigator, fixed and variable errors and how to apply them.

(6)   The use of Consol, and how to obtain a count.

SUCCESS AND FAILURE IN THE EXAMINATIONS.

The examinations for certificates of competency are divided into three parts—written, oral and signalling, and the written and oral examinations must in the first instance be taken together.

The marking of the whole of the written portion of the examination, in Home Trade examinations, with the exception of the papers on chart work, will be carried out by the Central Board of Examiners. In the Fishing examinations, the marking of the whole of the written portion will be carried out by the Examiners.

For his written work, the candidate will be furnished with sheets of blank ruled paper on which he will be required to answer in a clear and legible hand the questions on the paper and to start each answer by writing in the margin the number of the question to which it relates.

To pass in the written portion, a candidate will be required to obtain the appropriate percentage pass in the subjects shown in the following tables and also to obtain 70 per cent of the total marks for all subjects. The time and marks alloted for each written part of the examination for each grade of certificate will be as follows:—

MATE (HOME TRADE).

First Day				Time	Marks	% Pass
(1)	Chart Work	– –	–	2 hrs.	150	70%
(2)	Practical Navigation		–	3 hrs	150	70%
Second Day						
(3)	Ship Knowledge	–	–	2 hrs.	150	50%
(4)	Essay –	– –	–	1½ hrs.	100	—
					550	70%

MASTER (HOME TRADE).

		Time	Marks	% Pass
FIRST DAY				
(1) Chart Work – – –		2 hrs.	150	70%
(2) Practical Navigation –		2 hrs.	150	70%
SECOND DAY				
(3) Stability – – –		2 hrs.	200	50%
(4) Compass Deviation –		1½ hrs.	100	—
THIRD DAY				
(5) English – – –		1 hr.	100	—
			700	70%

SECOND HAND (LIMITED).

		Time	Marks	% Pass
FIRST DAY				
(1) Chart Work – – –		3 hrs.	200	70%
(2) Practical Navigation –		2 hrs.	200	70%
			400	70%

SECOND HAND (FULL)

	Time	Marks	% Pass
FIRST DAY			
(1) Chart Work – – –	3 hrs.	200	70%
(2) Practical Navigation, I –	2 hrs.	150	70%
SECOND DAY			
(3) Practical Navigation, II	3 hrs.	200	70%
(4) Principles of Navigation	2 hrs.	150	—
		700	70%

SKIPPER (LIMITED)

	Time	Marks	% Pass
FIRST DAY			
(1) Chart Work – –	3 hrs.	200	70%
(2) Practical Navigation I –	2 hrs.	150	70%
SECOND DAY			
(3) Practical Navigation, II	3 hrs.	200	70%
		550	70%

SKIPPER (FULL)

	Time	Marks	% Pass
FIRST DAY			
(1) Practical Navigation, I –	3 hrs.	200	70%
(2) Practical Navigation, II	2 hrs.	150	70%
SECOND DAY			
(3) Chart Work – – –	3 hrs.	200	70%
(4) Navigational Aids – –	2 hrs.	150	50%
THIRD DAY			
(5) Ship Stability – –	2 hrs.	100	—
		800	70%

SECOND HAND (SPECIAL)

	Time	Marks	% Pass
FIRST DAY			
(1) Chart Work – – –	3 hrs.	See below	
(2) Navigation – – –	2 hrs.	See below	

All questions in the Second Hand (Special) Examination must be answered correctly if a pass is to be obtained. If, when a candidate hands in his papers, the errors are not too numerous and the time allowed for working the papers has not expired, the incorrectly worked problems will be returned by the Examiner to the candidate for correction. The incorrectly worked problems will not be returned to the candidate a second time.

YACHTMASTER (COASTAL).

Qualifications.—This examination is open to British yachtsmen and yachtswomen of 21 years of age or over. Candidates are not required to have served any specified time afloat, since their sea knowledge will be sufficiently tested by their examination in seamanship.

SYLLABUS OF EXAMINATION IN NAVIGATION.
Chartwork and Pilotage. (3 hours).

(*a*) To use a chart or plan and understand the meaning of all the marks, signs and abbreviations thereon. (Candidate will be examined orally on this section.)

(*b*) To find the compass course (or courses) and the distance (or distances) between two points on the chart.

(*c*) To find the ship's position by cross bearings of two objects and the set and drift experienced.

(*d*) To find the ship's position from two bearings of the same object, the course and distance run between taking the bearings being given, making due allowance for a given tide or current, and to find the distance of the ship from any given position at the time of the second bearing.

(*e*) To find on a chart or plan the course to steer by compass in order to counteract the effect of a given tide or current and find the distance the ship will make good towards a given position in a given time.

(*f*) To fix the ship's position by two horizontal sextant angles.

(*g*) The use of horizontal and vertical danger angles and use of clearing marks. Range of lights.

(*h*) The use of a line of soundings. Leeway.

Navigation (2 hours).

(*a*) To obtain the deviation of the compass by time azimuth or amplitude of the sun by means of tables, diagrams or any other method the candidate may select.

(*b*) The care of chronometers and other navigational timepieces; rating and daily comparisons. Radio time signals. Time-keeping at sea. Standard time, zone time, summer time. Use of Admiralty list of Radio Signals and Nautical Almanac.

(*c*) To use the Nautical Almanac to obtain the time of sun's and moon's rising and setting.

(*d*) To use the Tide Tables to find the times and heights of high and low water at standard and secondary ports in Admiralty Tide Tables, Vol. I. To find the height of tide at a standard port at a given time.

(*e*) How to find the correct count from a Consol station. Correction of Radio bearings before laying off on a Mercator chart.

(*f*) Requirements for the choice of suitable objects to obtain a fix from horizontal sextant angles.

SUCCESS AND FAILURE IN THE EXAMINATION.
(Written portion).

First Day				Time	Marks	% Pass
(1)	Magnetic Compass –	–	–	3 hrs.	150	50%
(2)	Meteorology	–	–	2 hrs.	100	50%
Second Day						
(3)	Chart Work –	–	–	3 hrs.	150	70%
(4)	Navigation –	–	–	2 hrs.	150	70%

HOME TRADE NAVIGATION GUIDE
FOR HOME TRADE, FISHING AND COASTAL YACHTMASTER EXAMINATIONS

Navigation for Home Trade and Fishing Examinations.

PART I.

CHAPTER 1.

THE DECIMAL SYSTEM.

Fractions.—A fraction of a number is any part which is less than a whole number, or less than unity. Thus, a half is written as $\frac{1}{2}$, which represents unity as being divided into 2 equal parts; a quarter is written as $\frac{1}{4}$, which represents unity as being divided into 4 equal parts, and so on.

If a number is divided into, say, 260 parts, the fraction is written as $\frac{1}{260}$, the lower part of the fraction always being the number of parts into which unity has been divided.

These fractions are called "Vulgar Fractions".

Decimal Fractions.—When the decimal system is used, the "broken up" form of figures (*e.g.* $\frac{7}{12}$) is not used, the whole number being divided from the fraction by the simple insertion of a dot, thus:—175·63, which represents 175 units, and 63 hundredths.

The name "decimal" is derived from the Latin word "decem", meaning ten, and thus a decimal fraction means that unity has been divided into tenths, or hundredths, or thousandths, and so on, according to whether there are one, two, three or more figures in the decimal fraction.

Thus, ·1 is equal to (=) $\frac{1}{1}$, ·2=$\frac{2}{1}$, and so on. So ·5, which is equal to $\frac{5}{10}$, is also equal to $\frac{1}{2}$, since $\frac{5}{10}$ is half of $\frac{10}{10}$, or of 1.

Now, ·5 can also be written as ·50000, because as many ciphers (0's) as are desired can be added without altering the value of the fraction. If it is desired to find the value of half of ·5, it must be divided by 2. When the number to be divided by 2 is an "odd" number (that is, 1, 3, 5, 7, or 9): add a cipher to it, making (in this case) ·50, which, divided by 2, becomes ·25.

Thus, the half of ·5 ($\frac{1}{2}$) is ·25 ($\frac{1}{4}$) and, similarly, $\frac{3}{4} = $ ·75. In this latter case, the ·7 is equal to $\frac{7}{10}$, and the second figure—which, if appearing on its own, would be written as ·05—is equal to $\frac{5}{100}$.

It should be noted that while any number of ciphers can be added AFTER the figures comprising the decimal fraction without altering its value, a cipher placed IN FRONT of the figures, immediately after the decimal point, has the same effect as dividing the fraction by 10.

1

Thus, ·5 is equal to five-tenths, ·05 is equal to five-hundredths, ·005 is equal to five-thousandths, and so on.

The rule for converting decimal fractions into vulgar fractions is: Write down the figures of the decimal fraction as the top half of the vulgar fraction. The lower half of the vulgar fraction then consists of a 1 in place of the decimal point, and a cipher for every figure in the decimal fraction. An illustration will make this clear⸴ ·

Convert ·063 to a vulgar fraction.   ($\frac{63}{1000}$)

Again, ·145 $=\frac{145}{1000}$ and so on.

Addition by Decimal Fractions.—To perform addition, subtraction, etc., by the use of decimals is very simple, and except for a few easily remembered rules as to the placing of the decimal point is as easy as performing the same operations with whole numbers.

For instance, add together—

$$
\begin{array}{r}
943675 \\
58253 \\
187462 \\
\hline
1189390 \\
\hline
\end{array}
$$

Now, had the problem been given as follows:—

Add together 943·675, 58·253, and 187·462, it would have been worked like this—

$$
\begin{array}{r}
943 \cdot 675 \\
58 \cdot 253 \\
187 \cdot 462 \\
\hline
1189 \cdot 390 \\
\hline
\end{array}
$$

The figures add up in precisely the same way as did the whole numbers. In the example given above, when the figures immediately to the RIGHT of the decimal point were added, the total came to 13. The 3 was written in the answer, and the 1 was carried to the column on the left of the decimal point, exactly as if the decimal had not been there, and the decimal point was inserted immediately underneath the other decimal points in the question.

It is important that this fact should be noted. **Always keep the** decimal points underneath each other.

Example.—

Add together	1654·974	742·48
	3·875	55·79
	391·087	138·41
	2049·936	936·68

Subtraction by Decimals.—Subtraction by decimals is carried out under the same rules. That is to say, keep the decimal points underneath each other, and perform the operation as if these points did not

exist. In the answer, the decimal point is placed immediately underneath the decimal points in the two numbers.

Example.—

Subtract	943·77	4371·6294
	816·86	895·9375
	126·91	3475·6919

Multiplication by Decimals.—When multiplying numbers in which decimal fractions are involved, first perform the operation as if the numbers were two whole numbers and write the answer as a whole number, thus—

Multiply	18·562		18·562
by	9·88	**or**	9·88
	148496		167058
	148496		148496
	167058		148496
	18339256		18339256

Next count the total number of figures which lie to the RIGHT of the decimal point in the two numbers given to be multiplied.

In this case, there are 3 figures to the right of the point in the top number, and 2 in the lower number, 5 in all.

The decimal point in the answer has to be placed immediately in front of the fifth figure *from the right,* and the completed answer reads 183·39256.

Example.—

Multiply	49·774		49·774
by	8·7	**or**	8·7
	348418		398192
	398192		348418
	433·0338		433·0338

Division by Decimals.—The operation of dividing is to find out how many times one number contains another. Thus the problem has three parts—the DIVIDEND, which contains the DIVISOR a certain number of times, this latter number being called the QUOTIENT.

Thus	Divisor	Dividend	Quotient
	4)	12	(3

If the problem does not work out evenly, a decimal point is inserted in the quotient as soon as the figures given in the question have all been disposed of, and any required number of ciphers can then be added to the dividend, the division being carried on to as many "places of decimals" as may be required, or until the remainder is zero.

Thus—

```
4)13·00(3·25
   12
   ──
   10
    8
   ──
   20
   20
   ══
```

Explanation.—The first remainder, after dividing, is 1. To this remainder, a cipher is added, and immediately this is done a decimal point is placed after the 3 in the quotient, and the division is continued. The second remainder is 2. Another cipher is added to this, and the division continued. The third remainder is zero, so the problem is now complete.

The above is the simplest form of division by decimals. When both the divisor and the dividend contain decimal fractions, there are two methods which can be used, according to the individual choice.

METHOD 1.—*Example.*—Divide 94·654 by 17·32.

Mentally, find how many times the WHOLE NUMBER of the divisor will divide into the dividend.

In this case it will go 5 times. The quotient, therefore, will be 5, with the decimal point coming immediately after that figure, and the division can then be continued as far as is desired.

Thus—

```
17·32)94·654(5·465
      86 60
      ─────
       8 054
       6 928
       ──────
       1 1260
       1 0392
       ──────
         8680
         8660
         ────
           20
           ══
```

Explanation.—After dividing, the last figure of the dividend (4) is added to the first remainder, and the sum is continued. The second remainder, and those following, each requires to have a cipher added, and the quotient is carried as far as required, to 3 places of decimals in this case.

METHOD 2.—*Example.*—Divide 745·61 by 9·342.

Convert the divisor into a WHOLE NUMBER by moving the decimal point 3 places to the right.

The dividend must have the decimal point moved the *same number of places* to the right at the same time, which sometimes, as in this example, makes it necessary to add a cipher to it.

The problem now appears as follows:—

```
9342)745610(79·81
     65394
     ─────
     91670
     84078
     ─────
     75920
     74736
     ─────
     11840
      9342
     ─────
      2498
```

Explanation.—After the first operation, the last figure of the dividend (0) is placed after the remainder. The second remainder (7592) is, of course, smaller than the divisor, and has a cipher added after it, the decimal point being inserted in the quotient AT THE SAME TIME, and the division is continued, adding as many ciphers as are necessary.

When the divisor is larger than the dividend the quotient will be a fraction, and there will be no whole number in the answer.

Example.—Divide 17·6432 by 41·164.

411640)176432·0(0·428
164656 0
⎯⎯⎯⎯⎯
11776 00
8232 80
⎯⎯⎯⎯⎯
3543 200
3293 120
⎯⎯⎯⎯⎯
250 080
⎯⎯⎯⎯⎯

Explanation.—Since, even after the decimal points in divisor and dividend have each been moved 4 places to the right, the dividend is the smaller, a cipher is placed as the first figure in the quotient. A cipher is then added after the last figure of the dividend, and the decimal point is put after the 0 in the quotient at the same time. The problem is then carried on.

Note the difference in the following example:

Divide 4·53 by 131·6

13160)45300(0·034
39480
⎯⎯⎯⎯⎯
58200
52640
⎯⎯⎯⎯⎯
5560
⎯⎯⎯⎯⎯

Explanation.—In this case, the decimal points in divisor and dividend were shifted 2 places to the right, and the problem reads as follows—

13160)453   (

When dividing, a cipher was put as the first figure of the quotient, and another cipher was added to the dividend, the decimal point being entered in the quotient at the same time. The problem then appeared thus—

13160)4530   (0·

Even then, the divisor was larger than the dividend, so the next figure after the decimal point in the quotient was 0, and another ciph·r had to be added after the dividend before the normal operation of division could be carried on.

Another method of performing division is shown in the following example:—

Divide 6437·75 by 218·94

29·4
⎯⎯⎯⎯⎯
21894)643775(
43788
⎯⎯⎯⎯⎯
205895
197046
⎯⎯⎯⎯⎯
88490
87576
⎯⎯⎯⎯⎯
914
⎯⎯⎯⎯⎯

Explanation.—Count the number of figures in the divisor, in this case 5. If the FIRST figure of the divisor is smaller than the first figure of the dividend, place the first figure of the quotient, (the answer) over the 5th figure of the dividend. If the first figure of the divisor should be larger than the first figure of the dividend, the first figure of the quotient would be placed over the 6th figure of the quotient. (See *Example* 2.) Immediately all the figures in the dividend have been accounted for, put in the decimal point in the answer, and dd as many ciphers to the dividend as are required.

Example 2.—Divide 3216·79 by 48·31

```
          66·58
4831)321679(
      28986
      ─────
      31819
      28986
      ─────
      28330
      24155
      ─────
      41750
      38648
      ─────
```

Explanation.—**The first figure of** the divisor (4) is larger than the first figure of the dividend (3), so the first figure of the answer is not placed over the 4th figure of the dividend, but over the 5th. As soon as all the figures of the dividend have been divided, and a cipher has been added to it, the decimal point is put in the answer.

EXERCISE 1.

1.	Add	743·69
		538·51
		132·77
		255·94
		613·23

2.	Add	3513·742
		7826·417
		5548·335
		2874·162
		5137·265

3.	Add	74·629
		138·455
		8·262
		15·819
		327·665

4.	Add	283·1
		16·294
		5·83
		161·54
		28·916

5.	Subtract	46·91
		33·27

6.	Subtract	7421·365
		6268·497

7.	Subtract	2382·7
		589·947

8.	Subtract	28·35
		17·419

9.	Multiply	17·62	by	5·8
10.	,,	94·225	by	13·71
11.	,,	421·3	by	8·94
12.	,,	74·61	by	3·38
13.	Divide	1769	by	43
14.	,,	196·7	by	55·3
15.	,,	216·39	by	44·8
16.	,,	663·947	by	132·72
17.	,,	48	by	75
18.	,,	33·97	by	102·4
19.	,,	75·617	by	2131·7
20.	,,	3 7	by	24·652

CHAPTER 2.

ANGLES—OBLIQUE ANGLES AND RIGHT ANGLES—DIVISION OF DEGREES—CONVERTING MINUTES TO DECIMAL FRACTIONS OF DEGREES, ETC.

When two straight lines meet each other, as in Fig. 1, they form angles. In the accompanying diagram, CDB and CDA are two angles, unequal to each other.

These are called OBLIQUE ANGLES.

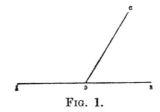

FIG. 1.

In Fig. 2, the angles PQS and PQR are equal to each other, and PQ stands perpendicular to RS.

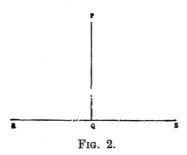

FIG. 2.

Each of these angles is called a RIGHT ANGLE.

In Fig. 1, angle CDB, which is smaller than a right angle, is called an ACUTE ANGLE, while angle CDA, which is larger than a right angle, is called an OBTUSE ANGLE.

Division of Degrees.—The right angle is taken as the standard for the measurement of angles, and is divided into 90 degrees (°). Each

8

degree is subdivided into 60 minutes ('), and each minute is further subdivided into 60 seconds (''). Thus, in a right angle, there are 90°, or $(90 \times 60)'$, or $(90 \times 60 \times 60)''$.

Converting Minutes to Decimal Fractions of Degrees.—When dealing with degrees, etc., in navigation problems, it is often necessary to reduce minutes to decimal fractions of degrees, or to reduce seconds to decimal fractions of minutes.

Since there are 60'' in 1', it follows that 6'' are equal to (=) $\frac{1}{10}$ of 1', or to ·1'. 12''=$\frac{2}{10}$ of 1', or to ·2', and so on. Thus we find the rule— To reduce seconds to a decimal fraction of a minute, divide the seconds by 6. Since also there are 60' in 1°, the same rule applies when reducing minutes to a decimal fraction of a degree, or, if working with time, the same rule holds good when reducing seconds or minutes to a decimal fraction of a minute or of an hour respectively. For example—

Reduce   17' 18'' to minutes.   Ans. 17·3' } By dividing the
          31' 42'' to minutes.   Ans. 31·7' }   seconds by 6.
          25° 54' to degrees.   Ans. 25·9° } By dividing the
          28° 36' to degrees.   Ans. 28·6° }   minutes by 6.

It is usually sufficient, when thus reducing, to work only to one place of decimals, in which case

       12' 17'' becomes 12·3' (nearest)
       12' 19''   ,,   12·3'   ,,
       12' 20''   ,,   12·3'   ,,

But if it should be desired to work very accurately, then the rule already given in Chapter 1 should be used. A cipher should be added to the last figure, and the dividing carried one place further. In that case, the above examples would read.

       12' 17'' = 12·28'
       12' 19'' = 12·31'
       12' 20'' = 12·33'

In each case, a cipher was added to the 17'', 19'', and 20'' before dividing by 6.

The Reverse Process.—To reduce decimal fractions of degrees (or minutes) to minutes (or seconds) the above rule is reversed, and the fraction is MULTIPLIED by 6.

Thus—   19·4° = 19° 24'
            17·7' = 17' 42''
            25·83°= 25° 49·8' or 25° 49' 48''

The same rules hold good for hours and minutes of time.

Complements and Supplements of Angles.—The COMPLEMENT of an angle (or of the arc of a circle) is the difference between that angle, or arc, and 90° (one right angle). In Fig. 3, the angle ABD is the complement of angle DBC.

The SUPPLEMENT of an angle, or of an arc, is the difference between that angle, or arc, and 180°. In Fig. 4, angle *CDA* is the supplement of angle *CDB.*

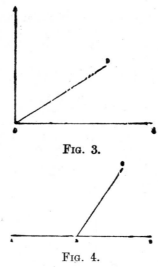

FIG. 3.

FIG. 4.

A simple method of remembering which is "complement" and which is "supplement," is by noting the number of times the letter "P" appears in the word. In "complement", "P" appears once, so "one right angle". In "supplement", "P" appears twice, so "two right angles".

Later on, we shall regularly use the complements of what are called "functions" of angles, but the word "complement" will then be reduced to the first two letters—"CO".

EXERCISE 2.

Reduce to decimal fractions.

1. 23° 18'
2. 75° 42'
3. 12° 36'
4. 16° 30'
5. 38' 24''
6. 5' 06''
7. 29' 35''
8. 2 hr. 17 min.
9. 5 hr. 40 min.
10. 3 hr. 24 min.
11. 18 min. 53 sec.
12. 48 min. 22 sec.

Reduce to minutes and seconds.

13. 17·7°
14. 25·3°
15. 42·9°
16. 38·6'
17. 51·4'
18. 22·2'
19. 1·5 hr.
20. 3·1 hr.
21. 11·64 hr.
22. 9·48 hr.
23. 6·32 min.
24. 54·93 min.

CHAPTER 3.

LOGARITHMS.

The usual textbook definition of a logarithm is not very helpful to a beginner. It is as follows: A LOGARITHM IS THE EXPONENT OF THE POWER TO WHICH THE BASE MUST BE RAISED TO PRODUCE ANOTHER NUMBER. Having chewed this definition over, the beginner probably feels that he knows less about logarithms than before! However, let us try to get at it with all its finery stripped off, to find what a "log" really is.

In navigation tables, logs are used which have been calculated from a starting point (or "base") of 10.

Now, $10 \times 10 = 100$, and another way of writing 10×10 is 10^2, the small 2 indicating the number of 10's which have been multiplied together. This same number 2 is the "log" of 10×10, or, the log of 100.

As stated above, 10×10 can be written as 10^2, so that 10 by itself can be written as 10^1. Similarly, we can say that $10^1 \times 10^1 = 100$, instead of saying that $10^2 = 100$. These little 1's are called indices, and thus it is seen that by ADDING the indices when the 10's are being MULTIPLIED we arrive at the log.

Thus, $10^1 \times 10^1 \times 10^1 = 1000$, and can be written as 10^3. The log of 1000 is therefore 3, and if the indices of the 10's are ADDED the result is, of course, 3.

Similarly, $10^1 \times 10^1 \times 10^1 \times 10^1 = 10,000$ and can be written as 10^4. The log of 10,000, therefore, is 4.

10 itself, as stated above, can be written as 10^1, and the log of 10 is therefore 1.

Study these figures for a moment, and it will be seen that—

The log of 10 is 1 ⎫ Therefore the log of any number between
The log of 100 is 2 ⎭ 10 and 100 must be 1 and a fraction.

The log of 100 is 2 ⎫ Therefore the log of any number between
The log of 1000 is 3 ⎭ 100 and 1000 must be 2 and a fraction.

The log of 1000 is 3 ⎫ Therefore the log of any number between
The log of 10000 is 4 ⎭ 1000 and 10000 must be 3 and a fraction, and so on.

The figures 10, 100, 1000, and so on are called the NATURAL NUMBERS, and the log itself is divided into two parts—the 1, 2, 3, and so on, which is called the INDEX NUMBER, and the fraction, always expressed in decimals, which is called the *mantissa*.

Analysing the facts we have collected, we see that—

M

The natural number 10 contains 2 figures, and its log is 1.
  ,,   ,,   100 ,, 3 ,,   ,,   2.
  ,,   ,,   1000 ,, 4 ,,   ,,   3.

From that analysis we find that—

THE INDEX NUMBER OF A LOG IS 1 LESS *in value* THAN THE *number* OF FIGURES IN THE WHOLE NATURAL NUMBER.

That is to say—

The log of 100·00 is 2·00000, the fraction being given to 5 places of decimals.

The log of 999·76 is 2 and a fraction, since there are only 3 fig ıres in the whole natural number. The figures in the fraction of the natural number are not counted.

Similarly the log of 17·65 is 1 and a fraction, the index number of the log being 1 less in value than the number of figures (2) contained in 17, the whole natural number.

Also the log of 7·625 is 0 and a fraction, the index number (0) being 1 less in value than the number of figures (1) contained in 7, the whole natural number.

When converting natural numbers to logarithms, if the natural numbers do not contain more than 4 figures, both *Norie's Tables* and *Burton's Tables* use the same method. Or when converting logarithms to natural numbers, and the logarithms can be found exactly in the tables, both methods are again the same.

Table of Logs in *Norie's* is found to commence on page 188. In *Burton's*, Table 18 (Logs) commences on page 118.

In *Norie's* (older editions) the logs are given to 6 places of decimals, while in the newer edition and in *Burton's* the logs are given to 5 places of decimals.

In a small prefatory table, logs are given from 1 to 100, each with the index number prefixed.

The second, and larger part, of the table gives logs from 1000 to 9999 and in this part of the table the MANTISSA only (the decimal fraction) is given, the index numbers being omitted. It is, however, simple to find and prefix the required index number of any log by the rule given above—that the index number is 1 less in value than the number of figures contained in the whole natural number.

The first 3 figures of the natural number are found in the left-hand column of the table and the 4th figure is found in the column along the top of the page.

Suppose it is required to find the log of 15·47. (Note—when studying these, or any, examples, the student should invariably look up the examples in the tables to gain the fullest knowledge.) First, before even looking at the table, write down the required index number from the rule. There are 2 figures in 15, therefore the index number will be 1 less than 2, that is, 1.

This operation disposes of the decimal point in the natural number, and the question could now read, "Find the log of 1547".

Look for 154 in the left-hand column of the table, then follow that level across the page till the column headed 7 (the last figure) is reached. The log there reads (*Norie's*) 18949. The answer to the question is therefore 1·18949.

If the question had read, "Find the log of 154·7," the mantissa would have been the same as above (18949), but the index number would have been 2. Again, "Find the log of 1·547." The mantissa still remains the same, but the index number is 0, and the answer is 0·18949.

Using the same figures for still another example, "Find the log of 154700". The mantissa remains 18949, but the index number is now 5. So that ciphers added to the figures of the natural number make no difference to the mantissa, only to the index number.

To Find Natural Numbers from Logs.—To find the natural number corresponding to a given log the operation is performed in the opposite way, when the log can be found exactly in the table. When the log has been found, the first three figures of the natural number are taken from the left-hand column abreast of the log, and the fourth figure is taken from the proper column at the top of the page.

Having found the natural number, it still remains to fix the decimal point in your answer. This is done by reversing the rule already explained. That is, if the index number of the log is 2, there are 3 figures in the whole natural number. If the index number of the log is 4, there are 5 figures in the whole natural number, in which case it would be necessary to add a sufficient number of ciphers to the natural number to make up the number of figures required in the answer.

Example 1.—Find the natural number corresponding to log 3·99273.

Look first in the table of logs for the MANTISSA, leaving the index number of the log out of account entirely for the time being.

In the table, abreast 99273, in the left-hand column, you will find 983, and the log is in the column headed "4" at the top. The natural number is therefore 9834, but the decimal point has still to be inserted. The index number of the log is 3. This means that there are 4 figures in front of the decimal point and the answer is thus 9834·00.

Example 2.—Find the natural number corresponding to the log 1·79539.

The mantissa is found in the table, giving the corresponding natural number 6243. The index number of the log, 1, shows that there must be 2 figures in front of the decimal point, so the answer is 62·43.

Example 3.—Find the natural number corresponding to log 5·67779.

The mantissa gives the natural number 4762. The index number shows there must be 6 figures in front of the decimal point, so, by adding the necessary number of ciphers, the required answer becomes 476200·00.

B

Exercise 3.

Finding Logarithms from Natural Numbers and Vice Versa.

Find the logs of—	Find the natural numbers of logs—
1. 1737	13. 2·86356
2. 2581	14. 1·73783
3. 153700	15. 0·93692
4. 137·3	16. 4·31702
5. 65·21	17. 6·70243
6. 1·559	18. 2·32593
7. 12·74	19. 4·17202
8. 4·000	20. 2·44311
9. 8·004	21. 1·70484
10. 653·9	22. 4·87823
11. 56·41	23. 1·55182
12. 7632·00	24. 3·35794

The number of figures in natural numbers can, and very often does, exceed 4, and we have now to consider finding the logs of such numbers.

The method used in *Norie's* and the method used in *Burton's* are slightly different, so each method is discussed separately. Students who use one set of tables need not study the method used for the other tables.

BY NORIE'S TABLES.

Example 1.—Find the log of 196·74. Here we have 3 figures in the whole number, and two in the decimal fraction, 5 in all. The index number of the log is 2. Look in the table for the first 4 figures of the natural number, exactly as was done before, and write down the log 2·29380.

We have now to consider the last figure (4) of the given natural number.

Continue right across the page to the extreme right, keeping on the same level of figures, and in the last column of all, which is headed "Diff." are the figures 22.

Write these figures in the margin, and multiply them by the figure, or figures, of the natural number which have not yet been taken into account. In this case, multiply by 4, the result being 88.

Now cut off from the right of this result the same number of figures as you have multiplied the diff. by. In this case, you multiplied by one figure (4), so cut off one figure from the right of 88, which leaves 8·8 or 9. (See note, p. 15.) This has to be added to the mantissa already obtained, and the whole problem appears as follows:—

Log of 196·7	2·29380	Diff. 22
Log of ·04	9	4
Log of 196·74	2·29389	8͟8͟

Example 2.—Find the log of 7356·63.

The index number is 3, and the log of 7356 is 3·86664. The diff. 6.

has to be multiplied by the 2 figures remaining, 63, which gives 378. Since 2 figures were used to multiply, 2 figures have to be cut off from that result, leaving 4 (nearest).

The problem is worked thus:—

Log of 7356	3·86664	Diff.	6
Log of ·63	4		63
Log of 7356·63	3·86668		3 8̶

Example 3.—Find the log of 546·307.

The index number is 2, and the log of 546·3 is 2·73743. The diff. (8) is multiplied by 07, the remaining figures. The result is 56.

Although one of the figures by which the diff. was multiplied is 0, you have to count this figure when cutting off the figures from the right of the result. So that 2 figures have to be cut off, not 1, which leaves nearly 1 to be added to the original log as found from the tables.

Note.—When the figure cut off is 5, or more than 5, add 1 to the remaining amount. Thus, in this example, the figures 56 were cut off. The correction will be 1.

The problem would be put down thus:—

Log of 546·3	2·73743	Diff.	8
Log of ·007	1		07
Log of 546·307	2·73744		·5̶6̶ = 1

When converting a logarithm into its corresponding natural number, the exact log very usually cannot be found in the table. The procedure then is as follows:—

Example 1.—Find the number of which 4·75978 is the log.

Write down the mantissa, and underneath it, write from the table the mantissa next smaller than the given log. In this case, the next smaller mantissa is 75974, the natural number corresponding to which is 5751. Subtract these logs. The problem is set down thus—

$$\begin{array}{l} 75978 \\ 75974 \\ \hline 4 \ \text{(diff.)} \end{array}$$

Add a cipher to the 4, and divide by the diff. from the "Difference" column of the table—in this case 8.

The index number of the log shows that there must be 5 figures in the whole number of the answer.

The whole problem is set down thus—

$$\begin{array}{l} 4·75978 \\ 75974 \ \text{(next less log)} \\ \hline \text{(Diff.)} \quad 8)40(5 \\ 40 \quad \textit{Answer.}—57515 \\ \overline{} \end{array}$$

Example 2.—Find the number of which 5·50264 is the log.

$$
\begin{array}{r}
5\cdot50264 \\
50256 \text{ (next less log)} \\
\hline
\end{array}
$$

(Diff.)   14)80(5714
              70
             ———
             100
              98
             ———
              20
              14
             ———
              60
              56   *Answer.*—318157·14.

Note very carefully that if the diff. does not divide into the dividend with *one cipher only* added, a cipher must then be inserted in the answer before putting in an extra cipher in the dividend. Thus—

Example 3.—Find the number of which 4·11762 is the log.

$$
\begin{array}{r}
4\cdot11762 \\
11760 \\
\hline
\end{array}
$$

              33)200(0606
                 198
                 ———
                 200   *Answer.*—13110·606.

Explanation.—The difference between the two logs, AFTER a cipher was added, was only 20, which could not be divided by 33. Another cipher, therefore, had to be added to make it divide, but first a cipher had also to be inserted in the answer.

BY BURTON'S TABLES.

The right-hand column in each page gives the "5th figure" of the natural number, with the "log diff." (the amount which has to be added to the log of the first 4 figures) just adjoining.

Example 1.—Find the log of 57·678.
The log of the first 4 figures, 57·67, is 1·76095.
In the right-hand column, on the same level as the log, look for the 5th figure, which is 8. Abreast of this is the "log diff." 6, which has to be added to the log of the first 4 figures. The completed problem appears thus—

Log of 57·67	1·76095
5th fig. (8)	6
Log of 57·678	1·76101

When there are 6 or more figures in the natural number, proceed as follows:—

Example 2.—Find the log of 1532·659.

Log of 1532	3·18526	
5th fig. (6)	17	
6th fig. (5)	14	(move 1 place right)
7th fig. (9)	25	(move 2 places right)
	3·1854465	

or, to 5 places of decimals, 3·18545.

Explanation.—First write down the log of the first 4 figures, 1532. The 5th figure (6) is looked for in the right-hand column, and the corresponding log diff. written under the last 2 figures of your log.   The 6th figure is then looked for under the heading of "5th fig.", but the log diff. has to be moved ONE PLACE TO THE RIGHT.   The 7th figure is found in the same column, the log diff. being moved 2 PLACES TO THE RIGHT.   After completing the addition, the log is taken to 5 places of decimals, the remaining figures being disregarded.

Example 3.—Find the log of 1137·379.

Log of 1137	3·05576	
5th fig. (3)	11	
6th fig. (7)	26	
7th fig. (9)	34	
	3·0558994	or 3·05590

When turning logs into natural numbers, if the exact log cannot be found in the tables, take the log next less than the given log, and find the difference between the two.   This is the "log diff." and the number corresponding to it in the right-hand column of the table is the 5th figure of the natural number.

Example 1.—Find the number of which 3·24859 is the log.

3·24859	
24846	next less log
13	log diff.—5th fig.=5

Answer=1772·5

Example 2.—Find the number of which 4·14787 is the log.

4·14787	
14768	next less log
19	log diff.—5th fig.=6 (nearest)

Answer=14056

Exercise 4.
Logarithms.

Turn the following numbers into logs:—

1. 74·63	2. 131·8	3. 3·839	4. 5·661
5. 8754	6. 437·92	7. 334·615	8. 3351·79
9. 12·1539	10. 55521·7	11. 510·005	12. 74973·4
13. 3216·28	14. 1241·089	15. 432·76	16. 883·56

Turn the following logs into natural numbers:—

17. 2·99304	18. 3·41128	19. 0·24724	20. 3·16017
21. 4·40901	22. 5·59169	23. 1·71395	24. 2·86720
25. 3·65192	26. 4·51544	27. 6·58720	28. 0·20173
29. 3·35284	30. 4·46496	31. 2·60176	32. 4·70000

The Use of Logarithms.

By the use of logs, the arithmetical operation of multiplication is transformed into addition, and the operation of division is transformed into subtraction.

To illustrate this, take a set of logs in their simplest form—calculated to the base of 2.

$$2^1 \quad 2^2 \quad 2^3 \quad 2^4 \quad 2^5 \quad 2^6 \quad 2^7 \quad 2^8 \quad 2^9 \quad 2^{10} \quad 2^{11} \quad 2^{12}$$
$$=2 \quad 4 \quad 8 \quad 16 \quad 32 \quad 64 \quad 128 \quad 256 \quad 512 \quad 1024 \quad 2048 \quad 4096$$

and so on.

If, now, we take the multiplication problem 256×16. The log of 256 to base 2 is 8 (from our table above), and the log of 16 from the same table is 4.

Adding these two logs, we get 12, and 12 is the log of 4096. So then, 256×16 should be 4096.

Multiplying in the ordinary way, we find that this is correct. Again take the following: Divide 2048 by 128.

The log of 2048, from our table, is 11, and the log of 128 is 7. Subtracting these, the answer is 4, which is the log of 16. If we divide 2048 by 128, in the ordinary way, we find the answer is 16.

So, then, if we wish to perform multiplication or division by the use of logs, we find the logs of the natural numbers, and either add or subtract these logs, according to whether we are multiplying or dividing, and the result is the log of the answer, which, in turn, has to be turned back into a natural number.

Example 1.—Multiply 1682 by 325, using logs.

By Norie's			By Burton's
1682	log	3·22583	3·22583
325	log	2·51188	2·51188
Log of ans.		5·73771	5·73771
Next less		73767	73767
		8)40(5	4
		40	

Answer.—546650·0   *Answer.*—546650·0

Example 2.—Multiply 17·758 by 12·339.

By Norie's

17·75	log	1·24920		diff.	25
	corr.	20			× 8
17·758	log	1·24940			200
12·33	log	1·09096			
	corr.	32		diff.	35
					× 9
Log of ans		2·34068			
Next less		34064			31$

20)40(2
40

Answer.—219·12.

By Burton's

17·75	log	1·24920
5th fig.		20
17·758	log	1·24940
12·33	log	1·09096
5th fig.		31
Log of ans.		2·34067
Next less		34064
Log diff.		3

Answer.—219·115

Example 3.—Divide 756·83 by 19·48.

By Norie's.

756·8	log	2·87898		diff.	6
	corr.	2			×3
756·83	log	2·87900			18
19·48	log	1·28959			
Log of ans.		1·58941			
Next less		58939			

11)20(18
11

90

Answer.—38·8518.

By Burton's

756·8	log	2·87898
5th fig.		2
756·83	log	2·87900
19·48	log	1·28959
Log of ans.		1·58941
Next less		58939
Diff.		2

Answer.—38·852

Logs of Decimal Numbers.—It has been seen that all the natural numbers with which we have been working so far are greater than 1. We have now to consider numbers which are **less than 1, or** numbers which only contain decimals.

We know that the index of the log of

57·55 is 1
5·755 is 0

therefore the index of the log of 0·5755 is —1. We know also that the mantissa of a log does not alter when the position of the decimal point in a natural number is altered. The mantissa is always considered to be *positive*.

Thus, Log 0·5755 = —1 + (+ 0·76005) = —1·76005.

This is usually written as $\bar{1}$·76005, the minus sign being written over the index. It is called "Bar One". Carrying the example a stage further, Log 0·05755 is —2 + (+0·76005) = $\bar{2}$·76005.

The rule for this is: To find the index number of the log when the natural number is a decimal, count the decimal point as one figure, and each cipher immediately after the decimal point as one figure. Thus the index number of the log of ·000367 would be $\bar{4}$.

To do away with this minus sign, a little subterfuge is employed. Add 10 to the index number of the log, and the log of 0·5755 becomes $\bar{1}$·76005+10=9·76005. Similarly, the log of 0·05755 becomes 2·76005 +10=8·76005.

Involution.—

8 × 8 × 8 can be written as 8^3 (or 512).
5 × 5 × 5 × 5 can be written as 5^4 (or 625).

If it is required to multiply these numbers, take the log of each number, and multiply each log by the "power".

Example.—Multiply 8^3 by 5^4.

Log of 8	= 0·90309		log of 5	= 0·69897
Multiply by	3		Multiply by	4
Log of 8^3	= 2·70927		Log of 5^4	= 2·79588

2·70927
2·79588

Log of answer 5·50515   *Answer.*—320000

Evolution.—(To find the root of a number).

The expression, $\sqrt{9}$, means that the value is required of a number which, when multiplied by itself, makes 9. The answer, is, of course, 3, since $3 \times 3 = 9$. The expression $\sqrt{}$ is called a "square root".

The expression $\sqrt[3]{27}$ means that the value is required of a number which, multiplied twice over by itself makes 27. The answer is again 3, since $3 \times 3 \times 3 = 27$. The expression $\sqrt[3]{}$ is called a "cube root".

To find such a number by using logarithms, take the log of the given number and divide it by the power given in the question. The result is the log of the required number.

If the expression is $\sqrt{}$, divide the log of the number by 2. If the expression is $\sqrt[3]{}$, divide the log by 3. If the expression is $\sqrt[4]{}$, divide the log by 4, and so on.

Thus—

Find $\sqrt[5]{643700}$.
643700 log $\quad = 5 \cdot 80868$
Divide by 5 $\quad = 1 \cdot 16174 = $ log of answer
Answer.—$=14 \cdot 512$

EXERCISE 5.

Solve the following examples by using logarithms:—

1. 743×391

2. $13 \cdot 55 \times 2 \cdot 68$

3. $241 \cdot 65 \times 44 \cdot 562$

4. $5342 \cdot 22 \times 8 \cdot 43$

5. $5874 \div 948$

6. $554 \cdot 18 \div 68 \cdot 4$

7. $34 \cdot 749 \div 139 \cdot 3$

8. $125 \cdot 86 \div 111 \cdot 7$

9. $\dfrac{34 \cdot 61 \times 28 \cdot 49}{542 \cdot 79}$

10. $\dfrac{12 \times 69 \times 56}{431 \times 47}$

11. $\sqrt{4} \times \sqrt[3]{7}$

12. $\sqrt[3]{56} \times \sqrt[3]{28}$

13. $\sqrt[4]{65} \times \sqrt{23}$

14. $\sqrt[3]{45} \div \sqrt{76}$

15. $\sqrt[3]{32 \cdot 1} \div \sqrt{3 \cdot 8}$

16. $12 \cdot 3^2 \times 9 \cdot 1^3$

17. $816 \cdot 1^2 \div 75^3$

CHAPTER 4.

TRIANGLES—RATIOS OF ANGLES—USE OF RATIOS— FINDING SINES, TANGENTS, ETC., OF ANGLES PRACTICAL USES OF "FUNCTIONS"—EQUATIONS.

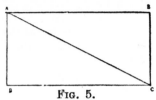

Fig. 5.

Fig. 5 represents a rectangular figure in which there are 4 right angles, one at each corner.

When a straight line is drawn diagonally from one corner, or angle, to another, it divides the figure into two triangles, each of which is equal to the other. Each triangle is therefore equal to half of the rectangle, and, since any rectangular figure contains 4 right angles, the sum of the three angles in each triangle must be 2 right angles.

In the triangle ACD, the angle at D is a right angle, therefore the two remaining angles, DAC and DCA, must together be equal to one right angle. That is to say, these two angles are COMPLEMENTARY.

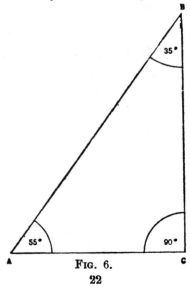

Fig. 6.

22

The same fact is common to all right-angled triangles, and in **Fig.** 6, if the angle $ABC=35°$, then the angle BAC must be 55°.

The sides of a Triangle are Proportionate to the Angles.—In **Fig.** 7, in the series of triangles shown, angle B is the same in each, and the angles at J, G, E and C are all right angles. Thus the angles at H F, D and A must all be equal.

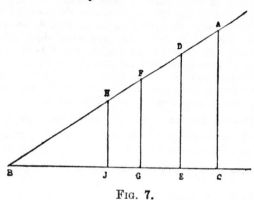

Fig. 7.

Each triangle HBJ, FBG, DBE, and ABC is therefore called SIMILAR to the others, and in their relationship to each other—

$$\frac{BJ}{BH}=\frac{BG}{BF}=\frac{BE}{BD}=\frac{BC}{BA},$$ and so on, in the same way as we can

say $\frac{3}{4}=\frac{9}{12}=\frac{15}{20}=\frac{18}{24}$

So we say that the sides of a triangle are proportionate to the angles, since the actual lengths of the side do not matter. What does matter

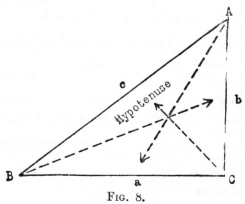

Fig. 8.

is the measurement of the various angles. Any number of triangles can be drawn in which the three angles measure 90°, 35°, and 55°.

In dealing with triangles, it is usual to label the various angles with capital letters, as in Fig. 8, and the side immediately opposite each angle is then named with the corresponding small letter. Thus the side AC, which is opposite to angle B, is called side "b"; the side AB, which is opposite to angle C, is called side "c", and so on.

The side opposite to the 90° angle in any right-angled triangle is called the HYPOTENUSE. Referring again to Fig. 8, let us consider angle B. The side "b" is called the OPPOSITE side, side "a" the ADJACENT side (or side next to the angle), and side "c", being the HYPOTENUSE is, of course, the longest side of the triangle,.

Still considering angle B, the 3 sides of a right-angled triangle have 6 RATIOS towards the angle, and the student is recommended to to learn these ratios very thoroughly. They are—

SINE, and the complement of the sine, called the COSINE.

SECANT, and the complement of the secant, called COSECANT.

TANGENT, and the complement of the tangent, called COTANGENT.

For everyday use these names are contracted to sin, cos, sec, cosec, tan and cot.

Referring to Fig. 8, angle B.

$$\text{Sin} = \frac{\text{opp. side}}{\text{hyp.}} = \frac{b}{c} \qquad \text{Cosec} = \frac{\text{hyp.}}{\text{opp. side}} = \frac{c}{b}$$

$$\text{Cos} = \frac{\text{adj. side}}{\text{hyp.}} = \frac{a}{c} \qquad \text{Sec} = \frac{\text{hyp.}}{\text{adj. side}} = \frac{c}{a}$$

$$\text{Tan} = \frac{\text{opp. side}}{\text{adj. side}} = \frac{b}{a} \qquad \text{Cot} = \frac{\text{adj. side}}{\text{opp. side}} = \frac{a}{b}$$

Two quantities, like $\frac{3}{4}$ and $\frac{4}{3}$, are called RECIPROCAL quantities, and when multiplied are equal to 1. Thus $\frac{3}{4} \times \frac{4}{3} = 1$.

If letters are substituted for the figures, thus, $\frac{a}{b} \times \frac{b}{a}$, the result is also 1. since the letters a and b represent a definite value.

When studying triangles, that fact should be understood. The use of letters instead of figures merely indicates that the relationship $\frac{a}{b}$ is ALWAYS the same, no matter what the lengths of the sides are, provided the angles are the same measurement.

So, referring back to the table of ratios, we see that sin and cosec are reciprocals, as also are cos and sec, and tan and cot.

Now refer to angle A in the figure, and we see that—

$$\text{Sin } A = \frac{\text{opp. side}}{\text{hyp.}} = \frac{a}{c} = \cos B$$

$$\mathbf{Cos}\ A = \frac{\text{adj. side}}{\text{hyp.}} = \frac{b}{c} = \sin B$$

$$\mathbf{Tan}\ A = \frac{\text{opp. side}}{\text{adj. side}} = \frac{a}{b} = \cot B$$

Thus, in any right-angled triangle, leaving the right angle out of consideration for the moment,

Sine of one angle is equal to the cosine of the other

Tan   ,,   ,,   cot   ,,

Sec   ,,   ,,   cosec   ,,

It is plain that this must be so, one angle being the complement of the other, and the cosine is the complement of the sine, etc.

How the Trigonometrical Ratios of Angles are Found.—It may assist the student in understanding these ratios, or FUNCTIONS, of angles, if we explain here how these various functions are found.

The unit for measurement is the length of a radius of the circle, which is the same in every case. Each side of the triangle in turn is divided by the unit of measurement (a radius), which is taken as equal to 1.

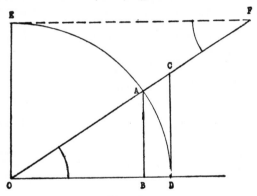

FIG. 9.

Note also that in Fig. 9 the angle **F** is equal to the angle **O**.

$$\text{Sin}\quad O = AB = \frac{AB}{\text{rad}} = \frac{AB}{OA} = \frac{\text{opp.}}{\text{hyp.}}$$

$$\text{Cos}\quad O = OB = \frac{OB}{\text{rad}} = \frac{OB}{OA} = \frac{\text{adj.}}{\text{hyp.}}$$

$$\text{Tan}\quad O = CD = \frac{CD}{\text{rad}} = \frac{CD}{OD} = \frac{\text{opp.}}{\text{adj.}}$$

$$\text{Cot}\quad O = EF = \frac{EF}{\text{rad}} = \frac{EF}{OE} = \frac{\text{adj.}}{\text{opp.}}$$

$$\text{Sec}\quad O = OC = \frac{OC}{\text{rad}} = \frac{OC}{OD} = \frac{\text{hyp.}}{\text{adj.}}$$

$$\text{Cosec}\ O = OF = \frac{OF}{\text{rad}} = \frac{OF}{OE} = \frac{\text{hyp.}}{\text{opp.}}$$

Note that the radius used as the denominator is in each case part of the same triangle with which the numerator is associated.

Note also that for the cot and the cosec, the angle F has been used instead of the angle O, to which it is equal.

Use of Ratios.—In navigation, it is sometimes necessary to add or to subtract various ratios, in which case the NATURAL ratios (or functions) must be used. More frequently, however, it becomes necessary to multiply or to divide these functions, in which case the logs of the functions are used.

These are usually written L sin, L cos, etc., but it is proposed to refer to them simply as sin, cos, etc., and when dealing with natural functions to label these as such.

To Find Functions of Angles from the Tables.—

BY NORIE'S (pp. 238-327).

Since the sin $40°=\cos 50°$, it is unnecessary to extend the tables further than $45°$ and angles of more than $45°$ are found at the foot of the pages.

Each degree in the tables occupies two pages, and the particulars for the first 45 degrees are given at the top of the pages.

Taking these angles first, the student will find that in the top left hand corner of each page is given the degrees, converted into time. The first vertical column on the left hand side gives the odd seconds of time corresponding to half-minutes of arc, which appear in the second vertical column.

This second column is the one in which we are interested at the moment.

As stated above, it gives each half-minute of arc, and to find the function of any angle to the nearest half-minute, turn to the degrees at the top of the page, then follow the arc (') column DOWN the page. Then go across the page till the column of the particular function required is reached.

As was seen on page 24, sines and cosecants are reciprocals, so in the tables these two are bracketed together. Tangents and cotangents, secants and cosines are also bracketed together, and each pair has a double column of figures between them.

It may be noted, in passing, that the logs of any pair of reciprocals in this table, added together, total 20·00000.

The double column of figures between each set of reciprocals is headed "Parts for ''''", and, when the angle exceeds 9°, the first column, headed '', runs from 1'' to 30''. The figures adjoining represent the amount to be added to, or subtracted from, the required function when applying the odd seconds in the angle.

Examine the table, and it will be seen that sines, tangents and secants all increase as the angle itself increases, but the "co's" decrease as the angle increases. When applying corrections for odd seconds in the angle, these must be subtracted if the function is a "co", but added if the function is a sine, a tangent, or a secant.

The two pages which are given over to each degree are handily subdivided for ease in reading. The first half of the first page gives minutes of arc, from 0' to 15', and the second half from 15½' to 30'. The first half of the second page gives from 30' to 45', and the second half from 45½' to 60'.

When the angle is 45° or more, all the particulars are given at the foot of the page, the column which is SINE for angles of less than 45° being the COSINE column for angles of over 45° and so on. A little care is necessary at first, but working from the foot of the page soon becomes easy. Always remember to look for the "heading" at the foot of the page when the angle exceeds 45°. The odd half-minutes of arc are also read from the foot of the page *upwards*, using the second column (headed ') from the *right hand* side of the page.

Example 1.—Find the sine of 29° 36' 30''.

Turn to the pages headed 29°, and in the second vertical column on the left-hand side look for 36½'. Abreast this, under the heading "sin", will be found the answer 9·69379.

Example 2.—Find cos 60° 23' 30''.

The angle is over 45°, so look for the degree at the foot of the page. Then find 23½' in the second column from the *right*, reading from the foot of the page upwards. Taking the "heading" from the foot of the page, the **cos** is found to be 9·69379, which is also the sin 29° 36' 30'', as we have just seen. Adding 29° 36' 30'' and 60° 23' 30'', the result is 90° 00' 00''. Thus sin 29° 36' 30''=cos 60° 23' 30''.

Example 3.—Find cot 35° 23' 00''.

Look for 35° at the top of the page, 23' in the left-hand column, follow this across the page to the column headed "cotangent", and it is found to be 10·14860.

Example 4.—Find sec 40° 35' 11''.

First find sec 40° 35' which is 10·11950. In the double column between sec and cos, look for the odd 11'', and abreast of it in the same columns is found "2". This is the log difference, and since secants increase with the angle, 2 has to be added to the log already found. It would appear thus—

Sec 40° 35'	10·11950
Parts for 11''	+ 2
Sec 40° 35' 11''	10·11952

Example 5.—Find cos 40° 35' 11''

This would appear—

Cos 40° 35'	9·88051
Parts for 11''	− 2
Cos 40° 35' 11''	9·88049

In this case, the correction has to be subtracted, the **function** being a "co", which decreases as the angle increases.

Angles Smaller than 6°.—Except in the case of logs of sec and cos, the various functions of angles alter more rapidly when the angle is smaller than 6°, and in the *parts for''* column, it will be seen that the difference between one log and the next is only given, and not the difference for each second of arc.

When taking out the correction for odd seconds, therefore, keep to that part of the column which is abreast of the minutes which are being dealt with.

Example 6.—Find **tan** 5° 11′ 09″.

Tan 5° 11′	8·95767	
Parts for 9″	23	(1/3 of Diff. 70)
Tan 5° 11′ 09″	8·95790	

Example 7.—Find sin 5° 50′ 50″.

Sin 5° 50′ 30″	9·00766	
Parts for 20″	41	(2/3 of Diff. 62)
Sin 5° 50′ 50″	9·00807	

Example 8.—Find cosec 5° 28′ 07″.

Cosec 5° 28′	11·02106	
Parts for 07″	16	(¼ of Diff. 66)
Cosec 5° 28′ 07″	11·02090	

The correction is subtracted, being a "co".

Should the sine of a very small angle (less than 4°) be required, or the cosine of a very large angle (over 86°), turn to the table immediately in front of the one that has just been used (pp. 214-237), where sines and cosines of these angles are given for each single second. Corrections are unnecessary then, the exact log being taken out at sight.

Example 9.—Find sin 0° 18′ 35″.

Find the column headed 0° 18′ in the table. Look **down** the left-hand column of the page for the seconds (″).

The answer is 7·73285, which is the sine of the angle.

Example 10.—Find cosine of 88° 44′ 25″.

At the foot of the page, look for cos 88° 44′. Follow the seconds column *up* the page on the right hand side for the 25″, and cosine is found to be 8·34212.

To Convert Functions to Angles.—To convert functions to angles, the process described above has to be reversed.

First find the appropriate column in the table, being careful to note whether the angle is greater or less than 45°. When finding the function, watch the index number of the log carefully, and remember again that sines, secants and tangents increase with the angle, while cosines, cosecants and cotangents decrease.

Example 1.—Find the angle of which 9·38037 is the sine.

In the table, under the heading of sine, look for the figures given, and the sine is found to be for the angle 13° 53½'.

Example 2.—Find the angle of which 9·77777 is the tangent.

When the index number of a tangent is 9, the angle is less than 45°. When the index number is 10, the angle is over 45°. For cotangents, reverse this rule.

We therefore know to look at the top of the page for this angle, and, following the appropriate column, we find the required angle is 30° 56½'.

Example 3.—Find the angle of which 9·63911 is the cosine.

This log cannot be found in the cosine column at the top of the page, so we conclude the angle is more than 45°, and look for it from the foot of the page and the angle is found to be 64° 10½'.

When the log cannot be found exactly in the table, always take the one next smaller than the given log, and find the difference between them. This "log diff." is then found in the second column of figures under the heading of *parts for*", and the required number of seconds is found in the first column abreast of this difference.

Example 4.—Find the angle of which 10·58232 is the cotangent.

The log next smaller to the given log is 10·58216.

Given log	10·58232	
Next less	10·58216	(angle 14° 40')
Log diff.	16	Correction — 18"

From the "parts" column, 16 (nearest) gives correction as 18". The log being a cotangent, this correction has to be subtracted.

Angle	14° 40' 00"
Corr.	— 18"
Reqd. Angle	14° 39' 42"

Example 5.—Find the angle of which 10·04244 is the cosecant.

Given log	10·04244			
Next less	10·04243	Angle	65° 05' 00"	Correction may
Log. diff	1	Corr.	— 10"	be from 5" to 14", so take the
		Reqd. angle	65° 04' 50"	mean.

BURTON'S TABLES.

The Table of Logarithmic Functions is No. 19, pp. 133 to 162.

In *Burton's Tables*, the "functions" of the angles are given for every minute of arc, the cosine, secant and tangent being found from the top of the page, from 0° to 90°. Their complements, the sine, cosecant and cotangent, are given from the foot of the page, working backwards, from 0° on page 167 to 90° on page 138.

To read the various functions, look for the degrees at the top or the foot of the page. If the function is from the top, the odd minutes of arc will be found in the left-hand column and are to be read downwards. If the function is from the foot of the page, the odd minutes are found in the right-hand column and are read upwards.

Between the cosine and the secant (top of page) or between the sine and cosecant (foot of page), is a column headed "D"—the difference between the log of one minute and the log of the next. The diff for the tangent or cotangent comes just after these logs.

To Find the Function.—*Example* 1.—Find sec 21° 38′ 00″.

This is from the top of the page, and is found to be 0·03172.

Note that the index numbers of the various functions are given at the heads of their respective columns.

Example 2.—Find the cotangent of 70° 12′ 35″.

Cotangents are found from the foot of the page.
Cot 70° 12′ = 9·55633.
The "diff" between cot 70° 12′ and 70° 13′ is given as 40. The correction is required for 35″ only, not for a full minute. This represents ·6 of a minute, so "D" has to be multiplied by ·6, the required correction being then 24.

Since sines, tangents, and secants increase as the angle increases, corrections for them have to be added. Cosines, cotangents, and cosecants decrease as the angle increases, so that the corrections for them have to be subtracted.

$$
\begin{array}{lll}
\text{Cot} & 70°\ 12′ & = 9·55633 \\
\text{Corr for } 35″ & & = -\ \ \ \ 24 \\
\hline
\text{Cot} & 70°\ 12′\ 35″ & = 9·55609
\end{array}
$$

Example 3.—Find secant of 46° 23′ 19″

Sec	46° 23′	= 0·16126	"D" =	13
Corr		= + 4	19″ =	× ·3
Sec 46° 23′ 19″		= 0·16130		3·9

Example 4.—Find cosine 77° 47′ 13″.

Cos	77° 47′	= 9·32553	"D" =	59
Corr		= − 12	13″ =	× ·2
Cos	77° 47′ 13″	= 9·32541		11·8

To Find Angles Corresponding to Functions.—When finding the angles corresponding to the various functions, look for the given log in the appropriate column.

If the log is a cosine, a secant or a tangent, the degrees will be found at the top of the page, and the minutes of arc in the left-hand column, abreast the log. If the log is a sine, a cosecant or a cotangent, the degrees will be found at the foot of the page, and the minutes of arc in the right-hand column, reading upwards from the foot of the page.

Example 1.—Find the angle of which 0·08435 is the secant. The answer is 34° 34'.

Example 2.—Find the angle of which 9·83540 is the sine. The answer is 43° 12'.

Example 3.—Find the angle of which 0·60647 is the cotangent. The answer is 13° 54'.

If the given log cannot be found exactly in the table, always take the next smaller log and find the difference between the two logs. Add a cipher to this difference, and divide it by the "D" from the table. The answer will be a decimal fraction of a minute of arc, which, multiplied by 60, will give the required number of seconds of arc.

Example 4.—Find the angle of which 9·72915 is the sine.

Given log   9·72915
Next less   9·72902   (Angle = **32° 24'**)
"D" = 20)130(·65
        120
        ‾‾‾‾
        100

Answer is 32° 24·65' or 32° 24' 39".

Example 5.—Find the angle of which 0·29771 is the tangent.

Given log   0·29771
Next less   0·29753   (Angle = 63° 15')
"D" = 31)180(·6
        186
        ‾‾‾

Answer is 63° 15·6' or 63° 15' 36"

Example 6.—Find the angle of which 0·16065 is the cosecant.

Given log   0·16065
Next less   0·16060   (Angle = 43° 42')
"D" = 14)50(·4 (approx.)
        56
        ‾‾

The correction for a "co" has to be subtracted, so
Answer is 43° 41·6' or 43° 41' 36".

Angles Greater than 90°.

It often happens that the function is required of an angle which is greater than 90°.

In that case, subtract 90° from the angle, and then find the complement of the required function for the smaller angle. For instance—

Find the sine of   112° 30′
Subtract   90° 00′   then

Sin 112° 30′ = cos   22° 30′ = 9·96562

Find the cosecant of   97° 45′ 20″
Subtract   90° 00′ 00″   then

Cosec 97° 45′ 20″ = Sec   7° 45′ 20″

                       = 10·00399

Another method is to subtract the function from 180°, and find the
same function for the remainder.

Example.—Find the cosecant of 135° 37′ 30″.

                       180° 00′ 00″
                       135° 37′ 30″
Cosec   44° 22′ 30″ = 10·15530

The student is recommended to choose one method, and to stick
to it. Either one gives the same result.

Example.—Find the cosecant of 103° 37′ 42″.

Method 1.   Cosec   103° 37′ 42″
                          90

            Sec   13° 37′ 42″

                  = 0·01240

Method 2.   103° 37′ 42″
                         180

            Cosec   76° 22′ 18″

                  = 0·01240

EXERCISE 6.

Find the log functions of the following angles:

1.	Sin	23°	17′	00″	9.	Sin	2°	37′	48″
2.	Tan	53	47	30	10.	Cos	87	22	12
3.	Cos	48	19	24	11.	Cosec	69	46	06
4.	Cosec	39	51	16	12.	Tan	45	00	00
5.	Cot	12	32	18	13.	Sec	12	52	11
6.	Sec	126	11	42	14.	Tan	6	21	53
7.	Sin	6	33	53	15.	Sin	142	16	37
8.	Sec	74	21	38	16.	Cot	85	28	21

Find the angles corresponding to the following logs:

17.	Cosec	10·29080		23.	Cos	9·90418
18.	Tan	9·89476		24.	Cosec	10·13962
19.	Sin	9·96493		25.	Tan	8·91328
20.	Sec	10·04699		26.	Sin	8·95386
21.	Cot	9·65722		27.	Cot	10·63976
22.	Sin	9·36287		28.	Cosec	10·74699

Note.—When using *Burton's Tables*, the "10's" in the indices are dropped. For example, Question 17 would read—Cosec 0·29080.

Practical Uses of Functions.—When Parts III. and IV. of this book are being studied, it will be found that log functions of angles are used extensively in problems concerning "celestial" navigation. The same functions, or the "natural" functions, can also be used to solve many problems, navigational and otherwise, which often crop up on board.

In any triangle, there are 6 parts—3 sides and 3 angles. To "solve" a triangle—that is, to find the measurements of all the sides and all the angles—it is necessary in the first place to know the measurements of at least three of these parts.

But if the measurements given are of three *angles* only, the actual lengths of the sides could not be found. We could only discover the *ratio* between the lengths of the various sides.

Plane (straight-lined) triangles are of two varieties—right-angled and oblique-angled. We are only concerned at the moment with the first variety, where one of the angles measures 90°.

Equations.—Equations are problems written in such a way that one side of the problem is equal to the other side, the dividing line between the two sides being shown by the equating sign (=).

For instance, $\frac{3}{4} = \frac{9}{12}$ is an equation. Its truth can be proved in two or three ways. We could, for instance, multiply the top and the bottom figures on the left-hand side (3 and 4) by 3, and the equation would then read

$$\frac{9}{12} = \frac{9}{12}$$

Conversely, we could divide both the 9 and the 12 of the right-hand side by 3, and the equation would read

$$\frac{3}{4} = \frac{3}{4}$$

A third way is to "cross-multiply". That is, multiply the TOP figure or figures of the left-hand side by the BOTTOM figures of the right-hand side. Insert the equating sign, and multiply the BOTTOM left-hand figures by the TOP right-hand figures. In our example, the result would read

$$36 = 36$$

When 3 parts of the equation are known, a fourth part can be found in the same way. The usual procedure is to make the "unknown" factor the top part of the left-hand fraction. Suppose the figure 3 in the original equation is an unknown quantity, whose value is required. Call it "x", as is usual. Then

$$\frac{x}{4} = \frac{9}{12}$$

By cross-multiplying, this becomes

$$12x = 36$$

and by dividing each side of the new equation by 12, to eliminate the "coefficient" of x, it is seen that $x=3$.

We have now found:

First, an equation containing fractions can easily be solved by cross-multiplying;

Second, when an equation contains an unknown quantity, this quantity should be made the TOP part of a fraction.

When a ship at sea is in sight of a point of land, or a lighthouse, it is always good policy to fix her position as exactly as possible, to obtain a "departure" position for the next leg of the journey. A single compass bearing of, say, a lighthouse gives only the direction of the ship from the light, but not the distance off. From a chart, however, we can find the height of the lighthouse, and if a vertical sextant angle is taken between the top of the lighthouse and its base, or the sea-line, the distance of the ship from the light can be found with very little difficulty.

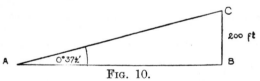

FIG. 10.

Example 1.—A lighthouse is 200 feet high, and a vertical sextant angle, base to top, is 0° 37½′. How far off the lighthouse is the ship?

In Fig. 10, the angle at "B", the base of the lighthouse, is 90°, and the side $AB=x$, the unknown side. The angle at A, the observer's position, is the vertical sextant angle. The equation is written

$$\frac{x}{200} = \frac{\text{some function of } A}{1}$$

Referring to page 24, it is seen that $\dfrac{x}{200}$ is $\dfrac{\text{adj.}}{\text{opp.}}$, or the cotangent of A. So

$$\frac{x}{200} = \frac{\cot A}{1} \quad .. \quad .. \quad .. \quad .. \quad .. \quad (a)$$

Cot A has been written "over 1" just to complete the four parts of the equation. Really, it is not necessary to do so, for when cross-multiplying, $1x=x$.

By cross-multiplying, we find that

x (dist. off light) $= 200 \times \cot A$ .. .. (b)

Using logs

Log dist. (in feet) $= \log 200 + \log \cot A$. .. (c)

The result would give the distance off in feet, which would have to be divided by 6080 to bring it to miles. So if we subtract the log of 6080 from the log found in (c), we obtain the log of the distance off IN MILES. The worked problem would appear like this:

$$
\begin{array}{lll}
200 & \log = 2 \cdot 30103 \\
0° 37\tfrac{1}{2}' & \log \cot = 1 \cdot 96200
\end{array} \Big\} +
$$

$$
\begin{array}{lll}
\text{log dist in feet} & = 4 \cdot 26303 \\
6080 & \log = 3 \cdot 78390
\end{array} \Big\} -
$$

log dist. in mls. $= \overline{0 \cdot 47913}$ $= 3$ miles (nearly).

Not infrequently, a ship may pass a light off which a reef lies for a considerable distance. At Skerryvore, rocks extend for a distance of almost 3 miles off the light. Thus a ship must be kept a safe distance to seaward of the danger.

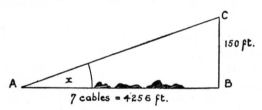

FIG. 11.

Example 2.—A 150-ft. lighthouse has a reef extending 5 cables from it. The ship wishes to pass not nearer than 7 cables off the light. What is the largest angle that should appear on the sextant? (Note.—The nearer the lighthouse, the larger the sextant angle.)

7 cables $= 7 \times 608$ ft. $= 4256$ feet.

Here the angle is the "unknown quantity".

$$\frac{4256}{150} = \cot \text{ angle (see page 24)}$$

$$
\begin{array}{ll}
4256 \log = 3 \cdot 62900 \\
150 \log = 2 \cdot 17609
\end{array} \Big\} -
$$

log cot $= \overline{1 \cdot 45291}$ Angle $= 2° 1'$ (nearly).

Example 3.—A 6-ft. man, standing 40 feet away from a flagpole, finds the vertical sextant angle, top to bottom, to be 32° 32'. How high is the flagpole?

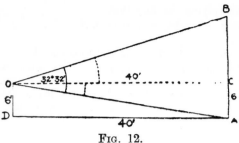

FIG. 12.

From Fig. 12, it can be seen that here we have two triangles with which to deal.   In the smaller triangle

$$OC = DA = 40 \text{ ft., and}$$
$$OD = CA = 6 \text{ ft.}$$

With this information, we can find the angle *COA*.

$$\frac{CA}{OC} = \frac{6}{40} = \tan COA$$

Nat. tan $COA=0{\cdot}15000$, and so $COA=8° \; 32'$.   Angle BOA is $32° \; 32'$, and COA is $8° \; 32'$, so $BOC=24°$.   In the second triangle, it is now known that

$OC=40$ ft., and angle $BOC=24°$. BC is unknown. $\dfrac{BC}{40}=\tan 24°$

$BC=40\times\tan \; 24°.$ $=17{\cdot}8$ feet.
Length of flagpole$=(17{\cdot}8+6)$ ft.$=23{\cdot}8$ ft.

Example 4.—What length of shrouds will be required in a vessel of 26 feet beam.   The houndsband on the mast is 22 feet above the deck, and the rigging-screw is 2 feet above the deck.

(Note.—The vessel's half-breadth is used.)

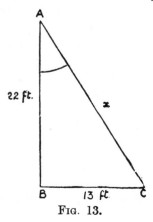

FIG. 13.

1. $\dfrac{AB}{BC} = \dfrac{22}{13}$ = cot angle A. Nat. cot.=1·6924. Angle A=30° 35'.

2. $\dfrac{x}{22}$ = sec angle A. x=22×1.1616. =25·56 feet (nearly).

3. Length of shroud=(25·56—2) feet=23·56 feet.

EXERCISE 7.

(Answers to nearest minute of arc, and to one place of decimals.)

1. A vessel approaching a headland 500 feet high, with a 50-ft. lighthouse on top, wishes to remain at least 0·8 miles off. What sextant angle would be put on the sextant?

2. A vessel is 1½ miles off a headland, and the sextant angle of the hill-top is 1° 10'. What is the height of the headland?

3. The vertical sextant angle of a 310-ft. lighthouse is 0° 16'. What distance is the observer off the lighthouse?

4. A flagstaff in a garden is fitted with a houndsband 23 feet up the staff. The stays have a spread of 8 feet from the staff. Allowing that the length of the rope-lashing is 9 inches from the ground to the lower end of the stay, find the length of each stay.

5. In water of 60 fathoms depth, a trawler pays out 500 fathoms of warp. How far astern of the gallows is the mouth of the net?

6. A 5' 6'' man, standing at the break of the forecastle, 30 feet from the mast, finds the vertical angle from deck to masthead to be 62° 16'. Deck of forecastle is 7' 6'' above main deck. How high is the mast?

7. The breadth of a ship is 30 feet, and the houndsband is 40 feet above the deck. How long are the shrouds, measured to the deck level at the ship's side?

The Use of Reciprocals.—Reciprocal relationships are mentioned on page 24. It is important that these relationships should be fully understood, as in later problems it will be shown that reciprocals are used regularly in order to simplify calculations and lessen chances of making mistakes.

Earlier in this chapter, it was shown that the sine of an angle in a right-angled triangle is found by dividing the length of the side opposite to the angle by the length of the hypotenuse, or

$$\text{sin angle} = \frac{\text{opp}}{\text{hyp}}$$

If, in a particular angle, these values were 3 and 7 respectively,

$$\text{sin angle} = \frac{3}{7}$$

The reciprocal quantity is $\dfrac{7}{3} = \dfrac{\text{hyp}}{\text{opp}}$ = cosec of the same angle

The quantity $\dfrac{7}{3}$ is called reciprocal, because $\dfrac{7}{3} \times \dfrac{3}{7} = 1.$

In another triangle, given the length of the opposite side=2 feet, and the hypotenuse=10 feet, then

$$\text{cosec angle} = \frac{10}{2} = 5, \quad \text{and the reciprocal,}$$

$$\text{sin angle} = \frac{2}{10} = \frac{1}{5} = 0\cdot2$$

If in some particular problem it became necessary to divide 16 by the sine of this angle. It would be written as

$$\frac{16}{0\cdot2} = 80.$$

The same result can be obtained by MULTIPLYING 16 by 5, and it has just been shown that 5 is the value of the cosecant of the angle, and the reciprocal of the sine. Thus $\frac{16}{\text{sin angle}} = 16 \times \text{cosec angle}.$

The process of multiplying is more simple than that of dividing, and this artifice is used as a matter of course in certain problems.

PART II.

DAY'S WORK, CHARTWORK, TIDES.

CHAPTER 5.

THE EARTH—MOVEMENTS OF THE EARTH—LATITUDE AND LONGITUDE—HOW TERRESTRIAL POSITIONS ARE EXPRESSED— DEFINITIONS.

The Earth.—The Earth is a huge sphere, which keeps continually spinning round in space, its movements controlled by the pulling power of the Sun. Its diameter is approximately 6875 nautical miles, and its circumference is 21,600 nautical miles.

Although the Earth is called a sphere, its shape is not truly spherical. Careful measurements and calculations have established that the diameter in a North-South direction is almost 26 nautical miles smaller than the diameter in an East-West direction. But for all practical purposes the Earth can be, and is, considered as a sphere.

Movements of the Earth.—The sphere turns on its own axis once every day in a direction from West to East, and the axis round which it turns meets the surface of the Earth at two points which are called the North and South geographical poles. In addition, the Earth completes one full revolution round the Sun in 365¼ days, the path it follows being called its "orbit".

The axis of the Earth does not lie perfectly vertical to this orbit, but it is inclined to the orbit at an angle of 23° 27'. This fact is of great importance, and is discussed later in Chapter 16.

Latitude and Longitude.—When a ship is on the high seas, her progress from the point of departure towards her immediate destination has to be checked frequently. Thus it becomes necessary to have some means of indicating terrestrial positions, whether on land or on the high seas, and to do so easily and quickly.

A method of doing so has been devised, and is used universally, by which the Earth is divided into imaginary portions.

In Fig. 14, the circle represents the world, and the straight line represents a circle drawn round the sphere, midway between the North and South Poles.

This circle, as can be seen from the sketch, divides the sphere into two equal parts, and for this reason it is called the "Equator". This particular circle also serves as an excellent jumping-off place from which to measure positions on the sphere.

The Earth is presumed to be a solid mass, and if the sphere were

41

to be sliced right round at the equator, a flat surface called a "plane" would be exposed. This plane passes right through the centre of the sphere.

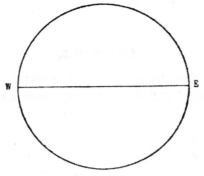

FIG. 14.

Any number of such circles, in any direction, could be drawn, with their planes passing through the sphere's centre. Such circles are called "Great Circles", and the equator itself can be defined as a great circle round the Earth, midway between the poles. When a second great circle is drawn through the North and South poles, as in Fig. 15, it can be seen that four right angles have been formed. Each of these is divided into 90°, so that the angle between the equator and the North Pole, or between the equator and the South Pole, can be divided into ninety degrees.

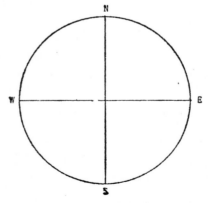

FIG. 15

The Earth, as stated above, revolves round a North-South axis, and thus it is natural and convenient to think of the direction of the equator as "broadwise". Divisions of the Earth in an East-West direction **are** therefore named "Latitude", and if we name the equator Latitude 0°, the degrees of latitude can be numbered from zero at the equator to 90° N. and 90° S. at the poles.

Circles are drawn on the sphere to represent latitude. These are all parallel to the equator and to each other, so they are called "Parallels of Latitude". From Fig. 16, it can be seen that none of them except the equator have planes which pass through the centre of the Earth. Such circles are called "Small Circles".

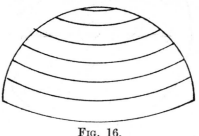

Fig. 16.

Parallels of latitude serve to indicate terrestrial positions "broadwise", but we still require to indicate positions "longwise" in order to pinpoint any required spot. All circles which indicate "longitude" pass through the North and South poles, and they therefore cut the equator at right angles.

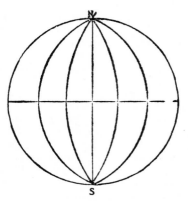

Fig. 17.

Unlike circles of latitude, circles of longitude are not parallel to each other, since they meet at the poles, but they are all great circles with planes passing through the Earth's centre.

In the case of longitude, there is no natural jumping-off place from which to base measurements. However, Greenwich Observatory is well-known throughout the civilised world, and a great circle through both poles, and passing through the position of the Observatory is now almost universally accepted as Longitude 0°.

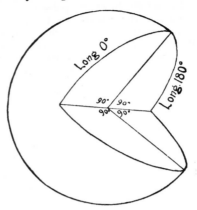

FIG. 18.

It can be seen from Fig. 18 that the only natural place to finish the measurement of longitude, short of going right round the world, is half-way round the world from Greenwich. This angle measures 180°, and so longitude is measured from 0° at Greenwich to 180° E. and 180° W.

Each degree of arc can be sub-divided into 60', as has already been shown in Chapter 2, and each minute further sub-divided into 60''.

How Terrestrial Positions are expressed.—When a ship at sea is in sight of land, her position could be expressed as, say, 10 miles North from Cape Wrath. This would give her position with sufficient accuracy.

More often than not, however, the vessel is out of sight of land, and a handier method is required to express her position. It is for this reason that the sphere has been divided into imaginary portions.

If the ship's position were given only as Lat. 54° 15' N., she could be *anywhere* on a small circle 54° 15' North of the equator. In the same way, if the position were given simply as Long. 12° 30' W., the ship could be anywhere on a great circle 12° 30' West from Greenwich. But when both latitude and longitude are given, the ship's position is pinpointed accurately on the surface of the sphere.

Thus both Latitude and Longitude are required to express a ship's position at sea, or to express the position of a lighthouse or a point of land. When expressing this position, the universal convention used is that latitude is always given first, followed by the longitude, thus:

Lat. 54° 15' N., Long. 12° 30' W.

Definitions.—A list of definitions is given here, and these should be memorised and thoroughly understood.

Great Circle	.. ..	Is a circle on a sphere whose plane passes through the sphere's centre.
Small Circle	.. ..	Is a circle on a sphere whose plane does not pass through the centre.
Equator	.. ..	Is a great circle on the terrestrial sphere midway between the poles.
Poles	.. .. ..	The poles of the Earth are the points where the Earth's axis meets the surface.
Parallel of Latitude	..	Is a small circle on the terrestrial sphere, parallel to the equator.
Meridian of Longitude	..	Is a great circle on the terrestrial sphere passing through the poles and cutting the equator at right angles.
Prime Meridian	.. ..	Is the first meridian, or the meridian through Greenwich Observatory (Long. 0°). It is the meridian from which longitude is measured.
Plane	.. .. ..	Is any flat surface.

See also Chapter 37, page 397.

CHAPTER 6.

THE MARINER'S COMPASS—BOXING THE COMPASS—VARIATION —DEVIATION—ERROR OF THE COMPASS—CORRECTING COMPASS COURSES—LEEWAY—3-FIGURE NOTATION.

The Mariner's Compass.—Out of sight of land, a ship's head can only be kept in any required direction by steering a course by compass.

Briefly, the Mariner's Compass consists of a light circular card enclosed in a bowl. This bowl, usually made of brass, copper, or glass, may be filled with liquid—distilled alcohol—or it may only have air in it. In smaller vessels, and in vessels subjected to shocks, as by gunfire, etc., it is usual for the bowl to be filled with liquid, while in larger vessels, a "dry" compass card is more usual.

Whichever variety is used, the idea is the same—the compass card must float horizontally with the minimum of friction to make it as efficient an instrument of direction as pos ible.

The card itself is graduated at its outside edge either in "quarter-points" or in degrees. Many cards have both systems of graduation. A narrow vertical line is marked inside the bowl at the centre fore-and-aft line of the ship. This line represents the actual direction of the ship's head, and is called the "lubber-line". When the helmsman is given a course to steer—say N.N.E.—the N.N.E. point of the compass card must be kept as near as possible to the lubber-line.

Boxing the Compass.—Every seaman should be familiar with the graduations of the card, and should be able to "box the compass" to quarter-points with ease.

The "NORTH" point of the compass is always specially marked, and is kept pointing to magnetic North by a magnet, or magnets, fixed underneath the card, parallel to the North and South points of the card. At right angles to the North point, EAST lies to the right when you are facing North, and WEST lies to the left.

The four points North, South, East and West, are called the

"Cardinal" points of the compass, and the angle between each succeeding pair—North and East, East and South, and so on, is a right angle, 90°.

Each quarter of a circle, or "quadrant", can also be divided into 8 points. These points are read

From NORTH to EAST;

,, NORTH ,, WEST;

,, SOUTH ,, EAST;

,, SOUTH ,, WEST.

It is very seldom that the compass is read from East or f om West towards North or South. One navigational problem which requires such a reading is discussed in Chapter 18.

The method of naming the various points in each quadrant of the compass can be most easily understood if each successive act of subdividing the right angle is tackled separately, and the task of "boxing the compass" thereby becomes greatly simplified.

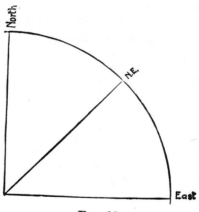

Fig. 19.

In Fig. 19, the North and East points of the compass are shown, at right angles to ea h other. (N. and E.).

When this ang e is divided into two equal parts of 45° each, a natural name to call the resulting point is NORTH-EAST (N.E.), which combines the names of the two limiting points of the right angle.

In the complete round of the compass, four such points are formed, —N.E., S.E., S.W. and N.W.—and these four points, being midway between the cardinal points, are called the "Inter-cardinal" points.

In Fig. 20, the two angles of 45° have each been bisected, dividing

the right angle into 4 angles, each measuring 22½°. The two new
points which have just been formed are definitely not North-East.

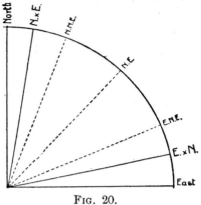

FIG. 20.

One is to the northward of N.E., the other is to the eastward. So they
are called respectively NORTH-North-East (N.N.E.), and EAST-North-
East (E.N.E.).

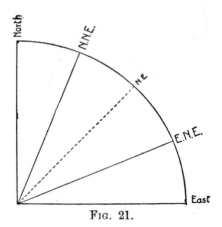

FIG. 21.

If next, the angles nearest to North and East are bisected, as in
Fig. 21, the angles formed each measure 11¼°. The one near North
lies to the eastward of that point, and is therefore called NORTH-BY-
EAST (N.×E.). The one near East lies to the northward of East, and
is similarly called EAST-BY-NORTH (E.×N.).

Finally, as in Fig. 22, the remaining two angles are bisected, so that now each angle contained within the right angle measures $11\frac{1}{4}°$.
The angle to the left of N.E. is nearer to North, and is named

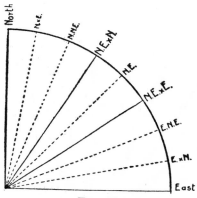

FIG. 22.

North-East-BY-North (N.E. × N.) and the other, which lies nearer to East, is named North-East-BY-East (N.E. × E.)

Each separate quadrant of the compass card is treated in the same way, and the points are named by the same process of reasoning. A full compass card, with the points named, is given in Fig. 23.

When the card is still further sub-divided into quarter-points, it can be seen that the value of a quarter-point is 2° 48′ 45″. That is $(11\frac{1}{4}° \div 4)$.

When boxing the compass, say between North and East, the quarter-points are, for a start, reckoned from North. Using that heading as a basic point, they work AWAY from North for two points, as far as N.N.E., the values of the quarter-points INCREASING—($\frac{1}{4}$, $\frac{1}{2}$, $\frac{3}{4}$). The basic point is then changed to N.E., and in the next two points, the quarters are reckoned from N.N.E. TOWARDS N.E., so that their values DECREASE—($\frac{3}{4}$, $\frac{1}{2}$, $\frac{1}{4}$). Still using N.E. as a basic point, the quarters are reckoned from there as far as E.N.E., with their values again increasing; from there the basic point is changed to EAST, with the quarter values DECREASING.

From the adjoining Table, it can be seen that in the 1st, 3rd, 5th, etc., sections, the values of the quarter-points increase, while in the 2nd, 4th, 6th, etc., sections, the values decrease.

Students should be able to repeat the quarter-points correctly in either direction, commencing at any quarter-point on the card.

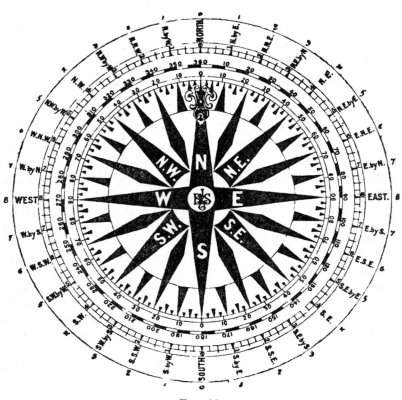

Fig. 23.

TABLE OF QUARTER POINTS

Sections 1, 3, 5, etc. increasing

N.W.	West	S.W.	South	S.E.	East	N.E.	North
NW¼N	W¼N	SW¼W	S¼W	SE¼S	E¼S	NE¼E	N¼E
NW½N	W½N	SW½W	S½W	SE½S	E½S	NE½E	N½E
NW¾N	W¾N	SW¾W	S¾W	SE¾S	E¾S	NE¾E	N¾E
NW×N	W×N	SW×W	S×W	SE×S	E×S	NE×E	N×E
NW×N¼N	W×N¼N	SW×W¼W	S×W¼W	SE×S¼S	E×S¼S	NE×E¼E	N×E¼E
NW×N½N	W×N½N	SW×W½W	S×W½W	SE×S½S	E×S½S	NE×E½E	N×E½E
NW×N¾N	W×N¾N	SW×W¾W	S×W¾W	SE×S¾S	E×S¾S	NE×E¾E	N×E¾E
N.N.W.	W.N.W.	W.S.W.	S.S.W.	S.S.E.	E.S.E.	E.N.E.	N.N.E.

Sections 2, 4, 6, etc. decreasing

N.W.	West	S.W.	South	S.E.	East	N.E.	North
NW¼W	W¼S	SW¼S	S¼E	SE¼E	E¼N	NE¼N	N¼W
NW½W	W½S	SW½S	S½E	SE½E	E½N	NE½N	N½W
NW¾W	W¾S	SW¾S	S¾E	SE¾E	E¾N	NE¾N	N¾W
NW×W	W×S	SW×S	S×E	SE×E	E×N	NE×N	N×W
NW×W¼W	W×S¼S	SW×S¼S	S×E¼E	SE×E¼E	E×N¼N	NE×N¼N	N×W¼W
NW×W½W	W×S½S	SW×S½S	S×E½E	SE×E½E	E×N½N	NE×N½N	N×W½W
NW×W¾W	W×S¾S	SW×S¾S	S×E¾E	SE×E¾E	E×N¾N	NE×N¾N	N×W¾W
W.N.W.	W.S.W.	S.S.W.	S.S.E.	E.S.E.	E.N.E.	N.N.E.	N.N.W.

Variation.—As has already been stated, the world revolves on its axis, and the points where that axis meets the surface are called the "True Poles" of the Earth.

In addition to other attributes, the world possesses that mysterious force called "Magnetism", and is itself, in fact, a huge magnet.

Every magnet must possess two poles, and regarding the world as a magnet these poles are named the North and South Magnetic Poles.

If these magnetic poles were at the same position as the true poles, compass needles would always point to true North, provided there was no local attraction.

Unfortunately, however, the magnetic poles are situated at some considerable distance from the true poles (in Lat. 70° N., Long. 97° W., and Lat. 73° S., Long. 155° E.) and it is to the North magnetic pole that the North point of the compass holds. The angle between true North and magnetic North is called the "Variation of the Compass."

The amount of variation depends upon the observer's position on the surface of the globe and can be calculated, and the variation for any particular area is usually to be found on charts of that area.

In Fig. 24, *T* represents true North, *M* represents magnetic North, and the angle between them, *MOT*, represents the variation. From this we get the definition. Variation of the compass is the angle between the true and the magnetic meridians.

This angle differs at different parts of the Earth, and it also varies slowly with time, in all probability owing to the fact that the position of the magnetic poles is slowly altering with reference to the true poles.

So long as a vessel remains in one place, the variation remains unchanged, no matter what may be the direction of the ship's head.

Deviation of the Compass.—Iron and steel are the metals principally

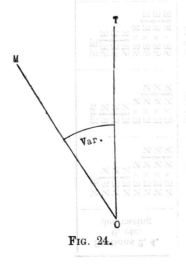

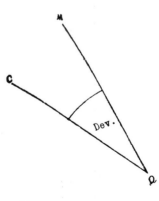

FIG. 24.   FIG. 25.

affected by magnetism, and it is in the midst of a vessel built of these materials that a ship's compass is placed.

Each part of a ship exercises a different magnetic effect on the compass, so, as the ship's head alters, a different effect, exercised at a different angle, alters the amount of attraction or repulsion on the compass needles.

This attraction, or repulsion, is called "Deviation of the Compass", and its amount depends on the direction in which the ship is steering, and it alters as the ship's head alters.

In Fig. 25, M represents magnetic North, C represents the ship's compass North, and the angle between them, MOC, represents the deviation of the compass.

Combining the information from Figs. 24 and 25, we find that the angle between true and magnetic North is the variation, and the angle

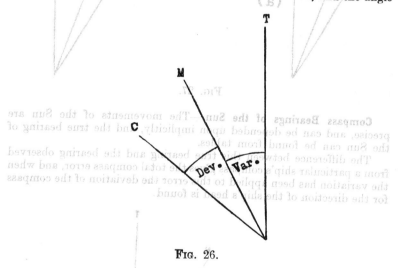

FIG. 26.

between magnetic and compass North is the deviation. From Fig. 26 it can be seen that, to convert a compass course to a true course, the deviation is first applied, converting compass course to magnetic course, and variation is then applied, converting the magnetic course to a true course.

Error of the Compass.—When variation and deviation are combined the result is the error of the compass and, as is seen from Fig. 26, the error is the angle between true North and compass North. If the variation were 20° W., and the deviation 10° W., it is easy to see that the error would be 30° W. If the variation were 10° W., and the deviation were 5° E., the error would be 5° W. (See Figs 27, (a) and (b).) Thus the Rule is: To find error, add variation and deviation when they are of the same name. When they are of different names, subtract them, calling the error the same name as the larger of the two. Error, variation and deviation are named either East or West—East when the North point of the compass is drawn to the right; West when the North point is drawn to the left.

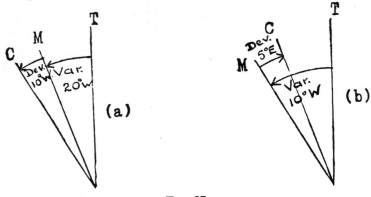

Fig. 27.

Compass Bearings of the Sun.—The movements of the Sun are precise, and can be depended upon implicitly, and the true bearing of the Sun can be found from tables.

The difference between this true bearing and the bearing observed from a particular ship's compass gives the total compass error, and when the variation has been applied to this error the deviation of the compass for the direction of the ship's head is found.

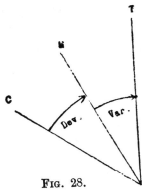

Fig. 28.

In the next chapter, a problem named "The Day's Work" is discussed. In this problem the courses given are almost invariably compass courses, and these, of course, have to be converted to true courses before the problem can be solved. To convert compass courses to true courses the deviation for the direction of the ship's head is

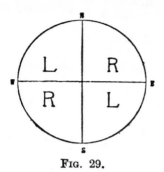

FIG. 29.

first applied to convert the compass course to magnetic. The variation is then applied, to convert the magnetic course to true.

When an observer standing at the centre of a compass faces North, the East point lies on his right hand, and the West point on his left hand. If the observer faces South, the West point is on his right hand, and the East point on his left.

The various quadrants, or quarters, of the compass are therefore marked "R" and "L", as in Fig. 29.

When converting compass courses to true courses, or vice versa, both in this problem and in chart problems, the "R" or "L" should always be used. There is nothing "lubberly" in doing so, and in an examination, if mistakes are made by omitting to use the "R" and "L", the candidate will probably be severely taken to task over the omission.

The order to be followed in correcting a course is from—

    (1) Compass   to
    (2) Magnetic   thence to
    (3) True

If, in travelling along that route, the deviation and the variation have the same names (both E. or both W.), they should each be applied the same way, the rule being—

From Compass to True apply E. to Right; W. to Left.

The word CaTERWauL helps the student to remember the rule—From Compass to True, East to Right, West to Left.

Example.—Ship's head was N. 72° E., deviation was 16° W., variation 12° W., find the true course.

Comp. course N. 72° E. R. ⎫
Deviation 16 W. L. ⎬ Contrary names subtract

Mag. course N. 56° E. R. ⎫
Variation 12 W. L. ⎬ Contrary names subtract

True course N. 44° E. R.

Example.—Ship's head S. 37° E., deviation 5° E., variation 16° W., find the true course.

Comp. course S. 37° E. L. ⎫
Deviation 5° E. R. ⎬ Contrary names subtract

Mag. course S. 32 E. L. ⎫
Variation 16 W. L. ⎬ Same names add

True course S. 48° E. L.

A short examination of these two examples will show that the variation and the deviation can be comb ned into compass error by adding them when they are of the same name, and by subtract.ng them when they have contrary names. In the latter case, the error is given the same name as the larger of the var.at.on and deviation.

Example.—Ship's head S. 42° W., deviation 13° W., variation 6° W., find the true course.

Comp. course S. 42° W R   Dev. 13° W.
Error 19 W L.   Var. 6 W.

True course S. 23° W.   Error 19° W.

Leeway.—When a stiff breeze is blowing, especially when it is at an angle to the ship's fore and aft line, the vessel will probably not make her proper course through the water, but will be blown to leeward. The amount of the leeway, which in actual practice can only be estimated by experience, depends on—

(a) The force of the wind.

(b) The direction of the wind relative to the ship's fore and aft line.

(c) Whether the vessel is loaded or light.

With regard to (b) it is easy to see that a wind which is broad on the beam will cause more drift than a wind which is fine on the bow.

With regard to (c), a deep-laden vessel has more "grip of the water" than a vessel flying light, and will, therefore, not make so much leeway.

The amount of the estimated leeway is always given in the question, and WHEN CONVERTING A COMPASS COURSE TO A TRUE COURSE, it has always to be allowed AWAY from the wind.

(Note.—The question of leeway is also discussed in the section on "Chartwork.").

Example.—Compass course N. 25° E., wind W.N.W., leeway 6°, deviation 12° W., variation 5° E., find the true course.

Comp. course	N. 25° E. R.	
Error	7 W. L.	

| | N. 18 E. R. | } Allow leeway to E'rd away from |
| Leeway | + 6 | } wind |

| True course | N. 24° E. R. |

Example.—Compass course N. 77° W., wind S.W., leeway 5°, deviation 12° E., variation 3° W., find true course.

Comp. course	N. 77° W. L.
Error	9° E. R.

| | N. 68 W. L. | } Allow to northward |
| Leeway | − 5 | } |

| True course | N. 63° W. L. |

The 3-Figure Notation.—When dealing with courses and bearings, increasing use is being made of the "3-figure notation," in place of dividing the compass card into four quadrants. In this notation, NORTH is expressed as 000°, and the degrees of courses, etc., increase in a clockwise direction round the card to 359°. Thus N.E. becomes 045°, EAST is 090°, S.E. is 135°, SOUTH is 180°, and so on.

Since East is 090°, it can be seen that any course whose value is less than 90° must lie in the N.E. quadrant. Conversely, any course in the N.E. quadrant must not exceed 90°. Similarly, any course whose value lies between 091° and 179° must be in the S.E. quadrant, while those between 181° and 269°, and between 271° and 359°, must be in the S.W. and N.W. quadrants respectively.

For many daily purposes at sea, quadrantal names will continue to be used, so it is vitally necessary for the seaman to be able to convert a course or bearing named by one method to the equivalent value of the other method. Very little practice indeed is required for this purpose, using the information just given.

Under the "quadrantal" method of naming courses, etc., courses in the N.E. and S.W. quadrants are read in a clockwise direction, while those in the S.E. and N.W. quadrants are read in an anti-clockwise direction. Under the "3-figure notation" method, all courses are read in a clockwise direction, so that when this notation is used, only one set of rules is necessary for the conversion of True courses to Magnetic or Compass, and *vice versa*.

With the aid of a little rhyme, this rule can be easily memorised— Given a True Course—

"*Variation West, Magnetic is best;*
Variation East, Magnetic is least."

That is to say, when converting a True Course or bearing to Magnetic by applying variation, or to Compass by applying total error, ADD if the variation or error is West. If East, subtract. When converting from Compass to Magnetic or to True, the rule must of course be the converse of the above, and can only be used with 3-figure notation.

True courses and bearings are given as 129° T, or simply as 129°. Magnetic and Compass courses and bearings are distinguished by affixing the letters M or C respectively, thus:

Course 129° T.   Var. 11° W. = 140° M.   Dev. 6° E. = 134° C.

Course 341° C.   Err. 19° W. = 322° T.

Example.—Compass Course 237°, wind N.W., leeway 3°, deviation 3° E., variation 12° W., find the True Course.

Course	237° C	}	subtract
Error	9 W.		
	223°	}	allow to southward
Leeway	−3		
Course	225° T		

Example.—Compass Course 353°, wind West, leeway 4°, deviation 2° E., variation 17° E., find the True Course.

Course	353° C	}	add
Error	19 E		
	372	}	allow clockwise to eastward
Leeway	+4		
	376	}	Course exceeds 360°, take 360° from it.
Subtract	360		
Course	016° T		

Example.—Compass course 019°, wind East, leeway 6°, deviation 2° E., variation 22° W., find the True Course.

Course   019° C   ⎫ Error greater than course, and subtrac-
          +360   ⎭ tive. Add 360° to course.
          ————
          379°
Error   20 W.
          ————
          359
Leeway   —6   ⎫ allow to westward
                     ⎭
Course   353° T

EXERCISE 8.

Given the following particulars, find the true course:—

	Comp. Co.	Wind	Lee	Dev.	Var.
1.	N. 42° E.	N.N.W.	4°	7° E.	18° W.
2.	S. 37 E.	South	3	5 W.	11 W.
3.	S. 7 W.	West	5	6 W.	9 W.
4.	N. 39 W.	N.N.E.	3	4 E.	15 E.
5.	South	E.S.E.	6	11 W.	17 W.
6.	S. 56 E.	North	4	2 E.	15 E.
7.	N. 39 W.	W.S.W.	2	14 W.	16 E.
8.	S. 33 E.	S.S.W.	4	14 E.	26 E.
9.	West	North	6	6 E.	6 W.
10.	S. 87 E.	S.E.	2	5 W.	12 W.
11.	113°	South	2	4 W.	11 W.
12.	090	N.E.	3	3 E.	9 W.
13.	002	E.N.E.	5	6 E.	4 E.
14.	349	West	4	2 W.	9 E.
15.	222	West	2	3 E.	16 W.
16.	101	North	3	5 W.	18 W.

CHAPTER 7.

MERCATOR'S PROJECTION—THE RHUMB LINE—DEPARTURE— DIFFERENCE OF LATITUDE—DIFFERENCE OF LONGITUDE— PLANE SAILING—PARALLEL SAILING—THE DAY'S WORK— MERCATOR SAILING—MERIDIONAL PARTS.

Charts.—From the earliest days of navigation, seamen and geographers have endeavoured to depict areas of land and sea on flat surfaces. Although nowadays we may be inclined to smile tolerantly at the glaring imperfections of these early maps, we must also recognise that the first cartographers used eyes and brains very efficiently. Wonderful voyages into the unknown were planned and carried through using these imperfect charts, or, as often as not, with no charts at all. It was not until the close of the 16th century that the method of drawing charts on what is known as "Mercator's Projection" was evolved. Today, practically all marine navigation is carried out with the aid of charts drawn on Mercator's Projection.

In Chapter 5 (p. 43) it was shown that terrestrial latitudes on a sphere are represented by "small" circles, each circle parallel to the Equator, and each, therefore, parallel to the other circles of latitude.

Terrestrial longitudes are represented by "great" circles, all of which cut the parallels of latitude at an angle of 90°. Circles, or meridians, of longitude are not parallel to each other, but meet at the Earth's poles. Meridians are at their greatest distance apart at the Equator.

On Mercator charts, circles of latitude are represented by parallel straight lines drawn horizontally on the chart in a true East-West direction, while circles of longitude are represented by *parallel* straight lines drawn vertically on the chart in a true North-South direction. The important point to notice about the meridians is that they too are drawn *parallel to each other*.

It must therefore be obvious that while this system of representing meridians is correct at the Equator, distances between the meridians in an East-West direction must become distorted as the meridians, shown as parallel lines, grow away from the Equator. The greater the distance from the Equator, the more will these distances be distorted. It will also be appreciated that if distortion is present in that direction, there must also be a compensating distortion in a North-South direction if a correct ratio between the two directions is to be preserved. The method used to resolve that difficulty is discussed later in this chapter.

60

The Rhumb Line.—A Rhumb Line, or Loxodromic Curve, is a line drawn on a sphere in such a manner that it cuts each m ridian of longitude at the same angle. On a sphere, it would appear as a curve winding round and round, and gradually approaching the pole. In theory, this curve would never reach the pole.

On a Mercator chart, the rhumb line becomes a straight line, still cutting each meridian at the same angle. As such, it represents on the chart the track across the ocean of a vessel pursuing a steady course. The course is the angle which the line makes with the North-South meridian, and the length of the li e is termed the distance, which is usually expressed in nautical miles, or, on large-scale charts, in cables.

Departure.—If a vessel is steering true East or West, the distance steamed is then named "Departure." Departure is defined as the distance made good in nautical miles to the East or West of the point sailed from. On the Equator, and *only on the Equator*, this Departure, expressed in miles, is equal to the Difference of Longitude expressed in minutes of arc. (See also p. 103).

Difference of Latitude.—Figure 30 represents the globe, partly dissected.

The arcs *PA* and *PB* represent meridians of longitude.

Let us suppose that there are towns situated in Lat. *A*, Lat. *C*, and Lat. *E*. Then *AC* represents the difference of latitude between the two places *A* and *C*. Similarly *CE* represents the difference of latitude (D. Lat.) between *C* and *E*.

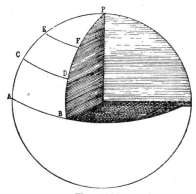

Fig. 30.

Difference of Latitude is the arc of a meridian between the parallels of latitude through two places, and *CE* therefore also represents the D. Lat. between *C* and *F*, and *AC* represents the D. Lat. between *A* and *D*, or between *B* and *C*.

On the globe 1' of latitude represents 1 sea mile (6080 feet) so that D. Lat. can be measured in miles without further trouble.

The Sailings.—When a vessel steams on a rhumb line course at a known speed from a known position of departure, the seaman is able at any time to plot the ship's approximate position on the course line drawn on the chart. He is also able to find the latitude and longitude of that position without direct reference to a chart.

The methods used to obtain the information required for that purpose are closely related to each other, and are called "The Sailings." They include:—

1. Plane Sailing, with which is linked Traverse Sailing;
2. Parallel Sailing, with which is linked Middle Latitude Sailing;
3. Mercator Sailing.

Plane Sailing and Parallel Sailing give good results only if used over restricted distances. The portion of the globe which is under consideration is treated exactly as if it were a plane surface. For that reason, the normal distances used should never exceed 600 miles, and the normal latitudes should if possible never exceed 60°. When greater distances or higher latitudes are used, better results are obtained by using Mercator Sailing.

PLANE SAILING.

When a vessel steers any rhumb line course except North, South, East or West, that course, and the distance covered, can be represented on the plane surface of a chart in the manner shown in Fig. 31, where *AC* is any meridian, *AB* is the distance, and the angle *BAC* is the course.

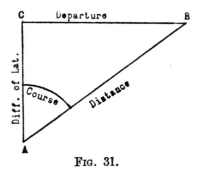

FIG. 31.

A line drawn in an E.-W. direction from *B* to *C* completes a right-angled triangle, in which D. Lat. is represented by *AC*, Dep. by *BC*. It can then be seen that, if the ordinary rules of right-angled triangles are used,

$$\frac{\text{Dep.}}{\text{Dist.}} = \text{Sin Co., and} \quad \text{Dep.} = \text{Dist. Sin Co.}$$

$$\frac{\text{D. Lat}}{\text{Dist}} = \text{Cos Co., and} \quad \text{D. Lat.} = \text{Dist. Cos. Co.}$$

Example 1.—Given course 312° T., distance 312 miles, find the D. Lat. and Dep.

Co. 312° = N. 48° W.

$$\frac{\text{D. Lat.}}{312} = \cos 48° \quad \text{D. Lat.} = 312 \times \cos. \ 48° = 208\cdot76'$$

$$\frac{\text{Dep.}}{312} = \sin. 48° \quad \text{Dep.} = 312 \times \sin. \ 48° = 231\cdot85'$$

Example 2.—A ship makes good D. Lat. 98' N., and Dep. 137' W. Find the course and distance.

$$\frac{98}{137} = \cot \text{co.} = 0\cdot7153. \qquad \text{Course} = \text{N. } 54° 25\tfrac{1}{2}' \text{ W.}$$

$$\frac{\text{Dist.}}{137} = \text{cosec co.} \quad \text{Dist.} = 137 \times \text{cosec co.} = 168\cdot44 \text{ mls.}$$

Example 3.—A vessel steers 041° T., 420 miles, from Lat. 48° 48' N. What will her latitude be then?

$$\frac{\text{D. Lat.}}{420} = \cos 41°. \quad \text{D. Lat.} = 420 \times \cos 41° = 316\cdot97' = 5° 16\cdot97'.$$

Lat. left	48°	48·00' N.
D. Lat.	5	16·97 N.
Lat. in	54	04·97 N.

Example 4.—A vessel alters her Dep. 139' E. after sailing 282 miles. What course did she steer?

$$\frac{139}{282} = \sin \text{Co.} = \cdot4929$$

Course N. or S. 29° 32' E.

Exercise 8a.

Plane Sailing.

(This exercise should first be worked using Plane Sailing formulae, and the results should be checked by using the Traverse Table.)

1. Given true course 207°, distance 260 miles, find D. Lat. and Dep.
2. Given Dep. 276', course 068° T., find the distance.

3. A ship sails from Lat. 47° 16′ N., and steers 333° T. for 10 hrs. at 13 knots. What is her latitude then?

4. A ship leaves Lat. 37° 18′ N., and on arrival in Lat. 43° 05′ N. she finds her Dep. is exactly half the D. Lat. What course has she steered, and for what distance?

5. After steaming for 314 miles from Lat. 40° 40′ N., an officer finds the ship has made a departure of 205′ E. If she sailed in a N.E'ly direction, what is her new latitude?

6. A ship in Lat. 18° 19′ S. wishes to reach Lat. 23° 45′ S. If her course is S. 38° E. T., how far will she have to steam?

7. After steaming for 500 miles, a vessel finds she has altered her latitude 4° 36′. What course has she steered?

8. If a ship's departure to the East is exactly one third the distance steamed, what course has she steered?

9. A rhumb line is drawn at an angle of 28° to a meridian. If the D. Lat. measures 7°, how long is the hypotenuse of the triangle?

10. After steering 340° T. for 465 miles, a vessel finds her latitude is 3° 51′ N. From what latitude did she sail?

Answers to Exercise 8a.

1. D. Lat. 231·66′. Dep. 118·04′.
2. Dist. 297·68 miles.
3. Latitude reached 49° 11·83′.
4. Course N. 26° 34′ E. or W. Distance 387·94 miles.
5. Latitude reached 44° 37·84′ N.
6. Distance to steam 413·7 miles.
7. Course N. 56½° E. or W. or S. 56½° E. or W.
8. Course N. or S. 19° 28·4′ E.
9. Hypotenuse=Distance=475·7 miles.
10. Sailed from Lat. 3° 26′ S.

Traverse Sailing.

In Traverse Sailing, all the true courses and distances sailed by a vessel during some specified period are tabulated. In practice the period taken is very often, but by no means always, from noon on one day to noon on the next day. The D. Lat. and Dep. for each separate course and distance are then found from a special "Traverse Table," and tabulated. From these particulars, the net D. Lat. and Dep. are obtained.

It is important to note that in Plane and Traverse Sailings, the component parts of the triangle include only D. Lat., Dep., Course, and Distance. *D. Long. does not enter into these sailings.*

In the Traverse Table, (pp. 2-93 in *Norie's*, Table 3 in *Burton's*) the right-angled triangle is "solved" for every degree of course from 1° to 89°, and for every separate mile from 1 to 600.

PARALLEL SAILING.

It has already been stated that an observer's exact position cannot be known unless both latitude and longitude are known. (p. 44).

When the position from which a ship has sailed is known, together with the course steered and the distance steamed, the D. Lat. can be obtained either by using the formula found in Plane Sailing, or by using the Traverse Table. From these known figures, the latitude reached by the vessel ("Lat. in") can be found. The Dep. is obtained in the same manner, but the Difference of Longitude, (D. Long.) must also be obtained in order to find the longitude reached. ("Long. in").

Difference of Longitude.—D. Long., like departure, is measured to the East or the West along a parallel of latitude. In Fig. 30, (p. 61) D. Long. between A and B=D. Long. between C and D=D. Long. between E and F. But it is quite noticeable that the actual *distance* between E and F is much smaller than the distance between C and D, or between A and B, although in each case the D. Long. is the same. The East-West distance, or departure, between places situated on the same two meridians decreases progressively as the pole of either hemisphere is approached, because of the fact that all meridians meet at the poles.

In Figure 32, PA and PB are two meridians.

P is the pole of the Earth.

C is the centre of the Earth.

$BC=EC=PC=$radii of Earth.

AB is the D. Long., an arc of the equator between A and B.

DE is the arc of a parallel of latitude between the same meridians, and is the departure in that latitude.

EF is the radius of a small circle of the parallel of latitude.

Arc BE (or angle BCE) represents the latitude of E.

The two arcs AB and DE bear the same proportion to each other as do the radii of their circles BC and EF. That is to say—

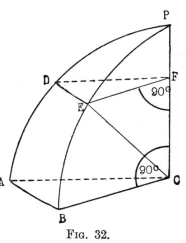

Fig. 32.

Arc $A B$ is to arc $D E$
as
Radius $B C$ is to radius $E F$
or
$$\frac{\text{arc } DE}{\text{arc } AB} = \frac{EF}{BC}$$

Also, $BC=EC$, since each is a radius of the Earth, so the above can be written as—

$$\frac{\text{arc } DE}{\text{arc } AB} = \frac{EF}{EC}$$

Now, $\dfrac{EF}{EC}$ is the sine of angle FCE, or the cosine of its complement, ECB, which is the latitude.

$$\text{Arc } AB = \text{D. Long.}$$
$$\text{Arc. } DE = \text{Dep.}$$

So that $\dfrac{\text{Dep.}}{\text{D. Long.}} = \cos \text{lat.}$

This is a simple equation, which we can transform to our own needs by following certain rules.

$$\text{For instance, } \frac{12}{3} = 4$$

If we wish to have the 3 on the other side of the equation, we have to change it from a divider to multiplier, thus—

$$12 = 4 \times 3$$

and the equation is still correct.

In the same way the equation $\dfrac{\text{Dep.}}{\text{D. Long.}} = \cos \text{lat.}$

can be transformed to Dep = D. Long. × cos. lat.

Thence, by transposing, D. Long.$= \dfrac{\text{dep.}}{\cos \text{lat.}}$, and since cosines and

secants are reciprocals, and to divide by a function is the same as to multiply by its reciprocal, we have

$$\text{D. Long} = \sec \text{lat.} \times \text{dep.}$$

which is the form we require it to take.

Thus, when a ship has made a certain specified course and distance from a known position, her ultimate latitude is found by applying a "Plane Sailing" formula to the Lat. left, while her ultimate longitude is found by applying a "Parallel Sailing" formula to a Departure already obtained from the Plane Sailing formula.

Two latitudes are usually involved—"Lat. left" and "Lat. in." When that is the case, the secant is taken of the "Mean Latitude"— the latitude numerically half-way between the latitude left and the latitude in.

The position found is approximate only, and assumes that the course and distance used is correct. It is called a "Dead Reckoning" (D.R.) position. Winds and ocean currents have an effect on the course and speed made good by the ship, and when these, too, are taken into account, the position is called an "Estimated position."

The name "Parallel Sailing" has been handed down from the days when means of finding a ship's longitude at sea did not exist. Vessels sailed as directly as possible to the latitude of the place to which they were bound, and then steered East or West along the parallel of latitude until a landfall was made.

Finding D. Long from Traverse Table.—Two equations, one taken from Plane Sailing and one from Parallel Sailing, can be used to demonstrate graphically a method by which Difference of Longitude corresponding to a particular Departure can be obtained by use of the Traverse Table only.

1. D. Lat. = Dist. × Cos Co.   (Plane Sailing)
2. Dep.   = D. Long. × Cos Lat.   (Parallel Sailing)

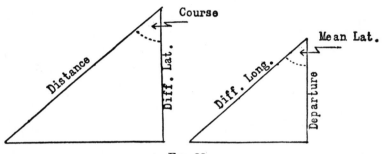

Fig. 32a.

In Fig. 32a, the left-hand triangle is the same as is used in Plane Sailing. (See also Fig. 31).

The right-hand triangle shows the relationship between D. Long. and Dep. $\dfrac{\text{D. Long.}}{\text{Dep.}} = \text{Sec. Lat.}$)

If the angles representing "Course" and "Latitude" respectively are made equal in these triangles, the two triangles are similar. Under these circumstances, it can be seen that the ratio between D. Lat. and Dist. in one triangle is equal to the ratio between Dep. and D. Long. in the other triangle. If "Dep" in the right-hand triangle is made equal to "D. Lat" in the left hand one, the D. Long. of one triangle must be equal to the Dist. of the other.

From these facts, the following rule is obtained:—

Using the Latitude (or Mean Latitude) as a Course in the Traverse Table, look for the given Dep. in the D. Lat. column.

The corresponding Dist. gives the required D. Long.

This rule should be memorised.

Most nautical Tables indicate the rule in the headings of the relevant columns of the Traverse Table.

Example 1.—Find the true course and distance from Lat. 31° 16′ N., Long. 87° 41′ W., to Lat. 34° 09′ N., Long. 83° 25′ W.

| Lat. left | 31° | 16′ N. | Long. left | 87° | 41′ W. | Lat. left | 31° | 16′ N. |
| Lat. to | 34 | 09 N. | Long to | 83 | 25 W. | ½ D. Lat. | 1 | 26½ N. |

| D. Lat. | 2 | 53′ N. | D. Long. | 4 | 16′ E. | Mean Lat. | 32 | 42½ |

| | =173′ | | | =256′ | |

Course and Dist. are required, for which D. Lat. and Dep. are needed. First find Dep.=D. Long × Cos. Mean Lat. Then,

$$\frac{\text{Dep.}}{\text{D. Lat.}} = \text{Tan Co.,} \quad \text{and} \quad \text{Dist.} = \text{D. Lat.} \times \text{Sec Co.}$$

| D. Long. 256′ | Log. | 2·40824 | $\Big\} +$ |
| M. Lat. 32° 42½′ | L. Cos. | 9·92502 | |

Dep.	Log.	2·33326	$\Big\} -$		
D. Lat. 173′	Log.	2·23805		Log.	2·23805	$\Big\} +$
	L. Tan. Co.	0·09521		L. Sec	0·20329	

Co. N. 51° 13·8′ E.   Dist. 276·28 mls.   Log. Dist. 2·44134

Example 2.—After steering a course of 144° T. over a certain distance, a ship altered her longitude 6° 18′ whilst making a departure of 170′. Between what latitudes had she sailed, and for what distance?

(1) $\dfrac{\text{Dep.}}{\text{D. Long}}$ = Cos. M. Lat.   (2) D. Lat. = Dep. Cot Co.

(3) Dist. = Dep. Cosec Co.

| Dep 170 | Log 2·23045 | $\Big\} -$ | Dep. 170 | Log 2·23045 | $\Big\} +$ |
| D. Long 378 | Log 2·57749 | | Cot. Co | 0·13874 | |

| Cos M. Lat | 9·65296 | | Log. D. Lat. | 2·36919 |

| | Dep. 170 | Log 2·23045 | $\Big\} +$ |
| | Cosec Co. | 0·23078 | |

| | Log. Dist. | 2·46123 |

Mean Lat.	63° 16·4′	$\pm$	*Latitudes*	*Distance* 289·22 miles.
½ D. Lat.	1 57·0		65° 13·4′	*D. Lat.* 234′
			61 19·4	

Example 3.—A vessel sailed in a N.E.'ly direction from Lat. 41° 27′ N. Long. 89° 19′ W. After 387 miles her latitude was 45° N. What was her longitude then, and what course had she made good?

(1) $\dfrac{\text{D. Lat.}}{\text{Dist}}$ = Cos. Co.   (2) Dep.= D. Lat. Tan Co.

(3) D. Long.= Dep. Sec M. Lat.

D. Lat.	213′	Log 2·32838	} −	2·32838		Lat. left	41° 27·0′ N.
Dist.	387	Log 2·58771			+	½ D. Lat.	1 46·5

Cos Course   9·74067 Tan. 0·18098   Mean Lat. 43 13·5 N.

Log Dep. 2·50936 } +
M. Lat. Sec 0·13747

D. Long. Log 2·64683

Long. left 89° 19·0′W } −
D. Long. 7 23·4 E.

Course N. 56° 36·4′ E.   Long. in 81 55·6 W.

Parallel Sailing.

1. Find the course and distance from Lat. 40° N., Long. 50° W., to Lat. 47° N., Long. 53° W.

2. Find the course and distance from Lat. 5° 16′ S., Long. 131° 48′ E., to Lat. 0° 55′ N., Long. 126° 31′ E.

3. Find the course and distance from Lat. 53° 11′ N., Long. 178° 36′ E., to Lat. 49° 26′ N., Long. 178° 36′ W.

4. A vessel sailed on a S. 61° W. course from Lat. 29° 19′ S., Long. 1° 33′ E., and changed her latitude 5° 52′. Find the position she arrived at, and the total distance sailed.

5. After steering a course of 141° T. from Lat. 41° 12′ N., long. 19° 53′ W. a vessel's latitude was 36° 48′ N. What was her longitude then?

6. A vessel steamed 495 miles from Lat. 51° 22′ N. till she reached Lat. 47° 40′ N. What was the D. Long. made good?

7. In the Northern hemisphere, a vessel changed her longitude 4° 43′, and her departure was 192′. Course steered was 230° T. Between what latitudes had she sailed?

8. After steering 063° T. for 516 miles, a ship arrived in Lat. 42° 08′ N., Long. 71° 25′ W. From what position had she sailed?

9. A vessel in Lat. 43° N. steers 090° T. from Long. 176° E. to Long. 176° W. How far has she steamed?

10. What is the hourly speed of rotation of a place in Lat. 53° 25′ N.?

1. Dep. 130·57'. Course N. 17° 16·15'W.   Dist. 439·8 miles.

2. Dep. 316·8'.   Course N. 40° 29·5' W.   Dist. 487·8 miles.

3. Dep. 105·02'. Course S. 25° 01·3' E.   Dist. 248·3 miles.

4. Dep. 635·03'   Dist.   726·05 mls. Lat. 35° 11' S. Long. 10° 57·9' W.

5. Dep. 213·8'.   D. Long. 275·1'.   Long. in 15° 17·9' W.

6. Course S. 63° 21·4' E. or W.   Dep. 442·5'.   D. Long. 11° 21·5'.

7. Mean Lat. 47° 16·7'.   D. Lat. 161·1'.   Latitudes 48° 37·2' N. and
   45° 56·2' N.

8. D. Long. 601·8'.   Lat. left 38° 13·7' N.   Long. left 81° 26·8' W.

9. Distance 351·5 miles.

10. Speed of rotation 536·4 miles per hour.

The Day's Work.

The problem known as the "Day's Work" consists, briefly, in reckoning up all the courses steered during a specified time, and the distance steamed on each course. These particulars are tabulated, and the D. Lat. and Dep. for each separate course and distance are found from the Traverse Table.

According to the direction of the course steered, the value of each D. Lat. is written in one or other of two columns headed "N" and "S," and the value of each departure is written in one or other of two columns headed "E" and "W."

Subtract the smaller D. Lat. value from the larger to obtain the net difference of latitude, or D. Lat. made good, and apply this to the latitude whence the ship has sailed (Lat. left) to obtain the "Lat. in."

In the same way, subtract the smaller Dep. value from the larger to obtain the Dep. made good. This departure multiplied by the secant of the mean latitude, as shown previously, gives the Difference of Longitude. Apply this to the Long. left to obtain the Long. in. The position thus found is named the "Dead Reckoning" position.

If, in addition to the particulars mentioned above, the estimated effects of set and drift of currents are included, the position is then called the "Estimated position."

The straight course and distance between the position left and the position arrived at—the "co. and dist. made good"—can also be found directly from the Traverse Table by using the D. Lat. and Dep. If, at the end of the period a position by astronomical observation is available, the set and drift of the current experienced during that time can also be calculated.

In the "Day's Work," courses are almost invariably given as *compass* courses, to which the necessary corrections for variation, deviation, and leeway must be applied as shown in Chapter 6.

Courses in the problem may be given in degrees of the "quadrantal" notation (*e.g.*, N. 36° E.), in points or quarter-points (*e.g.*, N.W. ¼ N.), or in degrees of the 3-figure notation (*e.g.*, 126° C.). The method to be followed in each case is discussed separately below.

. Courses Given in Degrees of Quadrantal Notation.—The two oblique angles in every right-angled triangle are complementary. That is, together they equal 90°. So the side which represents D. Lat. when the course (or angle) is, say, 30° becomes the Dep. side when the course is 60°.

When the course is less than 45°, it is found at the top of the page, and the necessary particulars—Dist., D. Lat., Dep.—are given in that order, also at the top of the page. When the course is more than 45°, it is found at the foot of the page, and the "headings" are altered to Dist., Dep., D. Lat. Note that the "Dist." heading does NOT alter, but the positions of Dep. and D. Lat. change over relative to courses less than 45°.

As in the Table of Log Functions, courses over 45° increase BACK-WARDS in the book.

The following points should be noted when studying the layout of the Traverse Table—

When the course is 45°, D. Lat. and Dep. are of the same value;

The nearer the course is to 45°, the smaller the difference between D. Lat. and Dep.;

When the course is less than 45°, D. Lat. is greater than Dep. When the course is over 45°, Dep. is the greater.

Courses Given in Points and Quarter-Points.—In these cases, variation and deviation are also usually given in points. The courses, corrected to true, should then be converted to degrees, remembering that

1 point $= 11\frac{1}{4}°$;

½ point $= 5° 37' 30''$, which can be counted as $5\frac{1}{2}°$;

¼ point $= 2° 48' 45''$, which can be counted as $2\frac{3}{4}°$.

For examination room purposes, accuracy is of great importance, and when a course contains a fraction of a degree, the required "mean" should always be taken.

Example.—True Course N.W. × N., dist. 40 miles.   **Find D. Lat.**
and Dep.   N.W. × N. = 3 points from North = $33\frac{3}{4}$°.

33° gives D. Lat. 33·5' ⎱ for $33\frac{3}{4}$°, use 33·3' D. Lat.
34° gives D. Lat. 33·2' ⎰

33° gives Dep. 21·8' ⎱ for $33\frac{3}{4}$°, use 22·2' Dep.
34° gives Dep. 22·4' ⎰

This process is called "interpolation".

Courses Given in 3-Figure Notation.—At the top of each page in
the Traverse Table—and also at the foot—the "3-figure" values of the
courses are given in addition to the "quadrantal" values. For instance,
for a course of 34°, the top of the page in *Norie's* is laid out thus:—

$$\frac{326°}{214°}\Big\uparrow \qquad\qquad \mathbf{34°} \qquad\qquad \Big\uparrow\frac{034°}{146°}$$

In *Burton's*, the same information is given as follows:—

$$\mathbf{34°} \qquad \frac{326°}{214°}\Big|\frac{034°}{146°} \qquad \mathbf{34°}$$

Interpreted, this means that

$$\begin{aligned}
\text{N. 34° E.} &= 034°\\
\text{S. 34 E.} &= 146°\\
\text{S. 34 W.} &= 214°\\
\text{N. 34 W.} &= 326°
\end{aligned}$$

Since the degrees in the S.E. and N.W. quadrants increase in an
anti-clockwise direction, it will be appreciated that in these quadrants
the 3-figure notation values will *decrease* as the quadrantal angles
increase.

If compass courses in the Day's Work problem are given in the
3-figure notation, the easiest way to deal with them is to convert
them, as they stand, to true courses, and then, before entering the
Traverse Table, convert them to quadrantal courses. In the actual
calculation, as will be seen, N. or S. must be used when dealing with
D. Lat., and E. or W. when dealing with Dep.

Example.—Compass course 333°, wind West, leeway 4°, deviation
6° W., variation 11° W. Find the true course.

$$\begin{array}{lr}
\text{Course} & 333° \text{ (C)}\\
\text{Leeway} & +4\\ \hline
& 337\\
\text{Error} & -17 \text{ W.}\\ \hline
\text{Course} & 320 \text{ (T)}
\end{array}$$

(See also Worked Example 5.)

In the following examples, each step is explained fully as we proceed.

Example 1.—Noon. Departure was taken from position in Lat. 47° 38′ N., Long. 5° 28′ W.

Hrs.	Comp. Co.	Dist.	Wind	Lee.	Dev.	Remarks
1 p.m.	N. 20° W.		West	4°	8° W.	
2 ,,						
3 ,,						
4 ,,						
5 ,,		60 m.	,,			Var. 16° W.
6 ,,	N. 43° W.			2°	2° W.	
7 ,,						
8 ,,						
9 ,,						
10 ,,						
11 ,,		64 m.	,,			
Midnt.	S. 82° W.			Nil	3° E.	
1 a.m.						
2 ,,						
3 ,,						
4 ,,						
5 ,,		66 m.	,,			
6 ,,	S. 41° W.			2°	6° E.	
7 ,,						
8 ,,						
9 ,,						
10 ,,						
11 ,,						
Noon		61 m.				

Find D.R. latitude and longitude, also course and distance made good in the 24 hours.

The first thing to be done is to correct each course for leeway, deviation and variation. A table is then drawn out, containing columns fo the true courses and the distances with, in addition, columns for N. and S. (D. Lat.) and E. and W. (dep.).

Put a dash through those columns which will NOT be used (this saves errors) and then write in the D. Lats. and deps. from the Traverse Tables.

Comp. Courses.

N. 20° W. L.	N. 43° W. L.	S. 82° W. R.	S. 41° W. R.
24 W. L.(err)	18 W. L.	13 W. L.	10 W. L.
N. 44 W. L.	N. 61 W. L.	S. 69° W.	S. 31 W. R.
—4 (lee)	—2		—2
N 40° W.	N. 59° W.		S. 29° W.

True Co.	Dist.	N.	S.	E.	W.
N. 40° W.	60	46·0	—	—	38·6
N. 59 W.	64	33·0	—	—	54·9
S. 69 W.	66	—	23·7	—	61·6
S. 29 W.	61	—	53·4	—	29·6

79·0 / 77·1   W. 184·7 dep
77·1

D. Lat. 1·9 N.

Explanation.—Each of the columns, N., S., E. and W., is added up separately, and taking the N. and S. columns, the lesser total is subtracted from the greater, the result (the D. Lat.) being named the same as the greater. The same procedure is followed for the departure.

In the above example, the net result of the courses steered is found to be—

D. Lat.   1·9′ to the North.
Dep.   184·7′ to the West.

There were no easterly courses.

Next write down the vessel's position at the beginning of the run. The D. Lat. (1·9′) is applied to the "Lat. left", and the result is the vessel's latitude by D.R. (lat. in)—(*a*) below.

To find the long. in, we first require to find the D. Long., which equals the secant of the latitude × the departure.

There are two latitudes to deal with—the "latitude left" and the "latitude in". Add these, and divide by 2. This gives the mean latitude, of which we take the secant.

Working in logs, add the L. sec mean lat. and the log of the departure. The result is the log of the D. Long. Find the D. Long.—(*b*) below— and apply it to the longitude left, obtaining the long. in—(*c*) below. This part of the problem appears as follows:—

	Lat. left	47° 38′ N.	Long. left	5° 28′ W.	
(*a*)	D. Lat	1·9 N.	D. Long.	4 34·2 W.	(*c*)
	Lat. in	47° 39·9′ N.	Long. in	10° 02·2′ W.	

	M. Lat.	47° 39′	sec	10·17156
(*b*)	Dep.	184·7	log	2·26647
	Log of D. Long.			2·43803	D. Long.=274·2′

To complete the problem, all that remains to be done is to find the course and distance made good by the vessel from noon to noon.

In the Traverse Table, look for either the D. Lat. or the dep., whichever is the larger, and find the page where the two quantities in adjoining columns most closely approximate the required D. Lat. and dep., remembering that—

(1) The closer the two are in value to each other the nearer the course will be to 45°; and

(2) When, as in this case, the dep. is the greater, the course has to be read from the foot of the page.

In this example, there is practically no D. Lat., and the answer is Course N. 89½° W., Dist. 185 miles.

The course is named N. because the D. Lat. is N. It is named W. because the dep. is W.

When the D. Lat. and the dep. in the tables do not satisfactorily approximate the given figures, it may become necessary to do some interpolating. (See Example 3.)

Example 2.—Noon. Vessel's departure was taken from a position in Lat. 57° 19′ N., Long. 3° 54′ E.

Time	Comp. Co.	Speed	Wind	Lee	Dev.	Remarks
1 p.m.	N. 78° E.	10·0 kts.	S.	5°	2° W.	
2						
3						
4						4·0 a/c S.65° E.
5	S. 65° E.	9·5	,,	4°	3° E.	
6						
7						
8						
9						
10						10·0 a/c S.50° E.
11	S. 50° E.	10·0	S.S.W.	4°	4° E.	
Midnt.						Var. 13° W.
1 a.m.						
2						2·0 a/c S.22° E.
3	S. 22° E.	10·0	West	5°	6° E.	
4						
5						
6						6·0 a/c S.19° W
7	S. 19° W.	10·5	,,	3°	8° E.	
8						
9						
10						
11						
Noon						

Correct the compass courses for leeway, deviation and variation, and find the position by D.R. at the end of 24 hours, also the course and distance made good from noon to noon.

Note that in this example, the SPEED of the vessel is given in knots =miles per hour.

First, correct the courses.

N.78° E. R.	S.65° E. L.	S.50° E. L.	S.22° E. L.	S.19° W.R.
15° W.L.	10 W.L.	9 W. L.	7 W. L.	5° W. L. Error

N.63 E. R.	S.75 E. L.	S.59 E. L.	S.29 E. L.	S.14 W. R.
−5	+4	+4	+5	−3 Leeway

N.58° E.	S.79° E.	S.63° E.	S.34° E.	S.11° W.

True Course	Dist.	N.	S.	E.	W.
N. 58° E.	40	21·2	—	33·9	—
S. 79 E.	57	—	10·9	56·0	—
S. 63 E.	40	—	18·2	35·6	—
S. 34 E.	40	—	33·2	22·4	—
S. 11 W.	63	—	61·8	—	12·0
		21·2	124·1	147·9	12·0
			21·2	12·0	

D. Lat. S. 102·9′   135·9′ Dep. E.

Lat. left	57°	19·0′ N.		Long. left	3° 54·0′ E.
Diff. lat.	1	42·9 S.	(a)	Diff. long.	4 06·0 E. (c)
Lat. in	55	36·1′ N.		Long. in	8 00·0 E.

Mean lat	56° 27·6′ N.	sec	10·25765	
Dep.	135·9′	log	2·13322	(b)

Log D. Long   2·39087   D. Long = 246·0′

Lat. by D.R.   55° 36·1′ N.
Long. by D.R.   8   00·0 E.
Course   S. 53° E.
Dist.   170 miles

To find the course and distance made good, look in the Traverse Table till you find where the required D. Lat. and dep. (102·9′ and 135·9′) are found in their respective columns, abreast of each other, and approximating the given quantities as nearly as possible.

Since the departure is the larger, the course must be taken from the foot of the page, and under 53°, distance 170, you will find—

Dep.=135·8, D. Lat.=102·3, which is very close.

The course is named S. because the D. Lat. is S. It is named E. because the dep. is E.

Example 3.—Noon. Departure taken from a point in Lat. 50° 02′ N., Long. 178° 31′ W. Find the ship's estimated position at the end of the run, also the course and distance made good from noon to noon.

Time	Comp. Co.	Speed	Wind	Lee	Dev.	Remarks
Noon –3 p.m.	N. 48° W.	11·0	N.	5°	3°W.	
3 p.m.–8 p.m.	N. 83° W.	11·0		7	7 W.	Var. 7° E.
8 p.m.–2 a.m.	S. 75 W.	11·5		7	9 W.	
2 a.m.–6 a.m.	S. 70 W.	11·5		6	9 W.	Current set
6 a.m.–noon	S. 65 W.	12·0		6	8 W.	170°, 2 kts.

Correct the compass courses, applying the leeway, and pick out the necessary particulars from the Traverse Table.

Note that in this example a current has been given. This current is treated as an extra course, and since 170° indicates a TRUE direction, no correction has to be applied to it. The current will therefore be written as S. 10° E. 48 miles, since 2 knots means 2 miles per hour.

The 2nd course, when corrected, comes to West. There is thus no D. Lat., and the distance becomes the departure, and is entered in the "W" column.

Course	Dist.	N.	S.	E.	W.
N. 49° W.	33	21·6	—	—	24·9
West	55	—	—	—	55·0
S. 66° W.	69	—	28·1	—	63·0
S. 62 W.	46	—	21·6	—	40·6
S. 58 W.	72	—	38·2	—	61·1
S. 10 E.	48	—	47·3	8·3	—

$$\begin{array}{cccc} & 21\cdot6 & 135\cdot2 & 8\cdot3 & 244\cdot6 \\ & & 21\cdot6 & & 8\cdot3 \\ \text{D. Lat. S.} & & 11\overline{3\cdot6}' & \text{Dep. W.} & 23\overline{6\cdot3}' \end{array}$$

Lat. left 50° 02·0′ N.   Long. left 178° 31·0′ W.
D. Lat.   1 53·6 S. (a)   D. Long.   6 00·8 W. (c)
Lat. in   48° 08·4′ N.   184 31·8 W.
                                       − 360

M. Lat. 49° 05′ sec 10·18379
Dep.   236·3 log 2·37346 (b)   175° 28·2′ E. Long. in

Log D. Long.   2·55725 D. Long.   360·8′

Answer—Lat.   48° 08′ 24″ N.
          Long. 175 28 12 E.
          Course S. 64½° W.
          Dist.   262 miles

D

Note in this example that the estimated longitude was more than 180°. Since longitude cannot be more than 180°, this was subtracted from 360°, and the name of the longitude changed from W. to E.

When finding the course and distance, the D. Lat. and the dep. do not come very near each other in the Traverse Table.

Course 64° gives 236·4 and 115·3, distance 263.
Course 65° gives 236·5 and 110·3, distance 261.

Take the mean (split the difference) of both course and distance in order to obtain the answer.

Example No. 4.—Noon. Departure taken from Lat. 49° 22′ N., Long. 8° 34′ W. Find ship's estimated position at the end of the run, and also the course and distance made good from noon to noon.

Time	Comp. Co.	Speed	Wind	Lee.	Dev.	Remarks
1 p.m.	N.W.×N.	10·0 kt.	S.W.	½ pt.	½ pt. W.	Noon, set co. N.W.×N.
2	.					
3						
4						
5						
6	N.W.½N.	9·5 kt.	S.W.	½ pt.	½ pt. W.	6·0 a/c N.W.½N.
7						
8						
9						Variation 11¼°W. throughout
10						
11						
Mid.						
1 a.m.						
2	N.W.×W.	9·5 kt.	S.	¼ pt.	¼ pt. W.	2·0 a/c N.W.×W.
3						
4						
5						
6	W.×N,	10·0 kt.	S.	½ pt.	½ pt. W.	6·0 a/c W.×N.
7						
8						
9						
10						
11						Current set S.S.E. (True) throughout day, 1¼ kts.
Noon						

Correct the compass courses as before, ready to obtain all the necessary particulars from the Traverse Tables. In this case again, a current has been given, to be treated as an extra course.

After correcting the courses, transform the points into degrees of the quadrantal notation.

Comp.	N.W.×N.L.	N.W.½N.L.	N.W.×W.L.	W.×N.L.	
Err.	1½pt. W.L.	1½pt. W.L.	1¼ pt. W.L.	1½ pt. W.L.	
	N.W.½W.L.	N.W.×W.L.	W ×N.¾N.L.	W.½S.R.	
Lee	½ pt.	½ pt.	¼ pt.	½ pt.	Current
True	N.W.	N.W.½W.	W.N.W.	West	S.S.E.
	(1) N.45°W.	(2) N.50½°W.	(3) N.67½°W.	(4) N.90° W.	(5) S.22½°E.
	60 mls.	76 mls.	38 mls.	60 mls.	30 mls.

Course	Dist.	N.	S.	E.	W.
N. 45° W.	60	42·4	—	—	42·4
N. 50½ W.	76	48·4	—	—	58·7
N. 67½ W.	38	14·5	—	—	35·1
West	60	—	—	—	60·0
S. 22½ E.	30	—	27·7	11·4	—
		105·3			196·2
		27·7			11·4

D. Lat. 77·6 N.   Dep. 184·8 W.

Lat. left	49° 22′ 00″ N.	(a)	Long. left	8° 34′ 00″ W.	(c)
D. Lat.	1 17 36 N.		D. Long.	4 47 36 W.	
Lat. in	50 39 36 N.		Long. in	13 21 36 W.	

M. Lat. 50 00 48   Sec 0·19205
Dep.   184·8   Log 2·26670   (b)

Log D. Long.   2·45875   D. Long. 287·6′.

Lat. in   50° 39′ 36″ N.
Long. in 13 21 36 W.
Course   N. 67° W.
Dist.   201 miles.

Example 5.—At noon, departure was taken from Lat. 52° 09′ N., Long. 3° 16′ E. Log set at zero. Compass Course 231°.

Time	Comp. Co.	Log	Wind	Lee	Dev.	Remarks
1 p.m.	231°	0	S.E.	3°	5°E.	
2						
3						
4	203	32	S.E.	2	2 E.	3.30 p.m., a/c 203° (C)
5						
6						
7						
8						
9						
10	257	102	S.E.	4	7 E.	10.15 p.m., a/c 257°(C)
11						
Mid.						Variation 13° W. throughout
1 a.m.						
2	173	140	East	3	1 W.	1.50 a.m., a/c 173° (C)
3						
4						
5						
6	169	184	N.E.	2	2 W.	6.00 a.m., a/c 169° (C)
7						
8						
9						
10	180	221	N.E.	2	Nil	9.40 a.m., a/c 180° (C)
11						Current set 033° (M), 1 knot
Noon		246				

Correct the courses for leeway and error, and find the estimated position of the ship at the following noon. Find also course and distance made good from noon to noon.

Comp.	231°	203°	257°	173°	169°	180°	033°
Err.	8W	11W	6W	14W	15W	13W	13W
	223	192	251	159	154	167	020
Lee	+3	+2	+4	+3	+2	+2	—
True	226	194	255	162	156	169	020
Mls.	32	70	38	44	37	25	24

Co.	Dist.	N.	S.	E.	W.
226	32	—	22·2	—	23·0
194	70	—	67·9	—	16·9
255	38	—	9·8	—	36·7
162	44	—	41·8	13·6	—
156	37	—	33·8	15·0	—
169	25	—	24·5	4·8	—
020	24	22·6	—	8·2	—
		22·6	200·0	41·6	76·6

$\longrightarrow$ 22·6 $\longrightarrow$ 41·6

D. Lat.   177·4 S.   Dep.   35·0 **W.**

Lat. left	52°	09′	00″ N.	(a)	Long. left 3° 16′ 00″ E.
D. Lat.	2	57	24 S.		D. Long. 55 12 W. *(c)*
Lat. in	49	11	36 N.		Long. in 2 20 48 E.
M. Lat.	50°	40′	18″		Sec 0·19808 (b)
Dep.	35				Log 1·54407

Log. D. Long.   1·74215   D. Long. 55·2′

Lat. in   49° 11′ 36″ N.
Long. in   2   20   48   E.
Course   191° (T)
Dist.   181 miles.

To Find Set and Drift of the Current.—It is sometimes required to find the set and drift of the current in the problem, instead of having a current given. In that case, the position of the vessel as found by sextant observations is given, and the difference between this position and the estimated (or D.R.) position gives the particulars required to find the set and drift of the current.

In the following example, the vessel crosses the equator, and it will be noted that when close to the equator, the secant of the mean latitude is very small, and there is, therefore, practically no difference between the dep. and the D. Long.

On the equator, D. Long.=Dep.

Example 6.—Noon. Departure taken from a position in Lat. 1° 23′ S., Long. 38° 17′ W. At the end of 24 hours, the position was found by observation to be Lat. 2° 36′ N. Long. 38° 36′ W.

Find the latitude and longitude by D.R., the course and distance made good from noon to noon, and also the set and drift of the current.

Time	Speed	Comp. Co.	Wind	Lee	Dev.	Remarks
Noon –4 p.m.	10·5	N. 32° E.	West	2°	6°W.	
4 p.m. –midnt.	11·0	N. 30 E.		2	6 W.	Var. 13° W.
Midnt.–noon	11·0	N. 5 W.		3	4 W.	

Correct the courses:—

	N. 32° E. R.	N. 30° E. R.	N. 5 W. L.
Error	19 W. L.	19 W. L.	17 W. L,
	N. 13 E. R.	N. 11 E. R.	N. 22 W. L.
Leeway	+2	+2	−3
True Co.	N. 15° E.	N. 13° E.	N. 19° W.

True Co.	Dist.	N.	S.	E.	W.
N. 15° E.	42	40·6	—	10·9	—
N. 13 E.	88	85·7	—	19·8	—
N. 19 W.	132	124·8	—	—	43·0

D. Lat. 251·1 N.   30·7   43·0

                            30·7

                 Dep.   12·3 W.

Lat. left	1° 23′	S.	Long. left	38° 17·0′ W.	
D. Lat.	4 11·1	N. (a)	D. Long.	12·3 W.	(c)
Lat. in	2° 48·1′ N.		Long. in	38° 29·3′ W.	

M. Lat.	0° 42′	N.	sec	10·00003	(b)
Dep.	12·3	W.	log	1·08991	
Log D. Long.				1·08994	D. Long. 12·3′

Note regarding the latitude. The difference of latitude is larger than the latitude left. The smaller is taken from the larger, and the "lat. in" is named contrary to the "lat. left".

To find the mean lat. when lat. left and lat. in have contrary names, subtract them and divide by 2. The mean lat. takes the same name as the greater.

To Find the Set and Drift of the Current.—Write down the position by D.R., and underneath it write the position by observation. Find the D. Lat. and the D. Long. thus—

Lat. D.R.	2° 48·1′ N.		Long. D.R.	38° 29·3′ W.	
Lat. obs.	2 36 N.		Long. obs.	38 36 W.	
D. Lat.	12·1′		D. Long.	6·7′	

Next convert the difference of longitude to departure by adding the log *cosine* of M. Lat. and the log of the D. Long. This gives the departure.

(Note.—The cosine is the reciprocal of the secant, therefore performing this operation becomes the reverse of the usual operation of turning dep. into D. Long.)

Mean Lat.	2° 42'	cos	9·99952	
D. Long.	6·7	log	0·82608	
		Log dep.	0·82560	Dep. 6·7'

Next look for the D. Lat. (12·1') and the dep. (6·7') in their respective columns in the Traverse Table, exactly as when looking for the course and distance.

Under 29°, 14 miles, we find D. Lat. is 12·2' and dep is 6·8'. These are as close as we can get. The current is then written as—

Set S. 29° W.   Drift 14 miles.

To find the *direction of the set* (South and West) it must be considered that the current sets FROM THE EXPECTED POSITION TO THE ACTUAL POSITION.

In this case, the current has set the vessel from Lat. 2° 48·1' N. to Lat. 2° 36' N.—in a southerly direction, and it has set the vessel from Long. 39° 29·3' W. to Long. 38° 36' W.—in a westerly direction.

To complete the problem, all that remains to be done is to find the course and distance made good, in the ordinary way.

D. Lat. 251·1. Dep. 12·3. The nearest is—
N. 3° W., 251 miles. The answers are set out:—

Lat. in	2° 48' 06'' N.
Long. in	38 29 18 W.
Current set	S. 29° W.
Drift	14 miles
Course	N. 3° W.
Distance	251 miles

Example 7.—Noon. Departure taken from a position in Lat. 38° 14' N., Long. 16° 48' E. Find the lat. and long. in by D.R., also the course and distance made good. If the position by observation at the end of the run was found to be Lat. 34° 22' N., Long. 15° 16' E., find also the set and drift of the current.

Time	Comp. Co.	Speed	Wind	Lee	Dev.	Remarks
Noon-midt.	S. 18° W.	10·0	East	7°	1° E.	Var. 11° W.
Midt.-noon	S. 25 W.	11·0	,,	6	1 E.	,,

True Course	Dist.	N.	S.	E.	W.
S. 15° W.	120	—	115·9	—	31·1
S. 21 W.	132	—	123·2	—	47·3

D. Lat. 239·1 S.   Dep. 78·4' W.

Lat. left	38°	14·0′ N.	(a)	Long. left	16°	48·0′ E.	(c)
D. Lat.	3	59·1 S.		D. Long.	1	37·2 W.	
Lat. in	34°	14·9′ N.		Long. in	15°	10·8′ E.	

M. Lat.	36° 14′	sec	10·09333	(b)
Dep.	78·4	log	1·89432	
	Log D. Long.		1·98765	D. Long. 97·2′

Lat. D.R.	34°	14·9′ N.	(a)	Long. D.R.	15°	10·8′ E.	(c)
Lat. obs.	34	22·0 N.		Long. obs.	15	16·0 E.	
D. Lat.		7·1′ N.		D. Long.		5·2′ E.	

M. Lat.	34° 18′	cos	9·91703	(b)
D. Long.	5·2	log	0·71600	
	Dep. log.		0·63303	Dep. = 4·3′

D. Lat.	7·1′	gives	{ Set	N. 32° E.	
Dep.	4·3		{ Drift	8 miles	*Current*
D. Lat.	239·1′	gives	{ Course	S. 18° W.	
Dep.	78·4		{ Distance	251 miles	

{ Lat.	34° 14′ 54″ N.	{ Current set N. 32° E.	{ Course S. 18° W.
{ Long.	15 10 48 E.	{ Drift 8 miles	{ Distance 251 miles

In all the previous examples, the position of the point of departure was given, but it often happens that, instead of giving the actual position of the vessel at the beginning of the run, her bearing and distance are given from a point of land whose position is known. (See Fig. 33).

Departure taken from a position with Bold Point (Lat. 45° 45′ N., Long. 7° 16′ W.) bearing S. 45° W. by compass, distance 13 miles. On a chart it would appear as in the figure.

The position of Bold Point is known, and from the particulars given in the question we must find the ship's position.

First find the deviation. To do so, we must know the direction of the ship's head. This will be given in the question, and let us suppose in this example that the deviation is 7° E., the variation being 15° W. (error 8° W.). The point of land, therefore, lies S. 37° W. (true) 13 miles from the ship, and the ship's position must consequently be N. 37° E., 13 miles from the point of land.

That is to say, the given bearing of the point of land has to be converted to a true bearing, *and reversed*.

Now consider this reversed bearing as a separate course, with its distance, and find the ship's position.

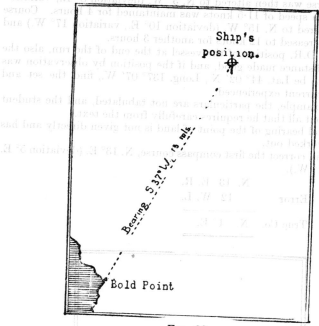

FIG. 33.

N. 37° E., 13 miles, gives D. Lat. 10·4' N., Dep. 7·8' E.
Position of point of land—

Lat.	45° 45' N.	(a)	Long.	7° 16·0' W.	(c)
D. Lat.	10·4 N.		D. Long.	11·2 E.	

Lat. of ship 45° 55·4' N.   7° 04·8' W. Long. of ship

M. Lat.	45°	50'	sec	10·15692	(b)
Dep.		7·8	log	0·89210	

Log. D. Long.   1·04902   D. Long. = 11·2'

The point of departure of the ship is therefore—
Lat. 45° 55·4' N. Long. 7° 04·8' W.,
and the problem is then continued in the ordinary way.

Example 8.—With ship steering N. 13° E. by compass (deviation 5° E., variation 17° W.) departure was taken from a position with a point of land in Lat. 42° 16′ N., Long. 136° 15′ W., abeam to starboard, distant 11 miles. Vessel continued on this course for 3 hours at 12 knots. Course was then altered to N. 3° W. (deviation 8° E., variation 17° W.) and a speed of 11·5 knots was maintained for 4 hours. Course was then altered to N. 15° W. (deviation 10° E., variation 17° W.) and speed was increased to 12 knots for another 3 hours.

Find the D.R. position of the vessel at the end of the run, also the course and distance made good, and if the position by observation was then found to be Lat. 44° 02′ N., Long. 137° 07′ W., find the set and drift of the current experienced.

In this example, the particulars are not tabulated, and the student has to pick out all that he requires carefully from the text.

The actual bearing of the point of land is not given directly and has also to be worked out.

To do this, correct the first compass course, N. 13° E. (deviation 5° E. variation 17° W.).

	N. 13° E. R.
Error	12 W. L.
True Co.	N. 1° E.

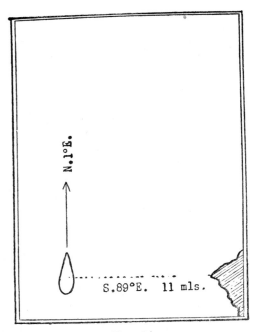

N. 1° E.

S. 89° E.   11 mls.

Fig. 34.

The point of land is abeam to starboard, that is, 90° to the right of N. 1° E., which is S. 89° E., distant 11 miles.

The ship's position is thus N. 89° W., 11 miles from the position of the point of land.

Find the ship's position, and using it as the point of departure, work the problem in the ordinary way thereafter.

Position of point of land—

Lat.	42° 16·0′ N.	(a)	Long.	136° 15·0′ W.	(c)
D. Lat.	——		D. Long.	14·9 W.	
Ship's Lat.	42 16·0 N.		Ship's Long.	136 29·9 W.	

M. Lat.	42° 16′	sec	10·13076
Dep.	11·0	log	1·04139	(b)

Log D. Long.   1·17215   D. Long. = 14·9′

True Co.	Dist.	N.	S.	E.	W.
N. 1° E.	36	36·0	—	0·6	—
N. 12 W.	46	45·0	—	—	9·6
N. 22 W.	36	33·4	—	—	13·5

D. Lat. 11·4′ N.   0·6′   23·1′
                              0·6

Dep.   22·5′ W.

Lat. left	42° 16·0′ N.	(a)	Long. left	136° 29·9′ W.	(c)
D. Lat.	1 54·4 N.		D. Long.	30·9 W.	
Lat. in	44° 10·4′ N.		Long. in	137° 00·8′ W.	

M. Lat.	43° 13′	sec	10·13741	(b)
Dep.	22·5	log	1·35218

Log D. Long.   1·48959   D. Long. 30·9′

D. Lat. 114·4′ } gives { Course   N. 11° W.
Dep.   22·5 }   { Distance   117 miles

Lat. D.R.	44° 10·4′ N.	(a)	Long. D.R.	137° 00·8′ W.	(b)
Lat. obs.	44 02·0 N.		Long. obs.	137° 07·0 W.	
D. Lat.	8·4′		D. Long.	6·2′	

M. Lat.   44° 06'   cos   9·85620   (c)
D. Long.   6·2   log   0·79239

        Log. Dep.   0·64859   Dep. 4·4'

D. Lat.   8·4' ⎫ gives ⎧ Set   S. 27° W.
Dep.   4·4 ⎭   ⎩ Drift   9½ miles

Lat. D.R.   44° 10' 24'' N.
Long. D.R.   137 00 48 W.
Co. N. 11° W.   Distance 117 miles
Set S. 27° W.   Drift   9½ miles.

Example 9.--At noon, departure was taken from a position with a point of land in Lat. 49° 36′ N., Long. 8° 40′ W., bearing 029° (C), dist. 16 miles. Ship's head on 1st course by compass. Var. and Dev. as per log.

Noon	Compass Course 302° Log set zero. Dev. 6° W.
	Var. 13° W.
4.30 p.m.	a/c 351° (C). Log 41. Dev. 3° W. Var. 13° W.
11.00 p.m.	a/c 011° (C). Log 104. Dev. 2° W. Var. 13° W.
	Wind East, leeway 3°.
9.20 a.m.	a/c 036° (C). Log 209. Dev. Nil. Var. 13° W.
Noon	Log 235.

Find the D.R. position of ship at noon, also the course and distance made good from noon to noon. If the position by observation at noon was found to be Lat. 52° 21′ N., Long. 10° 26′ W., find also the probable set and drift of the current.

    Pos. of land—Lat. 49° 36′ 00''N.   Long. 8° 40′ 00'' W.
          D. Lat.   15 48 S.   D. Long. 4 18 W.

Bearg.   (a) Lat. Ship 49 20 12 N.   Long. 8 44 18 W. (c)
of land

              M. Lat. 49° 28′ 06''   Sec 0·18718
029°   Dep. 2·8   Log 0·44716 (b)
Reversed   209°
Error   − 19 W.   Log. D. Long.   0·63434

T. Bg. Rev. 190   D. Long.   4·3'

	Comp. Co.	302°	351°	011° Lee−3°= 008°	036°
	Error	−19 W.	−16 W.	−15 W.	−13 W.
	True Co.	283	335	353	023
	Dist.	41 M.	63 M.	105 M.	26 M.

Course	Dist.	N.	S.	E.	W.
283	41	9·2	—	—	39·9
335	63	57·1	—	—	26·6
353	105	104·2	—	—	12·8
023	26	23·9	—	10·2	—

D. Lat.   194·4 N.   79·3
                                              10·2

Dep.   69·1 W.

Lat. left	49°	20′	12″ N.		Long. left	8° 44′ 18″ W.
D. Lat.	3	14	24 N. (a)		D. Long.	1 49 42 W. (c)
Lat. in	52	34	36 N.		Long. in	10 34 00 W.
M. Lat.	50° 57′ 24″	Sec	0·20072			
Dep.	69·1	Log	1·83948 (b)			

Log D. Long.   2·04020   D. Long. 109·7′

Lat. D.R.	52° 34′ 36″ N.	Long. D.R. 10° 34′ 00″ W.
Lat. Obs.	52 21 00 N. (a)	Long. Obs. 10 26 00 W. (c)
D. Lat.	13 36 S.	D. Long. 8 00 E.

M. Lat. 52° 27′ 48″ Cos 9·78481
D. Long.   8   Log. 0·90309 (b)

Log Dep.   0·68790   Dep. **4·9′**

Lat.	D.R.	52° 34′ 36″ N.
Long.	D.R.	10 34 00 W.
Course		340·5° (T)
Distance		206·5 M.
Set		160° (T)
Drift		**14·5 M.**

Exercise 9.

THE DAY'S WORK.

1. Noon.   Departure taken from Lat. 43° 11′ N., Long. 0° 25′ E.

Time	Comp. Co.	Speed Kts.	Wind	Lee-way	Dev.	Remarks
1 p.m.	S. 82° W.	9·5	South	5°	11°E.	
2		9·				
3		9·5				
4		9·5				
5	N. 82 W.	9·0	South	6	9 E.	
6		9·0				
7		9·0				
8		9·0				
9	N. 80 W.	9·0	South	4	9 E.	
10		9·0				
11		9·0				Variation
12 midt.		9·0				10° W.
1 a.m.	S. 65 W.	8·5	South	6	4 E.	
2		8·5				
3		8·5				
4		8·5				
5		8·5				
6		8·5				
7	S. 40 W.	9·0	South	0	Nil	
8		9·0				Current set
9		9·0				150° at ¾ knot
10		9·0				throughout
11		9·0				the day
12 noon		9·0				

Correct the above courses for leeway, variation and deviation; find the ship's estimated position at noon, also the course and distance made good.

2. Noon. Departure taken from a position in Lat. 49° 37′ N., Long. 12° 50′ W.

Time	Comp. Co.	Speed Kts.	Wind	Lee-way	Dev.	Remarks
1 p.m.	S. 74° W.	11·0	South	5°	11°E.	
2		11·0				
3		11·0				
4		11·0				
5	N. 40 W.	10·5	S.S.E.	2°	3 E.	
6		10·5				
7		10·5				
8		10·5				
9	N. 20 W.	11·0	S.S.E.	0	2 W.	Variation
10		11·0				16° W.
11		11·0				
12 midt.		11·0				
1 a.m.		11·0				
2		11·0				
3		11·0				
4		11·0				
5	N. 3 E.	11·0	East	3	6 W.	
6		11·0				
7		11·0				Current set
8		11·0				ship 106°, at
9		11·0				1 kt. through-
10		11·0				out day
11		11·0				
12 noon		11·0				

Correct the above courses for leeway, variation and deviation; find the ship's estimated position at noon, and also the course and distance made good.

3. Noon. Departure taken from a position in Lat. 42° 19′ N., Long. 1° 12′ W.

Time	Comp. Co.	Speed Kts.	Wind	Lee-way	Dev.	Remarks
1 p.m.	N. 66° E.	9·0	N.N.W.	4°	3°W.	
2		9·0				
3		9·0				
4		9·0				
5		9·0				
6	S. 83 E.	9·5	North	5	1 E.	
7		9·5				
8		9·5				
9		9·5				
10		9·5				
11		9·5				
12 midt.	S. 70 E.	9·0	,,	3	3 E.	Variation
1 a.m.		9·0				15° W.
2		9·0				
3		9·0				
4		9·0				
5		9·0				
6		9·0				
7		9·0				
8		9·0				
9	S. 40 E.	10·0	,,	1	5 E.	Current set
10		10·0				vessel 180°, ½
11		10·0				knot through-
12 noon		10·0				out the day

Correct the above courses for leeway, deviation and variation; find the estimated position at noon, and the course and distance made good from noon to noon.

4. Noon. Departure taken from Lat. 60° 00′ 30″ N., Long. 5° 23′ E.

Time	Comp. Co.	Speed Kts.	Wind	Lee-way	Dev.	Remarks
1 p.m.	S. 23° W.	11·0	North	0°	9°E.	
2		11·0				
3		11·0				
4		11·0				
5		11·0				
6		11·0				
7		11·0				
8		11·0				
9		11·0				
10		11·0				
11	S. 5 W.	11·0			11 E.	Variation
12 midt.		11·0				10° W.
1 a.m.		11·0				
2		11·0				
3		11·0				
4	S. 16 W.	11·0			10 E.	
5		11·0				
6		11·0				
7		11·0				
8		11·0				
9		11·0				A current set
10		11·0				ship 170°, 1
11		11·0				knot through
12 noon		11·0				out the day

Correct the above courses for leeway, deviation and variation; find the estimated position at noon, and the course and distance made good between noon and noon.

5. Noon. Departure taken from Lat. 41° 41′ N., Long. 0° 57′ E.

Time	Comp. Co.	Wind	Lee	Dev.	Remarks
1 p.m. 2 3 4	S.S.W.	West	¼ pt.	1 pt. E.	Noon, set co. S.S.W., Log set zero.
5 6 7 8	South	West	½ pt.	¾ pt. E.	6 p.m. a/c South, Log 52.
9 10 11 Midnt. 1 a.m. 2 3 4 5 6 7	S.E.×S.	West	Nil	¼ pt. E.	10 p.m. a/c SE×S, Log 86. Variation 11¼° W.
8 9 10 11 Noon	S.×E.	West	½ pt.	¾ pt. E.	8 a.m. a/c S.×E. Log. 170. Noon—log 205

Find the D.R. position after 24 hours, and also the course and distance made good between noon and noon.

6. **Noon.** Departure taken from Lat. 33° 47′ N., Long. 10° 55′ W. Course set 036° (C). Log set zero. Variation throughout 9° W.

Time	Comp. Co.	Wind	Lee-way	Dev.	Remarks
1 p.m.	036°	N.W.	2°	5° E.	
2					
3	051°	N.W.	2°	8° E.	2.40 p.m. a/c
4					051°(C), Log. 19.
5					
6					
7					
8	003°	N.W.	1°	1° W.	7.35 p.m. a/c
9					003°(C), Log 62.
10					
11					
Midnt.	349°	N.W.	Nil	4° W.	Mid., a/c 349° (C),
1 a.m.					Log 99.
2					
3					
4					
5					
6					
7					
8					
9	006°	N.W.	1°	1° W.	8 a.m. a/c 006°(C),
10					Log 165.
11					Current set 234°(T)
Noon					19 M. during the
					24 hours.
					Noon Log 200.

Find ship's estimated position at the end of the run, also the course and distance made good from noon to noon.

7. Noon.　Lat. 41° 31′ N., Long. 18° 33′ W.　Compass Course set 107°
Log set zero.　Variation throughout 8° W.

Time	Comp. Co.	Wind	Lee-way	Dev.	Remarks
1 p.m.	107°	S.S.E.	2°	7° E.	
2					
3					
4	136°	S.S.E.	0°	9° E.	4 p.m. a/c 136°(C),
5					Log 42.
6					
7					
8					
9					
10	087°	South	4°	5° E.	10 p.m. a/c 087° (C),
11					Log. 107.
Midnt.					
1 a.m.					
2					
3					
4					
5					
6	090°	N.E.	2°	5° E.	6 a.m. a/c 090° (C),
7					Log 180.
8					Current estimated
9					to set 293° (T),
10					1½ kts. through-
11					out.
Noon					Noon Log 233.

Find ship's estimated position at the end of the run, also the course and distance made good from noon to noon.

8. **Noon.**   Departure was taken from a position with a point of land
(Lat. 42° 37′ N., Long. 17° 59′ E.), bearing S. 56° W. by compass,
distant 16 miles.   Ship's head on 1st course by compass.   Variation and deviation as per log.

Time	Comp. Co.	Speed Kts.	Wind	Lee-way	Dev.	Remarks
1 p.m.	N. 78° E.	10·0	S.S.E.	3°	6°E.	
2		10·0				
3		10·0				
4	S. 82 E.	10·0	S.S.E.	4	10°E.	
5		10·0				
6		10·0				
7		10·0				
8		10·0				
9		10·0				
10		10·0				
11	S. 78 E.	9·5	S.S.E.	2	9 E.	Variation
12 midt.		9·5				15° W.
1 a.m.		9·5				
2		9·5				
3	S. 49 E.	9·5	S.S.E.	0	7 E.	
4		9·5				
5		9·5				
6		9·5				
7		9·5				
8		9·5				
9		9·5				Current set
10		9·5				325°, 1½ kts.
11		9·5				throughout
12 noon		9·5				the day

Find the ship's estimated position at the end of the 24 hours, also
the course and distance made good between noon and noon.

9. Noon. Departure taken from a position with a lighthouse (Lat. 40° 51′ N., Long. 7° 12′ W.), bearing 225° (C). distant 11 miles. Ship's head on 1st course by compass. Variation and deviation as per log.

Time	Comp. Co.	Speed Kts.	Wind	Lee-way	Dev.	Remarks
1 p.m.	315°	9·0	N.E.	3°	0°	
2		9·0				
3		9·0				
4		9·0				
5		9·0				
6	344°	9·0	N.E.	1	3 E.	
7		9·0				
8		9·0				
9		9·0				
10		9·0				
11		9·0				V a r i a t i o n
12 midt.		9·0				11° W. for
1 a.m.	012°	8·5	N.E.	0	5 E.	first 12 hrs.;
2		8·5				12° W. there-
3		8·5				after
4		8·5				
5		8·5				
6		8·5				
7		8·5				
8		8·5				
9	017°	9·0	N.E.	0	5 E.	Current set
10		9·0				254° (T), 1½
11		9·0				knot through-
12 noon		9·0				out the day

Correct the above courses for leeway, deviation and variation; find the vessel's estimated position at the end of the run, also the course and distance made good from noon to noon.

10. Departure was taken from a position with a lighthouse (Lat. 51° 12′ N., Long. 0° 14′ E.), bearing N. 85° W. by compass, distant 11 miles. Ship's head was on 1st course by compass. Variation and deviation as per log.

Noon—7 p.m.	Comp. Co. N. 5° E. Speed 10 knots. Wind N.W., leeway 1°. Deviation 8° E. Variation 11° W.
7 p.m.-11 p.m.	Comp. Co. North. Speed 9·5 knots. Wind N.W., leeway 4°. Deviation 6° E. Variation 11° W.
11 p.m. - 4 a.m.	Comp. Co. N. 7° W. Speed 9 knots. Wind N.W., leeway 0°. Deviation 10° E. Variation 11° W.
4 a.m. - noon	Comp. Co. N. 65° W. Speed 9 knots. Wind N.W. leeway 0°. Deviation 5° E. Variation 11° W.

Current set 171°, ½ knot throughout.

Find estimated position at the end of 24 hours, also the course and distance made good from noon to noon.

11. Departure taken from a position with a lighthouse (Lat. 5° 12′ N., Long. 74° 16′ E.), bearing 000° (C), distant 7 miles. Ship's head on 1st course by compass. Variation and deviation as per log.

Noon-5.30 p.m.	Comp. Co. 215°. Speed 12 knots. Deviation 5° E. Variation 1° E.
5.30-11. p.m.	Comp. Co. 230°. Speed 12 knots. Deviation 3° E. Variation 1° E.
11 p.m.-6 a.m.	Comp. Co. 271°. Speed 11·5 knots. Deviation 2° W. Variation 1° E.
6 a.m.-noon	Comp. Co. 283°. Speed 11·5 knots. Wind N.E., leeway 2°. Deviation 3° W. Variation 1° E.

Current set 094°, (T), ¾ knot throughout.

Find estimated position, also course and distance made good from noon to noon.

12. Departure taken from a position with a point of land in Lat. 37° 50′ N., Long. 5° 25′ W., bearing by compass N. 67° W., distant 9 miles. Ship's head on 1st course by compass. Variation and deviation as per log.

Noon-4.40 p.m.	Comp. Co. S. 51° E. Speed 12 knots. Wind South, leeway 3°. Deviation 3° E. Variation 7° W.
4.40-10.00 p.m.	Comp. Co. S. 71° E. Speed 12 knots. Wind South, leeway 3°. Deviation 5° E. Variation 7° W.
10.00 p.m.-noon	Comp. Co. N. 78° E. Speed 12 knots. Wind South, leeway 4°. Deviation 7° E. Variation 7° W.

Find latitude and longitude in by dead reckoning and distance made good from noon to noon, and if the position by celestial observation at the end of 24 hours was found to be Lat. 37° 57′ N., Long. 00° 34′ 30″ E., find also the set and drift of the current experienced.

13. Departure was taken from a position in Lat. 19° 25′ N., Long. 00°
00′. The following courses were then steered:—

Noon-midnt.   Comp. Co. S. 5° E.   Speed 10 knots. Deviation 8° E.
                     Variation 3° W.
Midnt.-noon   Comp. Co. S. 20° E. Speed 9·5 knots. Deviation 3° E.
                     Variation 3° W.

Find the latitude and longitude in by D.R., also the course and distance made good from noon to noon, and if the position by observation
was found to be Lat. 15° 51′ N., Long. 00° 32′ E., find also the set
and drift of the current experienced during the 24 hours.

14. Departure taken from a position in Lat. 37° 02′ N., Long. 19° 41′ W.
Ship steered North by compass for 5½ hours at 10 knots.
(Variation nil, deviation ½ point East.) Course was then altered
to N.W.×N. by compass (variation nil, deviation ¼ point East)
and the same speed was maintained for 6½ hours. Course was
again altered to W.×S. by compass (variation nil, deviation
¾ point West) and during the next 12 hours, the speed was 11
knots.
During the first 12 hours, the current set East (True), 2
knots; for the next 6 hours it set South (True), 2 knots, and
for the rest of the run it set E.S.E. (True) 1½ knots.

Find the ship's estimated position at the end of the run, also the
course and distance made good.

15. Departure taken from a position with a lighthouse (Lat. 56° 00′ N.,
Long. 3° 22′ W.), bearing 4 points on the starboard quarter,
distant 12 miles. Ship's head was on 1st course by compass,
332° (variation 17° W. deviation 5° W.). After steering this
course for 2 hours 36 minutes at 12 knots, course was altered
to 282° (C), variation being unchanged, deviation being 11° W.
This course was continued at the same speed for 1 hour 24
minutes, and was then altered to 225° (C) (variation 17° W.,
deviation 8° W.) for 2 hours at 11 knots. The current throughout
set 152° (T), 2 knots.

Find the estimated position, also the course and distance made
good during the run.

16. At noon, a point of land in Lat. 56° 35′ N., Long. 4° 23′ W., bore
abeam to port, distant 9 miles. Ship's head by compass was
S. 37° W. (variation 21° W., deviation 6° E.). At 5.30 p.m., ship
having steamed 9·5 knots throughout, course was altered to
S. 11° W. by compass (variation 21° W., deviation 3° E.)
Leeway of 4° was estimated for a westerly wind, and speed was
increased to 10 knots. At midnight, the wind having dropped,
the allowance for leeway was discontinued, and at 4 a.m. the
course was altered to S. 9° E. (variation 20° W., deviation 1° W.),
the speed of 10 knots being maintained.

Find the estimated position of the vessel at the following noon, also the course and distance made good from noon to noon, allowing for a current which set 065°, 1 knot, during the first 10 hours, and 286°, 0·8 knots, for the remainder.

17. At 8 p.m., May 26th, a point of land in Lat. 00° 35′ N., Long. 18° 27′ W., bore by compass 095° (C), distant 9 miles. Ship's head was 180 (C) (variation, 6° W., deviation 6° E.), and the log was then set at zero. When the log showed 53, course was altered to 193° (C) (variation 6° W., deviation 9° E.) The log was not reset. This course was continued till log showed 96, when course was altered to 138° (C) (variation 7° W., deviation 9° E.), and at noon on May 27th the log, which had not been set since 8 p.m. the previous evening, read 194. Till 4 a.m., current was estimated to set 320° (T), 1 knot, and thereafter it set 033° (T), 1¼ knots.

Find the estimated latitude and longitude of the vessel at noon on May 27th, also the course and distance made good from 8 p.m. the previous day.

Some Harder Examples.

(Suitable for foreign-going 2nd Mates).

18. Noon—Set course 248° C. Var. 20° E. Dev. 2° E. Log set zero.
8 p.m.—A light in Lat. 56° 31′ S., Long. 68° 43′ W. was abeam to starboard, dist. 6·8 mls. Log 64. A/c 310° C. Var. 20° E. Dev. Nil.

Noon—Log 192. Current estimated to set 090° T., 2 kts., throughout. Find ship's position at the end of 24 hours, also the course and distance made good from noon to noon.

19. Noon—set course 251° C. Speed 10 kts. Var. 4° E. Dev. 5° W.
2000—a/c 264° C. Same speed. Var. 4° E. Dev. 3° W.
2100—C. James (35° 46′ S., 136° 35′ E.) 4 pts. on port bow.
2200—C. James abeam to port.

Assuming same course and speed from 2000, find course and dist. made good from noon to noon, and also the position of the ship at noon on the following day.

20. At noon, departure course was 077° C. Var. 5° E. Dev. 2° W.
Speed 11 kts. At 1830 a light in pos. 37° 42′ S., 178° 51′ E., bore 26½° on the port bow. This was abeam at 1930. Ship then a/c 062° C. Var. 5° E. Dev. Nil. At 2130, a/c 060° C.

Var. 5° E., Dev. Nil, to allow for a N.N.W. wind. At 0500 next day, an observation of a star bearing 103° T. gave intercept 16' towards. A/c 090° C. Var. 5° E. Dev. 3° W. Find ship's position at following noon, also course and distance made good from noon to noon.

21. At noon, departure was taken from position with a 240 ft. lt. ho. in Lat. 43° 19' N., Long. 1° 44' W., bearing right astern and subtending a vertical angle of 0° 23'. Co. 157° C. Error 5° W. Wind E.S.E., leeway 2°. Log zero. At 10 p.m., Log 108, stopped for repairs. Wind E.S.E. Leeway ¾ kt. At 2 a.m., ship proceeded, co. 160° C. Err. 5° W., leeway 3°. At 6.30 a.m., Log 151, an observation of a star bearing 201° T. gave intercept 6·8' towards. A/c 158° C. Err. 5° W. Lee 3°. At noon, Log 201. Find ship's D.R. position at noon, also co. and dist. made good.

22. At 1600, a lt. ho. in Lat. 48° 13' N., Long. 27° 33' E., was abeam to port, dist. 13 mls. Co. 189° C. Err. 9° W. Wind S.E., leeway 2°. Log reading 65. At 1936, log reading 108, an S.O.S. was received from a vessel in Lat. 46° 53' N., Long. 28° 06½' E. Speed was immediately increased to 16 kts. to go to her assistance. Find compass course to steer, allowing same error, also expected time of arrival to the nearest minute.

23. At noon, co. was set 071° C. Err. 18° W. Speed 15 kts. At 1616, a/c 090° C. Err. 16° W. Current throughout is estimated to set 309°, T., 3 kts. At 2136, a light in 39° 16' N., 0° 42' E. was abeam to port, dist. 14 mls. A/c 057° C. Err. 19° W. Find position of vessel's departure, and also the estimated position at 0800 the following day.

ANSWERS TO HARDER EXAMPLES, EXERCISE 9.

18. Departure pos. 56° 37·8' S., 67° 16' W. D. Lat. 104·1' N. Dep. 32' W. D. Long. 56·7' W. Lat. in 54° 46·9' S. Long. in 69° 39·7' W. Course N. 36° W. Dist. 137½ miles.

19. Lat. in 35° 48·2' S. Long. in 133° 42' E. Co. S. 80° W. Dist. 238 mls.

20. Dep. pos.: Lat. 38° 01·7' S., Long. 177° 09·3' E. Arrival pos.: Lat. 37° 12·9' S., Long. 177° 09·7' W. Co. N. 80° E. Dist. 277 mls.

21. Lat. 40° 05·8' N. Long. 00° 04·8' E. Co. S. 23° E. Dist. 204 mls.

22. Comp. Co. 144° (S. 36° E.) E.T.A. 22h. 55 m.

23. Dep. pos.: Lat. 37° 43·8' N., Long. 1° 27·5' W. Pos. at 0800: Lat. 41° 25' N., Long. 2° 20·1' E.

MERCATOR SAILING.

Terrestrial Measurements.—On the equator, the measure of one degree of longitude is 60', or 60 nautical miles. Departure, as previously stated, is defined as the distance in nautical miles made good to the East or West of the place sailed from. Therefore on the equator, *but on the equator only*, Dep=D. Long. In any other latitude, it has been shown that Dep=D. Long. Cos lat. This point is very important.

For many purposes, the Earth is considered to be a perfect sphere. In actual fact, its real shape is an "oblate spheroid," as it is sligh.ly flattened at the poles. The polar radius is about 27 miles less than the equatorial radius. In practical navigation the difference, though slight, is appreciable. Nautical tables were accustomed to include relevant tables calculated both for "the sphere" and for the "spheroid," but the newer editions of both *Norie's* and *Burton's* Tables now use only tables for the spheroid.

Considering the Earth as a sphere, it will be appreciated that on this sphere, the measure of one degree of latitude is also 60', or 60 nautical miles. That is—

1' of latitude	=	1 nautical mile;
1 nautical mile	=	1 mile of departure;
1 mile departure	=	1' longitude *on the equator.*

On the sphere, parallels of latitude appear as concentric circles, each equidistant from the next. The distance between meridians drawn through adjoining degrees of longitude, on the other hand, varies from 60 nautical miles at the equator to zero at the poles.

The Mercator Chart.—It has already been stated that on a chart meridians of longitude are represented by parallel straight lines, each equidistant at all points from the next. (Page 60).

If a particular chart, drawn on Mercator's projection, represents a portion of the Earth from the equator to Lat. 60°, it will be appreciated that the measure of 1' of latitude (or departure) at the equator will be the same as the measure of 1' of longitude, but in Lat. 60°, the measure of 1' of latitude (or departure) will be 1' × nat. sec. lat.= 1' × 2·000. On the chart, the measure of 1' of latitude in Lat. 60° is double the length of 1' of latitude at the equator, solely on account of the fact that meridians on the chart are represented by parallel straight lines.

On the same chart, the exact measure of the *total* length of a meridian from the equator to Lat. 60° would be—

Length of 1' long. at equator ×   (1' × sec 1')⊣-(1' × sec 2')+(...)+
$$(1' \times \sec 60°) \}$$

or

Length of 1' long. at equator × (sec 1'+sec 2'+. . . . .+sec 60°).

Meridional Parts.—Tables of "Meridional Parts" are given in all Nautical Tables. In *Norie's*, they begin on page 159 (new edition), and in *Burton's*, Table 4, they begin on page 92. These Tables are very simple to understand, the values tabulated representing the measure, in minutes of arc, of the length of a meridian on a mercator chart from the equator to any required latitude, expressed in terms of minutes of longitude at the equator. For instance, in *Norie's*, the Meridional Parts for Lat. 27° 15′ are given as 1689·66′. We know that 27° 15′ = 1635′. The difference between these two values is due to the fact that, on a chart, the measure of the length of 1′ of longitude at the equator has been multiplied by

$$(\sec 1' + \sec 2' + \ldots\ldots + \sec 27° 15').$$

These tabulated values are termed the "Meridional Parts" (M.P.) for the appropriate degrees and minutes of latitude.

The D. Lat. between Lats. 27° 15′ N. and 36° 40′ N. is 9° 25′, or 565′. The M.P. for each latitude are given as 1689·66 and 2353·66 respectively, a difference of 664′. This is termed the "Meridional Difference of Latitude" or "Diff. Meridional Parts" (D.M.P.)

Mercator's Sailing.—When the difference of latitude between two places is large, or if the latitudes themselves are high or on opposite sides of the equator, the results obtained from Parallel Sailing methods can be surprisingly inaccurate. The same disadvantage is noticeable when the distance between two positions is large. Under these con-

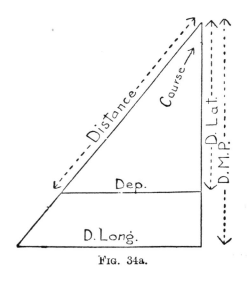

Fig. 34a.

ditions, "Mercator's Sailing" should always be used in preference to Parallel Sailing.

In Fig. 34a, D. Lat. has been increased to D.M.P., and Dep. has been increased *in the same ratio* to D. Long., so that

$$\frac{Dep.}{D.\ Long.} = \frac{D.\ Lat.}{D.M.P.} \quad \text{and} \quad \frac{Dep.}{D.\ Lat.} = \frac{D.\ Long.}{D.M.P.} = Tan\ Co.$$

Many students try to memorise the numerous formulae contained in Plane, Parallel, and Mercator Sailings, but a few minutes' study of the sketch will show that if the student possesses a very ordinary knowledge of the ratios of a right-angled triangle, there is no need to memorise formulae in a parrot fashion.

In the following worked examples, refer to Fig. 34a, and that fact will be fully appreciated.

Example 1.—Find the course and distance from Lat. 10° 44' N., Long. 5° 00' W., to Lat. 51° 16' N., Long. 63° 05' W.

Course and distance are required, and from Fig. 34a it can be seen

that $\frac{D.\ Long.}{D.M.P.} = Tan\ Co.$ $\therefore$ D. Long $= D.M.P.\ Tan.\ Co.$ and

$\frac{Dist.}{D.\ Lat.} = Sec\ Co.$ $\therefore$ Dist $= D.\ Lat.\ Sec\ Co.$

To find D.M.P., find the Meridional Parts for each latitude. Then, if both latitudes are the same name, subtract to obtain D. Lat., and also subtract M.P. to obtain D.M.P.

Lat. "A"	10° 44' N.	M.P.	643·44	Long. "A"	5° 00' W.
Lat. "B"	51 16 N.	M.P.	3576·03	Long "B"	63 05 W.
D. Lat.	40 32 N.	D.M.P.	2932·59	D. Long.	58 05' W.
	=2432' N.				=3485' W.

D. Long.	3485·00	Log 3·54220	D. Lat. 2432·0	Log 3·38596
D.M.P.	2932·59	Log 3·46725	Co. N. 49° 55' W.	Sec 0·19118
L. Tan Course		0·07495	Log Distance	3·57714

Course N. 49° 55' W.   Distance 3777 miles.

Example 2.—A ship takes her departure from Lat. 47° 50′ N., Long. 15° 18′ W., and steams 105° T. for 960 miles. Find her position at the end of the run.

First find D. Lat. $\dfrac{\text{D. Lat.}}{\text{Dist.}}$ = Cos Co. ∴ D Lat = Dist Cos Co.

Then find D. Long. $\dfrac{\text{D. Long}}{\text{D.M.P.}}$ = Tan Co. ∴ D. Long.=D.M.P. Tan Co.

Dist. 960	Log 2·98227	Lat. left	47°	50·0′ N	M.P.	3259·25
Co. S. 75° E.	Cos 9·41300	Diff. Lat.	4	08·5 S.		
D. Lat. Log	2·39529	Lat. in	43	41·5 N.	M.P.	2903·99
D. Lat.	248·5′				D.M.P.	355·26

D.M.P. 355·26	Log	2·55054	$\Big\}+$
Co. S. 75° E.	Tan	0·57195	
	D. Long. Log	3·12249	

D. Long.	1325·8′ =	22°	05·8′ E.
Long. left		15	18·0 W.
Long. in		6	47·8 E.

Example 3.—From Lat. 47° 30′ N., Long. 103° W., a vessel steered 250° T., and altered her longitude 47° 19′. Find the latitude reached and distance steamed.

To find D. Lat., we first require D.M.P. = D. Long. Cot Co.

Then, Dist. = D. Lat. Sec Co.

D. Long. 2839′ Log 3·45317	$\Big\}+$	Lat. left 47°30·0′N. M.P.3229·64′N.	$\Big\}-$
Course S. 70°W. Cot. 9·56107		D.M.P. 1033·33 S.	
D.M.P. Log 3·01424		Lat. in 34 31·5 N. M.P. 2196·31	
		D.Lat. 12 58·5 = 778·5′	

D. Lat. 778·5	Log 2·89126	$\Big\}+$	Lat. in 34° 31·5′ N.
Co. S. 70° W.	Sec 0·46595		
Dist.	Log 3·35721		Dist. 2276·2 miles

Example 4.—A vessel sailed on a course from Lat. 59° 20′ N. till her D.M.P. was twice the D. Lat., and equal to the Departure. Find the latitude reached and the Diff. Long.

Let value of D.M.P.=2. Then Dep=2, and D. Lat.=1

From Fig. $\dfrac{\text{D. Long}}{\text{D.M.P.}} = \dfrac{\text{Dep}}{\text{D. Lat.}}$

$$\text{D. Long} = \dfrac{\text{D.M.P.} \times \text{Dep}}{\text{D. Lat.}} = \dfrac{2 \times 2}{1} = 4$$

$\dfrac{\text{D. Long}}{\text{Dep}} = \dfrac{4}{2} = 2\!\cdot\!00000 = \text{Sec Mean Lat. (See Sketch)}$

Mean Lat. = 60° 00′ N.
Lat. left   59   20 N.

½ D. Lat.   40′   D. Lat. = 80′

D. Long.=80′ × 4 = 320′

Answer— Lat. in   60° 40′ N.
D. Long.   5 20

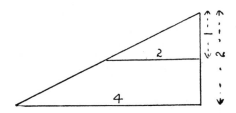

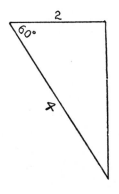

EXERCISE 9a.

Mercator Sailing.

1. Find the True Course and Distance from Lat. 23° N., Long. 7° E., to Lat. 40° N., Long. 15° W.

2. Find the True Course and Distance from Lat. 5° 42′ S., Long. 171° 16′ W. to Lat. 21° 47′ N., Long. 168° 25′ E.

3. A vessel steered 130° T. for 1167 miles. If she sailed from Lat. 49° 49′ N., Long. 87° 26′ W., what was her position at the end of the run?

4. After steering S.W. × S. (T) for 1200 miles, a ship arrived in Lat. 50° 18′ S., Long. 102° 44′ E. From what latitude and longitude had she sailed?

5. In the northern hemisphere, a vessel changed her longitude 12° 34′ while making a departure of 428′. If she left Long. 10° 44′ W. on a course of 242° T., find position arrived at, and the latitude of place of departure.

6. A vessel steered 300° T. from Lat. 40° 40′ N., and altered her longitude 11°. What distance had she steamed?

7. A ship in N. lat. steered 240° T., and altered her latitude 5° 43′, and her longitude 12° 08′. What distance and between what parallels had she steamed?

8. From Lat. 46° 14′ S., a ship steered on a course for 1418 miles, and made a departure of 905 miles West. If the course was to the northward, find the latitude arrived at, the D. Long. made good, and the course steered.

9. A vessel in Lat. 51° 11′ N. steered on a S'ly course till her D. Long. was 10° 57′ W., and her D.M.P. was 1063·85. Find latitude arrived at and the distance steamed.

10. A vessel left Lat. 10° 06′ N., Long. 50° 22′ W., and steered 202° for 1265 miles. Find position at which she arrived.

ANSWERS TO EXERCISE 9a.

1. D.M.P. 1198·15′. Course N. 47° 46′ 11″ W. Dist. 1517·5 miles.

2. D.M.P. 1671·23′. Course N. 36° 06′ 24″ W. Dist. 2041 miles.

3. D.M.P. 1037·35′. Lat. 37° 18·9′ N. Long. 66° 49·7′ W.

4. D.M.P. 1349·87′. Lat. 33° 40·2′ S. Long. 117° 45·9′ E.

5. D.M.P. 400·00′. Lat. left 57° 16·3′ N. Lat. in 53° 28·2′ N. Long. in 23° 18′ W.

6. D.M.P. 381·04′. D. Lat. 279·5′. Dist. 559 miles.

7. D.M.P. 420·3′. Dist. 686 miles. Lats. 38° 07½′ N. and 32° 23½′ N.

8. D.M.P. 1376·40′. Lat. in 28° 02′ S. D. Long. 1141′ (D.M.P. tan Co) or 1135′ (Dep. sec M. Lat.). Course N. 39° 39½′ W.

9. Lat. in 38° 39¾′ N. Dist. 883 miles

10. D.M.P. 1170·81′. Lat. 9° 27′ S. Long. 58° 15′ W.

E

CHARTWORK.

CHAPTER 8.

CONVERTING THE SPHERE TO MERCATOR'S PROJECTION— CHART ABBREVIATIONS — CORRECTIONS — NOTICES TO MARINERS—VARIATION CHARTS—LIGHT-VESSELS—MEANING OF "ABEAM"—MEASURING DISTANCES ON CHARTS— NORTH OR SOUTH, EAST OR WEST—EFFECTS OF REFRACTION, HEIGHT, AND TIDES.

In terrestrial navigation, outstanding landmarks, soundings of the sea bottom, etc., are used to give the seaman assistance in navigating his vessel along a coastline from one point to another. Special navigational charts are used for this purpose.

On these charts, the most noticeable feature is that while the landward portion is usually practically blank, except near the coastline, the seaward portion is teeming with figures and letters and lines.

It is, of course, the seaward part which is important to the navigator, and only that part of the land which can be seen from the sea is of any use to him when steaming along the coast.

To the initiated, the mass of figures, lines, and symbols printed on the seaward portion of a chart conveys important information required by mariners when navigating their vessels in clear weather and in fog.

Converting the Sphere to Mercator's Projection.—A chart represents, on a flat surface, part of the world. Since the world is actually a sphere, some distortion is necessary before it can be represented as a flat surface. This "distortion" has to be carried out in a strictly proportionate manner, in order that the shape of the land, compass bearings, and distances will still remain relatively correct.

Imagine a sphere to be dropped inside a cylinder of paper, as in Fig. 35. On the sphere is drawn the equator and each 10° of latitude and longitude, and the only part of the sphere which touches the cylinder of paper is the broadest part—the Earth's equator, in other words.

On the cylinder of paper, the equator becomes a straight line drawn across it. The points where the meridians of longitude touch this line are marked, and each meridian is then drawn on the paper at right angles to the line representing the equator.

When the cylinder of paper is laid flat, there is drawn on it the equator—a straight line right across the paper—and meridians of longitude for every 10° of longitude, which appear as parallel straight lines.

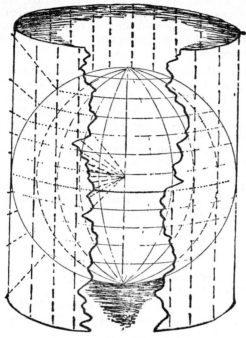

Actually, on a sphere, all meridians meet at the poles, and are therefore NOT parallel lines, so that the only place on the chart where the meridians agree with the meridians on the sphere is at the equator. The further North or South from the equator these parallel meridians are, the more they have been hauled out to the East or the West. It is therefore obvious that, when the parallels of latitude are drawn on the cylinder of paper, they will have to be hauled out, to North and South, in exactly the same proportion as the meridians have been.

To effect this purpose, lines are drawn from the centre of the sphere through each 10° of latitude and are produced straight out to the paper. The result is that there is no distortion at the equator, but the further North or South from the equator that any two succeeding parallels of latitude lie, the greater the distance between them, and on a chart it can be seen that the distance apart of Latitudes 0° and 10° is very much less than the distance apart of the parallels of, say, Latitudes 50° and 60°.

It can also be seen that it is impossible to show Latitude 90° on a chart, since a line from the centre of the sphere through its North or South pole would never touch the cylinder of paper. That is the reason why, on maps of the world on this projection, the North and South polar regions are always shown separately as circular maps, as though viewed from some place outside the Earth altogether.

The above method of "projecting" a map or chart is called "Mercator's projection".

Abbreviations.—On that part of the chart which represents the sea, the figures indicate the depth of the water at "low water ordinary spring tides". This is the least depth to be expected at that place under normal conditions, and if the depth shown on the chart is safe it is safe at any time. Information as to whether depths are in feet or in fathoms is given in the title-plate of the chart. Only charts on a large scale, covering an inshore area, give depths in feet. All other British charts give depths in fathoms.

Beside some of the figures, small letters can be seen, such **m., s., sh., st.,** etc. These are abbreviations for the nature of the bottom, and the examples given above indicate **mud, sand, shells,** and **stones.**

A special card of abbreviations is published by the Admiralty, and a good knowledge of them is very desirable. The list is divided into four parts, viz.—

(1) Quality of the Sea Bottom.
(2) General Abbreviations.
(3) Lights, Buoys, Beacons, Tides, etc.
(4) Conventional Signs.

It is important to note that the same abbreviation letter may mean two things, depending upon whether the letter is a small letter or a capital letter. For example,

"d" means "dark"; but "D" means "doubtful".

In the newer charts, referring to the quality of the sea bottom, when the initial letter is a capital letter, the word is a noun; when the initial letter is a small letter, the word is an adjective.

The candidate is recommended to study Admiralty Chart No. 5011 (inset) which contains ALL the abbreviations used on charts.

(Abbreviations in brackets are being brought into use gradually.)

Quality of Bottom.				*General Abbreviations.*		
b	....	blue		abt	....	about
blk	....	black	(bl)	Anche	....	anchorage
br	....	brown		Anct	....	ancient
brk	....	broken	(bk)	Approx	....	approximate
c	....	coarse		(Astrl)	....	astronomical
chk	....	chalk	(ck)	B	....	bay
cin	....	cinders	(Cn)	Blk	....	black
d	....	dark		Bk. Bks.	......	bank, banks
f	....	fine		Bn	....	beacon
g	....	gravel	(G)	Br.	....	bridge

grd	....	ground	(Gd)	C	.... cape
h	....	hard		Cas	.... castle
l	....	large		C.G.	.... coastguard
lt	....	light		Chan	.... channel
m	....	mud	(M)	Conspic	.... conspicuous
oys	....	oysters	(Oy)	Cov	.... covers
peb	....	pebbles	(p)	D	.... doubtful
r	....	rock	(R)	dr	.... dries
rd	....	red		fm	.... fathoms
s	....	sand	(S)	F.S.	.... flagstaff
sft	....	soft		ft	.... foot or feet
sh	....	shells	(Sh)	Hd	.... head
sm	....	small		Hr	.... harbour
st	....	stones	(St)	in	.... inches
stk	....	sticky	(sy)	L.B.S.	.... lifeboat station
w	....	white		L.S.S.	.... life-saving ,.
wd	....	weed	(Wd)	Lt.Ho.	.... lighthouse
y	....	yellow		Lt.Vl.	.... lightvessel
				occasl	.... occasional
				ord	.... ordinary
				P.D.	.... position doubtful
				P.A.	.... position approx.

Pecked lines on the chart indicate the limits of certain depths of water. Thus, — · · · — · · · — · · · — · · · — · · · — indicates that all depths OUTSIDE that line are over 30 fathoms. In general, for ordinary coasting work, the 5-fathom line (..... ....) should be taken as the danger line, special caution being used when inshore of that line.

Chart Corrections.—Lights, depths, shoals, etc., are liable to change and new information is constantly coming to hand which requires to be incorporated on charts.

When any such change occurs, it is notified to seamen in the "Admiralty Notices to Mariners", a publication which can be obtained free at any Mercantile Marine Office. The issue for fishermen and the home trade is printed on green paper; the issue for foreign-going vessels on white paper.

These Notices are printed on one side of the paper only, so that the information contained in them can be cut out, when necessary, without interfering with any other information. Very often extensive alterations on any part of a chart are shown by reproducing a part of the chart in the Notice. This reproduction, usually with the alteration given in red, can be cut out in its entirety and pasted on the chart in its proper place. Being given on the exact scale of the chart itself, such correction can be used on the chart with absolute confidence in its correctness.

Corrections from the "Notices to Mariners" are usually entered in red ink on the charts, unless they are listed as being of a temporary character, in which case they are entered in pencil. Every correction is given either a number or a date, and when a correction has been duly entered on the chart its number or its date should be immediately written in the bottom left-hand corner of the chart. This enables anyone to see at a glance whether the chart has been corrected up to date.

Variation.—The amount of the magnetic variation for the area covered by any particular chart is found in two or three places on the chart, incorporated on the "compass roses" which can be seen at various parts of each chart. A glance at the roses will show that the value of the variation alters quite appreciably within the area, so in actual practice the variation used is that given on the "rose" nearest the ship's position.

The compass roses themselves consist of (1) an outer ring, on which the degrees of the TRUE compass are graduated clockwise, from 000°, (North) through 090° (East) 180° (South), and 270° (West) to 359°; and (2) an inner ring, on which the degrees of the MAGNETIC compass are graduated. The inner rose also states the amount of the variation for a particular year, and the amount by which it increases or decreases annually.

On older charts, the graduations on the magnetic rose are given in the "quadrantal" method—North to East, North to West, South to East, and South to West—but as charts are being reprinted, the new editions are incorporating the 3-figure notation on the magnetic roses as well as on the true roses. Both systems are dealt with in this book.

In addition, a chart of the world, showing "curves" of equal magnetic variation, is published every five years. This chart, called an "isogonic" chart, shows the different amount of variation all over the world.

Light-vessels.—Light-vessels are denoted on charts by the adjoining symbol and, when measuring the actual position of a light-vessel, the tiny circle at the middle of the water-line is taken as the position.

Abeam.—In chart-work, the word "abeam" appears often. For a light, or a point of land, to be abeam of a vessel, is for it to be at an angle of 90° from the vessel's fore-and-aft line, or from the vessel's course, which is the same thing.

Measuring Distances.—Distances on a chart are invariably measured from the scale of latitude at the sides. Distances must NEVER be measured from the longitude scale.

1 minute of latitude	=	1 sea mile
1 degree of latitude	=	60 sea miles
1 sea mile	=	6080 feet

1 sea mile is also taken as being, approximately, 1000 fathoms
1 cable   = $\frac{1}{10}$ of a sea mile = 100 fathoms

Scales of latitude and longitude may not be given at the sides or the top and bottom of a harbour plan. In that case, a separate "scale of longitude" and a "scale of latitude and distance" are given on the chart, and the exact latitude and longitude of some conspicuous object on the chart are also given.

To obtain the latitude and longitude of any other point on the plan, draw two lines, one in a true North and South direction, the other in a true East and West direction, through the point whose position is given.

To find the position of any other point, measure with a pair of dividers from the point whose position is required to the E. and W. line through the given point. Refer this measurement to the "scale of latitude and distance", in order to obtain the difference of latitude between the given point and the point whose position is required. Next measure to the N. and S. line drawn through the given point, and refer this measurement to the "scale of longitude" to obtain the difference of longitude.

North or South, East or West.—The scale of latitude on a chart is given at both sides, and if the chart is of the Northern hemisphere, this increases upwards, or to the northward. If the chart is of an area in the Southern hemisphere, the scale increases downwards, or to the southward.

The scale of longitude is given across the top and the foot of the chart. If the area represented is in the Eastern hemisphere, the numerical value of degrees, etc., will increase to the right, or to the eastward. If the area is in the Western hemisphere, the numerical value of degrees, etc., will increase to the left, or to the westward.

Depth of Water.—The depths given on charts are the depths when the tide is at its normal lowest. That is, at "low water ordinary spring tides".

The distance that a light can be seen in clear weather, as given on charts, assumes the observer's eye to be 15 feet above sea level. So, if the observer's eye is less than 15 feet above sea level, the light will not be seen as far as is given on the chart. If, on the other hand, the observer's eye is at a greater height than 15 feet, the light will be seen at a greater distance.

The height of a lighthouse, or of a hill, is given above "high water ordinary spring tides". When the tide is below that level, the lighthouse (the centre of the light) will be higher out of the water than is stated on the chart and will thus be visible at a greater distance.

So, if an observer's eye is either higher or lower than 15 feet above sea level, it alters the range of visibility of a light. If the tide is not at H.W.O.S., it alters the range of visibility of a light. And if the night should be extraordinarily clear, with excessive refraction, the light under such circumstances might also be seen a great deal further than the normal distance.

CHAPTER 9.

LAYING OFF COURSES ON THE CHART—CONVERTING TRUE COURSES TO COMPASS COURSES—DEVIATION CARDS— LEEWAY.

"Parallel rulers" are used when laying off courses on a chart. These rulers (see Fig. 36) usually consist of two straight-edges joined together by two pieces of brass, which are also parallel to each other, so that no matter how far apart the separate straight-edges may be from each other, they always remain parallel. By this means, courses—or straight lines—can be projected from one part of a chart to another part with ease.

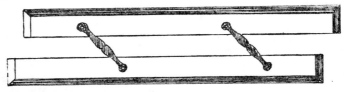

Fig. 36.

When a course has to be laid off from one definite point to another on a chart, first mark the latitude and longitude of each point, thus:—

Then lay the bevelled edge of the parallel ruler exactly on each of the two positions, and join them with a pencilled line. The line should be drawn lightly—no lines on a chart should be drawn heavily, and never under any circumstances should an indelible pencil be used. A sharp, fairly soft pencil is best. The more precisely the line is drawn, the more precise the answer will be.

When a course has to be laid to a position which is a stated distance off a lighthouse, first, with a pair of compasses, draw a circle whose radius is the required distance, using the position of the lighthouse as centre. Then draw the course-line so that it just touches the outside edge of the circle, as in Fig. 37.

Having drawn the course-line, shift the parallel rulers to the nearest compass rose, making certain that the rulers do not slip during the operation of shifting over the chart. Place the bevelled edge of the

rulers exactly at the centre of the compass rose—that is, just where the
four right angles meet—and read the number of degrees from the "true"
circle (the outer one).

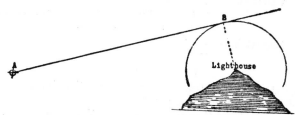

FIG. 37.

Make sure the reading from the compass rose is in the right
direction—FROM THE CENTRE OF THE ROSE TOWARDS THE DIRECTION
IN WHICH THE VESSEL IS GOING. Very little practice is required to
become adept at this.

Having found the true course, write it down exactly as it is read,
e.g., 026°, 097°, 321°, etc. To it, apply the given magnetic variation,
adding if this latter is westerly, subtracting if easterly. This operation
converts the true course to a magnetic course, and the same rhyme
that was used in the chapter on the Day's Work can be used here—
Given a true course:

"Variation west, magnetic best;
Variation east, magnetic least."

Example 1.—Using variation 10° W., convert true course 017° to a
magnetic course.

$$\begin{array}{ll} \text{True Course} & 017° \\ \text{Variation} & 10° \text{ W.} \\ \hline \text{Mag. Course} & 027° \end{array} \Big\} \;\; +$$

Example 2.—Using variation 15° E., convert true course 355° to
a magnetic course.

$$\begin{array}{ll} \text{True Course} & 355° \\ \text{Variation} & 15 \text{ E.} \\ \hline \text{Mag. Course} & 340° \end{array} \Big\} \;\; -$$

Example 3.—Using variation 12° E., convert true course 007° to
a magnetic course.

$$\begin{array}{ll} \text{True Course} & 007° \\ & +360 \\ \hline & 367° \\ \text{Variation} & 12 \text{ E.} \\ \hline \text{Mag. Course} & 355° \end{array} \;\; \Big\} \text{ Variation is subtractive and greater} \atop \text{than course, so add } 360°$$

Example 4.—Using variation 19° W., convert true course 352° to a magnetic course.

True Course   352° ⎫
Variation   19 W.⎭ +

$\overline{371°}$ ⎫ Course exceeds 360°, so subtract
         −360   ⎭   360 from it.

Mag. Course $\overline{\underline{011°}}$

EXERCISE 10.

Convert the following true courses to magnetic, giving the answers in both 3-figure and quadrantal notations.

1.	True Course	025°	Variation	13° E.
2.	,, ,,	078	,,	11 W.
3.	,, ,,	097	,,	10 W.
4.	,, ,,	011	,,	19 E.
5.	,, ,,	358	,,	12 W.
6.	,, ,,	017	,,	22 E.
7.	,, ,,	342	,,	18 W.
8.	,, ,,	202	,,	7 E.
9.	,, ,,	153	,,	14 E.
10.	,, ,,	000	,,	8 E.

To Convert Magnetic Courses to Compass Courses.—Until a vessel materially alters her geographical position, the magnetic variation remains unaltered, no matter what or how many courses the vessel steers.

But when a magnetic course has to be converted to a compass course, deviation is brought into use, and this, as stated in Chapter 6, alters every time the direction of the ship's head is altered.

In chart-work, although the quadrantal notation is still largely used, increasing use is being made of the 3-figure notation. Thus two distinct methods of conversion are involved, as each notation uses a different method. Both methods are fully explained below. The student should make himself equally adept in handling each method.

To Convert Magnetic Course to Compass Course (3-Figure Notation).—In Chapter 6, it was seen that the angle between the True and the Magnetic meridians is called Variation, and that the angle between the Magnetic meridian and the ship's Compass North is called Deviation. From Fig. 27 (page 54) it will also be appreciated that the rule we have already used when converting a True Course to a Magnetic Course must also hold good when converting a Magnetic Course to a Compass Course—that is, add westerly deviation, subtract easterly deviation.

Variation and deviation, when combined, give Compass Error, and when Error is applied, the same rule still holds good—add westerly, subtract easterly to obtain Compass Course.

Conversely, subtract westerly and add easterly when converting
    Compass Course to Magnetic Course;
    Magnetic Course to True Course;
    Compass Course to True Course.

Deviation Cards are supplied to vessels to enable the exact amount of deviation for *any* course to be found.

When the 3-figure notation is being used, these cards may show the value of the deviation of the compass for every 10° of "Ship's Head by Compass". Less usually, they may give the deviation for every 20° of Ship's Head by Compass. (See Deviation Cards 2 and 3, page 104).

In actual practice, vessels would not have deviations on their compasses nearly so large as those shown on the deviation cards. These deviations are purposely left large in order better to illustrate the working of the problems.

DEVIATION CARD. 1.

Ship's Head by Compass	Dev.
North	2°E.
N. by E.	4 E.
N.N.E.	6 E.
N.E. by N.	8 E.
N.E.	10 E.
N.E. by E.	12 E.
E.N.E.	14 E.
E. by N.	18 E.
East	22 E.
E. by S.	20 E.
E.S.E.	16 E.
S.E. by E.	14 E.
S.E.	12 E.
S.E. by S.	10 E.
S.S.E.	6 E.
S. by E.	4 E.
South	2 E.
S. by W.	2 W.
S.S.W.	7 W.
S.W. by S.	9 W.
S.W.	11 W.
S.W. by W.	14 W.
W.S.W.	16 W.
W. by S.	18 W.
West	22 W.
W. by N.	20 W.
W.N.W.	18 W.
N.W. by W.	16 W.
N.W.	12 W.
N.W. by N.	8 W.
N.N.W.	6 W.
N. by W.	2 W.
North	2 E.

DEVIATION CARDS.

Deviation Card 2			Deviation Card 3	
Comp. Co.	Dev.		Comp. Co.	Dev.
000°	2·0° E.		000°	12° W.
010	3·8 E.		010	10 W.
020	5·6 E.		020	8 W.
030	7·3 E.		030	7 W.
040	9·1 E.		040	6 W.
050	10·9 E.		050	4 W.
060	12·7 E.		060	3 W.
070	14·9 E.		070	1 W.
080	18·4 E.		080	2 E.
090	22·0 E.		090	3 E.
100	20·2 E.		100	5 E.
110	16·8 E.		110	7 E.
120	14·7 E.		120	8 E.
130	12·9 E.		130	10 E.
140	11·1 E.		140	11 E.
150	8·6 E.		150	12 E.
160	5·6 E.		160	14 E.
170	3·8 E.		170	15 E.
180	2·0 E.		180	13 E.
190	1·7 W.		190	12 E.
200	5·9 W.		200	10 E.
210	8·3 W.		210	9 E.
220	10·1 W.		220	7 E.
230	12·4 W.		230	5 E.
240	14·7 W.		240	4 E.
250	16·4 W.		250	3 E.
260	18·3 W.		260	2 E.
270	22·0 W.		270	0
280	20·2 W.		280	1 W.
290	18·4 W.		290	3 W.
300	16·7 W.		300	4 W.
310	13·8 W.		310	7 W.
320	10·2 W.		320	9 W.
330	7·3 W.		330	10 W.
340	5·1 W.		340	12 W.
350	1·6 W.		350	14 W.
000	2·0 E.		000	12 W.

Note particularly that the deviations given are for the "Ship's Head by Compass". The problem is to find the deviation to apply to any specified magnetic course to convert it to a compass course, using the information given on the card.

To do this, an appropriate compass course must be chosen from the deviation card, and this is converted to a magnetic course by applying the deviation given for that course.

Example 1.—The true course from "A" to "B" is 035°. Variation 11° W. Using Dev. card 3, find the compass course to steer.

$$\begin{array}{ll} \text{True Course} & 035° \\ \text{Variation} & +\ 11\ \text{W.} \\ \hline \text{Mag. Course} & 046° \end{array}$$

.rd, a COMPASS course of 050° (dev. 4° W.) seems

$$\begin{array}{ll} \text{Comp. Course} & 050° \\ \text{Deviation} & -\ \ 4\ \text{W.} \\ \hline \text{Mag. Course} & 046° \end{array}$$

ice a compass course of 050° gives a magnetic
plying its deviation of 4° W., this is the deviation

mpass course, after being converted to a magnetic
the same as the magnetic course for which the
When that is so, the necessary deviation must
n.

ι a MAGNETIC course 098°, find the deviation and
steer, using dev. card 3.
the deviation card a COMPASS course which,
deviation has been applied (E.+, W.—), will
e close to the given magnetic course.
·)0° or 100° seem appropriate. Write them down

℃)	098 (M)	100 (C)
ι.		+5 E.
093 (M)		105 (M)

Our course (098° (M)) lies between 093° (M) and 105°(M), so the required deviation lies SOMEWHERE between 3° E. and 5° E. That SOMEWHERE is in the same proportion as the difference between 093° and 098° (5°) is to the difference between 093° and 105° (12°). That is—

$$\text{Required correction to 3° E.} = \frac{(5-3)\ \times\ (098-093)}{(105-093)}$$

$$= \frac{2\times5}{12}$$

$$= \frac{10}{12}$$

$$= 0\cdot8 \text{ to the nearest decimal point.}$$

Since the required deviation is between 3° and 5°, this correction has to be ADDED to 3° E. The whole problem appears thus:—

090° C.	098° M.	100° C.	*Correction*
+3 E.	−3·8 E.	+5 E.	$\dfrac{2 \times 5}{12} = 0\cdot8°$
093 M.	094·2 C.	105 M.	

According to rule, easterly deviation is SUBTRACTED from the magnetic course.

If the above layout for the problem is followed, there is the advantage of knowing that all work at the two sides of the page follows the rule "E.+, W—", while work in the middle follows the reverse rule.

Example 3.—Given course of 230° (M), find the deviation and compass course, using deviation card 3.

By mentally adding the appropriate easterly deviations to compass courses 220° and 230°, we find that one of the two resultant magnetic courses is just smaller than the given course, the other just larger. So we choose these two compass courses.

220° (C)	230° (M)	230° (C)	*Dev. Corr.*
+7 E.	−6·2 E.	+5 E.	$\dfrac{2 \times 3}{8} = 0\cdot8$
227 (M)	223·8 (C)	235 (M)	

In this example, the *deviation* between 227° (M) and 235° (M) is DECREASING, therefore the correction (0·8°) is subtracted from 7° E.

Example 4.—Given course of 077° (M), find the deviation and compass course, using deviation card 3.

070° (C)	077·0° (M)	080° (C)	*Dev. Corr.*
−1 W.	−0·8 E.	+2 E.	$\dfrac{3 \times 8}{13} = 1\cdot8$
069 (M)	076·2 (C)	082 (M)	

In this example, the deviation alters from 1° W. to 2° E., a difference of 3°. The correction is 1·8°, to be applied to dev. 1° W. The sketch bel w indicates exactly how the required deviation of 0·8° E. has been arrived at.

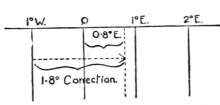

To Convert Magnetic Course to Compass Course (Quadrantal Notation).—Deviation cards supplied when quadrantal courses are required show the amount of deviation for every compass point of

"Ship's Head by Compass". (See Deviation Card 1, page 103). Candidates must therefore be familiar with the process of converting points to degrees. A table for this is given here.

No. of Points	Courses	Courses	Courses	Courses	No. of Degrees	
0	North		South		00°	00,
1	N. by E.	N. by W.	S. by E.	S. by W.	11	15
2	N.N.E.	N.N.W.	S.S.E.	S.S.W.	22	30
3	N.E. by N.	N.W. by N.	S.E. by S.	S.W. by S.	33	45
4	N.E.	N.W.	S.E.	S.W.	45	00
5	N.E. by E.	N.W. by W.	S.E. by E.	S.W. by W.	56	15
6	E.N.E.	W.N.W.	E.S.E.	W.S.W.	67	30
7	E. by N.	W. by N.	E. by S.	W. by S.	78	45
8	East	West	East	West	90	00

When finding the deviation for quadrantal courses, it is usually unnecessary to reckon the courses so closely as a quarter of a degree, so that 11° 15' can be read as 11°, 33° 45' as 34°, and so on.

The principles of finding the deviation for any particular course remain unchanged. A true course is laid off on the chart, the variation is applied to it, converting it to a magnetic course. This latter is then changed from the 3-figure notation to quadrantal notation.

This course should be "labelled". If an observer stands in the centre of a large compass card, facing North, the East point of the compass lies on his right hand side, the West point on his left hand side. Facing South, the East point lies on his left, the West point on his right.

This is ALWAYS the case, whether a course is True, Magnetic, or Compass, so that invariably a

> N.E. course is labelled "R";
> S.E.   ,,   ,,   ,,   "L";
> S.W.   ,,   ,,   ,,   "R";
> N.W.   ,,   ,,   ,,   "L".

An appropriate compass course must be chosen from the deviation card, and by applying the deviation given alongside of this course, it is converted to a magnetic course.

For help in performing this operation, the word CAMERA contains an easily remembered rule—

> From   **C**(ompass) to
>   a
>   **M**(agnetic) apply
>   **E**(asterly) deviation to
>   **R**(ight)
>   a

It then follows naturally that westerly deviation must be applied to the left. It will also be appreciated that when converting a magnetic course to a compass course, the rule must be reversed.

The compass course is "labelled" either "R" or "L", and the deviation to be applied is also labelled—easterly "R", westerly "L". If course and deviation are both "R" or both "L", they are added to obtain the magnetic course. If one is "R", and the other "L", they are subtracted.

Example 5.—Given TRUE Course 054°, and variation 14° W., find the deviation and compass course to steer, using deviation card 1.

$$
\begin{array}{ll}
\text{True Course} & 054° \\
\text{Variation} & \underline{14\ \text{W.}} \\
\text{Mag. Course} & \underline{\underline{068}} \quad = \text{N.68°E., R.}
\end{array}
$$

The magnetic course has been found. The next step is to choose an appropriate compass course from the deviation card, apply the deviation to it, using the rule CAMERA, and convert it to a magnetic course.

The compass course nearest to the given magnetic course is E.N.E.=N.67½°E.

$$
\begin{array}{ll}
\text{Comp. Course} & \text{N.67}\tfrac{1}{2}° \ \text{E., R.} \\
\text{Deviation} & \underline{14 \quad \text{E., R.}} \\
\text{Mag. Course} & \underline{\underline{\text{N.81}\tfrac{1}{2}\ \ \text{E., R.}}}
\end{array}
$$

This is obviously much too large, so the next smaller compass course must be tried—N.E. by E. = N. 56° E.

$$
\begin{array}{ll}
\text{Comp. Course} & \text{N. 56° E., R.} \\
\text{Deviation} & \underline{12 \quad \text{E., R.}} \\
\text{Mag. Course} & \underline{\underline{\text{N. 68 \ E.}}}
\end{array}
$$

From the operation just carried out, it has been found that a MAGNETIC course of N. 68° E. requires a deviation of 12° E., so our given magnetic course can be converted to a compass course by applying this deviation, to the LEFT. The problem should be set out thus:—

$$
\left.\begin{array}{ll}
\text{Comp. Course} & \text{N.56°E., R.} \\
\text{Deviation} & \underline{12 \ \text{E., R.}}
\end{array}\right\} + \qquad
\left.\begin{array}{ll}
\text{Mag. Course N. 68°E., R.} \\
\text{Deviation} \quad\quad\ \underline{12 \ \text{E., L.}}
\end{array}\right\} -
$$

$$
\begin{array}{ll}
\text{Mag. Course} \quad \underline{\underline{\text{N.68 E.}}} & \qquad \text{Comp. Course N. 56 E.}
\end{array}
$$

Note that when easterly deviation is applied to a magnetic course to convert it to a compass course, it is applied to the LEFT.

Note also that a N.E.ly course is always labelled "R", whether it is True, Magnetic, or Compass.

Example 6.—Given a *magnetic* course of N. 24° E., find the deviation and the compass course to steer, using the deviation card.

First choose from the deviation card a *compass* course, which, after its appropriate deviation has been applied (E. to R., W. to L.) will give a magnetic course close to the given magnetic course.

N.N.E. (N. 22½° E.) seems an appropriate course.

Comp. course	N. 22½° E. R.
Deviation	6 E. R.
Mag. course	N. 28½° E.

This magnetic course is slightly larger than the course given. Write the given magnetic course in the middle of the page, and this larger one on the right hand side, thus:—

Mag. Course.
N. 24° E. R.

Comp. Course	
	N. 22½° E. R.
Deviation	6 E. R.
Mag. Co.	N. 28½° E.

Next take the COMPASS course next less than N.N.E., namely, N. by E. (N. 11° E.). Write it on the left-hand side of the page, and apply its deviation, thus:—

Comp. Course		Mag. Course		Comp. Course	
	N. 11° E. R.		N. 24° E. R.		N. 22½° E. R.
Deviation	4 E. R.			Deviation	6 E. R.
Mag.	N. 15° E.			Mag.	N. 28½° E. R.

The given magnetic course is almost midway between the smaller and the greater MAGNETIC courses just found, and its deviation must therefore be almost midway between 4° E. and 6° E.

To find the exact deviation involves working a problem in simple proportion.

The given magnetic course is 9° greater than the SMALLER magnetic course we have found.

The larger magnetic course (to the nearest degree) is 14° greater than the smaller course.

The given magnetic course is thus $\frac{9}{14}$ of the way between the smaller and the larger courses, so the required deviation must be $\frac{9}{14}$ of the way between 4° and 6°.

Find the difference between the two deviations—(4° E. and 6° E.)=2°.

Multiply this by the difference between the smaller magnetic course and the given magnetic course (N. 15° E. and N. 24° E.)=9°.

$$9 \times 2 = 18°$$

Divide this result by the difference between the smaller magnetic course and the greater magnetic course (N. 15° E. and N. 28½° E.)= 13½°.

$$13\tfrac{1}{2})18(1\tfrac{1}{4}°$$

The result, to the nearest ¼ degree, is 1¼°.

This result is the correction to apply to THE DEVIATION OF THE SMALLER COURSE.

Since the deviation must be between 4° and 6°, the correction must obviously be added to the 4° E. deviation of the smaller course, giving the required deviation as 5¼° E.

This deviation is applied to the magnetic course (N. 24° E.), easterly deviation to the LEFT.

The entire problem, which is fully explained above, is laid out as follows:—

	Comp. Course	Mag. Course	Comp. Course	2
	N. 11° E. R.	N. 24° E. R.	N. 22½° E. R.	9
Dev.	4 E. R.	5¼ E. L.	6 E. R.	
				13½)18(1¼
Mag.	N. 15° E.	N. 18¾° E.	N. 28½° E. Mag.	

Comp. Course.

If the above form of layout for the problem is adhered to, there is the advantage of knowing that—

All work at the two sides of the page follows the rule CAMERA, and all work in the middle of the page follows the reverse rule.

Example 7.—Given a magnetic course of S. 55° W., find the compass course to steer, using the deviation card.

	Comp. Course	Mag. Course	Comp. Course	2
	S. 67½° W. R.	S. 55° W. R.	S. 79° W. R.	3½
Dev.	16 W. L.	16¾ W. R.	18 W. L.	
				10) 7 (¾
Mag.	S. 51½° W.	S. 71¾° W.	S. 61° W. Mag.	

Comp. Course

Note particularly that it does not matter whether the chosen COMPASS courses are greater or less than the given magnetic course. It is the MAGNETIC courses corresponding to these compass courses which must be smaller and greater than the given magnetic course.

Courses near North and South.—When the given magnetic course lies near North or South, or when the deviation is changing from E. to W., a little more care and thought may be needed.

Example 8.—Given magnetic course N. 4° W., find the compass course to steer, using the deviation card.

	Comp Course	Mag. Course	Comp. Course	4
	N. 00° E. R.	N. 4° W. L.	N. 11° W. L.	6
Dev.	2 E. R.	0½ E. L.	2 W. L.	
				15)24(1½
Mag.	N. 2° E.	N. 4½° W.	N. 13° W. Mag.	

Comp. Course

The difference between the deviations 2° E. and 2° W. is 4° and from N. 2° E. to N. 4° W. is 6°. Similarly from N. 2° E. to N. 13° W. is 15°. The correction is thus 1½°.

This correction has to be applied to the left-hand deviation (2° E.) and the resulting deviation has to be between 2° E. and 2° W.

In other words, the student might call the deviation 2° E.— "2 minutes *to* noon", and the deviation 2° W.—"2 minutes *past* noon."

Then, with the correction of 1½° to apply, he could ask, "What time would it be 1½ minutes after 2 minutes to noon?" The answer is, of course, ½ minute *to* noon, therefore the correct deviation is ½° E.

If the correction had been 2¼°, the question would be, "What time will it be 2¼ minutes after 2 minutes to noon?" In that case, the answer is ¼ minute *past* noon, or ¼° W.

When the deviation is changing its name, the working follows precisely the same rules as when correcting the Sun's declination, when the Sun is crossing the equinoctial on March 21st, or September 23rd.

Example 9.—Using the deviation card, find the compass course to steer, being given magnetic course S. 6° W.

	Comp. Course	Mag. Course	Comp. Course	
	S. 00° W. R.	S. 6° W. R.	S. 11° W. R.	4
Dev.	2 E. R.	0	2 W. L.	4
				—
				7)16(2
Mag.	S. 2° W.	S. 6° W.	S. 9° W. Mag.	

Comp. Course

Courses near East and West.—When the magnetic course is near East or West, it sometimes happens that one has to go from a southerly course to a northerly one, or *vice versa*, on the deviation card.

Example 10.—Given magnetic course S. 76° W., find the compass course to steer, using deviation card.

	Comp. Course	Mag. Course	Comp. Course	
	S. 90° W. R.	S. 76° W. R.	S. 101° W. R.	2
Dev.	22 W. L.	20¾ W. R.	20 W. L.	8
				13)16(1¼
Mag.	S. 68° W.	S. 96¾° W.	S. 81° Mag.	

—180°

N. 83¼° W.   Comp. Course

In this example, the appropriate smaller magnetic course, S. 68° W., is found from a compass course of West. This is the largest S. and W. course on the card, and the course which has to be taken as a larger course is therefore W. × N. (N. 79° W.).

In order to keep to the S. and W. names, it is quite in order to measure the angle from South, and N. 79° W. then becomes S. 101°W. (S. 90° W.+11°)

Between the smaller and the greater magnetic courses, the deviation decreases from 22° W. to 20° W., and the correction found has therefore to be subtracted from the *deviation of the smaller course.* This deviation is not necessarily the smaller deviation. That is an important point which must never be overlooked.

The final answer, being over 90°, is subtracted from 180°, the result being called N. and W.

Example 11.—Given magnetic course S. 88° W., find the compass course to steer, using deviation card.

	Comp. Course	Mag. Course	Comp. Course	2
	S. 101° W. R.	S. 88° W. R.	S. 112½° W. R.	7
Dev.	20 W. L.	19 W. R.	18 W. L.	
				13½)14(1
Mag.	S. 81° W.	S. 107° W.	S. 94½° W. **Mag.**	

—180

N. 73° W. Comp. Course

EXERCISE 11.

Given the following magnetic courses, convert them to compass courses in the quadrantal notation, using deviation card 1. Then change the magnetic courses to the 3-figure notation, and again convert to compass courses, using deviation card 2.

1. N. 35° E.	10. N. 77° W.	19. N. 90° E.
2. N. 48 E.	11. N. 83 W.	20. N. 90 W.
3. N. 62 E.	12. S. 20 W.	21. S. 80 W.
4. N. 75 E.	13. S. 38 W.	22. S. 3 W.
5. N. 88 E.	14. S. 67 W.	23. N. 2 E.
6. N. 24 W.	15. S. 20 E.	24. North
7. N. 35 W.	16. S. 43 E.	25. S. 2 E.
8. N. 51 W.	17. S. 56 E.	26. South
9. N. 64 W.	18. S. 80 E.	

Given the following magnetic courses, convert them to compass courses, using deviation card 3.

27. 144°	31. 073°	35. 353°
28. 230	32. 077	36. 358
29. 299	33. 268	
30. 009	34. 323	

Leeway.—The effect of a wind has often to be taken into account when "shaping a course" from one point to another, especially if a stiff breeze is blowing from nearly abeam.

The course laid off on the chart is a true course, and if leeway has to be allowed it must be allowed INTO THE WIND.

For instance, given a true course of N. 42° E., with a North wind blowing. If the leeway is estimated as 3°, the vessel would then require to steer N. 39° E. to counteract the leeway and to make good a N. 42° E. course.

Note that this reverses the rule used in the "Day's Work" problem. In the "Day's Work", a compass course is given, and leeway is allowed AWAY FROM the wind.

In "Chart Work", a true course is given, and leeway is allowed INTO the wind. The leeway should be allowed before applying either variation or deviation.

(NOTE.—All chart exercises are worked from *Brown's Practice Chart of the English Channel.* Students are advised to purchase this chart. Answers will probably show only slight differences if other copies of the English Channel chart are used.)

EXERCISE 12.

Laying off Courses without and with Leeway.

Using deviation card 1 on page 103, find the compass courses to steer, and the distances steamed.

1. From   Daunt Rk. Lt. VI.   To Smalls Lt.   (Var. 15° W.)
2. ,,   Smalls Lt.   ,, Hartland Pt. Lt.   (Var. 14° W.)
3. ,,   Hartland Pt. Lt.   ,, Pendeen Lt.   (Var. 14½° W.)
4. ,,   5 miles South (True) ,, 4 miles North (True) (Var. 12° W.)
            from Lizard Lt.   from C. la Hague
                                    Lt.
5. ,,   20 miles West (True) ,, 3 miles East (True)   (Var. 13° W.)
            from Ushant Lt.   from Eddystone
                                    Lt.
6. ,,   10 miles S. 20° W.   ,, 10 miles S. 20° W.   (Var. 12° W.)
            (mag.) from   (True) from
            Lizard Lt.   Beachy Hd. Lt.

Using deviation card 2 on page 104, find the compass courses to steer, and the distances steamed. Give courses to nearest half-degree.

7. From   5 miles 180° (M)   To Owers Lt. VI.   (Var. 12° W.)
            from Start Pt. Lt.
8. ,,   Coningbeg Lt. VI.   ,, Strumble Hd. Lt.   (Var. 14° W.)
            allowing 4° leeway for a southerly wind.
9. ,,   5 miles 180° (T)   To 3 miles 000° (T)   (Var. 11½° W.)
            from Beachy Hd.   from Casquets Lt.
            Lt.
            allowing 4° leeway for a north-westerly wind.
10. ,,   3 miles 000° (T)   To Eddystone Lt.   (Var. 12° W.)
            from Casquets Lt.
            allowing 2° leeway for a south-westerly wind.

CHAPTER 10.

POSITION BY CROSS BEARINGS—SET AND DRIFT OF CURRENT.

When a vessel is proceeding from one point to another, many factors tend to divert her from the course line laid down on the chart. Amongst the commonest are winds, currents and bad steering.

The responsible officer should always be on the alert to check up the vessel's position when in sight of land, and one of the easiest and best-known methods of doing this is by taking "cross-bearings" of two, or more, objects or lights.

The best results are obtained when the angle between two objects is as near as possible to 90°, though, of course, it is not always possible to obtain this.

A compass bearing of each object is taken, and these bearings are then converted to true bearings, and laid off on the chart, each bearing being drawn in the proper direction to its own respective object.

The argument is that, since the vessel must be somewhere on each of these two lines of bearing, as in Fig. 38, her position is where the two lines of bearing cross each other. This position, compared with the course line laid down on the chart, shows at a glance whether the vessel is keeping to her course, or is being set off it.

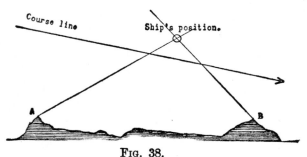

FIG. 38.

When a bearing can be obtained of a third object or light, the ship's position can be fixed even more accurately, provided all three bearings meet at a point. (See also Chapter 14.)

Correcting the Compass Bearings.—While compass bearings are being taken, the ship's head does not alter, but remains on the original course, the bearings themselves being taken by using a pelorus, or an "azimuth mirror", or even simply by "taking a bead" on the objects. So long as the ship's head remains on the original course, *the deviation of the compass remains unchanged.* So, when converting the compass bearing to a true bearing, the deviation FOR THAT COURSE is first applied to each bearing, converting each to a magnetic bearing, using the rule CAMERA.

Variation is then applied to these magnetic bearings, using the same rule, converting them to true bearings.

If desired, this operation can be performed by first combining the variation and the deviation. If both are E., or both W., add them to obtain compass error, naming the error the same as both. If one is E., and the other W., subtract them to obtain the error, naming the error the same as the greater.

Examples:—

Variation	17° W.	Variation	17° W.
Deviation	7 W.	Deviation	7 E.
Error	24° W.	Error	10° W.

When applying an error to a compass course or bearing to convert it direct to true, an easily remembered rule is contained in the word CATERWAUL.

From **C** (ompass)

a

to **T** (rue)

apply **E** (asterly)

to **R** (ight)

apply **W** (esterly)

a

u

to **L** (eft)

Having converted the bearings to true, lay them off on the chart. The point where the two lines cross is the vessel's position, as has already been explained. This position is expressed in degrees, minutes and seconds, the latitude always coming first, thus:—

Lat. 51° 23′ 30″ N., Long. 5° 18′ 00″ W.

To find the position on the chart, put the point of one leg of a pair of dividers on the ship's position. Stretch the other leg till it touches the nearest parallel of latitude on the chart—say Lat. 51°. Anywhere on that parallel is latitude 51°. Shift the dividers to the scale of latitude at the side of the chart, putting one leg on 51°. Now read the minutes and seconds at the point on the latitude scale reached by the other leg, making sure these are taken from BELOW the parallel of latitude if the ship's position is below it but from ABOVE it if the ship's position is above it. This reading gives the latitude.

The longitude is found in the same way, stretching the legs of the dividers from the ship's position to the nearest meridian of longitude and measuring from the longitude scale on the chart. The scales are marked very clearly for both latitude and longitude, but care must be taken to add or subtract the minutes and seconds according to whether the scale is increasing or decreasing in the appropriate direction.

To Find the Set and Drift of the Current.—In examination questions, sufficient information is given to indicate how far the vessel has steamed. The information may be given in a form such as: "The vessel reached this position after steaming for 1 hour at 10 knots".

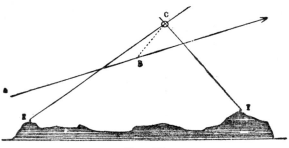

Fig. 39.

In Fig. 39, let us assume that the vessel starts off along her course line from position A. At the end of 1 hour, steaming 10 knots, she should have reached position B. By cross bearings, it is found that the vessel's actual position is at C.

Current has SET the vessel from her expected position at B to her actual position at C.

The direction from B to C, expressed as a true direction (*e.g.* 161°, 139°, etc.) is the set of the current experienced. It is found by laying the parallel rulers along the line B C, and shifting them to the nearest compass rose, the reading from the compass always being taken in the direction from the expected position to the actual position.

The DRIFT of the current is the distance in miles from B to C, measured in the usual way from the scale of latitude.

Example.—Using deviation card on page 103, and variation 12° W., find the course to steer from a position 180°, 5 miles from Lizard Head, to a position 180°, 5 miles from Start Point on "Brown's Practice Chart of the English Channel."

Comp. Course		True Course	Comp. Course	
N. 67½° E. R.		N. 77° E. R.	N. 79° E. R.	4
14 E. R.	Variation	12° W. R.	18 E. R.	7½
N. 81½° E. R.	Magnetic	N. 89 E. R.	N. 97° E. R.	15)30(2
	Deviation	16 E. L.		

N. 73° E. Comp. Course

With ship's head on above compass course, Eddystone Light bore N. 62° W. by compass, and Start Point bore N. 33° E. by the same compass. Find the ship's position, and the set and drift of the current experienced since the course was set, ship having run 5 hours and steaming 10 knots.

Deviation being 16° E., and variation 12° W., the error is 4° E.

Comp. bearings	N. 62° W. L.	N. 33° E. R.
Error	4 E. R.	4 E. R.
True bearings	N. 58° W.	N. 37° E.

Lay these true bearings off on the chart, and first find the ship's position.

Lat. 50° 00′ 15″ N., Long. 3° 52′ 30″ W.

Next lay off 50 miles ALONG THE ORIGINAL COURSE LINE from the position from which the vessel started. This gives the expected position. The current has set the vessel from the expected position to the actual position found by cross bearings, and the direction, usually expressed as a true direction, is the set. The drift is the distance in miles from the expected to the actual position.

Set 144½° Drift 5 miles

Using 3-figure notation, the same example would appear thus— Using deviation card 2 on page 104, and variation 12° W., find the course to steer from a position 180° (T), 5 miles from Lizard Head, to a position 180° (T), 5 miles from Start Point on "Brown's Practice Chart of the English Channel".

Course
077° (T)
12 W.

070° (C)	089 (M)	080° (C)	Correction
14·9° E.	16 E.	18·4° E.	3·5 × 4·1
084·9 (M)	073 (C)	098·4 (M)	13·5
			=1·1°

Comp. bearings were taken with the ship's head on the same course, as follows:—

Eddystone Lt. 298° (C); Start Point 033° (C)

Find the ship's position and the set and drift of the current experienced since the course was set, ship having run 5 hours, and steaming 10 knots.

Bearings	298° (C)	033° (C)
Error	4 E.	4 E.
Bearings	302 (T)	037 (T)

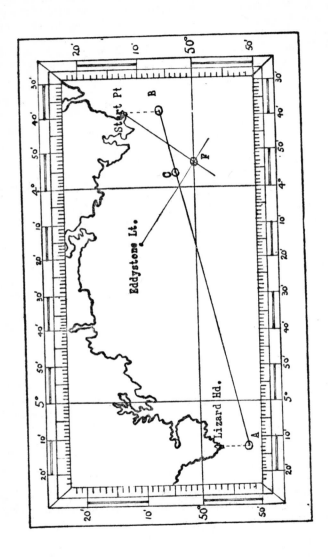

The ship's position, set and drift of the current would, of course, be the same as when working in the quadrantal notation.

EXERCISE 13.

1. (a) On "Brown's Practice Chart of the English Channel", and using variation 12° W., and deviation card No. 1, on page 103, find the compass course to steer from a position 180°, 6 miles from Beachy Head, to a position 180°, 6 miles from Start Point.

(b) With ship's head on above compass course, the following cross bearings were taken. Find the ship's position in each case, and the set and drift of the current experienced, ship steaming 10 knots throughout.

Time run from Beachy Head		Compass Bearings
(1) 1 hr 45 min	Owers Light Vessel Beachy Head	{ N. 35° W. { N. 80 E.
(2) 4 hr 30 min	St. Catherine's Owers Light Vessel	{ N. 28 W. { N. 85 E.
(3) 8 hr 36 min	Bill of Portland Needles Light	{ N. 40 W. { N. 76 E.
(4) 11 hr	Bill of Portland Anvil Point	{ N. 30½ E. { N. 77½ E.
(5) 13 hr 12 min	Start Point Bill of Portland	{ N. 59½ W. { S. 89 E.

2. (a) Using deviation card No. 2, and variation 14° W., find the compass course to steer from Seven Stones Light Vessel (Scillies) to Caldy Island (Bristol Channel).

(b) With ship's head as above, the following cross bearings were taken. Find the ship's position in each case, and the set and drift of the current experienced, ship steaming 12 knots.

Time run from Seven Stones Light Vessel		Compass Bearings
(1) 0 hr 55 min	Longships Trevose Head	{ 146° (C) { 066½ (C)
(2) 2 hr 10 min	Pendeen Trevose Head	{ 186° (C) { 086° (C)
(3) 5 hr	Trevose Head Hartland Point	{ 161° (C) { 073° (C)
(4) 6 hr 50 min	North Lundy Light St. Goven Light Vessel	{ 116° (C) { 019° (C)
(5) 7 hr 30 min	Caldy Island St. Ann's Head Light changing to *Red.*	006° (C)

CHAPTER 11.

RUNNING FIX ALLOWING FOR CURRENT—EXPLANATION OF THE PROBLEM.

Very often, only a single point of land, or lighthouse, is in sight, so that a somewhat different procedure has to be followed if the ship's position is desired.

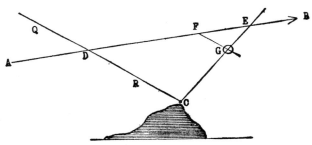

FIG. 40.

In Fig. 40, AB is the course line along which the vessel is supposed to be proceeding. It is not known whether she is exactly on that line or not, and the problem is to fix the position, having in sight one point of land only.

A compass bearing of the point is taken and converted to a true bearing, by applying first the deviation for *the direction of the ship's head*, and then the variation. This bearing is represented in Fig. 40 by the line CD.

All that is known now is that the vessel is heading in the direction AB, and that she is SOMEWHERE on the line of bearing CD. She *might* be at the point D, but she might just as easily be at the point R, or the point Q, for all we know.

For convenience (since the point D lies on the line of course), let the vessel's position be assumed to be at D, and if that happens NOT to be the correct position, any error must be in *the same direction as the line* CD, since the vessel is definitely somewhere on that line.

After running a set time—say 1 hour at 10 knots—a second bearing is taken of the point, converted to a true bearing, and laid off on the chart (line CE in Fig. 40.) The vessel is now somewhere on the second line of bearing.

From the point *D*, 10 miles (the distance steamed in the hour between the two bearings) is measured along the line of course (point *F*.)

If point *D* had been the vessel's position at the time of taking the first bearing, point *F* would coincide with point *E* on the line of bearing *CE*. If point *F* does not coincide, an error HAS been made in assuming the ship's original position to be at *D*. Such error, as was seen above, lies in the direction of the first bearing, *CD*. A line parallel to *CD* is therefore drawn through position *F*, and the point *G* where this line meets *CE*, the second bearing, must be the vessel's actual position at that time.

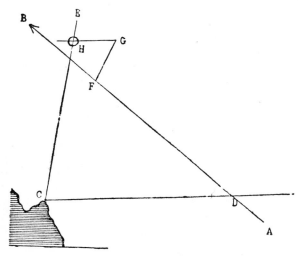

FIG. 41.

Example.—In Fig. 41, a vessel is steaming with her head N. 60° W. (true). Two bearings are taken of the lighthouse *C*, the ship steaming 1 hour at 9 knots between the bearings. A current is estimated to set 050°, 2 knots. Find the vessel's position at the time of taking the second bearing.

Convert both bearings to true bearings, and lay them off on the chart (*CD* and *CE*).

Assume position *D* to be the vessel's position, and from there, lay off 9 miles along the line of course (*F*).

From this point *F*, lay off *FG*, the set and drift of the estimated current.

If position *D* has been the vessel's correct position *F* would be her position at the time of taking the second bearing, and would, of course, be on the second line of bearing.

But the point *F* does NOT lie on the line of bearing *CE*, and current has to be allowed for, so that *D* was not the correct position, and the error in position must lie in the direction *CD*, since the vessel was somewhere on that line when the first bearing was taken.

A line parallel to *CD* is drawn through the point *G*, meeting the second line of bearing (*CE*) at *H*.

The position *H* is thus the vessel's position.

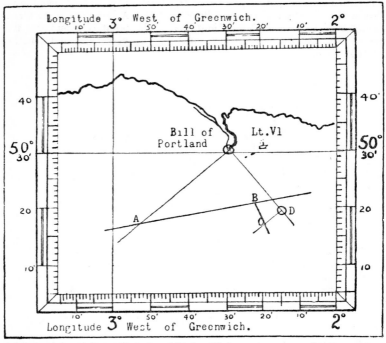

Example.—With ship's head E. by N. by compass, and using variation 12° W., and the deviation card No. 1 on page 103, Bill of Portland was observed bearing by compass N. 44° E., and after continuing on the same course for 2 hours at 10 knots the same light bore N. 48° W. by compass. Find the ship's position at the time of taking the second bearing, making due allowance for a current which set 150°, 2 knots.

Ship's head *by compass* is E. by N. From the deviation card, the deviation for that course is found to be 18° E.; variation is 12° W., giving an error of 6° E.

Comp. Bearings.

Comp. Course	N. 79° E. R.		N. 44° E. R.	N. 48° W. L.
Error	6 E. R.	Error	6 E. R.	6 E. R.
True Course	N. 85° E.		N. 50° E.	N. 42° W.

True Bearings

Lay off the true course on the chart, anywhere in the vicinity of the light. Lay off the two true bearings.

From the point where the first bearing crosses the course line, measure the distance steamed in 2 hours (20 miles) along the course line.

From this point, lay off the set and drift of the current (150°, 4 miles.)

Through this last point, draw a line parallel to the first bearing. The point where it cuts the second line of bearing gives the ship's position.

Lat. 50° 19′ 00″ N., Long. 2° 14′ 00″ W.

Using 3-figure notation, the same example would appear thus— Using deviation card 2 on page 104, and variation 12° W. Ship's head was 079° (C). Bill of Portland was observed bearing 044° (C), and after continuing on the same course for 2 hours at 10 knots, the same light bore 312° (C). Find the ship's position at the time of taking the second bearing, making due allowance for a current which set 150° (T), 2 knots.

The ship's course is 079° (C), which is ·9 of the way between 070° (C) and 080′ (C). The deviation for these two compass courses, from the deviation card, are respectively 14·9° E. and 18·4° E., a difference of 3·5°.

3·5×0·9=3·1°
14·9°+3·1° gives deviation 18° E.
Var. 12° W., Dev. 18° E., gives Error 6° E.

Bearings

Course	079° (C)	044° (C)	312° (C)
Error	+6 E.	+6 E.	+6 E.
Course	085° (T)	050° (T)	318° (T)

These courses and bearings are the same as were found when using quadrantal notation, so the ship's position will also be the same.

EXERCISE 14.

Finding Position by Running Fix.

1. With ship's head East (true), St. Catherine's Light bore 050° (T), and after continuing on the same course for 2 hours at 12 knots, the same light bore 320° (T). Find the ship's position at the time of taking the second bearing, making due allowance for a current which set 000° (T), 1½ knots.

2. With ship's head N. 70° E. (true), Owers Light Vessel bore 043° (T), and after steaming on the same course for 2 hours at 9½ knots the same light bore 310° (T). Find the ship's position at the time of taking the second bearing, making due allowance for a current which set 154° (T), 2 knots.

3. **Using** deviation card No. 1. With ship's head E.N.E. by compass, and using variation 13° W., Lizard Head Light bore by compass N. 27° E., and after continuing on the same course for 1½ hours at 10 knots, the same light bore by compass N. 55° W. Find the ship's position at the time of taking the second bearing, making due allowance for a current which set 147°, 2 knots.

(Note regarding above:—The compass course is given, and so the deviation for the ship's head E.N.E. is found direct from the deviation card to be 14° E. Variation being 13° W., the error is 1° E. The true course is laid off somewhere in the vicinity of Lizard Head. The precise distance off the light does not matter, as the answer will be the same no matter where the course line is laid down. The current is given true and requires no correction.)

4. With ship's head West by compass, and using variation 12° W., and deviation card No. 1, Casquets Light was observed to bear S. 34° W. by compass, and after continuing on the same course for 2 hours at 10 knots, the same light bore by compass S. 36° E. Find the ship's position at the time of taking the second bearing, making due allowance for a current which set 334°, 2 knots.

5. With ship's head W.N.W. by compass, and using variation 12½° W., and deviation card No. 1. Start Point Light bore by compass N. 27° W., and after steaming on the same course for a further 2 hours at 12 knots, the light bore N. 51° E. by compass. Find the ship's position at the time of taking the second bearing, making due allowance for a current which set 236°, 1¼ knots.

6. With ship's head 034° (C), and using variation 14° W., and deviation card No. 2, Smalls Light bore 068° (C), and after continuing on the same course for 2 hours at 11 knots, the same light bore abeam. Find the ship's position at the time of taking the second bearing, making due allowance for a current which set 166° (T), 1½ knots.

7. With ship's head 090° (T), Wolf Rock bore abeam, and after continuing on the same course for 3 hours at 10 knots, Lizard Head bore 330° (T). Find the ship's position at the time of taking the second bearing, making due allowance for a current which set 060° (T), 2 knots.

8. With ship's head 236° (C), and using variation 12° W., and deviation card No. 2, Casquets Lighthouse bore 172° (C), and after continuing on the same course for 3 hours at 12 knots, Les Hanois Light bore 113° (C). Find the ship's position at the time of taking the second bearing, making due allowance for a current which set 300° (T), 1½ knots.

9. With ship's head 146° (C), and using variation 14° W., and deviation card No. 2, Bishop Rock (Scillies) was observed to bear 103° (C), and after continuing on the same course for 1½ hours at 10 knots, the same light bore abeam. Find the ship's position at the time

of taking the second bearing, making due allowance for a current which set 260° (T), 2 knots.

10. With ship's head 067·5° (C), and using variation 15½° W., and deviation card No. 2, Galley Head bore 011·5° (C), and after continuing on the same course for 4 hours at 10 knots Old Head of Kinsale bore 309·5° (C) by the same compass. Find the ship's position at the time of taking the second bearing, making due allowance for a current which set 270° (T), 1 knot.

F

CHAPTER 12.

SETTING A COURSE TO COUNTERACT THE EFFECT OF A CURRENT.

As was seen in Chapter 11, when allowance has to be made for the probable effect of a known current, that allowance is applied *after* the vessel's course has first been set off.

But when setting a course which is to COUNTERACT the effect of a known current, the necessary steps have to be taken at the *commencement* of the run, since to counteract means to prevent.

This can easily be remembered by an ABC rule:—

A llow
fterwards

B ut

C ounteract at
ommencement

Example 1.—(See Fig. 42).—Find the course to steer by compass from position A to position B in order to counteract the effect of a current which set 090° (T), 2 knots. Find also the distance the vessel would make good towards her destination in 2 hours, ship steaming 10 knots.

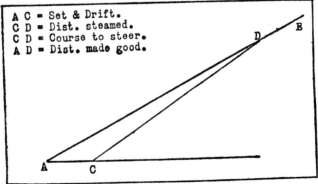

A C = Set & Drift.
C D = Dist. steamed.
C D = Course to steer.
A D = Dist. made good.

FIG. 42.

First lay off the course AB between the two points. From A, the commencement of the run, lay off 090°, the set of the current, and also the drift of the current in 2 hours at 2 knots=4 miles. (AC.)

142

From the point C (which is the position the vessel would reach in 2 hours under the influence of the current only), measure 20 miles, the distance the vessel would steam in 2 hours. This 20-mile distance meets the line AB at D.

Join CD. The line CD is the course the vessel will require to steer to counteract the effect of the current, in the same way as a sailing craft would require to steer that course to counteract the effect of a westerly wind, and since, by steering the course CD, she will maintain her position along the line AB, AD is the distance the vessel will make good towards her destination in the 2 hours.

It is important to notice that CD is the distance the vessel actually steams, and that it has to be measured from point C, the position to which the vessel would have been drifted by the effect of the current. CD is also the course she will have to steer, while AD is the vessel's actual line of progression, and also the distance she will make good in the stipulated time.

The distance to be made good may be given for any time, 1 hour, 2 hours, 3 hours, etc. Whatever time is given, the current must be laid off for that number of hours, and so also must the distance run by the ship.

The course thus found is, of course, a true course, to which variation has to be applied to convert it to a magnetic course. Thereafter the deviation has to be found, exactly as described in Chapter 9, in order to find the compass course to steer.

Example 2.—(See Fig. 43).—Find the course to steer by compass

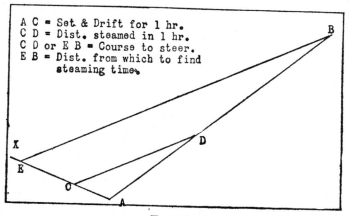

A C = Set & Drift for 1 hr.
C D = Dist. steamed in 1 hr.
C D or E B = Course to steer.
E B = Dist. from which to find
    steaming time.

FIG. 43.

from position A to position B, to counteract the effect of a current which set 295°, 1½ knots. Find also the time it would take the vessel to reach her destination, steaming 10 knots.

Note that, in this example, it is required to find the compass course and also the time it would take the vessel to reach her destination, not what distance she would make good in a stated time.

As before, lay off the course line AB. From A lay off AC, the set and drift of the current for, say, 1 hour. From the point C lay off the distance the vessel would steam *in the same time*, 1 *hour*, CD meeting the course line at D.

It is imperative that if the drift of the current has been laid off for 1 hour, the distance steamed must be laid off for the same time.

CD is the course required. A line parallel to CD is now drawn from position B, the destination, to AX, the line which represents the set of the current, meeting this line at point E.

The course is converted to a compass course in the ordinary way, and, to find the time required to reach the vessel's destination, measure the total distance EB, multiply this distance by the number of minutes the vessel takes to steam 1 mile, and reduce the answer to hours and minutes.

A vessel steaming 10 knots steams 1 mile in 6 minutes $\frac{(60)}{(10)}$

A vessel steaming 12 knots steams 1 mile in 5 minutes $\frac{(60)}{(12)}$

A vessel steaming 15 knots steams 1 mile in 4 minutes $\frac{(60)}{(15)}$

Example.—Find the course to steer by compass from a position 5 miles South (true) from St. Catherine's Point to a position 5 miles South (true) from Beachy Head, to counteract the effect of a current which set 228°, 2 knots. Variation 11° W. Find also (*a*) the distance the ship would make good towards her destination in 2 hours, steaming 12 knots; (*b*) the time it would take the ship to reach that destination off Beachy Head, steaming 12 knots.

Lay off the course from the position off St. Catherine's (A) to the position off Beachy Head (B). Since the effect of the current has to be counteracted, the steps to do so must be taken at the COMMENCEMENT of the run. From A lay off AX, the *set* of the current.

It is required to find the distance made good in 2 hours, therefore AC is measured=4 miles, the drift of the current in 2 hours. With the dividers, measure the distance the ship will steam in 2 hours=24 miles. With one leg of the dividers on C, lay the other leg on the line AB at D.

Then CD is the true course to steer (N. 76° E.) and AD is the distance made good in 2 hours (20¾ miles), since, by steering the course N. 76° E., the ship will maintain her position along the line AB.

To find the time taken to reach point B, draw the line EB parallel to CD, and measure along EB in lengths (or multiples) of 12 miles. The distance is 68 miles, so the time taken=5 hr 40 min.

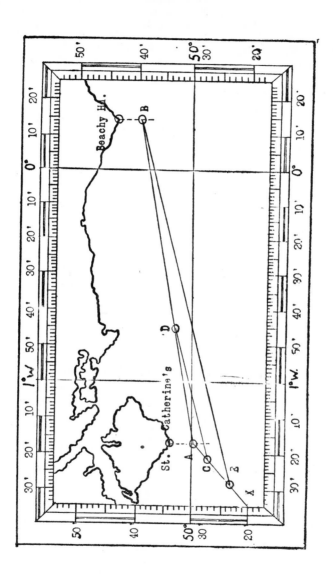

		True Course N. 76° E.R.		
	Var.	11 W. R.		
Comp. Course			Comp. Course	
N. 67½° E. R.	Mag.	N. 87 E. R.	N. 79° E. R.	4
14 E. R.		15½ E. L.	18 E. R.	5½
N. 81½° E.	Comp.	N. 71½° E.	N. 97° E. R.	15½)22(1½

Comp. Course N. 71½° E.
Deviation 15½ E.
Dist. made good 20¾ miles
Time to reach destination 5 hr 40 min.

The same example, using the 3-figure notation, is given below, and it will be seen that the required compass course is the same in each case.

Find the course to steer by compass from a position 5 miles 180° (T) from St. Catherine's Point to a position 5 miles 180° (T) from Beachy Head, to counteract the effect of a current which set 228° (T), 2 knots.

			Course	076° (T)			
			Var.	11 W.			
Course	070° (C)	Course	087	(M)	Course	080° (C)	Corr.
Dev.	14·9 E.	Dev.	15·5	E.	Dev.	18·4 E.	$\dfrac{3·5 \times 2·1}{13·5}$
Course	084·9 (M)	Course	071·5 (C)		Course	098·4 (M)	=0·6 nearly

EXERCISE 15.

Setting Course to Counteract a Current.

1. Using dev. card 1, find the course to steer by compass from a position 5 miles South (true) from Start Point to a position 5 miles South (true) from Lizard Head to counteract the effect of a current which set 106° (T), 2 knots. Find also the distance the ship would make good towards her destination in 3 hours, ship steaming 10 knots. Variation 13° W.

2. Using dev. card 1, find the course to steer by compass from a position 5 miles South (true) from Lizard Head to a position 10 miles North (true) from Ile de Bas to counteract the effect of a current which set 270° (T), 1½ knots. Find also the distance the ship would make good towards her destination in 4 hours, ship steaming 12 knots. Variation 13° W.

3. Using dev. card 1, find the course to steer by compass from St. Catherine's Light to the Casquets Light to counteract the effect of a current which set 060° (T), 3 knots. Find also the distance the ship would make good towards her destination in 2 hours, ship steaming 12 knots. Variation 12° W.

4. Using dev. card 1, find the course to steer by compass from Cape de la Hague to Bill of Portland to counteract the effect of a current which set 024° (T), 2 knots. Find also the distance ship would make good towards her destination in 2 hours, ship steaming 15 knots. Variation 12° W.

5. Using dev. card 1, find the course to steer by compass from St. Catherine's Light to Cape Barfleur to counteract the effect of a current which set 090° (T), 3 knots. Find also the distance the ship would make good towards her destination in 3 hours, ship steaming 10 knots. Variation 11° W.

6. Using dev. card 2, find the course to steer by compass from Trevose Head to the Smalls to counteract the effect of a current which set 214° (T), 2½ knots. Find also the time it would take the ship to reach this destination, ship steaming 12 knots. Variation 14° W.

7. Using dev. card 2, find the course to steer by compass from South Lundy Light to Pendeen Light to counteract the effect of a current which set 055° (T), 2 knots. Find also the time it would take the ship to reach her destination, ship steaming 10 knots. Variation 14° W.

8. Using dev. card 2, find the course to steer by compass from Smalls Light to Hartland Point to counteract the effect of a current which set 230° (T), 2 knots. Find also the time it would take ship to reach her destination, ship steaming 12 knots. Variation 14° W.

9. Using dev. card 2, find the course to steer by compass from Ushant (Creach Point) Light to Wolf Rock, to counteract the effect of a current which set 036° (T), 3 knots. Find also the time it would take the ship to reach Wolf Rock, ship steaming 10 knots. Variation 13° W.

10. Using dev. card 2, find the course to steer by compass from Cape d'Antifer to St. Catherine's Point to counteract the effect of a current which set 180° (T), 1 knot. Find also the time it would take the ship to reach her destination, ship steaming 10 knots. Variation 11° W.

CHAPTER 13.

EXPLANATION OF THE STATION POINTER—HORIZONTAL ANGLES—LAYING OFF BY PROTRACTOR.

AT best, a ship's deck is a very unsteady platform, unless in fine weather, and very often, especially in smaller craft, the platform is so unsteady as to render compass bearings unreliable. The compass bearing of an object, taken from the deck of a vessel which is jumping about in a seaway, can only be taken as approximate.

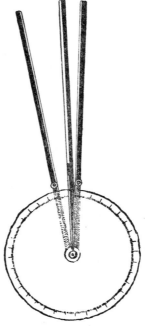

FIG. 44.

Even under bad weather conditions, however, a reliable and accurate position can be found by measuring the horizontal angles between objects, using a sextant for the purpose. The accuracy obtained by using these angles is very fine indeed.

148

With three conspicuous and well-charted shore objects available (*A*, *B* and *C*) the horizontal angle is first measured between *A* and *B*, and then the horizontal angle between *B* and *C*. When these angles are laid off on the chart, using a station pointer, the ship's position is given at once.

The Station Pointer consists, briefly, of a disc, made either of metal or of celluloid, graduated at the edge from zero to 180°, to the right and to the left. The centre of this disc, when the angles are laid off, gives the ship's position.

Three arms radiate from the centre, the middle arm being fixed at the reading of zero, the other arms free to rotate round the centre, and fitted with clamps to hold them in position. Each arm has a plain edge and a bevelled edge, thus:— and when clamping the arms at any required reading, it is always the bevelled edge which shows the angle.

The central (fixed) arm thus represents the middle object of the three, the right-hand arm represents the object to the right, etc.

After the horizontal sextant angles have been taken, the arms of the station pointer are clamped at the required angles. The instrument is then laid on the chart, the middle arm just touching the shore object which it represents, and the other arms are moved about till the bevelled edge of each arm just touches the object represented without, however, altering the angles. The position of the ship is then marked from the centre of the disc.

When selecting the three objects ashore, care must be taken that a circle passing through them does not also pass through or near the approximate position of the ship. Under these circumstances a great number of positions can be found which fulfil the angular conditions.

The "law" used in the station pointer problem is one, proved by Euclid, that the angle at the centre of a segment of a circle is twice the size of the angle at the circumference of the same segment.

In Fig. 45, *AB* (a line joining two lights or shore objects) cuts off a

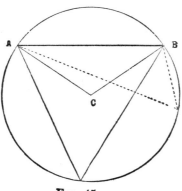

Fɪɢ. 45.

small portion of the circle drawn through the two objects, and the remaining portion is called a segment of the circle.

C is the centre of the circle, and the angle at C is **twice the size** of any angle drawn to the circumference from A and B.

If a horizontal angle is taken by sextant between the points A and B, and found to be, say, 60°, the position of the vessel is then SOMEWHERE on the circumference of the circle, since all angles "subtended" at the circumference between the two points measure 60°.

But when, as in Fig. 46, two circles are drawn, using two sets of angles, the position of the vessel is somewhere on the circumference of EACH circle, and must therefore be where the two circles cut each other, at point D.

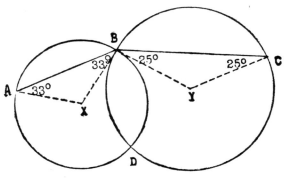

FIG. 46.

To Find the Ship's Position, Using a Protractor.—Station pointers are not always included in a vessel's navigational outfit, but the position can be found using horizontal sextant angles, by the help of an ordinary protractor.

Assume, in Fig. 46, that the horizontal angle between A and B is 57° and the angle between B and C is 65°. This would be written—

$$A-57°-B-65°-C.$$

The first thing to be done is to find the centres of the circles.

The three angles of any triangle are together equal to 180°, and, since the sides AX and BX of the first circle are equal, being radii of the circle, the angles at A and B are also equal.

The angle at X is twice the angle at the circumference, which is given as 57°. Angle X is therefore=114°.

Angles $A+B$ must=(180°−114°)=66°. Each of the two angles is therefore half of 66°=33°.

The same result can be arrived at by simply subtracting the given horizontal angle (57°) from 90° (90°−57°=33°).

From A and B lay off angles of 33°, and draw in the lines, completing the triangle ABX. "X" is the centre of the circle which passes through A, B and the ship's position.

With compasses, draw the circle. The ship's position is somewhere on the circumference of that circle.

Similarly, the angles at B and C in the second circle are $(90° - 65°)$ $= 25°$.

Lay off angles of 25° from B and C, and complete the triangle BCY. With centre Y, and radius BY, draw the circle.

The ship's position is somewhere on the circumference of that circle, hence it must be at D, where the two circles meet.

EXERCISE 16.

To Find Ship's Position by Station Pointer.

The following horizontal sextant angles having been taken to determine the ship's position, find in each case the latitude and longitude, using a station pointer:—

1. Fastnet Rock—62°—Galley Head—34°—Old Head of Kinsale.
2. Mine Head—69°—Hook Point—30°—Coningbeg Light-Vessel.
3. Strumble Head—48°—South Bishop—40°—Smalls.
4. Lizard Head—72°—Eddystone—35°—Start Point.
5. Bill of Portland—37°—Anvil Point—63°—St. Catherine's.
6. Cape Barfleur—67°—Cape de la Ha ue—51°—Casquets.

CHAPTER 14.

FOUR POINT AND 26½° BEARINGS—DOUBLING THE ANGLE ON THE BOW—VERTICAL ANGLES—BEARING AND RANGE— WIRELESS BEARINGS—DISTANCE AND HORIZONTAL ANGLE— THREE BEARING PROBLEM.

While coasting in any vessel, it is not only a matter of wisdom to keep a check on the vessel's position at every opportunity, but it is also the ordinary practice of seamen to do so. Many circumstances arise which tend to divert a vessel from its desired programme—winds may alter in direction and in force, currents or tides may be totally different from those which have been estimated, compass deviation may not be what was expected, steering may have been bad—all matters which help to put a vessel off her course.

There are various practical rules at sea which help towards safety. Among these are—

Use the 5-fathom line as a danger mark;

Keep close enough to the land to recognise it, but far enough off to avoid hitting it;

It is better to be a mile too far off than a yard too far in.

Various methods are employed to provide the vessel with a "running commentary" of her progress. Of these methods, probably the most extensively used is the 4-point bearing.

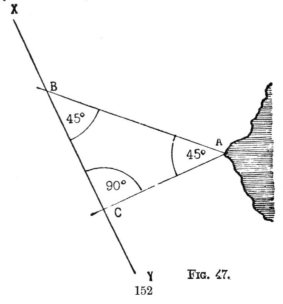

Fig. 47.

The 4-point Bearing.—In Fig. 47, "*A*" represents a lighthouse, *XY* the vessel's course.

When the vessel arrives at position "*B*", the lighthouse bears exactly 4 points (45°) on the port bow. When she arrives at "*C*", the lighthouse bears abeam.

The triangle *ABC* is a right-angled triangle, and, since angle *C*= 90°, angles *A*+*B*=90°. By observation, we have found that angle *B*=45°, so that angle *A* also = 45°. These angles being equal, the sides opposite them are equal, and *BC* equals *AC*.

BC represents the number of miles the vessel has steamed along the course between the 4-point bearing and the beam bearing. Hence this same distance also represents the distance the vessel was off the light when it was abeam.

The 26½° Bearing.—One big disadvantage of the 4-point bearing is that the distance off is not known till the vessel is actually abeam,

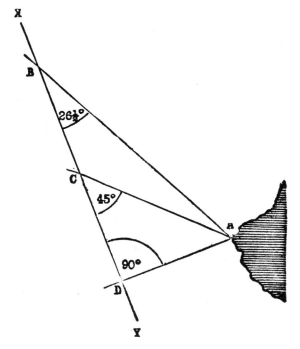

Fig. 48.

whereas it is often convenient to know beforehand what distance the vessel will pass off the light if the present course is continued.

In Fig. 48, "*A*" represents a lighthouse, *XY* represents the ship's course, and *B, C* and *D* the vessel's positions when the lighthouse is $26\frac{1}{2}°$, 4 points, and abeam, respectively.

By measurement, it will be found that $BC=CD=AD=$the distance off when abeam.

Hence the distance run between taking a bearing when the light is $26\frac{1}{2}°$ on the bow and when it is 4 points on the bow represents the distance the vessel will be off the light when it is abeam.

Suppose $AD=1$ mile, then $BD = 2$ miles. $\dfrac{BD}{DA}=\dfrac{2}{1}=$ cot angle ABD, and 2 is the nat. cot of $26\frac{1}{2}°$.

Doubling the Angle on the Bow.—If two bearings of a light are taken, the second one being double the number of degrees on the bow of the first one, the distance run between the two bearings gives the distance that the vessel is off the light at the time of taking the second bearing.

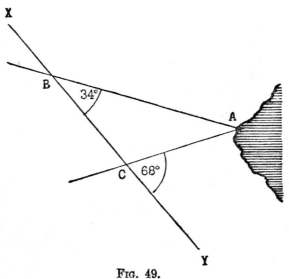

Fig. 49.

In Fig. 49, *A* represents the lighthouse, *XY* represents the vessel's course line, *B* the position of the vessel when the lighthouse bore 34° on the bow, and *C* its position when the lighthouse bore 68° on the bow.

Because the angle $ACY=68°$, the angle ACB must be $(180°-68°)$ $=112°$.

In the triangle ABC

$$\text{angle } B = 34°,$$
$$\text{angle } C = 112°,$$
$$\text{angles } B+C = (34°+112°)=146°$$

Therefore angle $A = (180°-146°)=34°=$angle *B*

Thus *BC*, the distance run between the two bearings=*AC*, the distance the vessel was off the lighthouse at the time the second bearing was taken.

Distances by Vertical Angles.—Distance off a lighthouse or a hill can be found by measuring by sextant the vertical angle between the light or the hill, and the water-line immediately below, provided the height of the light, or of the hill, is known. (See also Chap. 4.)

In Fig. 50, *A* is the position of the vessel, *CB* the lighthouse. The angle *CAB*, as taken by sextant, measures, say, 1° 10′. The height of the lighthouse (from water-line to the light itself) is, say 135 feet. It is required to find the distance the vessel is from the light, that is, the distance from *A* to *B*.

Referring to page 24, Part I, we see that the side *AB* of the triangle, divided by the side *CB*, is the cotangent of the angle *A*.

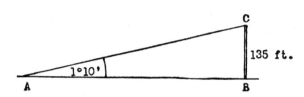

C

135 ft.

1°10′

A   B

FIG. 50.

That is, $\dfrac{AB}{CB}$ = cot angle

or, using *CB* as the height of the lighthouse—

$$\frac{AB}{135} = \text{cot } 1° \ 10'$$

The distance *AB* is required.

Taking an equation of similar form—

$$\frac{24}{6} = 4$$

it will be found that by a process called "cross-multiplying," it can be written as—

$$24 = 4 \times 6$$

That is, the denominator of the first part—(6)—has been taken over to the other side of the equation and transformed into a multiplier.

In the same way, our original equation can be written as—

$$AB = \text{cot } 1° \ 10' \times 135$$

or, using logarithms—

log dist. off = L. cot 1° 10′+log 135
        = 11·69112+2·13033
        = 3·82145 (rejecting 10's.)

This result gives the log of the distance off in FEET. To find the log of the distance off IN MILES, subtract from it the log of 6080 (which is the same as dividing the distance in feet by 6080).

$$\begin{aligned} \text{log dist. off} &= 3 \cdot 82145 \\ 6080 \text{ log} &= 3 \cdot 78390 \\ \hline \text{log dist. off (miles)} &= 0 \cdot 03755 \end{aligned}$$

Distance off in miles = 1·09 miles.

Example 2.—Vertical angle of a 200-ft. lighthouse was 1° 25′. Find distance off.

$$\left. \begin{aligned} \text{Vertical angle } 1° 25' \quad \text{cot} &= 11 \cdot 60677 \\ \text{Height of light 200 ft. } \quad \text{log} &= 2 \cdot 30103 \end{aligned} \right\} +$$

$$\left. \begin{aligned} \text{log dist. off in feet} \qquad &= 3 \cdot 90780 \\ 6080 \qquad\qquad \text{log} &= 3 \cdot 78390 \end{aligned} \right\} -$$

$$\text{log distance off in miles} \quad = \quad 0 \cdot 12390$$

$$\text{Distance off light} \quad = \quad 1 \cdot 33 \text{ miles}$$

Tables are included in *Norie's* and in *Burton's*, by which the distance off can be found on sight. In *Norie's*, the table is on pp. 104-109. In *Burton's*, the table is No. 35, pp. 254-258.

Position by Bearing and Range of a Light.—The distance of the sea horizon, in miles, is theoretically 1·15 √height of eye in feet. When, on a clear night, a light is observed to dip over the horizon, the position of the vessel can be found by using this formula.

First find the distance of the horizon from the observer, due to the height of his eye above sea-level, then find the distance the light is visible due to its height above sea-level, using the same formula. Add the two distances, and the result is the observer's distance off the light.

Both *Norie's* and *Burton's Tables* give special tables, using the formula, from which the distance can be found at sight. Used in conjunction with a compass bearing, it gives the position. Both tables are similar, *Nories'* being on page 161, *Burton's* being Table 2, inside the front cover.

Example.—A light 160 ft. high dips over the horizon. Height of eye 35 feet. Find the distance off the light.

$$\begin{aligned} \text{Height of eye} \quad \text{gives} \quad & 6 \cdot 8 \text{ miles} \\ \text{Height of light} \quad \text{gives} \quad & 14 \cdot 5 \quad ,, \\ \hline \text{Distance off} \qquad\qquad & 21 \cdot 3 \text{ miles} \end{aligned}$$

Wireless Bearings.—The position of a vessel can be found by crossing two or more wireless bearings of radio beacons, in exactly the same way as by crossing the bearings of two or more lights. The bearing of a light and a wireless bearing can also be crossed to obtain a position.

Up to a distance of about 50 miles, wireless bearings do not require any correction, but for distances of over 50 miles a correction is required, owing to the fact that the wireless waves follow the curvature of the earth in great circles, while they are laid off on the chart as "rhumb lines". (A rhumb line is a line which cuts each meridian at the same angle, of course, is constantly altering.)

When a vessel steams along a great circle, her course has to be altered every few hours, and the angle between the first course and the final course of a great circle track is the "convergency" of the meridians. To convert a wireless bearing to a mercatorial bearing, suitable for laying off on a chart, half this convergency is applied to the bearing as received.

In applying the half-convergency to a bearing, always look from the sending station towards the ship, and apply the correction in the direction of the equator.

In the Northern hemisphere, this means—

Add the half-convergency if ship is EAST of the station;

Subtract the half-convergency if ship is WEST of the station.

The formula is as follows:—

$$\text{Half-convergency} = \frac{\text{D. long.} \times \sin \text{mid lat.}}{2}$$

To work out the formula makes quite a bit of work, but the same result can be obtained easily from the Traverse Table.

Using mean latitude as a course, find the D. long. in the distance column. Convergency is then found in the dep. column. Divide this by 2 to obtain the half-convergency.

In *Norie's Tables*, the correction can be found at sight on page 150, and in *Burton's Tables*, in Table 6, page 113.

Most *Nautical Almanacs* also give a table for converting radio bearings to mercatorial bearings.

Position by Distance and Horizontal Angle.—Under certain conditions, a ship's compass might be useless, its deviation unknown, or its behaviour unsatisfactory. To obtain an exact position under these circumstances, assuming two objects are handy for observations, find the distance the vessel is off the nearer light by vertical angle. Say this was 2 miles. The position of the vessel is then somewhere on a circle of 2 miles radius, the object "*A*" being the centre, as in Fig. 51.

The horizontal angle between "*A*" and "*B*" is then taken. Say this was found to be 59°.

On the chart, join "*A*" and "*B*". Subtract the horizontal angle (59°) from 90°=31°. Using a protractor, lay this angle off from "*A*" and from "*B*". Where they meet, at *C*, is the centre of a circle which passes through *A*, through *B*, and through the ship's position.

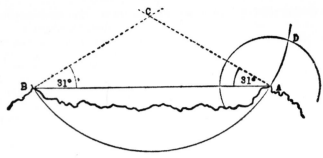

FIG. 51.

The required position is thus at D, where the larger circle cuts the circle of position off the object A.

The Three-bearing Problem.—This problem gives the actual course that a vessel is making good under the influence of a current whose effect is unknown. IT DOES NOT GIVE THE SHIP'S ACTUAL POSITION.

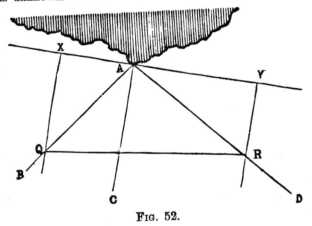

FIG. 52.

Three bearings AB, AC and AD, are taken of a point of land, and the distance run between each bearing noted.

Through the point "A", draw a line at right angles to the middle bearing (AC).

From A, lay off AX (the distance run between the first and second bearings) on the same side of A as the first bearing. In the opposite direction, lay off AY, the distance run between the second and third bearings. From X and Y, draw lines parallel to the middle bearing, meeting the first and third bearings at Q and R.

QR is the course the vessel is making good, but R is NOT the position of the vessel at the time of taking the last bearing.

The Cocked Hat.—Sometimes, when taking cross-bearings of three objects, these lines do not meet at a point, owing to the bearings not being taken precisely enough or to the fact that a wrong compass error is used, or to the fact that the objects are not correctly charted. When this is so, a small triangle is formed where the three bearings should meet. This triangle, from its shape, is known as the "Cocked Hat."

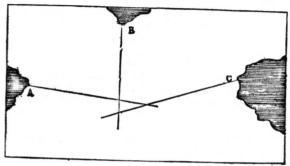

FIG. 53.

It is not by any means an easy matter to find out which of the variouf causes is responsible for the error which gives the cocked hat.

In practice, it is usually, and erroneously, assumed that the true position of the vessel is about the centre of the triangle thus formed, but in actual fact the vessel's position is inside the triangle only when the lines which join the three objects enclose the ship's position.

If the vessel lies outside the lines joining the three objects, her position lies outside the cocked hat.

If in doubt as to the vessel's exact position, it is always best to assume that she is at the most dangerous part of the cocked hat, and act accordingly.

To arrive at a Set Bearing and Distance off a Light.—It may sometimes be necessary to steer such a course as will allow the vessel to be on a certain bearing from a light when she has reached a specified distance off the light.

For instance: Find the course to steer from position *A*, in order to be 4 miles off lighthouse *B*, when the lighthouse is 3 points on the bow.

This problem is simply a variation of the "bearing and distance" problem, and two methods can be used to solve it.

If Traverse Tables are handy, use these tables. Using the given angle as a course, with the required distance off the light as a distance, pick out the corresponding departure from the table.

Then, with the lighthouse as a centre, draw the arcs of two circles—one with the required distance off as a radius, the other with the departure as a radius.

Lay off a line from the ship's position to form a tangent to the INNER circle. This gives the required course, and at the point where this course line meets the OUTER circle the light will be on the required bearing.

To use the other method: Join position "*A*" and the light "*B*". Three points (from the question)=34° on the bow is the required bearing. (90°—34°)=56°.

From "*A*" and again from "*B*", lay off lines making angles of 56° on the INSHORE side of the line joining the two points.

The point where these two lines meet is the centre of a circle which passes through points "*A*" and "*B*", and through the ship's position. Draw a circle of 4 miles radius from the light. Where this circle cuts the first circle is the required point for which to steer.

The question might have read " . . . . . to a position 4 miles off the lighthouse with the lighthouse 3 points ABAFT the beam."

3 points abaft the beam=5 points=56° from right astern. (90°—56°)=34°.

Lay off 34° at "*A*" and "*B*" on the OFFSHORE side of the line joining the two places, and proceed as before.

Field's Parallel Rulers.—These rulers, which are very generally used on board ships, are graduated along the top edge in degrees, and along the lower edge in quarter points, the "90°" mark on the top edge being exactly opposite to the "South" mark on the lower edge.

To obtain a "beam bearing" with these rulers, place them over the

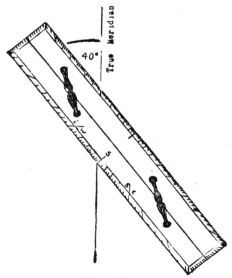

Fig. 54.

vessel's course line, with 90° on the top edge, and South on the lower edge, both cutting through the course line. The parallel ruler then lies at an angle of 90° to the course line, and can be moved in the usual way to whichever part of the chart is required.

To "lay off a course" with Field's ruler—if steering to degrees, put the "South" mark on any part of any meridian. Then, if the required course is, say, N. 40° W., swivel the ruler into a N.W.'ly direction keeping the South mark on the meridian, and bring the 40° mark to cut the same meridian. (See Fig. 54.) This gives the necessary course, and the ruler is then shifted to any part of the chart to lay off the course, in the usual way.

If steering to points, the 90° mark is kept on the meridian, and the necessary course (say N.W. ½ N.) is made to cut the same meridian.

Similarly, when the ship's position is somewhere on a certain line with a light "subtending a horizontal angle" of so many degrees, put the "South" mark of the lower edge on one side of the position line, and swivel the ruler till the required number of degrees (on the top edge) is on the other side of the same line. If the angle is less than 90°, always take the degrees from that half of the ruler which lies nearer to the light.

This gives the required horizontal angle, and the ruler can then be shifted over the chart in the usual way to cover the given light.

EXERCISE 17.

EXAMINATION PAPERS IN CHART WORK.

PAPER 1.

1. Using deviation card 1, and variation 11° W., on the chart of the English Channel, find the course to steer by compass from a position 10 miles South (true) from Beachy Head, to a position 10 miles South (true) from Bill of Portland; also the distance.

2. With ship's head on above compass course, St. Catherine's Head was observed to bear N. 23° W. by compass, and Owers Lt. Vl. was observed to bear N. 71° E. by the same compass. Find the position of the vessel, and the set and drift of the current experienced since the course was set, the vessel having run 4 hours steaming 12 knots.

3. With the ship's head as above, Anvil Point bore by compass N. 33° W., and after continuing on the same course for 1¼ hours steaming 12 knots, the same light was observed to bear abeam by compass. Find the ship's position at the time of taking the 2nd bearing, also the distance off the light, making due allowance for a current which set 180°, 2 knots.

4. Find the course to steer by compass from the position found in Question 3 to the destination off Bill of Portland, to counteract the effect of a current which set 210°, 2 knots. Find also the

distance the ship would make good towards her destination in 1 hour, ship steaming 12 knots.

5. The following horizontal sextant angles were taken in order to determine the ship's position:—
      Anvil Point—48°—St. Catherine's—65°—Owers Light Vessel.
Find the latitude and longitude, using a station pointer.

PAPER 2.

1. Using deviation card 2, and variation 12° W., find the courses to steer by compass from a position with Creach Point (Ushant) bearing 180° (T), distant 15 miles, to a position abeam of Cape D'Antifer, distant 10 miles, also the distance on each course, altering course when Casquets Light is abeam, distant 10 miles.

2. With ship's head on 1st course by compass, Ile de Vierge bore 192° (C), and Ile de Bas bore 126° (C) by the same compass. Find the position of the ship, and the set and drift of the current experienced since the course was set, the ship having run 3 hours, steaming 11 knots.

3. With ship's head on 2nd course by compass, Cape de la Hague was observed to bear 145½° (C), and after steaming on the same course for a further 2½ hours at 12 knots, Cape Barfleur was observed to bear 202½° (C) by the same compass. Find the ship's position and her distance off Cape Barfleur at the time of taking the 2nd bearing, making due allowance for a current which set 062° (T), 2 knots.

4. Find the course to steer by compass from Cape Barfleur to Cape d'Antifer to counteract the effect of a current which set 290° (T), 1½ knots. Find also the time it would take to reach Cape d'Antifer, vessel steaming 12 knots.

5. The following horizontal sextant angles were taken to determine the ship's position:—
      Cape de la Hague—60°—Casquets—33°—Les Hanois
Find the latitude and longitude, using a station pointer.

PAPER 3. (Dev. Card 1.)

1. Find the courses to steer by compass from a position 200° from Owers Lt. Vl., with St. Catherine's Head subtending a horizontal angle of 81°, to a position 180°, 15 miles from Bishop Rock Light (Scillies), also the distance on each course, altering course when the Casquets Light is right ahead, with Cape de la Hague abeam to port. Allow 4° leeway on each course for a northerly wind. Use variation 12° W. on the 1st course, and 13° W. on the 2nd course.

2. With ship's head on 1st course by compass, Casquets Light bore 1 point on the starboard bow, and Cape Barfleur Light bore by compass S. 23½° E. Find the position of the vessel, and the set

and drift of the current experienced since the course was set, the vessel having steamed 5 hours at 10 knots.

3. With ship's head on the 2nd course by compass, Lizard Head bore 4 points on the bow, and after continuing on the same course for 2 hours the same light bore 1 point abaft the beam. Find the ship's position and her distance from the light at the time of taking the 2nd bearing, making due allowance for a current which set 095°, 1½ knots, vessel steaming 10 knots.

4. Find the compass course to steer from Les Hanois Light to Lizard Head to counteract the effect of a current which set 064°, 2½ knots, using variation 12½° W. Find also the time it would take to bring Eddystone Light abeam by compass, vessel steaming 12 knots.

5. The following horizontal sextant angles were taken to determine the ship's position:—
Bishop Rock—62°—Wolf Rock—37°—Lizard Head
Find the latitude and longitude, using a station pointer.

PAPER 4.
Variation 14° W.   (Dev. Card 2.)

1. Find the courses to steer by compass from a position 17 miles to the southward of Smalls Light on the 40-fathom line, to a position in Lat. 49° N., Long. 6° W., also the distance on each course, altering course when Hartland Point bears 120° (T), with North Lundy Light subtending a horizontal angle of 108°, and again in Lat. 50° N., with Wolf Rock bearing 114° (T).

2. With ship's head on 2nd course by compass, Godrevy Light bore 210° (C), and Trevose Head bore 120° (C) by the same compass. Find the ship's position, and the set and drift of the current experienced since the course was set, the vessel having run 4 hours, steaming 11 knots.

3. With ship's head on the 2nd course by compass, Trevose Head bore 186° (C), and after continuing on the same course for 3 hours at 10 knots, Godrevy Light bore 134° (C) by the same compass. Find the ship's position and her distance from Godrevy Light at the time of taking the 2nd bearing, making due allowance for a current which set 252° (T), 2 knots.

4. Find the compass course to steer from the position found in Ques. 3 to Lat. 50° N., Long. 6° W., to counteract the effect of a current which set the same as was found in Ques. 3. Find also the time it would take vessel to reach this position, vessel steaming 10 knots.

5. The following horizontal sextant angles were taken to determine the ship's position:—
Trevose Head—57°—Godrevy—40°—Pendeen
Find the latitude and longitude, using a station pointer.

PAPER 5.
Variation 13½° W. (Dev. Card 1.)

1. Find the courses to steer by compass from a position midway between Tuskar Light and Strumble Head to a position 180°, 5 miles from Mumbles Light, also the distance on each course, altering course when on the 6th meridian, having passed 10 miles off Smalls Light, and again when North and South Lundy Island Lights are in transit, with Bull Point right ahead.

2. With ship's head on 1st course by compass, Strumble Head bore S. 80½° E. by compass, and Smalls Light bore 5 points on the port bow. Find the ship's position and the set and drift of the current experienced since the course was set, the vessel having steamed 2 hours at 9 knots.

3. With ship's head on 2nd course by compass, Smalls Light bore N. 4° W. by compass, and after continuing on the same course for 2 hours, Caldy Island Light bore N. 47° E. by the same compass. Find the ship's position and her distance from North Lundy Light at the time of taking the 2nd bearing, making due allowance for a current which set 270°, 2 knots, vessel steaming 10 knots.

4. Find the course to steer by compass from North Lundy Light to the Mumbles to counteract the effect of a current which set 270°, 2 knots. Find also the distance ship would make good towards her destination in 2 hours, ship steaming 10 knots.

5. The following horizontal sextant angles were taken to determine the ship's position:—
North Lundy Light—52°—Bull Point—75°—Foreland
Find the latitude and longitude, using a station pointer.

PAPER 6.
Variation 15° W. (Dev. Card 2.)

1. Find the course to steer by compass from Fastnet Light to Smalls Light, also the distance.

2. With ship's head on above compass course, Old Head of Kinsale was observed to bear 293° (C), and Ballycotton Light bore 006° (C) by the same compass at the same time. Find the position of the ship and the set and drift of the current experienced since the course was set, the ship steaming 10 knots and taking 5½ hours to reach this position.

3. With ship's head 090° (C), Hook Point (Waterford) bore 039° (C), and after continuing on the same course for a further 2 hours, the same light bore 315° (C). Find the ship's position at the time of taking the 2nd bearing, also her distance off the light, making due allowance for a current which set 270° (T), 3 knots, vessel steaming 11 knots.

4. Find the course to steer by compass from Hook Point to the Old Head of Kinsale to counteract the effect of a current which set

the same as the current in Ques. 3. Find also (a) the distance the ship would make good towards her destination in 2 hours, and (b) the time it would take the vessel to reach Old Head of Kinsale, vessel steaming 12 knots.

5. The following horizontal sextant angles were taken to determine the ship's position:—

Ballycotton—64°—Mine Head—49°—Hook Point

Find the latitude and longitude, using a station pointer.

PAPER 7.
Variation 14° W.   (Dev. Card 1.)

1. Find the course to steer by compass from a position 6 miles off Stiff Point (Ushant) with Ile de Vierge Light subtending a horizontal angle of 58°, to a position with Mumbles Light right ahead, and Bull Point Light bearing 2 points abaft the starboard beam, also the distance on each course, altering course when Seven Stones Light-Vessel (Scillies) is right ahead, with Longships and Wolf Rock in transit, and again when Pendeen Light bears 090°, distant 10 miles.   Allow 4° leeway for a S.W. wind on 1st and 2nd courses.

2. Two hours after altering course off Pendeen, Godrevy Light was observed to bear abeam by compass, and at the same time the Longships Light was observed to change from white to red.   Find the ship's position and the set and drift of the current experienced since the course was set, ship steaming 10 knots.

3. With ship's head on 3rd course by compass, Trevose Head was observed abeam, and after continuing on the same course for a further 2¼ hours, ship steaming 10 knots, Hartland Point Light bore 3 points on the starboard bow.   Find the ship's position and her distance from Hartland Point at the time of taking the 2nd bearing, making due allowance for a current which set 240°, 2 knots.

4. Find the course to steer by compass from Lat. 49° 20′ N., Long. 6° W., to Lizard Head to counteract the effect of a current which set in the normal direction for that position 1 hour before H.W. Dover, spring tides.   Find also the distance the ship would make good towards her destination in 3 hours, ship steaming 12 knots.

5. The following horizontal sextant angles were taken to determine the ship's position:—

Bishop Rock—52°—Wolf Rock—66°—Lizard Head

Find the latitude and longitude, using a station pointer.

PAPER 8.
(Dev. Card 2.)

1. At noon, latitude by meridian altitude was 50° 09′ N.   Ship then steered 124° (C) (variation 14° W.), at 11 knots.   At 1600 hours

S.A.T., Bishop Rock (Scillies) was abeam by compass. Using the deviation card, find the ship's position, making due allowance for a current which set 233° (T), 2 knots.

2. From the position found in Ques. 1, find the course to steer by compass to bring Casquets Light 3 points on the starboard bow when the vertical sextant angle subtended by the light is 0° 23', using variation 13° W. Find also the distance.

3. With ship's head as in previous question, at 2000 hours S.A.T., Wolf Rock bore 306° (C) and Lizard Head bore 036° (C) by the same compass. Find the ship's position and the set and drift of the current experienced since the course was set, the ship steaming 11 knots.

4. Find the course to steer by compass from the position off the Casquets Light found in Ques. 2 to a position with Bill of Portland right ahead and subtending a vertical sextant angle of 0° 20', to counteract the effect of a current found in that vicinity (Position 24) at 3 hours after H.W. Dover, spring tides. Find also the time it would take the vessel to reach this position, ship steaming 10 knots. Allow 4° for leeway for an easterly wind, and use variation 12° W.

CHAPTER 15.

TIDES—CAUSES OF TIDES—EARTH, MOON, AND SUN—TIDAL CONSTITUENTS—PRIMING AND LAGGING—AGE OF THE TIDE—TIDAL PECULIARITIES—INFORMATION FROM CHARTS—TIDAL PREDICTIONS—REDUCTION TO SOUNDINGS.

Tides are periodic VERTICAL movements of the surface of the sea over the Earth. When movements of masses of sea-water occur in a HORIZONTAL direction, they are called "currents" or "tidal streams".

How Tides are Caused.—Tides are the result of the intermixing of many different physical causes. Some of these are "diurnal"—once-daily—in their action, and others are "semidiurnal"—twice daily. Some of the causes can even be experienced four times daily, and between all these physical causes, the relative ranges of tides are infinitely variable.

Two of the most important of the physical forces which go to make up tidal changes are:

    1. Centrifugal force;

    2. Attractive force.

Centrifugal force is the tendency of matter to fly off from a revolving body. The Earth is a revolving body, so that the tendency to fly off is present in all terrestrial matter, but it is greater in a liquid than in a solid, owing to the smaller consistency of the former. The force of gravity bearing down on the Earth prevents matter from actually flying off into the air, but the tendency nevertheless does exist.

Attractive force is best explained by "Newton's Law", which states that every particle of matter attracts every other particle. The amount of this attraction depends (a) on the sizes of the "particles"; (b) on their distance apart. Cause (a) acts in a directly proportionate manner. That is, the larger the masses, the greater the attraction. Cause (b) acts inversely as the square of the distance. That is, the attraction of a mass of matter at a distance of, say, 4 miles would be only $\frac{1}{16}$ of the attraction of the same mass at a distance of 1 mile. (In the ratio of 1^2 to 4^2.)

Both the Moon and the Sun exercise an attractive force on the surface of the sea. The Sun has a much greater "mass" than the Moon, but its distance from the Earth is much greater than that of the Moon. The Moon's attraction is therefore greater than that of the Sun, being in the ratio of about 7 to 3. When considering tides, the Moon is the most important physical factor.

The Earth revolves on its axis once every twenty-four hours, and the Moon revolves round the Earth once every 29½ days. As the Moon always keeps the same face turned towards the Earth—no one has ever seen the other side of the Moon—we know that it turns on its axis only once every 29½ days.

To make the explanation of tides as simple as possible, let us suppose that the Earth's rotation does not exist, but that centrifugal force—which actually depends on rotation—DOES exist. In that case, the Earth and the Moon would revolve on an orbit round a common centre of gravity, and would remain in perfect balance. The centre of gravity would always be on a line joining the centres of the two bodies, and owing to the greater weight and bulk of the Earth, would be about 3000 miles from the Earth's centre.

The two main causes of tides—centrifugal force and attractive force—would balance each other at the Earth's centre, and at that point only. But on the side of the Earth nearest to the Moon, the force caused by the Moon's attraction, which causes tides, would be the more powerful of the two forces. The surface of the sea would be attracted towards the Moon, causing high tides on that side of the Earth. The water has to come from some other part of the Earth, and it is drawn from places situated as far as 90° away from the place of high tides, so that low tides would be experienced there.

Meanwhile, on the side of the Earth farthest away from the Moon, centrifugal force would overbalance attractive force, causing another high tide there.

The attraction caused by the Sun on the surface water of the Earth has a similar effect, but, as explained above, this effect is smaller, in the ratio of 3 to 7, owing to the Sun's greater distance away from the Earth.

Many other "constituents" enter into accurate computations of day-to-day variations in the heights and times of high and low water, but for practical purposes, four only of these constituents need be used. Before considering them, it is necessary in the first place that we have some understanding of the relative movements of the Sun, Moon, and Earth, since these play a very large part in the formation of tides.

Conjunction.—When the Earth, the Moon and the Sun are all in

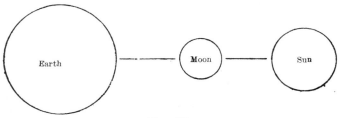

FIG. 55.

line, as in Fig. 55, with the Moon and the Sun on the same side of the
Earth, they are said to be "in conjunction". That is the relative
position of the three bodies at the period called "Change of the Moon",
a day or so before the new Moon can be seen close to the Sun just
about sunset.

At this period, the attractive force of both the Sun and the Moon
are being exerted in the same direction on the surface water of the Earth,
and high tides consequently rise higher at this time than at any other
time, and low tides fall to their lowest. These tides are called "Spring
Tides".

In Fig. 56, a particular place on the Earth is supposed to have

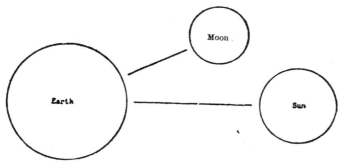

FIG. 56.

completed one full revolution from the position shown in Fig. 55.
This place has arrived back after 24 hours immediately underneath
the Sun. But as the Moon has in the meantime travelled about $\frac{1}{30}$
of the journey on its orbit round the Earth, the meridian of this particular place will not arrive underneath the Moon till 50 minutes after
it has passed underneath the Sun.

The Moon is therefore exerting its attractive force in a direction
slightly away from that of the Sun, and in consequence the height of
high water will not be so great as it was the previous day, when
the two bodies were pulling in the same direction.

Quadrature.—The angle between the Moon and the Sun gradually
widens until, about $7\frac{1}{4}$ days after conjunction, the Moon and the Sun
form a right angle with each other relative to the Earth, as in
Fig. 57.

The Moon's attractive force is now being exerted AGAINST the Sun's
force, with the result that the high tides experienced at these periods
are lower than those experienced at other times, and the low tides do
not fall so low as at other times. Such tides are called "Neap Tides",
and the relative positions of the Moon and the Sun are called

"Quadrature". The Moon is then at its first quarter, or what is more usually called "half-moon".

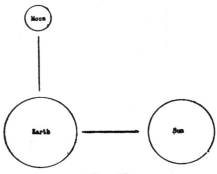

FIG. 57.

Opposition.—Continuing on its gradual daily divergence from the Sun, the Moon eventually arrives at the position shown in Fig. 58. Both bodies are again exerting their attractive force in the same line, although they are now on opposite sides of the Earth. Spring Tides are experienced again. This position is known as "Opposition", and

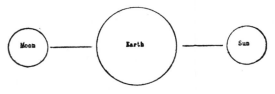

FIG 58.

takes place at the period of "Full Moon". The rays of the Sun light up the entire circle of the Moon which is facing the Earth, and the Moon is just rising in the East when the Sun is setting in the West.

Between conjunction (new Moon) and opposition (full Moon) more and more of the Moon's face has been illuminated every successive day. This is called the "waxing" of the Moon.

From the period of opposition, the Moon begins to "wane"—the amount of illuminated surface gets progressive y smaller each day—and in due course, the Sun and Moon arrive again at the position of quadrature, with consequent neap tides on the Earth. Thence the Moon continues its journey till once again it reaches the position of conjunction with the Sun.

From new Moon to quadrature, from quadrature to full Moon, from full Moon to quadrature, and from quadrature to new Moon each occupies about $7\frac{1}{4}$ days, the total period from "change of Moon back to change being about $29\frac{1}{2}$ days, as stated before. Thus the space of time from spring tides to neaps is about $7\frac{1}{4}$ days, and from springs to springs, about $14\frac{1}{2}$ days.

Tidal Constituents.

The four "constituents" which are generally considered sufficient for practical computations of times and heights of tides are as follows:—

1. Mean Lunar Semidiurnal Tide (M_2).—From the time the Moon crosses the meridian of a particular place on one day until it reaches the same meridian on the next day is an average period of 24 hours and 50 minutes. Each portion of the waters of the Earth therefore experiences two high tides due to the Moon's attraction during that time—one when the place is directly underneath the Moon, the other when it is 180° away from the Moon. Hence the name "semidiurnal".

The high tide that is formed can be traced on its passage round the world, keeping underneath the Moon. The angular distance from the "crest" of a tide to the "trough" is 90°, and on a graph would appear as a smooth curve. Thus the interval of time between each successive high and low tide is a quarter of 24 hours 50 minutes, or 6 hours 12 minutes.

2. Mean Solar Semidiurnal Tide (S_2).—This constituent is similar in its effects to M_2, but being caused by the attractive force of the Sun, is smaller. Like M_2, it causes two high tides and two low tides each day. The figure "2" attached to these constituents denotes the number of times each occurs in a day.

If we assume that tides caused by the Moon have a total range of 14 units (7 above Mean Tide Level, and 7 below) and that tides caused by the Sun have a total range of 6 units (3 above Mean Tide Level and 3 below) then at conjunction and opposition, the total effect on tides can be represented by (M_2+S_2). At periods of quadrature, the effects are (M_2-S_2). The variation between these two extremes is called the "phase inequality of heights".

The tides caused by M_2 and S_2 are due to the attractive force of the Moon and the Sun. So far, we have considered that these bodies remain at a constant distance from the Earth, and that during the Earth's journey round the Sun, and during the Moon's journey round the Earth, these bodies remain constantly over the Earth's equator. Actually, of course, this is NOT so. Their positions relative to the Earth's equator vary, and the effects from this fact have also to be taken into account.

3 and 4. Lunar Diurnal Inequality of Heights (K_1 and O_1).—In Fig. 59 the Moon's position has been shifted well North of the Earth's equator, and high tides are thus caused at the points H and H_1. Smaller high tides are also caused at S and S_1. When the Moon's latitude and the

latitude of the place are both North or both South, the highest high
tide occurs UNDER the Moon.   When the Moon is North and the place
is South, or *vice versa*, the highest high tide occurs 180° away from the
Moon.   In all cases the high tides at *H* and *H*₁ are higher than those

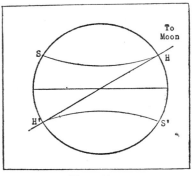

FIG. 59.

caused by M_2 alone, while at *S* and S_1, the high tide is smaller than
that caused by M_2 alone.

When the Moon is at its farthest distance North or South of the
equator, K_1 and O_1 act in conjunction.   When the Moon is directly
over the Earth's equator, they act in opposition.   These effects are
only experienced once daily, so they are given the suffix "1".   The
Moon alters its position from its highest North latitude to its highest
South, and back again to highest North, in the period of one month,
and so it crosses over the position of the Earth's equator twice every
month.

The constituents tabulated and discussed above are sufficient for
all practical purposes for tidal prediction, but when Tide Tables are
being computed, other constituents must be taken into account, including the varying distance between the Earth and the Sun, and
between the Earth and the Moon.   Friction in shallow water, geographical conditions, etc., have also to be considered.

Priming and Lagging.—This is caused by the attractive force of
the Sun, and its effects are felt both when the Sun is on the same side
of the Earth as the place at which H.W. is being considered, and when
the place is on the opposite side of the Earth from the Sun.

In Fig. 60, *Q*, *S*, *T*, and *V* represent places on the Earth, and the
pull of the Sun has the effect of causing H.W. to occur BEFORE the
Moon reaches the meridian of the place during the 1st and 3rd quarters
of the Moon.   (*Q* and *T*.)   This is called "priming".   Lagging occurs
during the 2nd and 4th quarters of the Moon, when H.W. occurs AFTER
the Moon has crossed the meridian of the place.   (*S* and *V*.)

At conjunction, opposition, and quadrature, there is no effect in this way from the pull of the Sun.

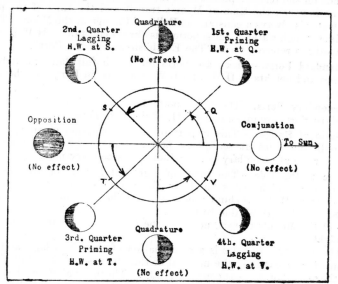

FIG. 60.

Incorrect

Definitions.

Chart Datum.—The depth marked on navigational charts is the depth of water at Low Water of Ordinary Spring Tides. (L.W.O.S.) That is, the depths are the lowest depths of water which may normally be expected there. Chart datum is the level of water below which the depths marked on the charts are calculated.

Height.—The height of tide at any specified time is the vertical distance between Chart Datum and the actual level of the water.

Rise.—Rise of tide is the height of any specified High Water above Chart Datum.

Range.—The Range of a tide is the difference between the heights of H.W. and L.W. of any particular tide.

Mean Tide Level.—This is half of the difference between MEAN High Water and MEAN Low Water.

Time of High Water.—This is the instant of time midway between the time that the tide apparently ceases to rise and the time at which it apparently commences to fall. The time of Low Water is defined in the same way.

H.W.F. & C.—This is the time of high water at any specified port at the periods of Full Moon and New Moon. The time of the Moon's

G

transit is then 00 hours and 12 hours respectively, and since "lag" depends on the relative positions of the Sun and the Moon, the interval of time between the time of Moon's transit and the time of the next high water is always a constant at Full and Change of the Moon. Thus the time of high water at these periods is always constant. H.W.F. & C. is sometimes referred to as "The Establishment of the Port".

Standard Ports.—These are ports for which full daily predictions of times and heights of H.W. and L.W. are given in Part I. of the *Tide Tables*.

Secondary Ports.—These are ports for which tidal differences on Standard Ports are given in Part II. of the *Tide Tables*.

Ratio of Ranges.—This is part of the information given to assist in predicting tides at secondary ports. Range of tide at standard port × ratio at secondary port = Range at secondary port.

Age of the Tide.—The times of high and low water are affected by friction, which tends to delay the action of tidal constituents. The crest of M_2 lags behind the Moon, and the crest of S_2 lags behind the Sun. Thus H.W. due to the former does not occur exactly at the time of the Moon's transit, nor does the H.W. of S_2 occur at noon and midnight.

The AGE OF THE TIDE is a combination of these two lags, and can be noted by measuring the interval of time between new or full Moon, and the arrival of the next composite M_2S_2. The interval of time between H.W.F. & C. and the time of the next following HIGHEST H.W. gives an approximation of the Age of the Tide.

The time lag of the semidiurnal tide due to the Sun is usually greater than that due to the Moon. Again, since the transit of the Moon at any particular place occurs about 50 minutes later each day, the interval between the high waters of M_2 and S_2 at full and change will also be reduced by that amount.

$$\text{Therefore age of tide} = \frac{\text{Lag of } S_2 - \text{lag of } M_2}{50}$$

For example, suppose the lag of $S_2 = 90$ minutes
and the lag of $M_2 = 40$ minutes

$$\text{then age of tide (in days)} = \frac{90-40}{50} = 1 \text{ day.}$$

Let us assume that the tide due to S_2 occurs at 13.30 at full and change, and that the tide due to M_2 occurs at 12.40. On the following day, S_2 still occurs at 13.30, and M_2, arriving 50 minutes later than the previous day, also occurs at 13.30. Thus the age of the tide is 1 day.

The age of the tide is subject to large variations within small areas, and for practical purposes is usually reckoned as $1\frac{1}{2}$ days in the vicinity of the British Isles.

Tidal Peculiarities.

At some places, the diurnal (once daily) constituents are larger than the semidiurnal constituents. When this is the case, the combined results of the various effects come nearer to being diurnal, and there may be only one H.W. and one L.W. in an entire day. These are called "single-day" tides.

In the Solent, and at various other places, QUARTER-DAY constituents (caused by terrestrial effects) are large compared to both the diurnal and the semidiurnal effects, and 4 high tides occur daily. These are called "double half-day" tides.

Bores.—When an oncoming tidal wave reaches shallow water, the front slope increases and the rear slope decreases in steepness. Thus the duration of the time of the rise of the tide is less than the duration of the time of the fall of the tide. In some tidal rivers, the incoming wave sometimes breaks, and "bores" occur, in which half, or more than half, of the total rise may occur within the space of a few minutes. Amongst other places, bores occur in the Rivers Severn, Seine, and Hoogly.

Meteorological Tides.—These are tides affected by the force and direction of the wind, and by the height of the barometer. The usual effects are that an off-shore wind decreases the predicted height, and an on-shore wind increases it. Higher tides occur when the barometer registers low pressure, and *vice-versa*.

Tidal Information from Charts.—On many charts tidal information for various districts shown on the charts is given in tabular form. On charts of British waters, this information is usually given with the direction and rate of the tidal streams referred to the time of H.W. at Dover, which is taken as the standard port for Britain. On some charts the information may be referred to H.W. at Liverpool.

Tidal Predictions.

The *Admiralty Tide Tables*, published in three volumes, provide a very comprehensive library. In these books, the seaman is able to find all necessary particulars of times and heights of tides at most of the world's ports. The three volumes are for:

1. European Waters, including the Mediterranean Sea;
2. Atlantic and Indian Oceans;
3. Pacific Ocean and Adjacent Seas.

Each volume is divided into two parts—Part I. tabulating the times and heights of high and low water for every day of the year at selected "standard" ports, while Part II. gives all information necessary to predict times and heights of high and low waters at secondary ports.

The predictions in Part I. have been worked out by very exacting methods, involving a great deal of calculation. This is usually carried out by mechanical devices, as otherwise the work would be laborious in the extreme.

H.W. by F. & C. Constant.—A very approximate method of finding the time of H.W. at a port, when no Tide Tables are handy, consists in finding—say from a chart—the "establishment of the port" in question. That, as explained above, is the time of H.W. at full and change of the Moon.

The Moon rises about 50 minutes later each day, so that approximately the time of H.W. occurs about 50 minutes later each day.

To the time of H.W.F. & C., add 50 minutes for every day that has elapsed from the last full Moon or new Moon. The result is the approximate P.M. tide for that day. To find the time of the A.M. H.W., subtract 12 hrs., 25 min. from this.

This method can only be taken as very rough and ready, as no account is taken of the configuration of the land, or of any peculiarities which tend to alter the time of H.W.

Reduction to Soundings.

As stated earlier, the times and heights of high and low water at standard ports are tabulated for every day of the year in Part I. of the *Admiralty Tide Tables*. (A.T.T.)

In the examination rooms, tidal problems may be worded in many different ways. However, when stripped down to the essentials, the problems require only one of two results—either:

(a) The HEIGHT of tide at the port at some specified time, or

(b) The TIME at which the tide will reach a specified height.

If an observer placed a "tide-pole" in position at any point, he could mark on the pole the highest point reached by the water during any particular tide. Later, he could also mark the lowest point reached by the falling tide. The difference between the two extremes would represent the "range" of that particular tide. The "half-range" would show the height of the tide midway between high and low waters. This point is called the Mean Tide Level. (M.T.L.)

In Fig. 61, the vertical line represents a tide-pole, with the heights of H.W., L.W., and M.T.L. marked to scale.

Using the M.T.L. mark as centre, a semi-circle has been drawn, the radius being the half-range of the tide. For simplicity, let us suppose the tide takes exactly 6 hours to rise from L.W. to H.W. It can thus be said that the tide has risen through an ANGLE of 180° in 6 hours. Therefore it must rise through an angle of 30° every hour.

Angles of 30° have been drawn to the circumference of the semi-circle, and horizontal lines from these points to the tide-pole show the heights of the tide at every hour. From the sketch, it can be seen that:

(a) The LEAST rise (or fall) of the tide occurs during the hour before (or after) high and low water;

(b) The GREATEST rise (or fall) occurs about the period of mid-tide.

This "graphic" method is very simple to use, and is of great help in solving tidal problems. We shall use this method in the first place to demonstrate the working of the problem. Later we shall see how the results can be checked by the use of Tables which are incorporated in the *Tide Tables*.

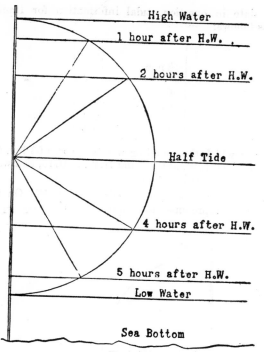

High Water

1 hour after H.W.

2 hours after H.W.

Half Tide

4 hours after H.W.

5 hours after H.W.

Low Water

Sea Bottom

FIG. 61.

All the examples given here are taken from Part I of the first volume of the Admiralty Tide Tables, 1959. It should be particularly noted that all times given in Part I are Greenwich Mean Time. This is also referred to as Standard Time. Should the answer be required in Local Mean Time, the longitude of the port—given at the top of each page—must be converted into time. If the port is in West longitude, the longitude in time is SUBTRACTED from Standard time. If the port is in East longitude, it must be ADDED. (See next chapter). On the other hand, if Local Mean Time is given in the question, the above rule is reversed—add for West longitude, subtract for East. When dealing with times from the Tide Tables, everything must be reduced to Standard Time.

Example 1.—On May 10th, at 03 hrs 02 m. Standard Time, being off Immingham, took a cast of the lead. Required the correction to be applied to the depth on the leadline before comparing it with the depth marked on the chart.

(Note.—A reproduction of the Admiralty Tide Table for the port of Immingham for part of the month of May, 1959, is given on page 480.)

On the date in question, tidal information for Immingham is tabulated as follows:

Time	Ht. Ft.
0107	2·4
0713	20·3
1326	2·2
1934	19·7

The time at which the sounding was taken was 03 hrs. 02m. This time occurs between L.W. at 0107 and H.W. at 0713, and was therefore taken on the morning rising tide.

Fig. 62 depicts a tide-pole erected at the port. On the sketch, "Chart Datum" represents low water of ordinary spring tides. (L.W.O.S.)

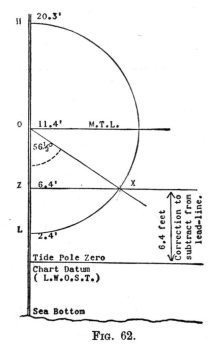

Fig. 62.

This is the height of the tide which was used when the depth actually marked on the chart was taken.

On this particular tide on May 10th, the height of L.W. is 2·4 feet above L.W.O.S., and the height of H.W. is 20·3 feet above L.W.O.S. It is required to find the height of the tide at 3·02 a.m.

	h. m.		h. m.		Ft.	
Time of L.W.	01 07	Time of L.W.	01 07	Ht. of L.W.	2·4	
Time of H.W.	07 13	Time of cast	03 02	Ht. of H.W.	20·3	┼
Dur: of rise	6 06	T. from L.W.	1 55		2)22·7	
= 366 min.		= 115 min.		M.T.L.	11·4 ft.	

The duration of the rise of the particular tide is found first by subtraction. For the purpose of using a graphic method of working the problem, this should be converted to minutes. In the same way, the period of time is found between the time of taking the sounding and either H.W. or L.W., whichever is the nearer. In this case, the time of the cast is 115 minutes from L.W.

The sum of the heights of H.W. and L.W., divided by 2, gives the height above *Chart Datum* of the sea surface at half-tide. This is the Mean Tide Level. (M.T.L.) The *Range* of the tide—the number of feet between the heights of H.W. and L.W.—is found by subtraction.

From the sketch, it can be seen that the problem could now be read as—"The tide rises through an angle of 180° in 366 minutes. Through what angle will it rise in 115 minutes?" The required angle is obviously less than 180°, in the proportion

$$\frac{180 \times 115}{366} = 56\tfrac{1}{2}°$$

When drawing a sketch, all heights and angles should be drawn accurately and to scale. The radius of the semicircle is from M.T.L. to the height of L.W. or H.W. (11·4—2·4)=9 feet.

Since the time of the sounding has been, in this case, referred to L.W., the angle of 56½° is measured from L.W. Lay the centre of a protractor at "0", the M.T.L., and measure 56½° from L.W. Through this point, draw a line from "0" to the circumference of the semicircle. From the point where the line meets the semicircle, draw another line, parallel to M.T.L. Where this line cuts the tide-pole represents the height of the tide above *Chart Datum* at the time of taking the sounding.

This is the number of feet to be SUBTRACTED from the depth read off the lead-line. By measurement, the amount to be subtracted is 6·4 feet.

TABLE I, A.T.T.—A Table printed on pp. xviii and xix of the Tide Table can be used to check the correctness of the working. If preferred, it can be used instead of the method given above.

The first and last vertical columns of figures in the top halves of the two pages are alike, and give durations of rise or fall of the tide to intervals of 10 minutes. Having found the duration of the appropriate tide, run a finger across the page at that level till the "Time from H. or L.W." is reached.

In Example 1, the duration of the rise of tide is 6 hours 6 minutes. This is roughly halfway between a duration of 6 hours and one of 6 hours 10 minutes.

A little more than halfway across the first page, we find—

	Int. from nearest H.W. or L.W.	
Dur. 6 hrs.	0148	0157
Dur. 6 hrs. 10 m.	0151	0200

The duration of the tide in question is practically halfway between 6 hrs. and 6 hrs. 10 m., therefore by interpolation, the interval— 1 hr. 55 m.—from L.W. is also practically halfway between the figures 0151 and 0157, read diagonally. In other words, the interval can be taken as being on the actual line dividing these times.

Follow this line down to the lower half of the page.

The RANGE of this particular tide (L.W. to H.W.) is (20·3—2·4) feet=17·9 feet. Call it 18 feet, which is quite near enough.

In the left—or right-hand column in the lower part of the page, abreast of Range 18 feet, and in the vicinity of the line that has been followed down, will be seen the figures 3·7 | 4·3.

The required correction—the mean of these two heights—is 4·0 feet, which MUST BE ADDED TO THE HEIGHT OF L.W. OF THIS PARTICULAR TIDE.

$$2·4+4·0=6·4 \text{ feet}=\text{height above chart datum.}$$

This final figure represents the amount that has to be subtracted from the depth shown on the leadline before it is compared with the depth marked on the chart.

It is seen that it agrees with the answer found by the graphic method.

Example 2.—At what time would there be 26 feet over a 2-fathom bank on the a.m. rising tide at Immingham on May 15th?

In this example it is required to find the TIME at which the tide would reach a specified height.

Draw the pole (Fig. 63) and fill in the necessary particulars— M.T.L., zero of chart datum, L.W. and H.W. Draw the semicircle.

Time of L.W.	04 06	Height of L.W.	5·5 ft.
Time of H.W.	1C 13	Height of H.W.	17·6 ft.

Dur. of rise 6 07

$= 367$ min.

2)23·1

11·5 ft. M.T.L.

A total depth of 26 feet above the sea-bottom is required, and since the depth at L.W.O.S. is 12 feet (2 fathoms) the required mark on the tide-pole must be $(26-12)=14$ feet.

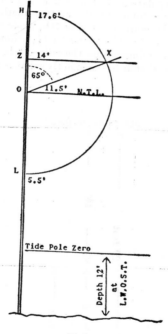

FIG. 63.

At 14 feet on the pole, mark "Z." Draw $Z X$ parallel to the M.T.L. Join OX, and measure angle HOX (from H.W.) This is found to measure 65°.

In 367 minutes, the tide falls through an angle of 180°. How long will it take to fall through an angle of 65°?

By proportion $\dfrac{367 \times 65}{180} = 132$ minutes $= 2$ hrs. 12 m.

The tide will reach the required height 2 hrs. 12 m. before H.W., at 08 hrs. 01 m. (Note that times need only be given to the nearest minute).

When using Table I from the A.T.T., and the required answer is in TIME, the work must be performed backwards.

Range of tide, H.W. to L.W., is 12·1 feet. Correction to the height of H.W. is (17·6—14)=3·6 feet.

In the fourth column across the page, abreast of Range 12 feet, is found 3·7 feet. This is quite close enough, and does not need interpolation.

Run a finger UP the page in this vertical column, and abreast of 6 hrs. 7 m. (by interpolation) is found 2 hrs. 15 m. This is within 3 minutes of the answer found by the graphic method.

Example 3.—On the morning of May 7th, up to what time would a vessel of 20 feet draught be able to cross a 1½-fathom shoal with 3 feet of clearance, leaving Immingham on the falling tide?

First draw a rough sketch to see exactly what is required.

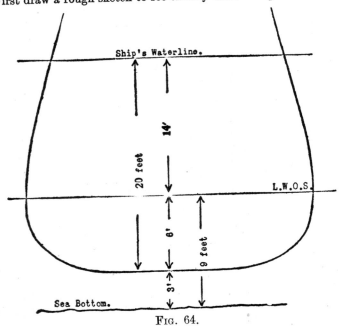

Fig. 64.

The vessel's draught is 20 feet. Clearance of 3 feet is required, so that there must be a total depth of 23 feet. At L.W.O.S. there is 9 feet, which is the zero mark on the tide-pole. Thus the pole will require to register a height of water of 14 feet above chart datum.

Time of H.W.	05 38	Height of H.W.	20·3 ft.
Time of L.W.	11 44	Height of L.W.	2·6 ft.
Dur. of fall	6 06		2)22·9
	=366 min.		11·5 ft. M.T.L.

Half-range (rad. of semicircle)
=M.T.L.−Ht. of L.W.
=11·5−2·6=8·9 ft.

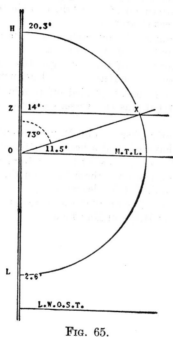

Fig. 65.

By measurement, angle $HOX=73°$.

Latest time to cross shoal$=\dfrac{366 \times 73}{180}=148$ min. after H.W.=2hrs. 28m.

Using Table I—Range of tide=17·7 ft.

Height *below* H.W.=(20·3−14) ft.=6·3 ft.

Duration of tide   6 hrs. 6 m.

Interval from H.W. (interpolating)=2 hrs. 29m.

EXERCISE 18.

1. On May 8th, at 01 hrs. 52m., standard time off Immingham, took a cast. Required the correction to be applied to the depth found before comparing it with the depth given on the chart.

2. On May 14th, at 14hrs. 16 m. standard time off Immingham, took a cast. Required the correction to be applied to the depth found by the leadline before comparing it with the depth marked on the chart.

3. At what time, a.m. at ship on May 3rd, would a 1-fathom shoal off Immingham have 20 feet of water over it on a falling tide?

4. At what time would a vessel drawing 17 feet, making for Immingham on the afternoon of May 8th, be able to cross a 2-fathom shoal with 3 feet clearance?

5. A vessel ran aground off Immingham at 11 a.m., May 10th. At what time would she be able to refloat?

6. What was the interval of time between the 10-ft. and the 13-ft. heights of water on the rising tide at Immingham on May 7th?

7. A vessel drawing 16 feet grounded off Immingham at 11 a.m. on May 13th. What was the vessel's additional freeboard at low water?

8. At what time, early afternoon on May 5th would the rising tide at Immingham have reached a height of 16 feet?

9. To what draught could a vessel load at Immingham on 1st May, to be able to cross a 1-fathom bank on the a.m. rising tide at 11 a.m.? Required 4-ft. clearance.

10. What would be the height of the a.m. rising tide at Immingham $1\frac{3}{4}$ hours before H.W. on May 14th?

PART III.
CELESTIAL NAVIGATION USING THE SUN.

CHAPTER 16.

MEASUREMENT OF TIME—DAY AND NIGHT—TWILIGHT—THE EARTH'S ANNUAL JOURNEY — THE SEASONS — APPARENT MOTION—RELATIONSHIP BETWEEN ARC AND TIME—TO CONVERT ARC INTO TIME—TO CONVERT TIME INTO ARC.

Measurement of Time.—So far as the inhabitants of the Earth are concerned, the Sun is by far the most important of all celestial bodies, providing, as it does, both heat and light to sustain life. Furthermore, the movements of the Earth relative to the Sun are subject only to very slight aberrations, so it is quite natural that all our measurements of TIME for our daily needs should depend on the Sun.

The average length of time that elapses between two successive "southings" of the Sun is called a day, and is divided into 24 hours. (The Sun is said to "south" when at noon it bears true South from an observer in the northern hemisphere.) As has been seen previously, each hour is divided into 60 minutes, and each minute is divided into 60 seconds.

Day and Night.—Some of the effects resulting from the Earth's daily rotation on its axis have already been considered. The same rotation is the cause of day and night on the Earth.

Within the period of a day, all the faces of the Earth are presented in turn towards the Sun. Those regions which are temporarily turned towards the Sun experience daylight, while those regions which are turned away from the Sun have the darkness of night.

Twilight.—The Earth is surrounded by a cushion of air, called the Atmosphere. Beyond this cushion, which extends only a few hundred miles above the Earth, lies Space, which is considered to be a vacuum.

If the atmosphere was perfectly pure, darkness would commence as soon as the Sun set in the evening, and would last in that place till sunrise next morning. But the air is full of particles of dust, on which the rays of light from the Sun are reflected. So long as this reflection can be seen, a modified light called Twilight is experienced.

"Civil twilight" lasts until the Sun has descended 6° VERTICALLY below the horizon. "Nautical twilight" lasts until it is 12° vertically below, and "astronomical twilight" continues until it has reached 18° below the horizon.

The "tropical zone" of the Earth is an area, extending right round

the world, between two imaginary small circles spaced 23° 27′ North
and South of the equator.   The Sun always keeps within these limits, and
in this zone it rises and sets almost vertically.   Twilight therefore
does not last long in the tropics.

In latitudes well North or South from the equator (high latitudes),
the period of twilight stretches out during the local summer months.
In very high latitudes—from just over 50° N. or S., during the height
of local summer, the Sun, at its lowest, does not reach 18° vertically
below the horizon, owing to the "falling off" of the Earth towards the
Poles.   During that period, real darkness is therefore not experienced,
twilight lasting throughout the night.   Even farther North or South,
the phenomenon known as "the midnight Sun" is experienced, where,
during summer months, the Sun remains above the horizon day and
night.

The Earth's Annual Journey.—In addition to rotating on its axis—
by which means we measure days and hours—the Earth also traverses
an almost circular path round the Sun at an average distance away
from it of 93 million miles.

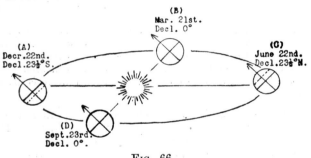

Fig. 66.

The space of time taken to perform this journey—365¼ days—is
called a year.

The Seasons.—In Chapter 5, it was stated that the axis of the Earth
is inclined at an angle of 23° 27′ to the orbit round which it travels
on its annual journey.   In Fig. 66, when the Earth is at position A,
the Sun will appear directly overhead at noon to an observer anywhere
in Lat. 23° 27′ S.   The date then is about December 22nd, which marks
the beginning of winter in the northern hemisphere.   Since the Earth's
orbit round the Sun is not quite circular, the distance between the
Sun and the Earth varies slightly at various times throughout the year,
and at this period the Earth is at its nearest approach to the Sun.

But because the Sun is so far South of the equator, its rays have
to pass very obliquely through the atmosphere before reaching the
Earth in high northern latitudes, and much of their heat has been
absorbed by the atmosphere before then.   The straighter the Sun's

rays descend to the Earth, the greater the proportion of heat which reaches the Earth's surface. The same effect can be demonstrated by a fire in a room. The person near the fire receives more of its heat than does a person at the far side of the room, for much of the fire's heat has been absorbed by the air before it reaches the latter person.

Proceeding along its orbit, the Sun reaches position B on March 21st. At noon on that day the Sun would be right overhead to an observer anywhere on the equator. All over the world, the Sun rises at 6 a.m. and sets at 6 p.m. Day and night are of equal duration, and in the northern hemisphere it is the spring equinox.

From then onwards till June 22nd, the Sun reaches a little farther North each day, and at noon on that date it would be right overhead to an observer in Lat. 23° 27′ N. In the northern hemisphere it is the beginning of summer (position C, Fig. 66) and though the Earth is now at its greatest distance away from the Sun, the rays of the latter reach the northern regions of the Earth more vertically, and we receive much more heat from them than we do in winter.

Thereafter the Sun commences its southward journey, and on September 23rd, it has reached the equator again (position D) at the period of the autumn equinox. From there it continues southward till, on December 22nd, it arrives back at position A.

Apparent Motion.—It must never be forgotten that it is the Earth which turns on its axis, and journeys on its orbit round the Sun. To a casual observer, it appears that the Earth is stationary, while the Sun and the Stars rise in the East and set in the West. This is known as "apparent motion", and it is often more convenient to work from this apparent motion than from the real motion of the Earth.

Under these circumstances the Earth becomes to all intents and purposes the centre of a ast universe, while the stars, fixed on the inside of a huge bowl called the sky, circle ceaselessly round the Earth.

The actual distance of the stars from the Earth is of no great importance for our present purpose. What *is* important is their positions relative to each other and to the Earth. Two stars may seem to us to be quite close together in the sky. The fact that they may actually be countless millions of miles apart is unimportant in practical navigation.

Relationship between Arc and Time.—When dealing with hours, minutes and seconds, these are always written as hrs., min., sec., and we are said to be dealing with TIME. When dealing with degrees, minutes and seconds, these are written as °, ′, ″, and we are said to be dealing with ARC, an arc being any part of the circumference of a circle. Minutes and seconds of time should never be confused with minutes and seconds of arc, each being entirely different from the other.

It is known that the Earth revolves once on its axis every 24 hours. That is to say, the Earth revolves through an angle of 4 times 90° (360°) in 24 hours. Thus it can be said that—

24 hours of time = 360° of arc.

This is called a simple equation, similar to 100/-=£5. If each side of any equation is divided by the same amount, the result is still an equation. For instance, using the same example 100/-=£5, divide each side by 5. The result is 20/-=£1, which, as we all know, is correct.

By performing the same operation with the equation between time and arc, we can establish a "table of relationship" between these two.

Time		Arc	
24 hours	=	360°	(Divide each side by 24)
1 hr (60 min)	=	15°	(Divide each side by 15)
4 min	=	1° (60')	(Divide each side by 4)
1 min (60 sec)	=	15'	(Divide each side by 15)
4 sec	=	1' (60'')	(Divide each side by 4)
1 sec	=	15''	

The second of these relationships (1 hour=15°) is highly important throughout navigation and should be carefully remembered.

Notice also that, with the exception of the first operation, division is performed by 15 or 4, which, themselves multiplied, make 60. In dealing with time and arc 60 is a standard figure.

A little study of the above table, which should be memorised, shows why it is important that minutes and seconds of time should not be confused with minutes and seconds of arc.

To Convert Arc into Time.—One of the most common operations in navigation is to convert arc into time, or time into arc. Both operations are simple, and some examples of the methods used, with a full explanation, are given here. To convert arc into time, the rule is: Multiply by 4 and divide by 60.

Example 1.—Convert 18° 09' 11'' into time.

$$18° \ 09' \ 11''$$
$$\times \qquad 4$$
$$60)\overline{72 \ \ 36 \ \ 44}$$
$$1 \ hr \ 12 \ min \ 36 \ sec \ \ \frac{44}{60}$$

Explanation.—When dividing by 60, always cancel the last figure of the 60 and also the last figure of the degrees. Then divide the remaining figure or figures of the degrees (7 in this case) by the 6. The result gives the hours of the answer.

The next step is to take the remainder of this division (12) and convert it into minutes by multiplying it by 60, thereafter adding to it the minutes in the question (36 in this case.)

If 12 is multiplied by 60, and then divided by 60, the result is still 12, so, in effect, all that has to be done after dividing the degrees by 60 is to write down the remainder calling it the minutes of time.

Similarly, 36' would become the remainder, to be multiplied by 60 to convert it to seconds. As it also has then to be divided by 60 the result would still be 36.

So, then, the 36' is simply put down in the answer as 36 sec. and the remainder, 44, is a fraction of a second.

If worked out by long division, the same problem would appear as follows:—

$$18° \ 09' \ 11''$$
$$\times \quad 4$$

60)72　36　44　(1 hr 12 min 36 sec
　60

　12
　60　Multiply by 60 to convert to minutes, and add 36'

60)756
　60

　156
　120

　36　Multiply by 60 to convert to seconds, and add 44''
　60
60)2204
　180
　404
　360
　44　Remainder

Example 2.—Convert 97° 43' 39'' into time.

In this case the seconds, when multiplied by 4, come to more than 60'', which is more than 1'. When multiplied, therefore, put the figures in the margin and divide them by 60 for the purpose of bringing them to minutes. The remainder is the number of seconds to transfer to the seconds column of the main problem, and the minutes to be added when the 43' have been multiplied by 4. Do the same with the minutes after multiplying, the problem appearing thus:—

97° 43' 39''
　×　　4

60)390　54' 36''

6 hr 30 min 54 sec $\frac{36}{60}$

60)156 = (39×4)

2' 36'' (Transfer 36'')
172

60)174

2° 54' (Transfer 54')
388

390　(Transfer)

Example 3.—Convert 137° 19′ 48″ into time.

137° 19′ 48″
×   4
───────────
60)549° 19′ 12″

9 hr 9 min 19 sec $\dfrac{12}{60}$

60)192

3′ 12″
76
───
60) 79
───
1° 19′
548
───
549

Example 4.—Convert 12° 37′ 19″ into time.

12° 37′ 19″
×   4
───────────
60)50° 29′ 16″

0 hr 50 min 29 sec $\dfrac{16}{60}$

60)76

1′ 16″
148
───
60)149
───
2° 29′
48
───
50

Note.—The degrees in this example are less than 15, therefore the hours, according to the table of relationship, must be less than 1.

A very common error, and one which has to be guarded against, is that of cancelling the last figure of the 60 and not cancelling the last figure of the dividend. Always remember that, if one figure has been cancelled, the other must be cancelled also.

To Convert Time into Arc.—The rule for performing this operation is the reverse of the one just used. That is, multiply by 60, and divide by 4.

Example 1.—Convert 10 hr 19 min 43 sec into arc. Now, when 43 sec are multiplied by 60, they become 43 min, since there are 60 sec in 1 min. The first step would then appear as follows:—

10 hr 19 min 43 sec
×   60
────────────────────
43   00 sec

Again, 19 min, when multiplied by 60, becomes 19 hr, since there are 60 min in 1 hr. And 10 hr, when multiplied by 60, remains in hours, so the next step in the problem, after that shown above, is to multiply the hours by 60, and add the minutes of the top line to the result. The problem then appears as follows:—

$$\begin{array}{r} 10 \text{ hr } 19 \text{ min } 43 \text{ sec} \\ \times \qquad 60 \end{array}$$

4)619 hr 43 min 00 sec

154° 55′ 45″ *Answer*

In dividing the hours by 4, the remainder is 3. This is multiplied by 60 to bring it to minutes, and the 43 minutes added. The result is 223, to be divided by 4. The remainder is again 3.

When dividing by 4, the remainder must be 0, 1, 2, or 3.

If remainder is 0, the seconds column is 0″.
If remainder is 1, the seconds column is $\frac{1}{4}$ of 60″, or 15″.
If remainder is 2, the seconds column is $\frac{1}{2}$ of 60″, or 30″.
If remainder is 3, the seconds column is $\frac{3}{4}$ of 60″, or 45″.

Example 2.—Convert 3 hr 48 min 19 sec into arc.

$$\begin{array}{r} 3 \text{ hr } 48 \text{ min } 19 \text{ sec} \\ \times \qquad 60 \end{array}$$

4)228 hr 19 min 00 sec

57° 04′ 45″

Example 3.—Convert 9 hr 18 min 51 sec to arc.

$$\begin{array}{r} 9 \text{ hr } 18 \text{ min } 51 \text{ sec} \\ \times \qquad 60 \end{array}$$

4)558 hr 51 min 00 sec

139° 42′ 45″

Divide by 15

EXERCISE 19.

Convert into time

1. 43° 12′ 08″
2. 18 46 52
3.   7 37 28
4. 126 42 37
5. 52 21 42
6. 37 18 24
7. 14 06 55
8. 59 22 34

Convert into arc

9.   5 hr 32 min 44 sec
10. 10   07   35
11. 7   49   25
12. 0   26   51
13. 2   15   14
14. 6   53   29
15. 1   04   24
16. 4   25   41

CHAPTER 17

GREENWICH TIME—MEAN AND APPARENT TIME—GREENWICH
HOUR ANGLE OF THE SUN—LOCAL HOUR ANGLE OF THE SUN—
DECLINATION—FIRST POINT OF ARIES—"THE NAUTICAL
ALMANAC"—EQUATION OF TIME—TO FIND G.M.T. FROM L.A.T.
—TO CORRECT DECLINATION—SPECIAL CASES AT SPRING AND
AUTUMN EQUINOXES—TO CORRECT G.H.A. OF THE SUN—WHY
SHIP'S TIME HAS TO BE ALTERED—INTERNATIONAL DATE
LINE.

Suppose an observer is situated anywhere on the meridian of Greenwich, longitude 0°. With a sextant he can note the angular height
of the Sun gradually increasing as it creeps higher in the sky. Then,
at a certain time, for an appreciable instant, the angular height appears
to remain constant, just before it begins to decrease. If he takes a
compass bearing of the Sun at the same time, he will find that it
bears true South from him, provided he is North of the Sun. If his
latitude is South of the Sun, it will bear true North from him.

That is to say, the Sun and the observer are now in the same
longitude, and at Greenwich, or at any place on the same meridian as
Greenwich, it is noon. (Hence the name "meridian", which is derived
from the Latin *meridies*, meaning mid-day.)

Greenwich Time.—Only places on the same meridian as Greenwich
have noon at that particular time, since all these places, like Greenwich,
are momentarily in the same longitude as the Sun. Places in other
longitudes will experience local noon either before or after noon at
Greenwich.

Suppose this observer is in communication with two other observers,
one in longitude 15° E., the other in longitude 15° W. The observer in
15° E. informs him that the Sun bore due South from him an hour ago
and *his* time is therefore 1 p.m. The observer in 15° W., on the other
hand, states that the Sun still has an hour to go before it will bear
true South from there, and it is 11 a.m. at that position. (It will
be remembered that 15°=1 hour.)

Thus it can be seen that TIME depends entirely on the relative
positions of the Sun and the observer. To an observer in longitude

180° the time would be midnight, while in longitudes 90° E. and 90° W. respectively, the times would be 6 p.m. and 6 a.m.

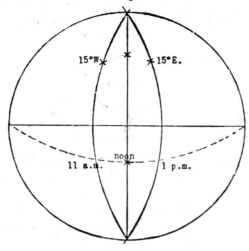

FIG. 67.

This gives us a little doggerel rhyme which comes in handy:—

"If longitude is East, Greenwich Time is least;
If longitude is West, Greenwich Time is best."

Mean and Apparent Time.—Greenwich Time is now taken as standard all over the world, and it is this time we shall now consider.

Our day is divided into 24 hours, and the length of an hour never alters. So it is natural to think, since our time depends on the Sun, that the Earth travels on its orbit at a steady consistent speed during its annual journey round the Sun.

This, however, is far from being the case. Actually, there is a slight day-to-day difference in the Earth's apparent speed. This difference is most pronounced at the periods of the spring and autumn equinoxes, about March 21st and September 23rd, and is least at the periods December 22nd, and June 22nd, when the Sun reaches farthest North and South respectively.

No clock could be made which would follow these changes accurately, and so the length of an hour on Earth has been taken from the average, or MEAN, length of an hour carefully calculated over a period of years.

In effect, astronomers have invented a purely imaginary Sun, round which the Earth is supposed to travel at a steady speed, and this Sun is called the MEAN (or average) Sun. The time as measured at Greenwich from this Mean Sun is called "GREENWICH MEAN TIME" (G.M.T.).

The real Sun is usually called the APPARENT Sun, because to us it *appears* to revolve round the Earth. Time measured by the real Sun is called APPARENT Time.

To follow the difference between Mean Time and Apparent Time, consider the case of two people cycling between two places 40 miles apart.

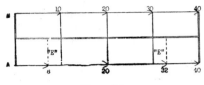

FIG. 68.

"M" cycles the distance at a steady speed of 10 miles an hour, and his progress each hour is indicated by the arrows in the top line in Fig. 68.

"A", on the other hand, cycles only 8 miles in the first hour. In the second and third hours, he increases his speed to 12 miles an hour, and during the last hour, he slows again to 8 miles an hour, arriving at his destination at the same time as "M".

The small spaces "E" in Fig. 68, which denote the difference of position between the cyclists, show us that sometimes "M" is ahead of "A", and sometimes astern of him.

The difference between Mean and Apparent Time is somewhat similar, and "E" represents the number of minutes that Mean Time is ahead or astern of Apparent Time.

This space of time, which never exceeds about 16 minutes, is called the "Equation of Time". To convert mean time into apparent time, or *vice versa*, the equation of time has to be added or subtracted, according to whether mean time is astern or ahead of apparent time.

Greenwich Hour Angle of the Sun (G.H.A. Sun).—The relationship between Time and Arc has already been explained. (See p. 174.) 189 This relationship is made use of in navigational problems by employing "Hour Angles".

If an observer were to take a bearing of the Sun at apparent noon, he would find it to bear due South, as previously explained.

The bearing of the Sun would gradually alter towards the West, and an hour later, presuming the observer to be on the meridian of Greenwich, the Sun would have arrived on the meridian of 15° W.

In Fig. 69, the circle represents the sky, usually termed the "celestial concave". O marks the position of an infinitesimal observer on the meridian of Greenwich on the earth below. N and S are the celestial poles, and X is the Sun. NOS is a meridian which passes through the celestial poles and also through the observer's ZENITH, a point in the sky immediately overhead from the observer. NXS is a meridian passing through the Sun. The angle ONX represents the Sun's "Hour Angle" West of Greenwich. This angle can be measured

either in time or in arc. The modern way is to perform the measurement in arc, and it is of great importance to remember that the Greenwich Hour Angle of the Sun, or of any other celestial body, is *always
measured to the westward.*

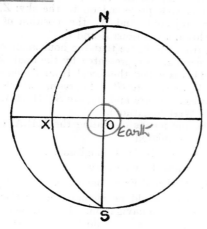

Fig. 69.

When the Sun is directly over the equator at the spring or autumn
equinox, it sets at 6 p.m., and its hour angle would then be 90°. At
midnight, though the Sun itself would be invisible to the observer on
the Greenwich meridian, its hour angle (H.A.) would be 180°. At
sunrise next morning, the H.A. would have increased to 270°, and would
continue to increase thereafter till it was 359° 59' 59'', when, at the
next apparent noon, it would start all over again from zero.

Local Hour Angle of the Sun (L.H.A. Sun).—In Fig. 70, the smaller

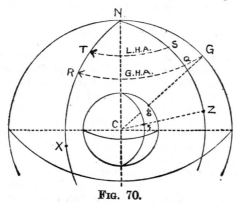

Fig. 70.

circle represents the Earth, with its centre (C), the position of Greenwich (g), and an observer in West longitude (z), all marked. A meridian of longitude is drawn through z.

The larger circle represents the celestial concave, showing G, the position of Greenwich projected on to the sky; Z, the observer's position similarly projected; and X, the position of the Sun, with meridians drawn through positions X and Z.

It can be seen from the figure that the hour angle of the Sun West of the observer's meridian is represented by the angle ZNX, or simply by the arc ST. This is called the Local Hour Angle of the Sun.

The angle GNX, or the arc GQR, represents the G.H.A. Sun, and the difference between this arc and the arc ST (L.H.A. Sun) is the arc GQ (the observer's West longitude).

From this, a simple means of finding the L.H.A. of the Sun from an observer can be formulated:

L.H.A.=G.H.A.—West longitude.

Similarly, it must also be true that

L.H.A.=G.H.A.+East longitude.

These two formulae should be memorised, for they are extremely important in all problems in navigation. By remembering one of them, the other follows naturally, as also do the converse formulae:

G.H.A. = L.H.A.+West longitude;
= L.H.A.—East longitude.

L.H.A., like G.H.A., is always measured to the westward.

Declination.—In Fig. 66, at the beginning of Chapter 16, it was noted that the Earth's axis is not at right angles to the path of its orbit, but is tilted quite noticeably away from the vertical. It should also be noted that the path traced out by the Earth's orbit round the Sun is not a true circle, but is slightly elliptical in shape. If it were not for these two facts, the Earth would not enjoy its differing seasons, and more or less each country would possess an unchanging, monotonous climate.

Owing to the Earth's tilt, and to its daily progress along its orbit, the Sun's "latitude" seems to alter slightly from day to day. This "latitude" is called the Sun's "declination", and it alters very gradually between two limits, which are 23° 27' North and South of the Earth's equator respectively. The angle of the Earth's tilt is also 23° 27'.

In Chapter 16, the equator was defined as a great circle round the Earth, midway between the poles. If this great circle is projected into the "celestial concave", it is then called the "Equinoctial", while the path that the Sun appears to describe across the celestial concave during a year—which is a great circle cutting the equinoctial at an angle of 23° 27'—is called the "Ecliptic".

On spring day—March 21st in ordinary years, and March 20th in Leap Years—the Sun's centre crosses the equinoctial and enters North declination. At this period, the Sun's declination alters at its most rapid rate, 1′ in every hour. It never exceeds that rate of change.

Its declination continues to increase to the northward until June 22nd, when it reaches 23° 27′ N., its greatest amount. During the preceding three months the rate of its hourly change has been slowing very gradually, and round about June 22nd, it practically does not change at all during a few days. This period is called a "solstice," or the stand-still of the Sun.

Then, very slowly, the declination begins to alter to the southward. The rate of change gradually quickens, and on September 23rd the Sun again crosses the equinoctial on its way South, and the rate of change is again at its maximum of 1′ every hour.

From then till December 22nd, its southerly declination gradually increases to 23° 27′ S., while the rate of change gradually decreases till once again the Sun seems to stand still for a few days. Then the declination alters to the northward till it reaches the equinoctial on spring day.

First Point of Aries.—This is the name given to a fixed point in the heavens, the point where the Sun's centre crosses the equinoctial on its northward passage in March each year. It is from this point that celestial longitude, or "Sidereal Hour Angle," is measured. It has already been explained that the Hour Angles of heavenly bodies are always measured to the westward.

Near the equinoctial and encircling the globe there are twelve "constellations" of stars. These make up the Zodiac. Hundreds of years ago, when the Sun crossed the equinoctial on spring day, its position was in one of these constellations, called the Ram. The Latin word for a Ram is "aries." In the course of centuries, due to a phenomenon known as "precession," the Sun on spring day has moved far from the actual constellation, but the name remains, and the symbol used to denote the First Point of Aries— ♈ —represents a ram's horns.

The point in the heavens directly opposite to Aries—the point where the Sun's centre re-crosses the equinoctial on or about September 23rd when changing from North to South declination, is named the "First Point of Libra." The two points are usually referred to simply as Aries and Libra respectively. "Libra" is the Latin name for a pair of scales, to which the constellation was likened. The symbol for this is ♎.

The Nautical Almanac.—Each year, Her Majesty's Stationery Office publishes *The Nautical Almanac* in a special edition abridged for the use of seamen. In the almanac is found all information regarding celestial bodies that is necessary for navigation. This information is tabulated as simply as possible, and presented in a concise way easy to understand.

There is a slow but continuous alteration in the tabulated numerical values, or "elements," so that the Almanac is of use in practical navigation for the year of issue only. Should a ship find herself at sea at the end of a calendar year without a copy of the succeeding year's *Almanac*, a paragraph on page 261 of the 1958 edition explains how this edition can be used during 1959 to obtain correct results till an up-to-date copy can be obtained.

On page 5 of the *Nautical Almanac* a calendar for the current year is printed, giving as well as the usual information, the number of days for each day since the beginning of the year.

The daily "elements" of the navigational bodies commence on page 10 and page 11, and the student should spend a little time studying the layout of these elements. Each pair of facing pages of the Almanac contains all the astronomical "ephemeris" for three days, each day occupying about a third of the two pages. On the first of the two pages the Greenwich Hour Angle of Aries is tabulated for every hour of Greenwich Mean Time. Aries is thus treated as a fixed point in the heavens. Then, reading across the page, we find the G.H.A. and the declination of each of the four "navigational" planets—Venus, Mars, Jupiter and Saturn—also given for every hour of G.M.T. At the right hand side of the page appears a list of navigational stars, together with their Sidereal Hour Angles and declinations. It will be noted that these alter very little indeed throughout the year.

On the second, or right hand page of the two, we are given the necessary information regarding the Sun and the Moon. For the present, we are concerned only with the Sun.

Each hour of G.M.T. for each of the three days is tabulated in a vertical column on the left hand side of the page. Each day commences at midnight (00 hours) and continues until 11 p.m. (23 hours). Abreast of this column, each day separate in its own panel, are found the numerical values of G.H.A. and declination of the Sun at each hour of G.M.T. These values are given in degrees, minutes, and decimals of a minute.

At the foot of the page, in the same panel, the measurement of the Sun's Semi-diameter (S.D.) is given. This value is applicable for all three days. The use of this information is explained in a later chapter. Close beside the S.D. there appears on, say, page 11, "*d* 0·2."

The item "*d*" is the mean hourly difference in the Sun's declination. The declination may be increasing or decreasing, according to the time of year. It will be seen that on 1st, 2nd and 3rd January, it is *decreasing* by an average amount of 0·2′ every hour. The method to be used to find the actual correction to apply to the tabulated declination for a time intermediate between two hours of G.M.T. is explained later in this chapter.

One highly important point to remember is that all time given in the *Nautical Almanac* is Greenwich MEAN Time. The G.H.A. and the declination of the Sun which are given are, however, those of the APPARENT, or TRUE SUN.

The hourly increase in G.H.A. of the MEAN Sun is 15°, but the hourly increase in G.H.A. of the APPARENT Sun differs slightly from 15°. To save trouble and calculation, the tabulated values of the Sun's G.H.A. have already been adjusted to allow for this slight difference, so no further correction is required.

Twilight, Sunrise and Sunset.—To the right of the middle of the second page there is a panel which tabulates the times of Sunrise, Sunset and morning and evening twilight (both nautical and civil) for a wide range of latitudes—72° N. to 60° S.—during these three days. (See also Chapter 16, p. 187). In these Tables, the symbol ▰ means that in the given latitude the Sun—and in the case of the Moon, that body also—is below the horizon all day. The symbol ▭ means the body is above the horizon all day and does not set in that latitude, while the symbol //// means there is no real darkness in that latitude—the Sun does not descend the required number of degrees vertically below the horizon. We shall have occasion to deal further with Times of Sunrise, Sunset and Twilight in the next chapter.

Equation of Time.—On page 195 it was explained that Equation of Time—usually abbreviated to Eq. T.—is the number of minutes and seconds of time that the Mean Sun is ahead or astern of the Apparent, or True, Sun.

At the foot of the panel containing particulars of Sunrise, etc., Eq. T. is given for 00 hrs, and 12 hrs, of each of the three days dealt with on that particular page. For each of these days there is also given, in hours and minutes, the time of the Sun's Meridian Passage (Mer. Pass.) That time is the G.M.T. when the Apparent, or True, Sun is momentarily in the same longitude as Greenwich, or Long. 0°. IT IS ALSO THE LOCAL MEAN TIME THAT THE TRUE SUN CROSSES THE MERIDIAN OF AN OBSERVER IN ANY LONGITUDE.

There is no sign (+ or —) attached to the Eq. T., but if the time of the Sun's Meridian Passage is later than 12 hrs., Eq. T. has to be added to APPARENT TIME to obtain MEAN TIME. Naturally it would have to be subtracted from MEAN TIME to obtain APPARENT TIME. If on the other hand the time of the Sun's Meridian Passage is earlier than 12 hours, Eq. T. has to be subtracted from Apparent Time and *vice versa*. It is a perfectly simple operation to find the correct Eq. T. to the nearest hour of G.M.T. or L.M.T. See worked examples later.

Like the Sun's declination, Eq. T. alters slowly, gradually, and smoothly, and keeps within well-defined limits. Like the changes in declination too, its *rate of change* is least when its value is greatest, and greatest when its value is least. A study of the *Nautical Almanac* will show that Eq. T. attains its greatest values about

February 11th	14 m. 20 s.	(+Apparent Time)
May 13th	3 m. 45 s.	(—Apparent Time)
July 25th	6 m. 24 s.	(+Apparent Time)
November 2nd	16 m. 24 s.	(—Apparent Time)

Its value is zero on or about April 15th, June 14th, September 1st, and December 25th each year. In the *Almanac*, the actual change from + to —, or from — to +, is shown thus:—

	Eq. T.				Mer.	
	00h		12h		Pass	
	m.	s.	m.	s.	h.	m.
13	00	16	00	10	12	00
14	00	04	00	03	12	00

In the particular case quoted above for June 14th, Eq. T. at 00 hrs. was 4 seconds to subtract, and at 12 hrs. was 3 seconds to add, a total difference of 7 seconds.

It is a point of interest to note that the greatest change in the values of the Eq. T. occurs between November of one year and February of the next year, at the period when the Earth is at its nearest approach to the Sun. Between these dates Eq. T. alters about 30¾ minutes, whereas between May and July, when the Earth is at its greatest distance away from the Sun, the change is only about 10 minutes.

To Correct the Equation of Time.—

Example 1.—Find the correct Eq. T. at 04 h. 15 m. G.M.T. on January 2nd.

Jan. 2nd, Eq. T. at 00 hrs. = 03m.   44s.
Eq. T. at 12 hrs. = 03   58

Diff. in 12 hrs.   _____14_ (increasing)

Diff. in 4 hrs. = $\dfrac{14 \times 4}{12}$ =4·7 sec. (say 5 sec.)   Eq. T. 00 h.= 03m   44s
Corr.   +   5

Corr. Eq. T.   03   49

Example 2.—Find the correct Eq. T. at 10 hrs. G.M.T. on June 14th.

June 14th, Eq. T. at 00 hrs. = 00m 04s (—App. T.)
Eq. T. at 12 hrs. = 00   03 (+App. T.)

Diff. in 12 hrs.   = 00   07

Diff. in 10 hrs. $= \dfrac{7 \times 10}{12} = 6$ sec.

Eq. T. 00 hrs.=00m 04s (−App.T.)
Corr.   −   6

Corr. Eq. T.00 02 (+App. T.)

Explanation.—To the nearest second, the correction to be applied to the Eq. T. at midnight is 6 seconds. The actual Eq. T. is *decreasing* from 4 sec. to zero, then *increasing* from zero to 3 sec. Thus a correction of 6 sec, to the original Eq. T. 00 m. 04 s. (−App. T.) gives a corrected Eq. T. of 00 m. 02s. (+App. T.)

To Obtain G.M.T. from L.A.T.

—When the Sun has reached its highest altitude for any particular day, it bears true North or true South from the observer, and the time is noon, local apparent time. This is written:

L(ocal) A(pparent) T(ime)=12 hrs. 00m. 00 sec.

The ship's longitude is then converted to time by the rule explained in Chapter 16. If ship's longitude is West, add the longitude in time to L.A.T. to obtain G.A.T. (Greenwich Time is best). If the longitude is East, subtract long. in time from L.A.T. to obtain G.A.T.

The Eq. T. corrected to the nearest hour of G.A.T., is then applied to the Greenwich Apparent Time. The result is Greenwich Mean Time.

G.M.T. is required when correcting the elements of all celestial bodies, as these elements are tabulated in the *Nautical Almanac* for each hour of G.M.T.

In the same way the G.M.T. corresponding to ANY L.A.T. can be found.

Example 1.—Find G.M.T. corresponding to noon, L.A.T. in Long. 37° 17′ W., on January 2nd.

	h m s			m s
L.A.T., Jan. 2nd	12 00 00	To convert	Eq. T., Jan. 2nd.	12h 03 58
Long. W.	+ 2 29 08	long. to time 37° 17′	Eq. T., Jan. 3rd, 00h	04 12
G.A.T., Jan. 2nd	14 29 08	× 4	Diff. in 12 hrs.	+ 14
Eq. T. (+App.T.)	4 01	60) 149 08	Diff. in 2½ hrs.=	3 sec.
G.M.T., Jan. 2nd	14 33 09	2 29 08	3m 58s+3 sec=4m 01s.	

Example 2.—Find G.M.T. at noon L.A.T. in long. 7° 19′ E. on June 14th.

	h	m	s		h	m	s
L.A.T., June 14th	12	00	00	Eq. T., June 14th. 00h	00	04	(−A.T.)
Long. E.	—	29	16	Eq. T., June 14th, 12h	00	03	(+A.T.)

	h	m	s		
G.A.T., June 14th	11	30	44	Diff. in 12 hrs.	7
Corr. Eq. T.	+		3	Diff. in 11½ hrs.	7
G.M.T., June 14th	11	30	47	Corr. Eq. T. 3 sec (+ A.T.)	

EXERCISE 20.
To Find G.M.T.

Find Greenwich Mean Time, being given Local Apparent Time
—Noon.

   1. January 2nd, in Long. 17° 22′ W.
   2. June 13th   ,,   21 22 W.
   3. July 16th   ,,   47 03 W.
   4. July 23rd   ,,   28 46 E.
   5. September 23rd   ,,   75 00 E.
   6. June 12th   ,,   55 30 W.
   7. October 9th   ,,   62 41 E.
   8. December 21st   ,,   41 29 W.
   9. June 12th   ,,   31 14 W.
  10. September 24th   ,,   40 11 E.
  11. January 3rd   ,,   12 41 E.
  12. June 14th   ,,   47 47 E.

Find Greenwich Mean Time, being given Local Apparent Time as
follows:—

  13. July 15th   16h 25m, in Long. 32° 14′ W.
  14. December 22nd   03 44   ,,   6 29 E.
  15. September 23rd 14 36   ,,   22 08 W.
  16. July 21st   21 09   ,,   10 18 E.
  17. January 1st   11 50   ,,   63 23 W.
  18. October 7th   08 22   ,,   25 19 W.
  19. June 13th   19 19   ,,   17 40 E.
  20. December 21st   10 27   ,,   8 52 E.

Equation of Time, as has already been pointed out, is used to convert Mean Time to Apparent Time, and *vice versa*. The use of Local (or Ship's) Apparent Time used to be very widespread, but with the introduction in the *Nautical Almanac* of the Greenwich Hour Angle of celestial bodies, the importance of Local Apparent Time (L.A.T.) has been greatly reduced. The Local Hour Angle (L.H.A.) of any body is found simply by applying the ship's longitude to the G.H.A. of the body at a specified time, expressed as G.M.T. Wireless time signals are broadcast at frequent intervals every day, so that no ship equipped with wireless should experience any difficulty in obtaining correct G.M.T.

To Correct G.H.A. Sun.—The G.H.A. of the Sun increases 15° every hour. The increase in every minute is therefore one-sixtieth part of 15°, which is $\frac{1}{4}$°, or 15′. Similarly the increase for every second of time is one-sixtieth of 15′, which is 15″ of arc.

To ease the work of finding the increase for any specified number of minutes and seconds of time, a Table of "Increments and Corrections" is incorporated in the latter pages of the *Nautical Almanac* commencing immediately after page 276. (See also extracts from the Table at the end of this book). Each page contains two panels. Each panel covers the corrections for one minute of time. The seconds of time, from 00 to 60, are printed in the vertical column on the left hand side of each panel. The three following columns give the "increments" to the G.H.A. of the Sun (and also Planets), Aries, and the Moon respectively. The remaining three columns of each panel are headed "*v* or *d* corrn.*" The use of these columns is discussed later in the chapter.

To find the correct G.H.A. of the Sun for any required time, open the Almanac at the page containing the given date, and write down from the panel on the right hand page, headed SUN, the G.H.A. for the given hour of G.M.T. It must be clearly understood that when using the elements from the *Nautical Almanac*, G.M.T. MUST ALWAYS BE USED.

Next turn to the Table of Increments at the page containing the required minutes of time, and abreast of the required number of seconds, in the column headed Sun (or Planets) you will find the increment to be used. This is added direct to the G.H.A. which has already been written.

Note particularly that in the Almanac the G.H.A. of the Sun at noon may not be exactly 360°. The reason for this lies in the fact already stated, that the time used is MEAN time, while the G.H.A. given is that of the APPARENT Sun.

Example 1.—Find G.H.A. Sun at 16 h. 33 m. 48 s. G.M.T. on January 3rd.

$$\text{G.H.A., Jan. 3rd, at 16 h.} = 58°\ \ 52\cdot2′$$
$$\text{Increment for 33 m. 48 s.} = \ \ 8\ \ \ 27\cdot0$$

$$\overline{\text{Corr. G.H.A. Sun}\quad\quad 67\quad 19\cdot2}$$

Example 2.—Find G.H.A. Sun at 07 h. 22 m. 11 s. G.M.T. on July 22nd.

$$\text{G.H.A. Sun at 07 h.}\quad = 283°\quad 25\cdot1′$$
$$\text{Increment for 22 m. 11 s.} = \ \ 5\quad 32\cdot8$$

$$\overline{\text{Corr. G.H.A. Sun}\quad\quad 288\quad 57\cdot9}$$

H ·

To Correct the Sun's Declination.—The Sun's declination for each hour of each day appears alongside the G.H.A. It will be noticed that the degrees of declination are normally given only at every sixth hour. This makes for clearness and ease in reading.

At the foot of the page, in the same panel, is given the letter "d," accompanied by a value. "d" is the mean hourly difference of the Sun's declination.

To find the correction to apply to the declination for a given number of minutes of time, turn again to the Table of Increments and Corrections, to the final three columns of the panel. Each column contains a double row of figures. The first figures, in small print, represent the value of "d" as read from the daily page. The larger figures represent the actual correction on account of the given number of minutes of G.M.T., to be applied to the declination shown at the given hour. If the Sun's declination is increasing, add the correction. If decreasing, subtract the correction.

Example 1.—Find the correct declination of the Sun at 16 h. 26 m. 23 s. G.M.T. on January 2nd.

$$\text{Decl. Jan. 2nd, 16 h.} = 22° 55·3' \text{ S.} \quad (d = 0·2')$$
$$\text{Corr. for 26 m.} \quad = \quad 0·1$$
$$\overline{\text{Correct declination} \quad 22 \;\; 55·2 \text{ S.}}$$

(Declination is decreasing; correction is subtracted).

Example 2.—Find the correct declination of the Sun at 19 h. 21 m. 48 s. G.M.T. on October 9th.

$$\text{Decl. Oct. 9th, 19 h.} = 6° 17·1' \text{S.} \quad (d = 1·0')$$
$$\text{Corr. for 21 m.} \quad = \quad 0·4$$
$$\overline{\text{Corr. declination} \quad 6 \;\; 17·5 \text{ S.}}$$

(Declination is increasing; correction is added).

To Correct Declination when Sun is Crossing Equinoctial.—On September 23rd the Sun, which is in North declination, is approaching the equinoctial at its greatest rate of change, its declination *decreasing* 1' every hour. A few minutes after 13 hours on that day its centre actually crosses the equinoctial. The declination then is zero, and changing to South—*increasing*.

In the *Nautical Almanac* the change-over appears thus:

$$\text{13 hrs. Decl. } 0° 00·2' \text{ N.}$$
$$\text{14 hrs. Decl. } 0° 00·8' \text{ S.}$$

To find the difference in one hour, it has to be remembered that in this case the Sun has moved in declination from $0° 00·2'$ N. to zero, and from zero to $0° 00·8'$ S. From Fig. 71 it can be seen that the total amount of change in the hour is $1·0'$, to obtain which result the declinations at the two separate hours have to be ADDED.

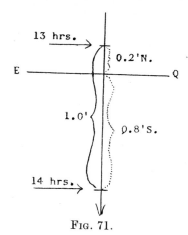

FIG. 71.

The same effect takes place on Spring Day, between 03 hrs. and 04 hrs., when the Sun's declination changes from South to North.

WHEN THE SUN'S DECLINATION IS CHANGING NAME, AND AT NO OTHER TIME, THE "DIFFERENCE IN 1 HOUR" IS FOUND BY ADDING THE TWO DECLINATIONS. It will be found that the difference at these times is always 1·0', or very nearly so.

It is also important to remember that the correction taken from the Table of Increments and Corrections must always be SUBTRACTED from the first of the two declinations.

If this correction is smaller than the value of the actual declination at the earlier of the two hours, the corrected declination retains its name—N. or S., as the case may be. If however the correction is larger than the value of the declination, the subtraction is performed "upside-down", and the corrected declination is then named opposite to the declination at the earlier hour. A few examples will make this clear.

Example 3.—Find the correct declination of the Sun at 13 h. 06 m., G.M.T. on September 23rd.

Decl., September 23rd, 13 h   =00° 00·2′ N.
Corr. for 6 m. at 1·0′ per hour=   0·1   (decreasing)

Corr. Decl., 13 h. 06 m. =00   00·1 N.

Example 4.—Find the correct declination of the Sun at 13 h. 12 m., G.M.T. on September 23rd.

Decl. Sept. 23rd, 13 h.   =00° 00·2′ N.
Corr. for 12 m. at 1·0′ per hour=   0·2   (decreasing)

Corr. Decl., 13 h. 12 m.   =00   00·0

Example 5.—Find the correct declination of the Sun at 13 h. 36 m., G.M.T. on September 23rd.

Decl. Sept. 23rd, 13 h.   =00° 00·2′ N.
Corr. for 36 m. at 1·0′ per hour=   0·6

Corr. Decl., 13 h. 36 m.   =00 00·4 S.

In the above example, the declination decreased 0·2′ to zero after 12 minutes, and in the remaining 24 minutes *increased* to 0° 0·4′ S. declination.

It is now possible to co-ordinate all that has been learned in this chapter, to obtain the correct G.H.A. and declination of the Sun at any time in any longitude, whether the time given is expressed as L.A.T., L.M.T., or G.M.T.

Example 1.—Find the correct G.H.A. and declination of the Sun on June 13th, at 05 h. 32 m. 21 s. G.M.T. in long. 28° 26′ W.

(Although longitude is given here, it is not required, as G.M.T. is also given).

G.M.T. June 13th, 05 h. G.H.A. =255°	03·3′	Decl. =23°	10·9′ N.
Increment, 32 m. 21 s.	8	05·3	Corr.	0·1 +
Correct G.H.A.	263	08·6	Decl. 23	11·0 N.

Example 2.—Find the correct G.H.A. and declination of the Sun on January 3rd, at 18 h. 16 m. 33 s. L.M.T. in long. 33° 10′ W.

(Apply longitude in time to L.M.T. to obtain G.M.T., then proceed as in Example 1).

L.M.T.   18h 16m 33s
Long. in time   + 2 12   40

G.M.T. 20 29 13

G.M.T., Jan. 3rd. 20 h. G.H.A. =118°	51·0′	Decl. =22°	48·7′ S.
Increment 29 m. 13 s.	= 7	18·3	Corr. −	0·1
Correct G.H.A.	126	09·3	Decl. 22	48·6 S.

Example 3.—Find the correct G.H.A. and declination of the Sun on December 22nd, at noon L.A.T. in long. 35° 24′ E.

L.A.T. Dec. 22nd	12h 00m 00s		Eq. T., Dec. 22nd, 00h=01m 47s (−A.T.)		
Longitude E.	− 2	21	36	12h=01	32
G.A.T.	09	38	24	Diff. in 12 hrs.	= 15
Eq. T. (−A.T.)	1	35			
G.M.T.	09	36	49	Diff. in 10 hrs.=12 sec.	
				Corr. Eq. T.= 1m 47s−12s	
				= 1m 35s	

G.M.T., Dec. 22nd, 09h G.H.A. =315° 23·7'   Decl. =23° 26·5' S.
    Increment 36m 49s   9   12·3   Corr.   0·0

        Correct G.H.A.   324   36·0   Decl.   23   26·5 S.

(First apply the longitude in time to L.A.T. to obtain G.A.T. Find the correct Eq. T. for G.A.T. to the nearest hour. Apply this to G.A.T. to obtain G.M.T. Then proceed as before).

Example 4.—Find the correct G.H.A. and declination of the Sun on October 7th, L.A.T. 02 h. 17 m., in long. 50° 43' W.

L.A.T., Oct. 7th, 02h 17m 00s   Eq. T., 00h   11m   54s   (−A.T.)
Long. in time + 3 22 52   Eq. T., 12h   12   02

G.A.T.   05 39 52   Diff. in 12h   8

Corr. Eq. T.   −   11 58   Diff. in 6h   4 sec.

G.M.T.   05 27 54

G.M.T., Oct. 7th, 05h G.H.A. 257° 59·4'   Decl. 5° 17·9' S.
Increment, 27 m. 54 s.   6   58·5   Corr.+   0·5

Correct G.H.A.   264   57·9   Decl. 5   18·4 S.

Exercise 21.

Find Correct G.H.A. and Declination of the Sun.

	Date	Time			Long.	
1.	Jan. 2nd			Noon, L.A.T.	19°	23'W.
2.	June 12th			Noon, L.A.T.	21	06 W.
3.	July 22nd			Noon, L.M.T.	51	51 W.
4.	July 15th	16h	28m	G.M.T.	36	19 E.
5.	Oct. 8th	21	57	L.A.T.	26	44 W.
6.	Dec. 21st	05	57	L.M.T.	6	18 E.
7.	Sept. 24th	01	28	L.A.T.	15	37 W.
8.	July 17th	10	02	L.A.T.	37	18 E.
9.	Oct. 7th	21	39	G.M.T.	40	07 W.
10.	June 14th	10	33	L.A.T.	14	43 E.
11.	July 23rd	18	18	L.M.T.	25	08 E.
12.	Jan. 3rd	02	10	L.M.T.	20	43 W.
13.	Dec. 23rd	17	50	L.A.T.	41	28 W.
14.	Oct. 9th	03	27	G.M.T.	00	00
15.	July 16th	19	08	L.A.T.	19	27 W.
16.	Jan. 1st	16	00	L.A.T.	7	20 E.

The Importance of Time at Sea.—The student may be tempted to think that the importance of minutes and seconds of time is being exaggerated. It will be seen later, however, that when out of sight of land at sea, a ship's position can be found with accuracy only when Greenwich Mean Time, correct to within one second, is available.

The actual time which is used on board individual vessels at sea depends a great deal on the vessel's trade, the distance to be travelled, etc. Local Apparent Time was very generally used by great numbers of ships. Nowadays, because of the ease with which ships can obtain G.M.T. by wireless signals, L.A.T. is used less. Local Mean Time to a large extent is taking the place of L.A.T.

Vessels engaged in the Home Trade routes and fishing vessels fishing in "home waters" usually stick to G.M.T., or to British Summer Time when that is being used ashore. Many warships and Atlantic liners use "Zone Time."

Zone Time.—For the purpose of Zone Time, the world is considered to be divided into 24 longitudinal compartments, each of 15° (1 hour). Zone 0 lies between long $7\frac{1}{2}$° E. and $7\frac{1}{2}$° W. To the eastward, where local time is fast of G.M.T., the twelve compartments, from $7\frac{1}{2}$° E. to $22\frac{1}{2}$°E., etc., are numbered Zone −1, Zone −2, etc. To the westward of $7\frac{1}{2}$° W., they are numbered Zone +1, Zone +2, etc.

In regions where the limits of the compartments cross the land, the areas of the zones are modified where necessary, to agree with boundaries of states or countries which use the same zone times.

Why Ship's Time has to be Altered at Sea.—Imagine yourself on board a ship on the Equator on Spring Day.

At 6 a.m., just at sunrise, the vessel commences her voyage, steering West. During the next 24 hours, let us say she steams 300 miles.

On the equator, 300 miles is equal to 5° of arc. As each degree equals 4 minutes of time, the vessel has thus steamed 20 minutes of time to the west of the position she had left at sunrise the previous day. Thus, on completion of 24 hours' steaming, the Sun would not be due to rise until 6·20 a.m., ship's time. In order to show correct apparent time, the clock would require to be retarded 20 minutes, thus lengthening the day by that amount.

If the vessel were able to continue to steam 300 miles to the westward each day throughout the voyage, the clock would require to be retarded 20 minutes each day. By the time the ship had completed circumnavigating the world, and arrived back at her original starting-point, the clock would have been retarded a full 24 hours, and the ship would appear to be one full day behind the calendar.

If the voyage had been performed to the eastward, the clock would have required to be *advanced* each day, thus shortening the length of the day, and at the end of a round-the-world voyage, that vessel would be one day ahead of reckoning.

The International Date Line.—In order to preserve the correct date on board ships which are circumnavigating the earth, one day has to be dropped at some part of the voyage when steaming westwards, or one day has to be added when steaming eastwards. The natural place for this to happen is half-way round the world from the meridian of Greenwich.

By coincidence, or by providence, there is very little inhabited land lying on the 180th meridian, so this meridian, with only slight deviations, is used internationally as the longitude where ships change date. The vessel steaming West comes to midnight on, say the 10th of a month, and calls the next day the 12th. The vessel steaming East comes to midnight on the 10th, but to her the next day is still the 10th. The first vessel had been in West longitude on the 10th, (+12 hrs. to obtain G.M.T.) Next day she is in East longitude (—12 hrs. to obtain G.M.T.)

CHAPTER 18.

TO FIND DEVIATION OF THE COMPASS BY AMPLITUDE OF THE SUN.

Compass Bearings of Celestial Bodies.—During a voyage, the deviation of a ship's compass may alter from a variety of reasons. Change of latitude, alteration of the ship's course, rolling of the ship, etc., all contribute towards making deviation an elusive and changeable quantity. Every opportunity should therefore be taken to verify the deviation of the compass. Given clear skies, compass bearings of celestial bodies can be taken at any hour of the day or night. The methods by which the deviation of the compass can be found by such bearings involve two different problems.

The first of these is called the "Amplitude" problem.

Definition.—The amplitude of a heavenly body is the angle between the true East point of the compass and the object when rising, or between the true West point and the object when setting.

Thus amplitudes of the Sun can be observed only when that body is just rising, or just setting, and at no other time.

It should be noted that amplitude bearings are restricted more or less to the Sun, the Moon, and, perhaps on exceptionally clear nights, to two large planets. Amplitudes of stars can practically never be observed, as they are rarely visible when their altitudes are less than 4° or 5° above the horizon.

The practical part of the operation consists of taking a bearing of the body at rising or setting, using an "azimuth mirror" on a standard compass, or using a pelorus. This bearing is then compared with the true bearing of the body, which is found by calculation. This is, in the case of the Sun, the true bearing of the Sun's centre when it is on the horizon, its altitude then being 0°.

Before the Sun's rays reach the Earth, they have travelled through numerous layers of atmosphere of varying densities. During that journey, they have been bent upwards by "refraction." (See also Chapter 21.) The amount of refraction varies with the body's altitude, being at its greatest when the body's altitude is least.

A "Table of Refractions" is included in all nautical tables. In *Norie's* it is found on page 168. In *Burton's* it is given on page 115. From either of these tables it can be seen that refraction for altitude 0°=33', which is practically the angle at the Earth's surface between the top and the bottom of the Sun. This is more usually stated as "the angle between the Sun's Upper Limb and its Lower Limb." At rising or setting, the Sun appears too high by that amount, so that to obtain a bearing at the time the centre is actually just on the horizon, the observer must take the bearing when the Sun appears to be *half its own height* above the horizon, as in Fig. 72.

FIG. 72.

A very important point to remember is that in the amplitude problem, and *in that problem only*, the compass bearing must not be read as, say, N. 75° E., but as E. 15° N. The bearing of the Sun obtained by calculation is the angle between the East or West point of the compass and the Sun, and the observed bearing must be expressed in the same way. The use of the 3-figure notation in this problem is not recommended, as it would serve to complicate matters.

In the problem, the time may be given as (a) G.M.T., (b) L.M.T., or (c) L.A.T. In the case of (a), the Sun's declination is corrected for that G.M.T. In the case of (b), apply longitude in time to L.M.T., to convert it to G.M.T. In the case of (c), convert L.A.T. into G.M.T. by the rules already given in Chapter 17, page 203.

Care should be taken to notice whether ship's time is a.m. or p.m. If given as 6 a.m., it is written as 06h 00m 00s. But if it is given as 6 p.m., it is written as 18h 00m 00s.

To Calculate the True Amplitude.—The elements required in the problem are the latitude—given in the question—and the Sun's declination, corrected for the G.M.T. of the problem.

The log secant of the latitude is added to the log sine of the corrected declination. The result is the log sine of the true amplitude. The two logs are ALWAYS added, whether the latitude and the declination have the same or different names.

When the value of the true amplitude has been found, it is named according to the following rule—

Prefix "E" if a.m., or if the Sun is rising. Prefix "W" if p.m., or if the Sun is setting. After it, affix *the same name as the declination.*

Thus far, the problem would be set down as follows:—

Example 1.—Find the true amplitude of the Sun when rising on December 21st, G.M.T., 10h 36m in lat. 55° 00′ N., long. 33° 15′ W.

Decl. at 10h., Dec. 21st	23° 26·3′ S.	Lat. 55°	L. sec	0·24141
Corr. for 36m.	0·0	Dec. 23° 26·3′	L. sin	9·59963

Correct Decl.	23 26·3 S.	L. sin true amp.	9·84104

True Amp. E. 43° 54·4′ S.

Notes:
1. The true amplitude is named East because the Sun is rising. It is named South because the declination is South.
2. When using *Norie's Tables*, the secant appears as 10·24141, and the L. sin of the true amplitude is therefore 19·84104. The "10" from the index number of the log is dropped, leaving 9·84104.

To Find Compass Error and Deviation.—Compass error and deviation are found from the true amplitude as calculated, and from other information which must be given in the question. In actual practice at sea, this information is found from (1) the observed compass bearing of the rising (or setting) Sun; and (2) the variation as given at the ship's position on the chart.

For the example worked above, the full question would read:—
On December 21st, G.M.T., 10h. 36m., in Lat. 55° 00′ N., long, 33° 15′ W., the Sun was observed to rise bearing S. 35° E. by compass (or 145° C.). Find the true amplitude and the error of the compass, and supposing the variation to be 16° W., find also the deviation of the compass for the direction of the ship's head.

The true amplitude is calculated as above. Underneath this is written the observed amplitude. In the question, this is given as S. 35° E., but to conform to the true amplitude, it must be expressed as the number of degrees from EAST, i.e., E. 55° S. (90°—35°=55°)

If both true and observed amplitudes are named North or both South, obtain the difference between them by subtracting the smaller from the greater. If on the other hand one is named North and the other South, add them. The result is the total compass error.

True Amp.   E. 43° 54·4′ S.
Obs. Amp.   E. 55 00·0 S.
_____
Error   11 05·6

Like variation and deviation, compass error is named simply East or West. To find the correct name, draw a rough cross in the margin of the page, marking the four points N., S., E., and W. On this sketch draw the *relative* positions of the true and the observed bearings, as in Fig. 73.

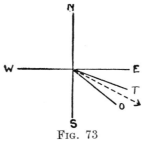

FIG. 73

If the observer then imagines himself to be standing in the centre of the compass, looking outward between the two bearings, in the direction of the arrow in the sketch, the error will be named East if the true bearing lies to the right of the observed bearing. If true lies to the left of the observed, the error will be named West. This rule can be easily remembered by using the word TROE.

T(rue) to the
R(ight) of
O(bserved) it's
E(ast).

In the example above, the true bearing lies to the LEFT of the observed, so the error is named West.

Finally, write the variation—given in the question—underneath the error. The rule as to whether these two are to be added or subtracted is the same rule as was used with the true and the observed amplitudes —if both have the same names, subtract them; if they are of different names, add them. The result is the deviation of the compass.

To Name the Deviation.—When the total error is smaller in value than the variation, and they have the same name—in other words, if error and variation have to be *subtracted "upside-down"*—the deviation is named opposite to the error. In all other cases, deviation is named the same as the error.

The completion of the example given above appears as follows:—

True amp.	E. 43° 54·4′ S. ⎫	
Obs. Amp.	E. 55 00·0 S. ⎭	Both S. Subtract.

Error	11 05·6 W. ⎫	
Var.	16 00·0 W. ⎭	Both W. Subtract.

Deviation	4 54·4 E.

Using the rule given above, deviation is named opposite to the error.

The correctness of the answer can be checked very simply. Compass error is a combination of variation and deviation. In the example above, if we had named the deviation West, the error would be 21° W. (Var. 16° W.+Dev. 5° W.=21° W.) Therefore the deviation can only be named East.

Special Cases.—When the Sun is very close to the equinoctial, with a declination close to 0°, it rises at 6 a.m., and sets at 6 p.m., no matter what the observer's latitude is. At these times, its true bearing is 090° when rising, 270° when setting.

When the observer's latitude is 0°, the true amplitude has the same value as the Sun's declination.

Example 2.—On October 8th, L.A.T. 06h. 35m. in lat. 58° 17′ N., long. 11° 06′ E., the Sun rose bearing by compass E. 10° S. Var. 8½° W. Required the true amplitude, error and deviation of the compass.

L.A.T.	06h 35m 00s	Lat. 58° 17′ N.	sec	0·27925
Long. —	44 24	Dec. 5 41·5	sin	8·99640

G.A.T.	05 50 36	Sin true amp.		9·27565

Eq. T. —	12 16	True Amp.	E. 10° 52·4′ S.

G.M.T.	05 38 20	Obs. Amp.	E. 10 00·0 S.

Decl.	5° 41·5′ S.	Error	0 52·4 E.
		Var.	8 30·0 W.

		Dev.	9 22·4 E.

Example 3.—On June 12th, L.M.T. 18h. 51m. in lat. 25° 11′ N., long. 67° 47′ W., the Sun set bearing 313° C. Var. 20° 15′ W. Required the true amplitude, error and deviation of the compass for the direction of the ship's head.

L.M.T.	18h 51m 00s	Lat. 25° 11′	sec	0·04337
Long. W.	+ 4 31 08	Dec. 23 10	sin	9·59484

G.M.T.	23 22 08	Sin true amp.	9·63821

Decl.	23° 10·0′ N.	True Amp.	W. 25° 46·0′ N.
		Obs. Amp.	W. 43 00·0 N.

		Error	17 14·0 W.
		Var.	20 15·0 W.

		Dev.	3 01·0 E.

Sunrise, Sunset and Twilight.—The tables of Sunrise, Sunset and Twilight have already been described on p. 201. The times listed in the *Nautical Almanac* for these phenomena in various latitudes is L.M.T. When required, interpolation can be performed mentally with ease. If the G.M.T. of Sunrise or Sunset is required—as, for instance, to calculate the correct declination or the G.H.A. of the Sun—longitude in time is applied to L.M.T. in the usual way.

The times for both civil and nautical twilight are listed. It will be remembered that civil twilight lasts from sunset until the Sun is 6° vertically below the horizon, or from the time the Sun is 6° vertically below the horizon until sunrise. Civil twilight is the space of time . during which, under normal conditions, the horizon at sea is sufficiently visible to be used when taking celestial observations.

Nautical twilight is the space of time which elapses from the time the Sun is 6° vertically below the horizon until it is 12° vertically below the horizon.

Example 1.—Find the G.M.T. of Sunrise on December 22nd, in lat. 56° N., long. 19° 21′ W.

From Table.

L.M.T. Sunrise, lat. 56° N.	08h 30m 00s
Longitude W.	+ 1 17 24
G.M.T. of Sunrise	09 47 24

Example 2.—Find the G.M.T. of Sunset on July 23rd, in lat. 51° 30 N., long. 81° 33′ W.

From Table.

L.M.T. Sunset, lat. 51½° N.	20h 04m 00s
Long. W.	+ 5 26 12
G.M.T. Sunset, July 24th	01 30 12

Example 3.—Find the time and duration of civil twilight on the evening of June 12th, in lat. 29° N.

From Table

Time of Sunset	19h 00m
Time of civil twilight	19 27
Duration of twilight	27m

EXERCISE 22.

	Date		Time	Lat.	Long.	Obs. Amp.	Var.
			h m	° ′	° ′	°	°
1.	Jan.	1	07 19 L.A.T.	40 13 N.	32 30 W.	E. 43 S.	16 W.
2.	Oct.	8	06 17 ,,	43 22 N.	8 13 W.	E. 22 S.	12 W.
3.	July	16	20 18 ,,	54 11 N.	11 27 E.	W. 38½ N.	3¼ W.
4.	Dec.	21	18 37 ,,	17 22 S.	61 33 E.	S. 47 W.	16 E.
5.	June	13	06 50 L.M.T.	28 41 S.	47 30 W.	063	5 E.
6.	July	23	05 08 ,,	31 42 N.	18 48 W.	E. 16 N.	12½ W.
7.	Sept.	24	17 56 ,,	18 55 N.	19 31 E.	S. 77 W.	7½ E.
8.	Jan.	3	21 23 G.M.T.	5 33 S.	46 15 W.	230	8 E.
9.	Dec.	23	07 24 ,,	38 29 N.	02 43 W.	S. 57 E.	9 W.
10.	July	16	04 38 ,,	52 19 N.	10 16 W.	E. 25 N.	11½ W.

11. On July 17th, in lat. 31° 42′ N., long. 37° 35′ W., the Sun rose bearing by compass East. L.A.T. 05h. 02m. Find the true amplitude and error of the compass, and if the variation was 20° W., find also the deviation of the compass for the direction of the ship's head.

12. On September 23rd, in lat. 45° N., on the prime meridian, at 0600 L.M.T., the Sun rose bearing by compass S. 75° E. If the variation was 12½° W., find the deviation of the compass for the direction of the ship's head.

13. On October 9th, in lat. 33° 25′ N., long. 50° 22′ W., the Sun rose bearing 119° C. L.A.T. 06h. 13m. If the variation was 22° W., find the deviation of the compass.

14. On December 21st, in lat. 34° 28′ N., long. 43° 26′ E., G.M.T. 03h. 39m., the Sun rose bearing by compass E.S.E. Var. 2° E. Required the true amplitude, error and deviation of the compass for the direction of the ship's head.

15. On June 14th, in lat. 52° 20′ N., long. 14° 19′ W., the Sun was observed to set bearing 318° C. G.M.T. 21h. 23m. 16s. Find the deviation of the compass for the direction of the ship's head, supposing the variation to be 13° W.

16. On January 3rd, in lat. 53° 16′ N., long. 17° 52′ W., L.M.T. 15h. 54m., the Sun set bearing 248° C. The variation being 14° W., find the compass deviation.

17. On July 22nd, L.M.T. 07h. 14m. in lat. 40° 09′ S., long. 72° 15′ E., the Sun rose bearing 038° C. If the variation was 16° E., find the deviation of the compass.

(In the remaining examples, the student should find the L.M.T. of sunset or sunrise from the appropriate table in the daily page of the *Nautical Almanac*, and thence the G.M.T., from which time the correct declination is found.)

18. On September 23rd, in lat 56° 39′ N., long. 11° 46′ E., the Sun rose bearing by compass N. 88° E. Find the true amplitude, and if the variation was 7° W., find also the deviation of the compass.

19. On January 1st, in lat. 43° 09′ N., long. 28° 40′ W., the Sun was observed to rise bearing S. 38° E. by compass. The variation being 14½° W., find the deviation of the compass for the direction of the ship's head.

20. On July 15th, on the equator in long. 84° E., the Sun set bearing 282·5° C. If the variation at that place was 15° 20′ E., find the true amplitude and the deviation of the compass.

CHAPTER 19.

TO FIND DEVIATION BY TIME AZIMUTH OF THE SUN.

Definition.—The Azimuth of a heavenly body is the angle at the observer's zenith between the observer's meridian and a vertical circle through the body's centre.

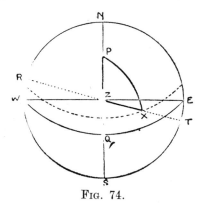

FIG. 74.

In Fig. 74, Z is the observer's zenith. NS is a meridian drawn through this point. P is the elevated pole, WQE, the equinoctial, and X the position of the Sun on its circle of declination. RT is a "vertical circle" through X. The angle PZX in the sketch represents the true bearing, or azimuth, of X.

As was explained in the previous chapter, the Amplitude problem is used only when finding the deviation of the compass at sunrise or sunset.

To find the deviation of the compass at any other time when the Sun is visible, the "azimuth" problem is used. In this problem, the observer requires to know the values of three items, or arguments. These are:

      (1) Latitude of observer;
      (2) Declination of Sun;
      (3) Local Apparent Time or Local Hour Angle of the Sun.

In an examination, time may be given as L.A.T., G.M.T., or L.M.T.

219

Methods of Finding Sun's True Azimuth.—There are two methods in general use in practical navigation for finding the Sun's true bearing, or azimuth.   These are—

By A.B.C. Tables (*Norie's* or *Burton's*)
By Time Azimuth Tables.

Each of these methods needs a different approach, and each is discussed separately.   The arguments required for each method also differ, and at this stage it is recommended that the student should choose one method, and stick to that, leaving the other method till a later period.

Time Azimuth by A.B.C. Tables.

Both in *Norie's* and in *Burton's* Tables, G.M.T. is required in order to find G.H.A. and declination of the Sun.

(1) **G.M.T. Given.**—Find the correct declination of the Sun, and also its G.H.A.   To this latter, apply the longitude (West—, East+) in order to find the L.H.A. of the Sun.   This is the angle required when entering the A.B.C. Tables.

(2) **L.A.T. Given.**—Find G.M.T. from L.A.T. as has already been explained in Chapter 17, page 203, and then proceed as described in (1) above.

(3) **L.M.T. Given.**—Convert this to G.M.T. by applying longitude in time (West+, East—), and proceed as described in (1) above.

The A.B.C. Tables, whether *Norie's* or *Burton's*, are in three parts —"A" and "B," which, when combined produce the value of "C."

In *Norie's* (1957 edition) they are given on pp. 532—580.   In *Burton's*, (Fifth Edition, 1955), they occupy pp. 242 to 315 (Tables 29 and 30).

In Table A the arguments required are the body's L.H.A. and the observer's latitude.   In Table B, the arguments are the L.H.A. and the body's declination.

Except for small differences—which will be noted in due course— Tables A and B are practically similar in both books.   Thus the description of A and B in *Norie's Nautical Tables* which follows can be taken as covering the same Tables in *Burton's*, with the exceptions noted.

(1) By Norie's Tables.

The Hour Angles in *Norie's* A and B Tables are given in arc only. They are the body's Local Hour Angles, and L.A.T. is not required. The G.H.A. Sun is found from the *Nautical Almanac* in the usual way, using G.M.T.   To G.H.A., longitude in arc is applied to obtain L.H.A. When the hour angle of a celestial body is small, its bearing changes rapidly.   In the Tables, values of L.H.A. in A and B are given for every 15' of arc (every minute of time) until L.H.A. is 15° (1 hour). From 15° to 30°, values are given for every 30' of arc, and thereafter for every 1°. When the body's true bearing is in the first or fourth quadrant of the compass, it is found at the top of the page—0° to 90° reading the pages in *ascending* numerical order, 270° to 360° in *descending* ORDER. Bearings for the second and third quadrants are given at the foot of the page—second quadrant read in *descending* order, third quadrant in *ascending* order.

Both A and B tables require the same Hour Angle, and are printed on adjoining pages—A, on the left-hand pages, B on the right. This arrangement saves turning over pages. On each page of A the Rule for naming the correction is given—always named opposite to the latitude unless L.H.A. is between 090° and 270°, and read from the foot of the page. Similarly the Rule for naming B is given on each right-hand page—named the same as the declination *under all conditions*.

If A and B are both named N. or both S., they are added. If they are of different names, the smaller is subtracted from the larger, and the result—"C"—is named the same as the larger.

Table C follows immediately after the A and B Tables. In it, the combined values of A and B are tabulated across the top of the page, the latitudes being given in the first and last vertical columns of each page. The true bearing of the body for each particular value of C is given in the body of the table abreast the appropriate latitude. It will be found that in all the three tables, interpolation has usually to be used.

Example 1.—Find the Sun's true azimuth in lat. 36° N., L.H.A. (E) 49°, decl. 12° N.

Turn to the appropriate page (546) of Table A. Follow the column headed 49° down the page until, about halfway down, latitude 36° is reached. A is found to have a value of ·63. Latitude being North, A = ·63 S.

On the adjoining page, follow the 49° column downwards to the level of decl. 12°. The value of B is ·23. Declination being North, B = ·23 N.

$$\left. \begin{array}{l} A = ·63 \text{ S.} \\ B = ·23 \text{ N.} \end{array} \right\} \text{ Different names, subtract.}$$

$$C = ·35 \text{ S.} \quad \text{A is larger; C is named S.}$$

Turn to Table C, and look for ·35 along the top or bottom. Follow that column till abreast of latitude 36°, and the true bearing of the Sun is given as 74·2°, or 74° 12'.

This bearing, following the Rule quoted at the foot of each page of Table C, is named S. because C is South. It is named E. because L.H.A. is East.

Example 2.—L.H.A. Sun is 43°.   Sun's declination is 21° N.   Find the true azimuth in lat. 50° N.

$$A=1·28 \text{ S.}   \text{(Opposite to latitude).}$$
$$B= ·56 \text{ N.}   \text{(Same as declination)}$$

$$C= ·72 \text{ S.}   \text{(Named same as greater)}$$

True bearing, S. 65·2° W. or S. 65° 12′ W.
S. because C is South.
W. because L.H.A. is West.

Example 3.—Find the true bearing of the Sun in lat. 46° 35′ N., decl. 18° 13′ N., L.H.A. 35° 30′. (W).

In this problem, there are odd minutes of arc in all three arguments, therefore interpolation must be carried out.

L.H.A. in the Table is given for 35° and 36°.   The given L.H.A. is half-way between these, while the latitude is almost half-way between 46° and 47°.   At the appropriate place, Table A reads—

	35°	36°	
Lat. 46°	1·48	1·43	The mean is 1·48
Lat. 47°	1·53	1·48	

To find the mean between the four entries used above, split the difference between *any* two entries, reading diagonally as shown above. There is no difference between the two readings chosen, and the required answer is 1·48.

If the other two entries of these four had been chosen instead, the answer would have been—

$$\frac{(1·53+1·43)}{2} = 1·48$$

At the appropriate place, Table B, on the adjoining page, reads—

	35°	36°	(L.H.A.)
Decl. 18°	·57	·55	Mean = ·58
Decl. 19°	·60	·59	

Then—

$$A=1·48 \text{ S.}$$
$$B= ·58 \text{ N.}$$

$$C= ·90 \text{ S.}$$

In Table C, Lat. 46°, this value gives true azimuth 58·0°.
        Lat. 47°, ,,   ,,   ,,   ,,   ,,   58·5°.
Difference in azimuth for 1° of latitude=·5°, or 30′.   Interpolation is required for 35′ (·6°) of latitude.

$$30′ \times ·6 = 18′.$$

Sun's true bearing in lat. 46° 35′ N.=S. 58° 18′ W.

Example 4.—Find the true azimuth of the Sun in lat. 16° 40′ N., L.H.A. 53° 30′ W., decl. 21° 25′ S.

		53°	54°			53°	54°
Table A	Lat. 16°	·22	·21	Table B	Decl. 21°	·48	·47
	Lat. 17°	·23	·22		Decl. 22°	·51	·50

A = ·22 S.
B = ·49 S.

C = ·71 S.

Table C	(C)	(C)
	·70	·72
Lat. 16°	55·8	55·1
Lat. 17°	56·3	55·6

True azimuth = S. ·55° 42′ W.

(Note the method to use when interpolation is required both for latitude and value of C.)

(2) By Burton's Tables.

(Students who use *Burton's Nautical Tables* should read the description of the *A* and *B Tables* which appear in *Norie's* (see pp. 220 to 221) before continuing here.

In *Burton's*, the A and B Tables give Local Hour Angles both in arc and, at the top of the page only, in time. They are given for every 15′ of arc—every minute of time—for all hour angles from zero to 30° (2 hours of time). From 30° to 60° (2 hours to 4 hours) they are given for every 30′ (2 minutes) and thereafter for every 1° (4 minutes). The Rules for applying signs are different from the Rules used in *Norie's*, but, like them, they are given at the top of each page of the Table. If the value of the L.H.A. in arc has to be taken from the top of the page, the sign of A is +. If taken from the foot of the page, the sign is —. The sign of B depends on whether latitude and declination are of the same name (—), or are of different names (+).

If both A and B are +, or both —, they are added to obtain the value of C, and the sign of C is the same as both A and B. If they have different signs, they are subtracted, and C is given the same sign as the greater.

In Table C, latitudes are given in the vertical columns on the right and left side of each page. The value of C is looked for in the body of the Table, and the required azimuth—to the nearest half-degree—is given at the top of the page. In most cases, it will be found that interpolation is necessary to arrive at the true value of the azimuth.

It is of great importance to note that if the body's Hour Angle is being read *in TIME*, the time used is *LOCAL APPARENT TIME*. If the Hour Angle is being read in arc, *LOCAL MEAN TIME* must be used. Students are advised to use Hour Angles in arc, as this saves work and minimises the chances of mistakes.

The Rules for naming the true azimuth are given at the top of each page in the C Table.

Example 1.—Find the true azimuth of the Sun in lat. 50° N., decl. 21° N., L.H.A. 43° (2h. 52m.)

In the *A* and *B* Tables, find the appropriate L.H.A., and follow down the page to the level of latitude 50°. The value of A is found to be 1·28. The L.H.A. was taken from the top of the page, so the sign is +.

In the same way, follow down the L.H.A. in Table B to the level of declination 21°. B is given as ·563. Latitude and declination both being North, the sign is —.

$$A= 1\cdot28+ \atop B= \cdot563-\}\quad \text{Contrary names} -$$

$$C= \underline{\cdot717+}\quad \text{(Sign of the greater)}$$

In Table C, on the level of latitude 50°, follow across the page to find ·717.

This value is not given exactly. It lies between the given values of ·725 (az. 65°) and ·709 /az. 65½°). The true azimuth is therefore between 65° and 65½°.

Disregarding decimals, the difference between the two given values (725 and 709) is 16. The difference between the larger (725) and the required value (717) is 8. The true azimuth is 8/16 (½) of the way between 65° and 65½°, e.g., 65° 15′. A handy way of performing this operation is as follows:—

	Az. 65°	Az. 65½°	
Lat. 50°	·725	·709	Diff.=16.
Required "C"	·717		

Diff. 16) 80(·5 of 30′=15′

Explanation.—Find the difference between the two values of C— one just larger, one just smaller than the given value, (16). Under the larger one, write the given value, and subtract (8). Add a cipher to this, and divide by the 16. The result is the decimal fraction of 30′ which is to be added to the azimuth with the lower value.

According to the Rule given at the top of the page, the azimuth (H.A. less than 180° in North latitude) is named S. and W.

True bearing, S. 65° 15′ W.

Example 2.—In lat. 37° N., Sun's decl. 13° N., L.H.A. 53° (15h. 32m.), find the Sun's true bearing.

Table A—Lat. 37°, L.H.A. 53°, corr. is   ·568+

Table B—Dec. 13°, L.H.A. 53°, corr. is   ·289—

$$C = \text{·279+}$$

Table C—Lat. 37°, the appropriate values are ·289 and ·278.

Az. 77°	Az. 77½°	
·289	·278	Diff. 11
·279		

Diff. 11) 100(·9 of 30′=27′.
    True azimuth S. 77° 27′ W.

Very usually it is necessary to use interpolation in the A and B Tables for all three arguments—latitude, declination, and L.H.A. In Example 3, below, the necessary working is performed first, and the full explanation is given after each step.

Example 3.—In lat. 32° 18′ N., Sun's decl. 18° 36′ N., L.H.A. Sun 319° 40′, find the Sun's true azimuth.

The L.H.A., being in the 4th quadrant, appears at the top of the page, the H.A. values increasing *from right to left*, thus—

	L.H.A. 320°	L.H.A. 319½°
Lat. 32°	·745	·732
Lat. 33°	·774	·760

Similarly, in Table B, the appropriate readings are—

	L.H.A. 320°	L.H.A. 319½°
Dec. 18°	·505	·500
Dec. 19°	·536	·530

			Diff. *Prop.**	*Corr.*	*Result*
"A" (Lat. 32°, H.A. 319½) = ·732 + 12 = ·744+	{	H.A. 13 × 0·3=3·9+			
		Lat. 28 × 0·3=8·4+ }		12·3+	
"B" (Dec.18°, H.A. 319½°) = ·500+19·5 = ·520−	{	H.A. 5 × 0·3=1·5+			
		Dec. 30×0·6=18·0+ }		19·5+	

$$\text{"C"} = \text{·224+}$$

Explanation.—The given L.H.A. (319° 40′) is ⅓ (0·3) of the way between 319½° and 320°, The difference in the "A" values of these angles in Lat. 32° is 13, which, multiplied by the required *"proportion"* (prop.) gives 3·9. Values of "A" are increasing between 319½° and 320°, so the correction is +. Similarly, the given latitude (32° 18′) is 0·3 of the way between latitudes 32° and 33°. The differences in

"A" values between these latitudes in the $319\frac{1}{2}°$ column is 28, increasing. This, multiplied by prop. 0·3, gives a correction of 8·4 to add. Both corrections are+, so the result—the total correction to the original ·732—is 12+. True "A" is therefore ·744.

Exactly the same procedure is carried out in Table B, using the arguments of declination and L.H.A. The H.A. difference is 5, increasing, the proportion, as before, being 0·3. Correction=1·5+. Declination difference is 30 increasing, the declination proportion (36′)=0·6. This gives correction 18·0. The result is a total correction of 19·5, or 20, to add to the original ·500. True "B" is thus ·520.

A is+, B is—. Subtract them to obtain C, naming this+, the same as the greater.

In Table C, we must interpolate again. First find the true azimuth for lat. 32°, and then find it again for lat. 33°.

Az. 79° Az. $79\frac{1}{2}°$

Lat. 32°   ·229 ·219 Diff. 10
        ·224

Diff 10) 50(·5 of 30′=15′ True Azimuth 79° 15′
Lat. 33° ·232 ·221 Diff. 11
     ·224   Diff. 6′

Diff. ·11) 80(·7 of 30′=21′ True Azimuth 79 21

The difference of the Sun's true bearing for 1° of latitude is 6′. What is the difference in its bearing between latitudes 32° and 32° 18′ =0·3°?

Answer=·3 of 6′=1·8′ or 2′, to add to true bearing at lat. 32° True bearing=S. 79° 17′ E.

The above problem seems very complicated when accompanied by the full explanation, but after a few examples have been worked carefully, step-by-step, it becomes surprisingly simple and straightforward.

Example 4.—Find the true bearing of the Sun in lat. 45° 12′ N., decl. 11° 42′ S., L.H.A. 47° 15′.

	Diff. Prop. Corr.	*Result*
"A" (Lat. 45°, H.A. 47°) = ·933− 2=·931+	H.A. 17 × ·5 = 8·5 − Lat. 33 × ·2 = 6·6 +	1·9 −
"B" (Dec. 11°, H.A. 47°) =.266+ 17=·283+	H.A. 2 × ·5 = 1·0 − Dec. 25 × ·7 =17·5 +	16·5 +

C=1·214 +

"C" — Lat. 45°   (No interpolation needed)   49° 30'⎫
     Lat. 46°   (No interpolation needed)   50   00 ⎭

Diff. for 1° lat.   30' × ·2=6'.
True azimuth=S. ·49° 36' W.

Example 5.—Find the Sun's true azimuth in lat. 52° 25' N., decl. 14° 40' S., L.H.A. 305° 11'.

		Diff.	*Prop.*	*Corr.*	*Result*

"A" (Lat. 52°, H.A. 305°) = ·896+18= ·914+ ⎰ H.A. 17 × ·3= 5·1+ ⎱ 18·3+
                                  ⎱ Lat. 33 × ·4=13·2+ ⎰

"B" (Dec. 14°, H.A. 305°) = ·304+17= .321+ ⎰ H·A. 2 × ·3= 0·6+ ⎱ 16·7+
                                  ⎱ Dec. 23 × ·7=16·1+ ⎰
               "C"   =1·235+

=1·24

C—Lat. 52°   1·25   1·25
          1·22   1·24

            3   )   10(·3 of 30'=   9' True Az.   =52° 39'⎫
Lat. 53°   1·25   1·25
          1·23   1·24

           2   )   10(·5 of 30'=15' True Az.   53   15 ⎭

Diff. for 1° =   36' ×.4
                    =14·4'
True Azimuth=52° 39'+14'
                =S. 52° 53' E.

(3) By Time Azimuth Tables.

(1) **Davis's Alt-Azimuth Tables.**—These are the Tables provided in the examination rooms, and they cover all cases between—

      Latitudes   30° to 64°, N. or S.;
      Declinations   0° to 24°, N. or S.

As the name implies, these Tables give both the azimuth and the altitude of any heavenly body whose declination is less than 24°.

Latitude is given for every degree, four separate pages being required for each degree. Declination is also given for every degree, in vertical columns—declination 0° to 12° on the left-hand pages, and 12° to 24° on the right-hand pages.

Ship's apparent time is tabulated in the first and last vertical columns on each page, the hours being shown in Roman numerals (V, VI, VII, etc.) and time is listed for every 4 minutes, except in some cases near noon, when it is given for every two minutes. The azimuth of a body alters more rapidly when it is near the meridian. Apparent

Time A.M. is shown in the left-hand columns, Apparent Time P.M. in the right-hand columns.

Every alternate line, reading across the page, is in somewhat heavy type, the others being in relatively light type. The lines in *light* type are the azimuths. The lines in heavy type are the altitudes, which are not required for our present purpose, and can therefore be entirely disregarded. Thus azimuths are ordinarily given for every 8 minutes of time.

The azimuths given in the first part of the book are those of bodies when latitude and declination have the same names. When latitude and declination are of different names, these azimuths are in the latter part of the book.

A few minutes' study of the book is strongly advised in order to gain facility in handling the Tables.

When following the changes in the Sun's true bearing throughout the day, from sunrise to sunset, start at the *foot* of the first left-hand column—headed "App. TIME A.M."—on page 3 of the required latitude if the declination does not exceed 12°, or on page 4 if the declination does exceed 12°. Time increases *upwards* to the top of the page. Then turn back to the *previous* page (either page 1 or page 2 of the required latitude) and read that page upwards till noon is reached at the top of the page. Then transfer across to the right-hand vertical column on the same page—headed "App. Time P.M."— and commence to read downwards, continuing on pages 3 or 4 till sunset.

This appears complicated, but in actual practice it rapidly becomes perfectly simple to read and easy to follow.

All particulars for the examples worked by Time Azimuth Tables in this book have been taken from *Davis's Alt-Azimuth Tables*. It will be noted that in the book, bearings are given in degrees and decimal fractions of a degree. The student will find his work made easier and more accurate if he converts the decimal fractions to minutes of arc by multiplying by 6.

It should also be noted that answers in the examination room are required to within a degree of accuracy of half-a-degree.

(2) **Burdwood's Azimuth Tables.**—The Table reproduced in the appendix of this book is from *Burdwood's Azimuth Tables*, which are used at sea more generally than *Davis's Tables*. Altitudes are not given, and the azimuths are calculated for every 4 minutes of time. Another difference lies in the fact that bearings are given in degrees and minutes of arc, instead of in degrees and decimals. This is not only easier but leads to greater accuracy. Students who work from the Table in the appendix may find that some of their answers will differ slightly from the results given, owing to these facts. They should not find any difficulty in negotiating the slight differences between

the two sets of tables if it is remembered that the normal time interval in *Davis's* for azimuths is 8 minutes, while in *Burdwood's* it is 4 minutes. It should also be noted that in *Burdwood's*, azimuths for "Lat. & Dec. Contrary Names" for every separate degree of latitude follow immediately after "Lat. & Dec. Same Names" of the same latitude.

Some of the Time Azimuth Tables now published give the Local Hour Angles of heavenly bodies in arc, instead of using Local Apparent Time. When that is so, intervals of time if 4 minutes are, of course, replaced by intervals of arc of 1°.

When working from either Alt-Azimuth or from Time Azimuth Tables in which Local Apparent Time is used, G.M.T. is also required to correct the Sun's declination. The method of dealing with time depends on the particulars available.

(1) **L.A.T. Given.**—Use this time without change in the Tables. G.M.T. is obtained from L.A.T. as has been explained in Chapter 17, page 203, and this is used to correct the Sun's declination-

(2) **G.M.T. Given.**—Use this time only to correct the declination. To find L.A.T., reverse the order of applying corrections in (1) above, thus—

$$
\begin{array}{ll}
\text{G.M.T.} & \text{..........} \\
\text{Eq. T. } (\pm\text{M.T.}) & \text{————} \\
\text{G.A.T.} & \text{..........} \\
\text{Long. (E.+W.--)} & \text{————} \\
\text{L.A.T.} & \text{========}
\end{array}
$$

(3) **L.M.T. Given.**—This must be converted to G.M.T. for use when correcting the declination, and also for obtaining the correct Eq. T. It must also be converted to L.A.T., required for entering the Tables. The following lay-out of work is advantageous—

L.M.T.	....		L.M.T.	....
Long. (E.--W.+)	....		Eq. T.	....
G.M.T.	....		L.A.T.	....

Example 1.—Find the true azimuth of the Sun at 10.16 a.m., L.A.T. in Lat. 52° N., given Decl. 19° N.

Open the Tables at Lat. 52°, Lat. same name as Decl.

The time is A.M., so look in the first vertical column on the left-hand side of the page (declination exceeding 12°) and follow up or down the page till X hrs. 16 m. is reached.

The line abreast of this, across the page, is in light type, showing that the figures give the values of Azimuths. Follow this line across till the vertical column headed 19° is reached. The azimuth is found to be 138·6°, or 138° 36'.

Instructions as to the naming of the azimuth are found at the foot of the page. These read—

In North Latitude, if time is A.M., name Azimuth N. and E.;
if time is P.M., name Azimuth N. and W.

The true azimuth is therefore N. 138° 36′ E.

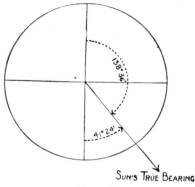

SUN'S TRUE BEARING

FIG. 75.

Subtract this from 180° and it is seen that N. 138° 36′ E.=S. 41° 24′ E.

Example 2.—Find the true azimuth of the Sun at 2.32 p.m., L.A.T. in Lat. 52° N., given declination 15° N.

The time is P.M., so is found in the right-hand vertical column on the right-hand page, the declination exceeding 12°. The azimuth is seen to be 126° 30′, and is named North because the latitude is North, and West, because the time is P.M.

Answer—N. 126° 30′ W., or S. 53° 30′ W.

Example 3.—Find the true azimuth of the Sun at 10.48 a.m. L.A.T., in Lat. 52° N., when the declination is 22° N.

Answer—N. 148° 18′ E., or S. 31° 42′ E.

These three examples demonstrate the problem in its simplest form. More usually, latitude and declination contain odd minutes of arc, and often, too, the given L.A.T. lies somewhere between two times listed in the Tables. In these cases, "interpolation" has to be carried out for each argument which contains odd minutes.

Example 4 (a).—Find the true azimuth of the Sun at 10.48 a.m., L.A.T. in Lat. 52° N., when the declination is 13° N.

The answer is found to be N. 153° 00′ E.

Let the above question now be altered to read—

Example 4 (b).—Find the true azimuth of the Sun at 10.48 a.m., L.A.T., in Lat. 52° N., when the declination is 13° 45′ N.

Here the declination is between 13° and 14°, so that interpolation is required for declination.

First find true azimuth for Lat. 52° N., Dec. 13° N., L.A.T. 10.48, exactly as before. (N. 153° 00′ E.)

Next, to the right of this, write the same figures again and below them write the true azimuth for Lat. 52° N., *Dec.* 14° *N.*, at 10.48, thus:—

Corr. for dec.
13° N. = 153° 00′
14 N. = 152 36

Diff. for 1° of decl. = — 24 (decreasing).

Then, since the azimuth decreases 24′ for a difference of 1° in declination, for a difference in declination of 45′ (=·75°) it must decrease ·75 of 24′= 18′. In this way, the proportional decrease due to the odd minutes of declination is found. The whole problem thus far would be written as follows:—

Az. for Lat. 52° N.,			*Corr. for dec.*		
Dec. 13° N.,		=N. 153° 00′ E.	Dec. 13° N.	= 153°	00′
10.48 L.A.T.					
Correction		= — 18 E.	Dec. 14 N.	= 152	36
Corrected Azimuth		=N. 152 42 E.	Diff.		— 24
				×	·75
			Prop. Diff. =		— 18

Example 4 (*c*).—Find the true azimuth of the Sun in Lat. 52° 18′ N., at 10.48 L.A.T., when the declination is 13° N.

In this case, interpolation is required for the odd minutes in the latitude.

As before, write down the true azimuth for Lat. 52° N., Dec. 13° N., at 10.48, and, to the right of this, find the correction for 18′ lat. (=·3°.)

Azimuth	N. 153° 00′ E.		*Corr. for lat.*	
Corr.	+ 9 E.	Lat. 52°	= 153°	00′
		Lat. 53	= 153	30
Corr. Azimuth	N. 153° 09′ E.			
		Diff. for 1° lat. + 30 (increasing).		
		× ·3		
		Prop. Diff. + 9		

Example 4 (*d*).—Find the true azimuth of the Sun at 10.53 a.m., L.A.T., in Lat. 52° N., declination 13° N.

In this case, the time in the original question has been altered. In the Table, the true azimuth is given for 10.48 and for 10.56. The time for which the azimuth is required is 10.53, which is 5/8 (·6) of the way between the two listed times. Therefore the correction to the azimuth given at 10.48 will be ·6 of the difference between the azimuths at 10.48 and 10.56.

Azimuth	N. 153° 00′ E.		*Corr. for time*
Corr.	+1 44	10.48	= 153° 00′
		10.56	= 155 54
Corrected Az.	N. 154 44 E.		
		Diff.	+ 174 (incr.)
			× ·6
		Prop. Diff.	+104·4

Analysing these last four examples, it can be seen that in every case the start was made from the same basic azimuth—N. 153° 00′ E.—and that each separate correction has been applied to that azimuth. So, if a question contains interpolations for ALL arguments—latitude, declination, and time—the same basic azimuth is used for each.

Thus it becomes a simple matter to correct each element separately, and afterwards to apply the total correction to the basic azimuth in one operation.

The same example as has been used above can be used to illustrate this:—

Example 4 (*e*).—Find the true azimuth of the Sun at 10.53 a.m., L.A.T., in Lat. 52° 18′ N., when the declination is 13° 45′ N.

As before, the azimuth for Lat. 52°, Dec. 13° (same names), L.A.T. 10.48, is 153° 00′.

Corr. for lat.		*Corr. for dec.*		*Corr. for time.*	
52°	= 153° 00′	13°	= 153° 00′	10.48	= 153° 00′
53	= 153 30	14	= 152 36	10.56	= 155 54
Diff.	+ 30		− 24		+ 174
	× ·3		× ·75		× ·6
Corr.	+ 9·0		− 18·0		+104·4

Combine the three corrections, according to their signs—

$$(+9·0+104·4)−18·0=+95·4=+1° 35·4′$$

Azimuth	N. 153° 00′ E.
Tot. Corr.	+1 35·4
Corr. Az.	N.154 35·4E.

Example 5.—Find the true azimuth of the Sun at 2.07 p.m., L.A.T., in Lat. 52° 43′ N., Decl. 12° 35′ N.

Basic Az.	N. 137° 48′ W.		Corrections for		
Corr.	−2 03·1		*Lat.*	*Dec.*	*Time*
			137° 48′	137° 48′	137° 48′
Corr. Az.	N. 135 44·9′ W.		138 24	137 12	135 24
			+ 36	− 36	− 144
			× ·7	× ·6	× ·88
		Corr.	+ 25·2′	− 21·6′	−126·7′

$(-21·6-126·7)+25·2=-123·1=-2°\ 03·1'$.

Answers to the nearest minute of arc are generally sufficiently accurate.

Hour Angles.—It is very probable that future editions of the Time Azimuth Tables will show "Hour Angles" instead of L.A.T., and that these Hour Angles will be expressed in arc instead of in time.

So far as the Sun is concerned, its H.A. is simply the time from apparent noon. Thus—

L.A.T. 09h 30m = H.A. 2h 30m East.
08 22 = 3 38 East.
14 18 = 2 18 West.

Hour angles can be converted from Time to Arc in the usual way or by using a special table appearing on page 379, *Norie's Tables*.

EXERCISE 23.
Finding True Azimuth.

	Lat.	Decl.	L.A.T.	L.H.A.
1.	52° 00′ N.	15° 00′ N.	9.20 a.m.	320° 00′
2.	52 00 N.	18 00 N.	10.24 a.m.	336 00
3.	52 00 N.	21 00 N.	12.26 p.m.	006 30
4.	52 00 N.	12 00 N.	2.32 p.m.	038 00
5.	53 00 N.	23 00 N.	3.44 p.m.	056 00
6.	53 00 N.	20 00 N.	9.12 a.m.	318 00
7.	52 30 N.	16 30 N.	10.40 a.m.	340 00
8.	52 30 N.	18 30 N.	1.16 p.m.	019 00
9.	52 18 N.	13 48 N.	10.35 a.m.	338 45
10.	52 24 N.	20 54 N.	2.29 p.m.	037 15
11.	52 12 N.	17 24 N.	1.51 p.m.	027 45
12.	52 42 N.	12 12 N.	9.27 a.m.	321 45
13.	52 36 N.	19 42 N.	2.47 p.m.	041 45
14.	52 06 N.	21 18 N.	9.55 a.m.	328 45

The following examples of the full problem are worked out:

(a) By *Norie's A.B.C. Tables*;
(b) By *Burton's A.B.C. Tables*;
(c) By *Davis's Alt-Azimuth Tables*.

The slight differences which appear in the respective methods should be noted. Students are again advised to choose one particular method, and should stick to it, disregarding the others.

Example 1.—On June 14th, at 15h. 22m. 05s. L.M.T. in lat. 32° 30′ S., long. 100° W., the Sun was observed to bear 287° C. Find the true azimuth, error and deviation of the compass for the direction of the ship's head, supposing the variation to be 27° E.

	h. m. s.		h. m. s.
L.M.T., June 14th	15 22 05	L.M.T.	15 22 05
Long. W. +	6 40 00	Eq. T. (—M.T.)	08
G.M.T., June 14th	22 02 05	L.A.T.	15 21 57

Dec. 22h.	23° 16·4′ N.
Corr.	Nil.
Corr. Dec.	23 16·4 N.

G.H.A Sun, 22h.	149° 57·9′
Increment	31·3
Corr. G.H.A.	150 29·2
Long. W.—	100 00·0
L.H.A. Sun	50 29·2

(*a*) By *Norie's A.B.C. Tables.*

A. (Lat. 32° 30′ S., L.H.A. 50° 30′) = ·53 N.
B. (Dec. 23 16 N., L.H.A. 50 30) = ·56 N.

C = 1·09 N.

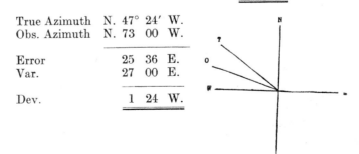

True Azimuth	N. 47° 24′ W.
Obs. Azimuth	N. 73 00 W.
Error	25 36 E.
Var.	27 00 E.
Dev.	1 24 W.

(*b*) By *Burton's A.B.C. Tables.*

A. (Lat. 32° 30′ S., L.H.A. 50½°) = ·525+
B. (Dec. 23 16 N., L.H.A. 50½) = ·556+

$$C = 1·081+$$

True Azimuth Lat. 32° = N. 47° 30′ W.
                  Lat. 33° = N. 47 45 W.*

Lat. 32½° = N. 47 37 W.
Obs. az.   N. 73 00 W.

Error   25 23 E.
Var.   27 00 E.

Dev.   1 37 W.

* In lat. 33°, "C" (1·08) is halfway between 47° 30′ and 48° 00′ =47° 45′.

(*c*) By *Alt-Azimuth Tables.*

T. Az. (Lat. 32°, Dec. 23°, L.A.T. 15h 20m=132° 30).

Lat. corr.   Dec. corr.

Lat. 32° = 132° 30′   Dec. 23° = 132° 30′
Lat. 33° = 132 42   Dec. 24° = 133 12

Diff. = 12   Diff. = 42
        × · 5   × ·25

Corr.   6+   Corr.   10·5+

Az. from Table 132° 30°
Tot. corr.   +   17

True Az.   S. 132 47 W.

True Az. N. 47° 13′ W.
Obs. Az. N. 73 00 W.

Error   25 47 E.
Var.   27 00 E.

Dev.   1 13 W.

Example 2.—On July 16th, at 14h 42m L.A.T. in lat. 35° 20′ S., long. 157° 30′ E., the Sun bore 333° C. Var. 16° W. Required the true azimuth, error and deviation of the compass for the direction of the ship's head.

	h	m	s		G.H.A. 04h,	238°	31·8′	Dec. 04h	21° 27·6′ N.
L.A.T., 16 July,	14	42	00	Increment		4	28·3	Corr.	−	·1
Longitude E.	−10	30	00						

				Corr. G.H.A.	243	00·1	Corr. Dec.	21 27·5 N.
G.A.T.	04	12	00	Long E.	+ 157	30		
Eq. T. (+ A.T.)		5	53					
					400	30		
G.M.T. 16 July,	04	17	53		− 360			

L.H.A.   40   30

(a) By *Norie's A.B.C. Tables.*

Table A—Lat. 35° ·82 }
        Lat. 36° ·85 } Mean for Lat. 35° 20′ = ·83 N.

Table B—Dec. 21° ·60 }
        Dec. 22° ·62 } Mean for Dec. 21° 27′ = ·61 N.

C=1·44 N.

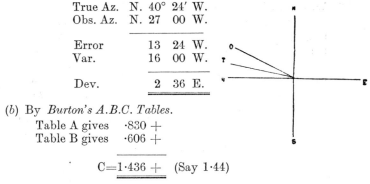

True Az. N. 40° 24′ W.
Obs. Az. N. 27   00 W.

Error   13 24 W.
Var.   16 00 W.

Dev.   2 36 E.

(b) By *Burton's A.B.C. Tables.*

Table A gives ·830 +
Table B gives ·606 +

C=1·436 + (Say 1·44)

Lat. 35° —C=40°20′ }
Lat. 35½°—C=40 40 } Mean for 35° 20′=40° 27′

True Az. N. 40° 27′ W.
Obs. Az. N. 27   00 W.

Error   13 27 W.
           16 00 W.

Dev.   2 33 E.

(c) By *Alt-Azimuth Tables.*

			Lat. corr.		
Lat. 35°	}	139° 36′	35°	= 139°	36′
Dec. 21°		— 4	36	= 139	48
L.A.T. 14·40			Diff.		12
			×		·3
			+		3·6

Dec. Corr.			*Time corr.*		
21°	=139° 36′		14h. 40m.	=139°	36′
22	=140 12		14 48	=137	54
Diff.	36		Diff.		102
	× ·5			×	·25
+	18·0		—		25·5

True Az.	N. 40°	32′	W.
Obs. Az.	N. 27	00	W.
Error	13	32	W.
Var.	16	00	W.
Dev.	2	28	E.

Tot. corr. $(+3·6+18·0)-25·5=-3·9$

Supplementary Methods of Finding Compass Deviation.

The deviation of the compass can also be found easily and quickly by the following methods:—

(1). **A Bearing of the Sun at Noon.**—In latitudes north of 24°N., the Sun at noon always bears true South. The difference between this true bearing and the bearing observed by compass gives compass error. Apply variation to the error, as shown in the examples above, and the result is the deviation. (The full explanation of the methods used to name Error and Deviation is given on page 215.)

Example 1.—The Sun at noon bore S. 11° W. (191°) by compass. The variation was 14° W. Find the deviation of the compass.

True bearing	180°
Obs. bearing	191
Error	11 W.
Var.	14 W.
Dev.	3 E.

I

Example 2.—In a high northern latitude the Sun at noon bore by compass S. 5° E. (175° C.) From the chart, variation was 3° E. Find the deviation of the compass.

True bearing	180°
Obs. bearing	175

Error	5 E.
Var.	3 E.
Dev.	2 E.

2. A Bearing of the Sun at Rising or Setting, Using Tables.—Tables

giving the TRUE AMPLITUDES of the Sun at rising or setting are given in *Norie's Nautical Tables* (pp. 582—583), and in *Burton's Nautical Tables* (pp. 238—241). When using these Tables, two important points must be remembered—

(*a*) An AMPLITUDE is the angle between the true East point and the bearing of the Sun when rising, or between the true West point and the bearing of the Sun when setting. The angle must not be measured from North or South.

(*b*) The compass bearing of the Sun should be taken when the body is half its own height above the horizon. (See Chapter 18, page 212).

Example 3.—In latitude 50° N., when its declination was 20½° N., the Sun was observed to rise bearing by compass N. 67° E. Variation 12° W. Find the deviation of the compass.

(Using *Burton's Tables*). True amplitude=E. 33° N. (E. because the Sun is rising. N. because the declination is North).

True Amp.=E. 33° N. True bearing	=N. 57° E.
Obs. bearing	=N. 67° E.

Error	10 W.
Var.	12 W.
Dev.	2 E.

Example 4.—In latitude 42½° N., when the declination was 11° N., the Sun set bearing by compass 300°. Variation 11° W. Find the deviation of the compass.

True Amp.=W. 15° N. True bearing	N. 75° W.
Obs. bearing	N. 60 W.

Error	15 W.
Var.	11 W.
Dev.	4 W.

3. **A Bearing of the Pole Star at any Time.**—The Pole Star is situated very close to the true North Pole of the heavens, circling round the "celestial pole" at an angular distance of about 1° from it. Thus a bearing of the star at any time provides a good *approximate* deviation.

Example 5.—From a position where the variation was 6° E., the Pole Star was observed to bear 350° C. What was the approximate deviation of the compass?

True bearing	000°
Obs. bearing	350
Error	10 E.
Var.	6 E.
Dev.	4 E.

Example 6.—The Pole Star bore 017° C. Var. 12° W. Find the approximate deviation of the compass.

True bearing	000°
Obs. bearing	017
Error	17 W.
Var.	12 W.
Dev.	5 W.

4. **A Bearing of Two Known Shore Lights in Line, or "In Transit"**— When two shore navigational lights are in transit—in one line—a compass bearing can be taken of them. The true bearing of the same lights in line can be obtained from a chart of the area.

Example 7.—Two lights, 216° T. in transit, bore 235° C. Var. 16° W. Find the deviation of the compass.

True bearing	216°
Obs. bearing	235
Error	19 W.
Var.	16 W.
Dev.	3 W.

Example 8.—Two lights, 053° T. in transit, bore by compass N. 40° E. Var. 16° E. Find the deviation of the compass.

True bearing 053°
Obs. bearing 040

Error	13 E.
Var.	16 E.
Dev.	3 W.

EXERCISE 24.

(A) Time Azimuth of the Sun.

(NOTE:—With the exception of No. 4, the first 10 problems of this exercise can be worked by using the "Time Azimuth Tables" reproduced at the end of this book. All the problems in the exercise can be worked by using A.B.C. Tables.)

	Date		Time	Lat.	Long.	Obs. Brg.	Var.
			h m	° '	° '	°	°
1.	Jan.	2	09 44 L.A.T.	52 00 S.	5 27 W.	N. 42 E.	5 E.
2.	Dec.	23	12 46 ,,	52 30 S.	43 19 E.	N. 28 W.	11 E.
3.	Jan.	3	14 50 ,,	52 23 S.	16 22 W.	317	18 W.
4.	Oct.	9	13 05 G.M.T.	52 17 N.	37 42 W.	South	27 W.
5.	June	13	14 05 ,,	52 41 N.	5 06 E.	252	10 W.
6.	July	15	12 44 ,,	52 05 N.	31 21 W.	170	24 W.
7.	July	16	13 26 ,,	52 11 N.	0 17 W.	230	18 W.
8.	July	23	11 12 L.M.T.	52 19 N.	58 12 E.	148	9 E.
9.	Jan.	3	09 31 ,,	52 35 S.	29 44 W.	062	10 W.
10.	Dec.	21	10 52 ,,	52 53 S.	87 12 E.	044	18 W.

11. On January 3rd, L.A.T. 08h. 43m. in lat. 46° 23' N., long. 17° 28' W., the Sun bore 145° C. Var. 15° W. Required the true azimuth, error and deviation of the compass for the direction of the ship's head.

12. On October 9th, in lat. 49° 37' N., long. 28° 33' E., L.A.T. 15h. 10m., the Sun bore by compass S. 57° W. Var. 9° W. Required the deviation of the compass.

13. On September 24th, L.A.T. 0705, in lat. 36° 11' N., long. 73° 11' E., the Sun bore East by compass. Var. 13° E. Required the deviation of the compass.

14. On July 21st, in lat. 61° 29' N., long. 34° 51' W., G.M.T. 18h. 32m., the Sun bore by compass N. 79° W. Var. 25° W. Required the true azimuth and deviation of the compass.

15. On June 14th, G.M.T. 10h. 27m., in lat. 56° 06′ N., long. 00° 48′ E., the Sun bore 152° C. Var. 11° W. Required the true azimuth and deviation of the compass.

16. On July 15th, at 16h. 03m., L.M.T., in lat. 49° 49′ N., long. 36° 05′ W., the Sun bore by compass N. 81° W. Var. 22° W. Required the deviation of the compass.

17. At 1300h. G.M.T., on October 7th, in lat. 36° 53′ S., long. 84° 11′ W., the Sun bore by compass East. Var. 8° W. Required the true azimuth and deviation of the compass.

18. On September 22nd, L.M.T. 11h. 18m., in lat. 35° 17′ N., long. 94° 30′ E., where the variation was 10° W., the Sun bore 181·5° C. Required the true azimuth, error and deviation of the compass.

19. On October 9th, L.M.T. 1718 in lat. 38° 19′ N., long, 49° 32′ W., the Sun bore 283° C. Var. 27° W. Required the deviation of the compass.

20. On December 21st, L.M.T. 14h. 51m., in lat. 58° 12′ N., long. 8° 19′ W., the Sun bore 232° C. Var. 15° W. Required the deviation of the compass.

(B) Deviation by Supplementary Methods.

Bearing of the Sun at Noon.

21.	Compass bearing S. 25° W.	Var.	13° W.
22.	S. 11 E.		5 E.
23.	South		5 W.
24.	S. 7 W.		10 W.
25.	S. 20 E.		23 E.

Bearing of the Pole Star.

26.	Compass bearing	N. 17° E.	Var.	12° W.
27.		North		4 W.
28.		N. 8 W.		6 E.
29.		N. 2 E.		3 E.
30.		N. 18 W.		20 E.

Bearing of Lights in Transit

31.	True bearing 103	Obs. bearing	East	Var.	9° E.
32.	282		N. 60° W.		15 W.
33.	139		S. 43 E.		2 W.
34.	211		S. 10 W.		16 E.
35.	010		N. 7 W.		11 E.

Amplitude Bearing of the Sun.

36.	Lat. 47° N.	Decl. 7° S.	Obs. b'rg (rising)	085°	Var.	20° E.
37.	51 N.	10 N.		East		20 W.
38.	55½ N.	19½ N.		050		2 W.
39.	42 N.	22½ N.		069		12 W.
40.	37 N.	13½ N.	(setting)	270		14 E.

CHAPTER 20.

EQUIPMENT FOR "TAKING SIGHTS"—THE SEXTANT—CHRONOMETERS, THEIR CARE AND MANAGEMENT—RATING CHRONOMETER TIMES—TIMEKEEPING AT SEA—ZONE TIMES.

Celestial navigation—position-finding by using altitudes and bearings of the Sun or other heavenly bodies—is only possible if the navigator is provided with the necessary equipment. Four items, in addition to a compass, comprise the bare minimum of necessities. These are—

1. A set of Nautical Tables;
2. *Nautical Almanac* for the current year;
3. A sextant;
4. A chronometer, or chronometer-watch.

The use of the first two items has already been discussed in a previous chapter.

The Sextant.—This instrument enables an observer to measure the vertical angle at his position between the horizon at sea and the object being observed.

Briefly, its essential features consist in the first place of a triangular metal frame, the lower part of which forms part of the circumference of a circle. (See Fig. 76.) For this reason, this part of the instrument is named the "Arc". (*A*).

A mirror (*I.M.*) perpendicular to the frame, whose centre is also the centre of the circle of which the arc is part of the circumference, is attached to a bar (*I.B.*) whose outer end is free to move round the arc. This bar can be securely clamped in place when desired. The arc itself is graduated very accurately to register every degree and every 10′ of arc, from zero to about 120°. The lower part of the bar is expanded to contain a "vernier" (*V*), which enables the observer to read measured altitudes to an accuracy of 10″ of arc. The mirror is called the "Index Mirror", and the bar is called the "Index Bar". A second glass, also perpendicular to the frame of the sextant, consists of half mirror and half plain glass. (*H*). An observing telescope (*G*) is screwed in place in a "collar" fixed to the frame of the instrument.

In use, the sextant is held in the observer's right hand by means of a handle. The observer looks through the telescope, and can then see the horizon through the plain part of the horizon glass (*H*). The clamp screw—behind the vernier—is loosened, and looking in the direction of the object whose altitude is required, the observer moves the index bar (*I.B.*) along the arc till the object, reflected from the

242

index mirror into the horizon glass, can be seen through the telescope, seeming to rest on the horizon, which is visible through the plain half of the horizon glass. The clamp screw is then tightened, and the "tangent screw" (*T*) is turned till the reflection of the object just touches the horizon when the sextant is perfectly vertical. The altitude is then read from the graduations on the arc and the vernier. The tangent screw is provided with a very fine thread on the screw which enables small movements of the index bar along the arc to be made smoothly while the clamp screw remains tightly clamped.

In modern sextants, the index bar clips itself automatically on the arc without the use of a clamp screw, and a "micrometer screw", on

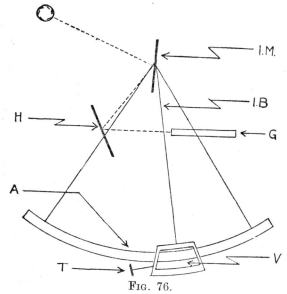

FIG. 76.

which the finer readings of the altitude are graduated, takes the place of the older tangent screw. This type is much easier and quicker to read than the older type, which is being rapidly ousted by the modern variety.

The sextant can also be used to measure the "angular height" at the observer between the horizon and the top of a lighthouse or a hill, and to measure the horizontal angle between different shore objects when finding the ship's position by using terrestrial objects.

Coloured shades of different densities are provided on the sextant to prevent glare from the Sun or from the sea hurting the observer's eye. Those which shade the index mirror are called "index shades", and similarly, the ones which shade the horizon glass are called "horizon shades". These shades are so arranged and hinged that each one can be used separately, or, if required, more than one can be used at the same time, according to the observer's personal inclination.

The sextant is carried in a specially-fitted wooden case, inside which it fits snugly without movement. After use, it should always be returned to its case, and never left lying about, as it is a very finely adjusted instrument, and careless handling could easily upset the adjustments.

Chronometers and Chronometer Watches.—These are expensive timekeepers, very accurately made and adjusted, and so actuated that neither the operation of winding them up, nor the motion of a vessel in a seaway affect their rate. Both require to be carefully handled, and as much as possible they should be kept at an even temperature and wound daily at the same time, by the same person, at the same rate.

Chronometers supplied to merchant vessels are generally of the 2-day (54 hour) or the 8-day types. Both types should be wound daily, the former type requiring about 8 left-handed half-turns of the winding key, the latter type requiring about 4 half-turns.

Winding a Chronometer.—Chronometers are kept in special wooden boxes, fitted with both wooden and glass lids and are slung in gimbals, like a compass, inside the boxes, to neutralise as much as possible the motion of the vessel at sea.

To wind a chronometer, turn it over gently in the gimbal ring, and hold it face down with the left hand. The dust cap at the bottom is opened with one finger of the same hand. The key is then inserted, and the chronometer wound, using the right hand, till the key "butts". Under no circumstances should any force be used.

When the key has been taken out, the dust cap is let go and the chronometer gently turned face up again. On the dial is a small gauge which shows whether the chronometer is wound "UP" or run "DOWN". The gauge should point to "UP".

Chronometer watches have no key, but are fitted with a winding-stem, like an ordinary watch, and the same procedure for winding is required, using this winding stem.

The hands of chronometers should never be shifted, as the time required to be registered is G.M.T.

When received on board ship, chronometers should be stowed in a special place, preferably a box, lined with green baize, in such a manner that, by the provision of a glass top to the box (additional to the wooden top), the box, or locker, does not require to be opened except for the purpose of winding the chronometers.

When more than one chronometer is kept on board they should be compared daily, so that any change in the rate can be detected immediately. Chronometers usually have a half-second tick, and to compare one with another is a simple matter when the tick is used to help.

The accuracy of the chronometer is very important when it is remembered that 4 seconds of time mean a difference of 1′ of longitude·

Finding the Chronometer Error.—Chronometers should be compared with G.M.T. at regular and short intervals.

Generally speaking, very few chronometers keep exact G.M.T., but possess a "daily rate", either losing or gaining, but this rate is always liable to change and various methods are used to "rate" chronometers.

The most modern method is by W/T time signal. These signals can *Wireless Telegraph* be obtained several times daily. The error is then obtained direct, and by applying the error to the reading of the timepiece, G.M.T. is obtained at once. If the chronometer is slow, add the error. If fast, subtract the error.

If W/T is not available, there are *time signals* given at many of the principal ports. These signals usually consist of a ball, hoisted on a staff on a lighthouse, or some other very conspicuous place, the ball dropping down the staff at some known Greenwich time. By comparing the chronometer reading with the Greenwich time of dropping, the error is found.

This error is compared with the last chronometer error found some time before, and the number of seconds which the chronometer has lost or gained in the meantime, divided by the number of days between the two observations, gives the "daily rate" of losing or gaining.

Then, when at any time the exact G.M.T. is required, this last error is applied to the chronometer reading, and the number of days which have elapsed since that error was obtained, multiplied by the "daily rate", gives the "accumulated rate" to be applied to the chronometer time.

1st Method.—When the "daily rate" of losing or gaining is known.

Example 1.—On May 10th, chronometer showed 11 hr. 59 min. 12 sec. On April 16th, chronometer was 3 min. 22 sec. fast of G.M. noon, and was losing 3·6 sec. daily.

First of all, note that when rating chronometers, *Greenwich Mean* NOON is always used. For this purpose, we have to find the number of complete days from NOON on one date to NOON on the other.

In this example, the chronometer time given is practically noon, so we find the number of days from April 16th to May 10th.

(NOTE.—In the *Nautical Almanac*, page 5, the "day of the year" for each calendar date is given. Thus April 16th is the 106th day, and May 10th is the 130th day. Subtracting 106 from 130, we have 24=required number of days.)

In each of these 24 days, the chronometer has been losing 3·6 seconds, so it has lost (24×3·6) seconds=1 min. 26 sec. during that period. This is called the "accumulated rate".

The problem is set down thus:—

		h.	m.	s.
Chron. time	May 10	11	59	12
Error fast		—	3	22
		11	55	50
Acc. rate losing		+	1	26
G.M.T.	May 10	11h 57m 16s.		

Example 2.—Chronometer showed September 11th, 00 hr. 03 min. 16 sec. On July 28th, chronometer was 1 min. 11 sec. slow of G.M. noon, and was losing 2·3 sec. daily.

In this example, the chronometer showed 00 hr. which is midnight. So, then, we cannot take the total number of days to NOON on September 11th, but only the number of days to midnight September 10th-11th.

July 28th (from the *Nautical Almanac*) is the 209th day, September 10th is the 253rd day, so the number of days from NOON, July 28th, to NOON, September 10th, is 44, and to MIDNIGHT, September 10th, is 44·5.

So we have 44·5 days at 2·3 sec. daily=1 min. 42 sec.

		h	m	s
Chron. time	Sept. 11	00	03	16
Error slow		+	1	11
		00	04	27
Acc. rate losing		+	1	42
G.M.T.	Sept. 11	00h 06m 09s		

Example 3.—Chronometer showed November 21st, 03 hr. 11 min. 42 sec. On September 19th, chronometer was 5 min. 15 sec. fast of G.M. noon, and was gaining 2·8 sec. daily.

In this example, the chronometer shows 3 A.M., so that the number of days required is from NOON on September 19th to NOON on November 20th, and thence from NOON on November 20th to 3 A.M. on November 21st, which is 15 hours more.

September 19th is the 262nd day, and November 20th is the 324th day, a period of 62 days and 15 hours.

To reduce hours to a decimal fraction of a day, add a cipher to the hours, and divide by 24, thus

$$24)150(·6$$
$$\underline{144}$$

We now have 62·6 days, with the chronometer gaining 2·8 sec. daily=2 min. 55 sec.

		h.	m.	s.
Chron. time	Nov. 21	03	11	42
Error fast		—	5	15

		03	06	27
Acc. rate gaining		—	2	55

G.M.T.	Nov. 21	03h 03m 32s

Example 4.—Chronometer showed April 19th, 17 hr. 12 min. 51 sec. On February 24th, chronometer was correct at G.M. noon, and was gaining 3·4 sec. daily.

Here the hours of the chronometer time come to 5 hours PAST noon of April 19th.

From noon, February 24th (55th day) to noon, April 19th (109th day) is 54 days, with 5 hours to add to bring it to 17 hours. That is, 54·2 days at 3·4 sec. daily=3 min. 04 sec.

		h.	m.	s.
Chron. time	April 19	17	12	51
Acc. rate gaining		—	3	04

G.M.T.	April 19	17h 09m 47s

Studying Examples 3 and 4, we shall find that, when correcting the chronometer—

(1) When the hours of the chronometer time are LESS THAN 12 we take noon of the day before, and ADD 12 hours to the chronometer hours before we find the decimal fraction of a day.

(2) When the hours of the chronometer time are MORE THAN 12 we take noon of the given day, and SUBTRACT 12 from the chronometer hours before we find the decimal fraction of a day.

2nd Method—When the "daily rate" has to be found.

Example 1.—On July 3rd, the chronometer showed 18 hr. 58 min. 25 sec. On April 4th, chronometer was 2 min. 16 sec. fast of G.M. noon, and on May 15th it was 4 min. 51 sec. fast.

Here we have no daily rate given to us, but we are told the error of the chronometer on two separate dates.

From April 4th to May 15th (41 days), the chronometer has gone from 2 min. 16 sec. fast to 4 min. 51 sec. fast, that is, it had gained 2 min. 35 sec.=155 secs.

To find the number of seconds it gained each day (in other words, to find the daily rate), divide the number of seconds by the number of days. 41)155(3·8 sec. (d.r.) gaining.

123

320
328

With this daily rate, we have now to find the accumulated rate, as previously, from THE DATE OF THE 2ND ERROR TO THE DATE OF THE QUESTION.

		h.	m.	s.
Chron. time	July 3	18	58	25
2nd error fast		—	4	51
		18	53	34
Acc. rate gaining		—	3	07
G.M.T.	July 3	18h	50m	27s

Notes:

(1) The accumulated rate was found from the date of the 2nd error to the date of the chronometer time.

(2) If one error is fast, and the other one slow, *add* the two errors to obtain the number of minutes lost or gained. (See Example 2.)

(3) A chronometer is gaining when it goes from—

SLOW TO LESS SLOW.
SLOW TO FAST.
FAST TO MORE FAST.

It is losing when it goes from—

FAST TO LESS FAST.
FAST TO SLOW.
SLOW TO MORE SLOW.

Example 2.—On August 14th, chronometer showed 05 hr. 16 min. 22 sec. On May 29th, chronometer was 1 min. 09 sec. fast of G.M. noon and on July 3rd it was 1 min. 47 sec. slow.

May 29th to July 3rd=35 days

35)176(5·0 sec. (d.r.) losing
175
———

1 min. 09 sec. fast
1 min. 47 sec. slow
———————————
2 min. 56 sec.=176 sec.

		h.	m.	s.
Chron. time	Aug. 14	05	16	22
2nd error slow		+	1	47
		05	18	09
Acc. rate losing		+	3	29
G.M.T.	Aug. 14	05h	21m	38s

Noon, July 3rd to noon, Aug. 13th=41 days   17 hr.
=41·7 days
× 5
—————
208·5 sec.

= 3 min. 29 sec.

EXERCISE 25.

From the following particulars find Greenwich Mean Time.

1. On September 9th, chronometer showed 11 hr. 14 min. 32 secs. On July 15th, chronometer was correct for G.M. noon, and was losing 3·5 sec. daily.

2. On June 19th, chronometer showed 00 hr. 17 min. 26 sec. On April 2nd, chronometer was 5 min. 44 sec. slow of G.M. noon, and was gaining 2·9 sec. daily.

3. On May 8th, chronometer showed 14 hr. 00 min. 21 sec. On March 3rd, chronometer was 6 min. 17 sec. fast of G.M. noon, and was losing 5·5 sec. daily.

4. On October 19th, chronometer showed 07 hr. 11 min. 29 sec. On August 2nd, chronometer was 12 min. fast of G.M. noon, and was gaining 2·8 sec. daily.

5. On June 10th, chronometer showed 19 hr. 03 min. 45 sec. On March 4th, chronometer was 2 min. 19 sec. fast of G.M. noon, and on April 25th it was 5 min. 22 sec. fast.

6. On December 14th, chronometer showed 10 hr. 27 min. 33 sec. On September 1st, chronometer was 22 min. 31 sec. slow of G.M. noon, and on November 3rd it was 19 min. 52 sec. slow.

7. On April 19th, chronometer showed 05 hr. 12 min. 48 sec. On February 12th, it was 00 min. 35 sec. fast of G.M. noon, and on March 14th it was 1 min. 42 sec. slow.

8. On October 1st, chronometer showed 02 hr. 05 min. 16 sec. On July 10th, chronometer was correct for G.M. noon, and on August 30th it was 3 min. 44 sec. slow.

9. On November 3rd, chronometer showed 22 hr. 32 min. 10 sec. On August 26th it was 2 min. 12 sec. fast of G.M. noon, and on September 30th it was correct.

CHAPTER 21.

LATITUDE BY MERIDIAN ALTITUDE OF THE SUN.

At noon, local apparent time, in any latitude North of the Sun's declination, the Sun bears true South.

At that time, the Sun reaches its highest apparent altitude for the day, and from that altitude, corrected, and from the Sun's declination, the observer's latitude can be found by a comparatively simple calculation.

In Fig 77, the circle represents the "Rational Horizon", which is that horizon that would be seen by an observer situated right at the Earth's centre, if that were possible. The point "Z" is the observer's

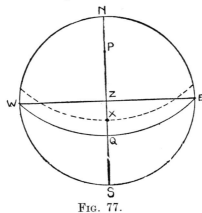

Fig. 77.

zenith, a point in the heavens directly over his head. WQE is the equinoctial—the Earth's equator projected into the sky. The dotted curve indicates the Sun's daily path along his small circle of declination, and the point X, on the same meridian as the observer, is the Sun's position at noon. P is the celestial North Pole.

In the sketch, the observer is in North latitude, represented by ZQ. The declination (XQ) is also North. The Sun's altitude at noon—from the southern horizon to the Sun—is represented by SX. The zenith distance of the Sun is (90°—altitude). Since $SZ=90°$, and $SX=$alt., then $ZX=$zenith distance.

The measurement from the celestial pole to the equinoctial is also 90°.

It can be seen from the figure that
$$ZX+XQ=ZQ, \text{ or}$$
zenith distance+declination=latitude,

provided the declination (N) and the direction X to Z (N) are both the same name.

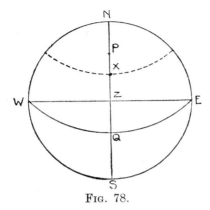

Fig. 78.

In Fig. 78, the declination is North, but the direction X to Z is South. In this case, $XQ—ZX=ZQ$, or
declination—zenith distance=latitude.

The practical part consists of measuring on the sextant the highest altitude reached by the Sun at apparent noon. This altitude is corrected as described below. The corrections are purely mechanical, and after a little practice, their application becomes very simple. The corrected altitude is then subtracted from 90° to obtain the zenith distance. The declination is found by methods described in Chapter 17. Then—Zenith distance $\pm$ declination=latitude.

In the first worked example given below, each step is described and explained very fully. This tends to make the calculation seem more lengthy than it is in actual practice.

The student is advised to go through each step in the calculation separately, checking the figures from the Tables used. He should also grasp thoroughly the *reason* for each correction, to ensure it is not being applied simply by "rule-of-thumb".

Example 1.—On October 8th, in long. 39° 15′ W., the sextant meridian altitude of the Sun's L.L. was 37° 22·5′, bearing South. Index error 5·5′ on the arc. Height of eye 30 ft. Required the latitude by meridian altitude.

The first step in the problem is to find the G.M.T. to the nearest minute, so as to obtain the Sun's correct declination at that time.

At the foot of the appropriate "daily page" in the *Nautical Almanac*, towards the right hand side, the time of the "Mer. Pass." of the Sun is given. This is the L.M.T. that the *Apparent* (or *True*) Sun crosses the observer's meridian in long. 39° 15′ W. To this time, apply longitude in time. The result is the G.M.T. of the Sun's meridian passage

for the particular meridian. The declination is then corrected for that
G.M.T. It cannot be too strongly emphasised that G.M.T. must be
used for all elements taken from the *Nautical Almanac*.

L.M.T. of Mer. Pass., Oct. 8th	11h 48m.	*To convert long. to time*
Long. in time West	+ 2 37	39° 15′ W.
		× 4
G.M.T. of Mer. Pass.	14 25	
		60)157 00
		2h 37m

Decl. at 14h.	5° 49·5′ S.
Corr. (from table)	+ ·4
Corr. Decl.	5 49·9 S.

Index Error.—Index error, the first particular given in the question
for which a correction is required, is an error of the observer's sextant.
The error differs with each sextant. It may be to add, or "off the arc".
It may be to subtract, or "on the arc". There may be no index error,
in which case the question would read "the *observed* meridian altitude"
instead of "the *sextant* meridian altitude".

Sext. mer. alt.	37° 22·5′ S.
Ind. err.	— 5·5
Obs. mer. alt.	37 17·0 S.

Dip.—The next particular given in the question is the height of
the observer's eye above sea level—30 feet.

At sea, the observer (*A* in Fig. 79) sees the horizon, which is the
circle where sea and sky meet. (*VH* in the sketch). This horizon
is called the "visible horizon", and the angle *XAH* is the actual angle
registered on the observer's sextant after eliminating index error.

To all intents and purposes, the observer is "on top of the world"
as he measures the Sun's altitude. Actually the angle *XAH* is not
the angle eventually required, and the next step is to find the amount
of difference made to the observed altitude by the height of the observer's
eye above sea level.

A line from his eye through his feet, and produced, would reach
the centre of the Earth. An imaginary plane drawn through his eye
at right angles to this vertical line provides an entirely imaginary
"SENSIBLE HORIZON", indicated in the figure by *SE*. The angle *EAH*
in the figure is termed the "dip of the sea horizon", and its size alters
as the height of the eye above sea level alters.

From the figure it can be seen that, to eliminate it, the "dip" has to be subtracted. The actual amount of dip for various heights of eye is found in the Nautical Tables. In *Norie's* the Table is on page 169, and in *Burton's* it is Table 9, page 115.

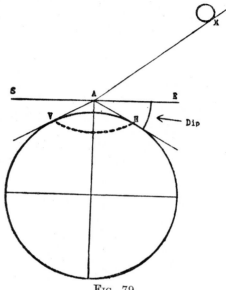

FIG. 79.

Refraction.—The next correction is termed "Refraction of the Atmosphere", or, more simply, refraction.

When a stick is plunged into water at right angles to the surface of the water, no apparent change takes place. But if it is partly immersed at an angle in the water, the stick itself appears to be bent at an angle, as in Fig. 80.

The reason for this apparent distortion is that one part of the stick is in air, while the other part is immersed in a substance of a totally different density from air.

FIG. 80.

Exactly the same effect takes place when a ray of light passes from the Sun to the Earth through countless layers of atmosphere each of a different density. The ray is apparently bent UPWARDS, and the amount of this bend, or "refraction", depends on how obliquely the ray has passed through the atmosphere. The lower the altitude, the greater the obliquity, and the greater the refraction. (See also Chapter 18.)

When the Sun is just rising, the amount of the refraction is at its greatest—33′—which is practically the diameter of the Sun as measured by a sextant on the Earth. As the altitude increases, the refraction decreases, and when the Sun is directly over the observer's head, at an altitude of 90°, refraction is zero.

Since refraction makes altitude appear too high, it must always be subtracted.

In *Norie's Tables*, the Table of Refraction is on page 168. In *Burton's*, it is on page 115, alongside the Table of Dip.

Parallax.—Hold a pencil upright at arm's length in front of the eyes, and close one eye. The pencil is seen to obscure some definite object. Without moving the head or the pencil, open that eye and close the other. The pencil will then obscure some different object. This illustrates "parallax".

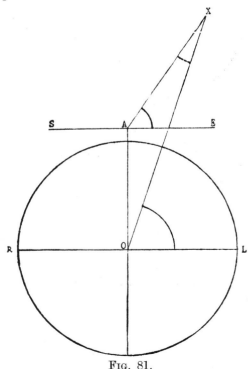

Fig. 81.

In Fig. 81, *XAE* is the Sun's observed altitude after being corrected for dip and refraction.

A plane *RL* through the Earth's centre, parallel to the sensible horizon (*SE*) is called the "rational horizon", and the altitude next required is the altitude of the Sun's Lower Limb (L.L.) above this plane at the centre of the Earth.

The angle *AXO* at the Sun—the angle at the object between the observer and the Earth's centre—represents the measurement of the parallax, which, added to the altitude already obtained, gives the altitude of the Sun's L.L. above the rational horizon.

Parallax, which never exceeds 0·15′ for the Sun, is found on page 169 in *Norie's Tables*, just below the Table of Dip. In *Burton's*, it is Table 14, page 116.

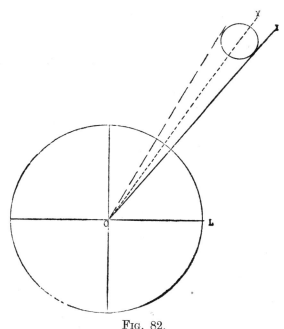

FIG. 82.

Semi-Diameter.—The altitude which has just been found is the *true* altitude of the Sun's lower limb above the Earth's centre, but it is the true altitude of the Sun's *centre* above the rational horizon that is wanted.

The angular measure from the Sun's "upper limb" to its "lower limb" varies slightly according to the Earth's distance from the Sun. The average measure is about 32′. Half of this—16′—is the "semi-diameter", and gives the angular measure to the Sun's centre from either the upper or the lower limb.

The Sun's semi-diameter is given at the foot of the "daily pages" in the *Nautical Almanac*, in the panel headed "Sun".

If the altitude originally measured on the sextant was that of the Sun's L.L., as in the present example (angle *XOL*), then the semi-diameter (*YOX*) must be ADDED to obtain the required angle *YOL*. Had the original altitude been that of the Sun's upper limb (U.L.), then the semi-diameter would have had to be subtracted.

The rule for applying semi-diameter, then, is L.L.+; U.L.—.

These corrections, applied to the original sextant altitude, provide the observer with the Sun's true altitude. In the present problem, the corrections would appear as follows:—

Sext. mer. alt.	37°	22·5′
Index error (I.E.) —		5·5
	37	17·0
Dip (30 ft.) —		5·37
	37	11·63
Ref. (Alt. 37°) —		1·27
	37	10·36
Par. (Alt. 37°) +		·11
	37	10·47
Semi-dia. (L.L.)+		16·00
True Alt.	37	26·47

A knowledge of the reasons for the various corrections is expected from all candidates, and so they have been fully explained above. In actual practice at sea, these separate corrections are shortened into "total corrections". Tables of total corrections are given in *Norie's* and in *Burton's*, are also given inside the front cover of the *Nautical Almanac*. The use of any of these tables is accepted in the examination. (See important note—page 259—with respect to altitudes of the Sun's Upper Limb.)

To use the tables given in the *Nautical Almanac*, first find the correction for Dip, given on the right hand side of the page. The given height of eye—30 ft.—lies between the heights of 29·2 ft. and 30·4 ft., which are listed in the table, and that correction (—5·3′) is used.

The table on the left hand side of the same page combines all the other corrections—refraction, parallax and semi-diameter. Care must be taken to use the correct table for the time of year. "Oct.—Mar."

comes first, "Apl.—Sept." next. Be careful also to note whether the sextant angle is of the Lower Limb or the Upper Limb, as the correction is very different in each case.

In the example given above, the apparent altitude—the sextant altitude corrected for index error and dip—is 37° 11·7'. This lies between two altitudes (36° 20' and 38° 36') listed in the main altitude correction table in the *Nautical Almanac*. The correction which appears between these two—+15·0'—is taken.

The whole of the work would appear thus:—

		37°	22·5'
Sext. mer. alt.		37°	22·5'
Index error	—		5·5
Obs. mer. alt.		37	17·0
Dip	—		5·3
App. alt.		37	11·7
Correction	+		15·0
True alt.		37	26·7

It will be observed there is a small discrepancy between the results given by the different methods, but this is not large enough to be of vital importance.

In Fig. 83, *Z* represents the observer's Zenith. *H* is the horizon, and *O* the observer.

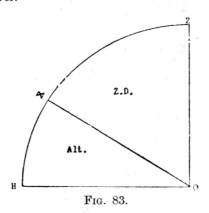

Fig. 83.

The angle *HOX* is the true altitude. This angle subtracted from 90° (angle *ZOH*) leaves angle *ZOX*, the Zenith Distance. Zenith Distance is always named opposite to the bearing of the altitude.

Underneath Z.D., write the Sun's true declination. Then, if both are N., or both S., add them to obtain the latitude, naming this the same as both. If one is N. and the other S., subtract them to obtain the latitude, naming this the same as the greater of the two.

Using the true altitude found by applying the total correction, the last part of the problem is written thus—

True alt.	37°	26·7′ S.
	90	
Z.D.	52	33·3 N.
Decl.	5	49·9 S.
Latitude	46	43·4 N.

NOTE.—When working navigational problems it is often of advantage to draw diagrams, which can be a great help in visualising what is being done.

Example 2.—On July 23rd, in long. 57° 18′ W., the sext. mer. alt. of the Sun's U.L. was 72° 16′, S. of observer. Index error 3·5′ off the arc. Height of eye 22 ft. Required the latitude.

L.M.T., Mer. Pass.	12h 06m	*To convert long. to time*
Long. in time W. + 3 49		57° 18′
		× 4
G.M.T. Mer. Pass.	15 55	
		60)229 12
Decl. at 15 hrs.	20° 06·1′ N.	
Corr. for 55 m. — ·5		3h 49m (to nearest min.)
Correct decl.	20 05·6 N.	

Sext. alt.	72°	16·0′ S.
I.E.	+	3·5
Obs. alt.	72	19·5
Dip	—	4·5
App. alt.	72	15·0
Corr. (U.L.)	—	17·4
True alt.	71	57·6 S.
	90	
Z.D.	18	02·4 N.
Decl.	20	05·6 N.
Latitude	38	08·0 N.

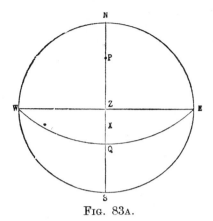

FIG. 83A.

In the sketch, *NESW* represents the rational horizon. *P* is the celestial pole, *Z* the Zenith, *X* the Sun. *WQE* is the equinoctial, *NZS* the observer's meridian, *ZX* the Zenith Distance, *SX* the True altitude, *XQ* the Declination, and *ZQ* the Latitude.

IMPORTANT NOTE.—The altitude corrections for the second example have been taken from the Table given in the *Nautical Almanac*. In these Tables an additional correction for "irradiation effect" is included in corrections for observations of the Sun's Upper Limb. It is not required for observations of the Lower Limb. This correction amounts to—1·2'. It is not included in the total corrections in *Norie's* or *Burton's Tables*, nor is any allowance made for it when separate corrections are made. Throughout this book, altitude corrections from the Almanac are used, and candidates are advised to use them at all times.

EXERCISE 26.

To Find Latitude by Meridian Altitude of the Sun.

1. On September 23rd, in long. 55° 45' W., the sext. mer. alt. of the Sun's U.L. was 23° 42·2' S. Index error 15' to add. Ht. of eye 30 ft. Required the latitude.

2. On October 7th, in long. 94° 17' W., the sext. mer. alt. of the Sun's L.L. was 43° 00', bearing North. Index error 3' to subtract. Ht. of eye 24 ft. Required the latitude.

3. On June 12th, in long. 49° 54' E., the Obs. mer. alt. of the Sun's U.L. was 75° 29·5', bearing North. Ht. of eye 25 ft. Required the latitude.

4. On July 16th, in long. 23° 04' W., the obs. mer. alt. of the Sun's L.L. was 45° 21', bearing North. Ht. of eye 30 ft. Required the latitude.

5. On October 9th, in long. 85° 19' W., the sext. mer. alt. of the Sun's L.L. was 63° 17', bearing S. I.E. 3·5' on the arc. Ht. of eye 16 ft. Required the latitude.

6. On December 21st, in long. 69° 22' E., the obs. mer. alt. of the Sun's L.L. was 81° 30·5', bearing N. Ht. of eye 22 ft. Required the latitude.

7. On January 2nd, in long. 97° 14' W., the obs. mer. alt. of the Sun's U.L. was 42° 13', bearing S. Ht. of eye 41 ft. Required the latitude.

8. On June 13th in long. 6° 34' E., the sext. mer. alt. of the Sun's L.L. was 47° 38', bearing S. I.E. 7' off the arc. Ht. of eye 25 ft. Required the latitude.

9. On September 22nd, in long. 9° 19' W., the obs. mer. alt. of the Sun's L.L. was 69° 31', North of observer. Ht. of eye 15 ft. Required the latitude.

10. On July 22nd, in long. 67° 14' E., the obs. mer. alt. of the Sun's U.L. was 67° 41', bearing S. Ht. of eye 38 ft. Required the latitude.

11. On October 8th, in long. 28° 06' W., the sext. mer. alt. of the Sun's L.L. was 32° 11', S. of observer. I.E. 2·5' off the arc. Ht. of eye 32 ft. Required the latitude.

12. On December 23rd, in long. 00° 00', the obs. mer. alt. of the Sun's L.L. was 66° 45', bearing S. Ht. of eye 28 ft. Required the latitude.

13. On January 1st, in long. 53° 40' W., the obs. mer. alt. of the Sun's L.L. was 68° 09', bearing N. Ht. of eye 36 ft. Required the latitude.

14. On June 14th, in long. 112° 08' E., the sext. mer. alt. of the Sun's U.L. was 74° 47', S. of obs. I.E. 3' on the arc. Ht. of eye 46 ft. Required the latitude.

15. On October 9th, in long. 18° 00' E., the obs. mer. alt. of the Sun's U.L. was 41° 12', bearing S. Ht. of eye 26 ft. Required the latitude.

16. On July 17th, in long. 66° 30' W., the obs. mer. alt. of the Sun's L.L. was 58° 02', S. of observer. Ht. of eye 18 ft. Required the latitude.

17. On September 22nd, in long. 81° 11' E., the obs. mer. alt. of the Sun's L.L. was 68° 22', bearing S. Ht. of eye 33 ft. Required the latitude.

18. On December 21st, in long. 20° 30' W., the obs. mer. alt. of the Sun's L.L. was 28° 51', bearing S. Ht. of eye 22 ft. Required the latitude.

CHAPTER 22.

LONGITUDE BY CHRONOMETER.

In earlier chapters, it has already been stressed that both latitude and longitude must be known in order to pinpoint a ship's position at sea. In Chapter 21, it has been shown that when using an altitude of the Sun, latitude can be found only at, or very near, local noon. On the other hand, an observation of the Sun for the purpose of finding the ship's longitude should be taken some hours before or after noon. The longitude thus found is correct only if the D.R. latitude used in the calculation is correct, or if the true bearing of the body at the time of observation is East or West. The methods used to combine the two observations in order to fix the ship's true position at noon are discussed in Chapter 23.

When a ship carries on board a chronometer or a chronometer watch, Greenwich Mean Time, to an accuracy of one or two seconds, is readily obtainable. At any desired G.M.T., the G.H.A. of the Sun or of any celestial body used for navigation is obtained from the *Nautical Almanac*. The difference between the G.H.A. of the body and its L.H.A. is the observer's longitude. It is necessary, therefore, in the first place to find the L.H.A. of the body.

In the case of the Sun, it might be thought that if G.M.T. were noted when the Sun was on the observer's meridian, the longitude could be found, since at local noon, L.H.A. Sun is zero. The argument is sound, but it has one insurmountable objection.

It will be remembered that, when dealing with longitude, one second of time=15″ of arc, or ¼′ of longitude. So that 4 seconds of time=1′ of longitude.

Even under the best conditions, it is not possible to judge to within a few seconds the exact instant when the Sun reaches the meridian. When the meridian altitude of the Sun is not high, it is not easy to judge the time of its meridian passage to within a few minutes. Therefore a longitude obtained by these means would be utterly unreliable. A separate problem must be worked to find the longitude.

The Practical Part.—In the case of the Sun, the practical part of the operation consists of observing the sextant altitude of the body between 3 and 5 hours before or after it reaches the meridian. At the same instant, the chronometer time is noted to the nearest second, usually by a person other than the observer.

261

The ideal time to take the observation is when the Sun is on "the prime vertical," either a.m. or p.m.   That is, when it bears either true East or true West.   Under these conditions any error in the estimated latitude used in the problem causes least error in the computed longitude.   (See Chapter 23, page 280.)   It is not always possible to obtain these conditions, but generally speaking an altitude taken within the time limits mentioned above gives very satisfactory results.   Altitudes should never be taken when the Sun is less than about 7° above the horizon.

The Haversine.—In Fig. 84, OA and OD are radii of a circle.   Being constant in value, that value can be said to be 1.

$$\text{The cosine of angle } O = \frac{\text{adj.}}{\text{hyp}} = \frac{OB}{OA} = \frac{OB}{1} = OB.$$

BD in the figure represents the *Versine* of the angle.   It can be seen that its value$=OD-OB$, or 1—cosine of angle.

The haversine is HALF THE VERSINE, or

$$\frac{1-\cos \text{ angle}}{2}$$

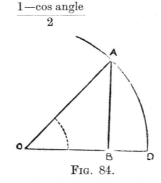

Fɪɢ. 84.

At sea, both "natural" and "log" haversines are in everyday use, and are given side by side both in *Norie's* and *Burton's Tables*.   In *Norie's* the table commences on page 458.   In *Burton's* it is Table 20, commencing on page 163.

The Tables of Haversines in the two books differ only in small details.   In *Norie's* the values of the haversines are listed in terms of arc only.   They are given for every half minute (30″) up to an angle of 135°, and from 225° to 360°.   From 135° to 225°, values are given for every 1′ of arc.   In *Burton's*, values are listed in terms of arc and also of time.   Up to a value of 120°, and again from 240° to 360°, tolerance is to every 30″ of arc, (2 seconds of time).   Between 120° and 240°, tolerance is to every 1′ of arc—4 seconds of time.

In both tables, the haversines of angles up to 180° are read from the top of the page, with the odd minutes and half-minutes of arc given in the left hand vertical column of the page.   This column is read *downwards*.   From 180° to 360°, the angular values are read from the

foot of the page, and the pages are read backwards. The odd minutes
and half-minutes are given in the right hand vertical column of each
page, read *upwards.*

Polar Distance.—In this problem, instead of using the Sun's declination, its "angular distance" from the celestial pole nearest to the
observer is used. This is termed "Polar Distance."

In Fig. 85, the observer is supposed to be situated where the meridian
crosses the East—West line. Say he is in lat. 30° N. The equator
must then be 30° South from him (WQE), and the Pole (P) 60° North
from him. The angular distance from P to Q is, of course, 90°.

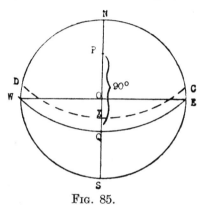

Fig. 85.

If the Sun's declination, indicated by the dotted line DXC, is also
North, the angular distance of the Sun (X) from the pole nearer to the
observer is (90°—declination). This is the Sun's Polar Distance.

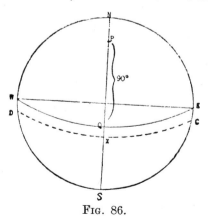

Fig. 86.

In Fig. 86, the observer's latitude is still 30° N., but the Sun's declination (*DXC*) is South. It can be seen that in this case the Sun's angular distance from the pole nearer to the observer is (90°+declination). The rule for finding P.D. is

Latitude and declination same names, P.D.=(90°—decl.)
Latitude and declination diff. names, P.D.=(90°+decl.)

G.H.A. and L.H.A.—G.H.A. of any heavenly body starts at a minimum value of 0°, when the body is momentarily on the meridian of Greenwich. In the case of the Sun, that is at a time near noon, G.M.T. The value of G.H.A. increases thereafter till the following meridian passage of the body over Greenwich, when it attains a maximum value of 360°, or 0°. In the same way, L.H.A. of a body is reckoned from 0° to 360°, using the observer's longitude instead of the longitude of Greenwich.

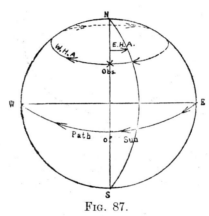

Fig. 87.

From Fig. 87, it can be seen that the path traced out by the Apparent Sun is always to the westward. At noon, local time, L.H.A. Sun=zero. At midnight, L.H.A.=180°. Therefore if an observation of the Sun for longitude has been taken a few hours *after* local noon, L.H.A. MUST BE LESS THAN 180°. If the observation has been taken some hours *before* local noon, L.H.A. must be between 180° and 360°. It is very important to remember this point.

"Elevated" and "Depressed" Poles.—When an observer is situated in any latitude North of the equator, observations are usually referred to the North Pole, and *vice versa*. In that case, the North Pole is called the observer's "Elevated" pole, while the South Pole, to an observer in the northern hemisphere, is the "Depressed" pole.

To Calculate the Observer's Longitude.—If an infinitesimally small observer on the Earth could trace out a triangle on the inverted bowl of the sky, with one line stretching from his zenith to the elevated pole, a second line from his zenith to the celestial body, and a third from the elevated pole to the body, each line would in fact be part of the circumference of a great circle. None of the lines—each of which is the side of a triangle—would be a straight line, as we understand it. Such a triangle is called a "spherical triangle," being drawn on the surface of a sphere, and it is generally referred to as the *PZX* tirangle. *P* represents the celestial pole, *Z* the observer's zenith, and *X* the body. The side *PZ* is the complement of the observer's latitude (the co-lat.); side *PX* is the Polar Distance of the body; and *ZX* the zenith distance (the complement of the true altitude). The angle formed at *P* is L.H.A., and the angle at *Z* represents the azimuth of the body.

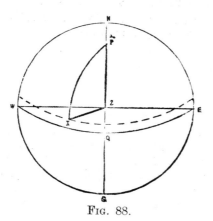

Fig. 88.

The same triangle can literally be brought down to earth by drawing the lines on a terrestrial globe—from the observer's D.R. position to the pole of the hemisphere in which he is; from his position to the terrestrial position immediately underneath the body (the body's "geographical position"); and from the elevated pole to the body.

In effect, that is just what is done when an observation for longitude is taken.

Various methods can be used to find the longitude by chronometer, all of which yield the same result to within very near limits. It is proposed to describe two methods.

Method 1.—Secant—Cosecant—Cosine—Sine Formula.

The formula used in this method is simple, straight-forward, and easily remembered. It is a method which can be strongly recommended to candidates for Fishing Certificates, by reason of its simplicity.

(*a*) Find:—

    G.M.T. from chronometer time.

    Correct declination and P.D.

    True Altitude.

    G.H.A. Sun.

(*b*) Find the Log haversine of the Sun's Local Hour Angle.

To do this, write down the following "arguments" in the order given, one below the other—

        Altitude

        Latitude

        Polar Distance.

Add these, calling the result the "Sum".

Divide the Sum by 2, naming the result "$\frac{1}{2}$ Sum".

From the $\frac{1}{2}$ Sum, subtract the Altitude, naming the result the "Remainder". The whole appears thus:—

    Alt. . . . .

    Lat. . . . .

    P.D. . . . .

    _____

    Sum . . . .

    $\frac{1}{2}$ S. . . . .

    Rem. . . . .

Now take the 2nd and 3rd arguments of the upper three (Lat. and P.D.) and the 2nd and 3rd arguments of the lower three ($\frac{1}{2}$ Sum and Remainder). For these quantities find respectively, from the Table of Log. Functions—

    1. Secant   (Lat.)

    2. Cosecant (P.D.)

    3. Cosine   ($\frac{1}{2}$ Sum)

    4. Sine   (Remainder)

Add the four logs together, rejecting 10's from the index. The result is the log haversine of the Sun's Local Hour Angle (L.H.A.) The whole of this sub-section appears thus:—

    Alt . . . .

    Lat. . . . .   Sec. . . . .

    P.D. . . . .   Cosec . . . .

    _____

    Sum . . . .

    $\frac{1}{2}$ S. . . . .   Cos. . . . .

    Rem. . . . .   Sin. . . . .

                         _____

      L. Hav L.H.A.   . . . .

(*c*) From the haversine table, find L.H.A. Sun. This, like the G.H.A., must be expressed as a WESTERLY H.A. Find the difference between L.H.A. and G.H.A. The result is the longitude, to be named

East, if G.H.A. is least;

West, if G.H.A. is best

If the difference between G.H.A. and L.H.A. is more than 180°, it must be subtracted from 360°, and the name of the longitude changed from E. to W., or *vice versa*. (See worked example 2.)

Example 1.—On July 23rd, A.M. at ship in est. lat. 41° 27′ N., the obs. alt. of the Sun's L.L. was 25° 38′. Height of eye 20 ft. Time by chronometer was 10h. 09m. 58s. On April 30th, chronometer was 3m. 40s. fast of G.M. noon, and on June 5th it was 6m. 22s. fast. Required the longitude by chronometer.

(*a*)	h	m	s		*To find Daily Rate*			
Chron. T., July 23	10	09	58		May	31d.	3m 40 fast
2nd error fast	—	6	22		June	5,,	6 22 ,,
	10	03	36		Tot.	36 ,,	2 42 gain.=162 sec.
Acc. rate gain'g	—	3	36				
					Daily rate=162 sec=4·5 sec. gain.
G.M.T.	10	00	00				/36

Corr. Decl.   20° 08·6′ N.   P.D. 69°51·4′   *To find Acc. Rate*

Corr. G.H.A. Sun 328° 24·4′.   June   25   days
                                             July   22·9   ,,

Obs. alt.   25° 38·0′   47·9   ,,   ×4·5 sec.
Tot. corr.   +   9·7   =3m 36s Acc. R.

True alt.   25   47·7

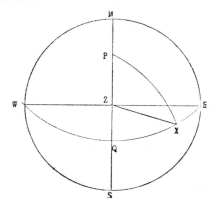

(b)

Alt.	25°	47·7′		
Lat.	41	27·0	Sec	0·12521
P.D.	69	51·4	Cosec	0·02741
Sum	137	06·1		
½ S.	68	33·0	Cos	9·56311
Rem.	42	45·3	Sin	9·83178

L. Hav L.H.A.   9·54751

(c)

L.H.A.	287°	07·4′
G.H.A.	328	24·4
Long	41	17·0 W.

Notes:
1. Time at ship was A.M., therefore L.H.A. must be more than 180°.
2. G.H.A. is best, therefore longitude is West.

Example 2.—On January 2nd, 1958 P.M. at ship in lat. 31° 14′ N., the obs. alt. of the Sun's U.L. was 19° 22′. Height of eye 25 ft. Time by chron. was 10h 19m 37s. Chron. was 1m. 12s. slow of G.M. noon on November 25th, 1957, and was losing 2·7 sec. daily. Required the longitude by chronometer.

(a)

Chron T., Jan. 2nd		10h	19m	37s
Error slow	+		1	12
		10	20	49
Acc. rate losing	+		1	42
G.M.T., Jan. 2nd		10	22	31

To find Daily Rate

Nov.	5	days
Dec.	31	,,
Jan.	1·9	,,
	37·9	,, at 2·7 sec.
		per day
=1m 42s.		

G.H.A. Sun 10h		329°	07·9
Increm.	+	5	37·8
Corr. G.H.A. Sun		334	45·7

Obs. alt.	19°	22·0′
Tot. Corr. —		24·9
True alt.	18	57·1

Decl.	23°	01·6′ S.
	90	
P.D.	113	01·6

(b)

Alt.	18°	57·1		
Lat.	31	14·0	Sec.	0·06800
P.D.	113	01·6	Cosec	0·03606
Sum	163	12·7		
½ S.	81	36·4	Cos	9·16426
Rem.	62	39·3	Sin	9·94854

L. Hav L.H.A.   9·21686

(c)

L.H.A.	47°	53·8′ W.
G.H.A.	334	45·7 W.
Long.	286	51·9 W.
	360	
	73	08·1 E.

NOTES:
1. Time at ship was P.M., therefore L.H.A. must be less than 180°.
2. Longitude was over 180°. It was subtracted from 360°, and its name changed from W. to E.

Method 2.—The Haversine Formula.

To find the Local Hour Angle of the body being observed, the following standard formula is used:

$$\text{Hav L.H.A.} = \frac{\text{Hav Z.D.} - \text{Hav (Co-lat} \smallfrown \text{P.D.)}}{\text{Sin Co-lat Sin P.D.}}$$

Study this formula in conjunction with Fig. 88. The haversine of the side opposite to the Hour Angle is subtracted from the haversine of the difference between the two sides which contain the Hour Angle. This result is then divided by the product of the sines of the same two sides.

One point which is handy to remember is that the difference between the object's polar distance and the observer's co-latitude is, of course, the same as the difference between the observer's latitude and the object's declination. For example:

Lat.   50°N.—Decl. 30°N.=20°, and
Co-lat. 40°   —P.D. 60°   =20°.

Further, sin co-lat=cos lat, and sin P.D.=cos decl.

Thus the standard formula given above can be altered and calculations somewhat simplified if we substitute Latitude for Co-latitude, and Declination for Polar Distance. The formula would then read:

$$\text{Hav. L.H.A.} = \frac{\text{Hav. Z.D.} - \text{Hav. (Lat.} \pm \text{Decl.)}}{\text{Cos. lat.} \quad \text{Cos. decl.}}$$

We have written (Lat.±Decl.) because the *difference* between these two arguments is:

Lat.+Decl. when they have different names;
Lat.—Decl. when they have the same names.

Example 1.—On July 23rd, A.M. a ship in est. lat. 41° 27′ N., the obs. alt. of the Sun's L.L. was 25° 38′. Ht. of eye 20 ft. Time by chronometer was 10h. 09m. 58s. On April 30th, chronometer was 3m. 40s. fast of G.M. noon, and on June 5th, it was 6m. 22s. fast. Required the longitude by chronometer.

(a)   Find: 1. G.M.T. from chronometer time and errors;
               2. Sun's true declination;
               3. Sun's true altitude and Z.D.;
               4. G.H.A. Sun;
               5. Difference between latitude and declination.

K

Chron. T., July 23rd	10h	09m	58s
2nd error fast	—	6	22
	10	03	36
Acc. rate gaining	—	3	36
G.M.T.	10	00	00

To find Daily Rate

May	31 days	3m	40s fast
June	5 ,,	6	22 ,,
Tot.	36 ,,	2	42 gaining

162 sec.
—––
36
=4·5 sec. D.R.

Corr. Decl.   20° 08·6′ N.

Corr. G.H.A. Sun 328° 24·4′

To find Acc. Rate
June   25 days.
July   22·9   ,,

Obs. alt.	25°	38·0′
Tot. Corr. +		9·7
True alt.	25	47·7
	90	
Z.D.	64	12·3

47·9 days × 4·5 sec.
     =3m 36s. Acc. R.

Lat.	41°	27·0′ N.
Dec.	20	08·6 N.
Diff.	21	18·4

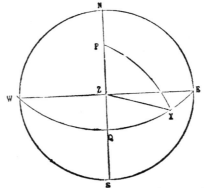

(*b*) The haversine formula can now be written, using actual values instead of letters.

$$\text{Hav. Sun's L.H.A.} = \frac{\text{Hav. } 64°\ 12\cdot3' - \text{Hav. } 21°\ 18\cdot4'}{\cos. 41°\ 27\cdot0'\ \cos. 20°\ 08\cdot6'}$$

It will be noted that the first operation is to *subtract* two haversines, so that logs cannot be used in this case. For performing subtraction, use *natural* haversines, and *convert the result to a log haversine.*

Z.D.	64°	12·3′	Nat. hav. 0·28242	—
(L.-D.)	21	18·4	Nat. hav. 0·03417	

0·24825 = log. hav. 9·39489

The next operation is to divide the answer just obtained by the product of two cosines. The operations of multiplication and division are most conveniently performed by using logs, so the natural haversine (0·24825) is converted to a log haversine, found in the Table just alongside the given natural haversine. Interpolation will usually have to be made.

On p.p. 37 and 38, it was shown that the process of dividing by a function yields the same answer as is found by multiplying by the *reciprocal* of the same function. As multiplication is more easily performed, the log sec of the latitude and the log sec of the declination are *added* to the log hav that has been found, the whole operation appearing as under:—

Z.D.	64° 12·3′	Nat hav 0·28242 ⎫ —
(L.-D.)	21 18·4	Nat hav 0·03417 ⎭

	Nat hav 0·24825 —Log hav	9·39489 ⎫
	Lat. 41° 27·0′ Log sec	0·12521 ⎬ +
	Dec. 20 08·6 Log sec	0·02741 ⎭

Log hav L.H.A.   9·54751

(*c*) Ship's time is A.M., therefore the L.H.A. must be more than 180°, and will require to be read from the foot of the page in the table of haversines.

L.H.A.	287°	07·4′
G.H.A.	328	24·4
Longitude	41	17·0 W.

G.H.A. is best, so longitude is West.

Example 2.—On Jan. 1st, P.M. at ship in lat. 31° 14′ N., the obs. alt. of the Sun's U.L. was 19° 22′. Height of eye 25 ft. Time by chron. was 10h. 19m. 37s. Chron was 1m. 12s. slow of G.M. noon on Nov. 24th, 1957, and was losing 2·7 sec. daily. Required the longitude by chronometer.

(*a*)	h	m	s
Chron. T., Jan. 1st	10	19	37
Error slow	+	1	12
	10	20	49
Acc. rate losing	+	1	42
G.M.T., Jan. 1st	10	22	31

To find accum. rate

Nov.   6 days
Dec. 31   ,,
Jan.   0·9 ,,

37·9 days at 2·7 sec. daily
=1m. 42s.

Decl. 23° 01·6′ S.

Obs. alt.   19° 22·0′
Corr.   —   24·9

G.H.A. Sun at 10h—329° 07·9′
Increment   5   37·8

T. alt   18   57·1

G.H.A. Sun   334   45·7

Z.D.   71   02·9

Lat.   31° 14·0′ N.
Dec.   23   01·6 S.

Diff.   54   15·6

(b)   Hav L.H.A. Sun = $\dfrac{\text{Hav } 71° 02·9' - \text{Hav } 54° 15·6'}{\text{Cos } 31° 14' \text{ Cos } 23° 01·6'}$

71° 02·9′ Nav hav 0·33762⎱ —
54 15·6   Nat hav 0·20794⎰

Nat hav 0·12968   Log hav   9·11286⎱
Lat. 31° 14′   Log sec   0·06800⎬ +
Dec. 23   01·6   Log sec   0·03606⎰

Log hav L.H.A.   9·21692

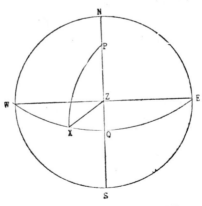

(c)   L.H.A.   47° 54·0′ W.
G.H.A.   334   45·7 W.

Longitude   286   51·7 W.
            —360

Longitude   73   08·3 E.

NOTES:

1. Time at ship was P.M., therefore L.H.A. must be less than 180°.
2. L.H.A. subtracted from G.H.A. yields a longitude of 286° 51·7′ W. Being over 180°, this must be subtracted from 360°, and its name is changed from W. to E.

EXERCISE 27.

TO FIND LONGITUDE BY CHRONOMETER.

Given the following particulars, find the longitude by chronometer.

1. On Jan. 2nd, A.M. at ship in est. lat. 7° 28′ N., the sext. alt. of the Sun's L.L. was 22° 17′. I.E. 3′ to add. Time by chronometer was 11h 19m 29s. The chronometer was 5m 12s slow of G.M.T. Height of eye 21 ft.

2. On Dec. 21st. A.M. at ship in lat. 11° 00′ N., the sext. alt. of the Sun's L.L. was 19° 25′. I.E. 7′ to subtract. Ht. of eye 18 ft. Time by chronometer was 10h 32m 18s. The chron. was 2m 19s slow of G.M. noon on Oct, 13th and was gaining 3·2s daily.

3. On July 16th, P.M. at ship in lat. 51° 12′ N., the obs. alt. of the Sun's L.L. was 19° 51′. Ht. of eye 23 ft. Time by chronometer was 20h 16m 43s. Chronometer was 2m 19s slow of G.M. noon on April 29th, and was 4m 35s slow on June 6th.

4. On Sept. 23rd, A.M. at ship in D.R. lat. 28° 20′ N., the sext. alt. of the Sun's L.L. was 17° 25′. I.E. 7′ to add. Ht. of eye 22 ft. Time by chronometer was 08h 15m 12s. Chronometer was 2m 16s slow of G.M. noon on August 10th, and was losing 5·2s daily.

5. On June 13th, P.M., at ship in lat. 40° 51′ N., the sext. alt. of the Sun's L.L. was 23° 45′. I.E. 3·3′ to subtract. Ht. of eye 19 ft. Time by chronometer was 14h 25m 37s. Chronometer was 13m 05s slow of G.M. noon on April 27th and was gaining 2·2s daily.

6. On Sept. 23rd, A.M. at ship in lat. 33° 05′ N., the obs. alt. of the Sun's L.L. was 38° 22′. Ht. of eye 24 ft. Time by chronometer was Sept. 22nd, 22h 22m 22s. This was correct G.M.T.

7. On June 14th, P.M. at ship in est. lat. 50° 36′ N., the obs. alt. of the Sun's L.L. was 40° 00′. Ht. of eye 20 ft. Time by chronometer was 14h 16m 48s. Chronometer was 5m 09s slow on April 20th, and was gaining 1·6s daily.

8. On Sept. 22nd, P.M. at ship is lat. 31° 26′ N., the sext. alt. of the Sun's L.L. was 25° 53′. I.E. 2·7′ to add. Ht. of eye 22 ft. Time by chronometer was Sept. 23rd, 02h 33m 19s. Chronometer was correct G.M.T. at noon, July 6th, and was 2m 19s slow on August 5th.

9. On June 13th, A.M. at ship on the equator, the obs. alt. of the Sun's U.L. was 27° 15'. Ht. of eye 17 ft. Time by chronometer was 14h 36m 39s. Chronometer was 2m 41s slow of G.M. noon on April 30th, and was gaining 3·9s daily.

10. On July 17th, P.M. at ship in lat. 49° 25' N., the obs. alt. of the Sun's L.L. was 41° 36'. Ht. of eye 28 ft. G.M.T. 12h 00m 00s.

11. On July 23rd, A.M. at ship in lat. 21° 08' S., the sext. alt. of the Sun's L.L. was 29° 14'. I.E.+4·5'. Ht. of eye 32 ft. Time by chronometer was 10h 39m 51s. Chronometer was 5m 22s fast of G.M.T.

12. On Oct. 7th, A.M. at ship in lat. 32° 41' N., the obs. alt. of the Sun's U.L. was 36° 05'. Ht. of eye 25 ft. G.M.T. 08h 31m 14s.

13. On Dec. 23rd, P.M. at ship in lat 11° 52' N., the obs. alt, of the Sun's L.L. was 39° 15'. Ht. of eye 29 ft. Time by chronometer was 17h 31m 20s. Chronometer was 6m 22s fast of G.M. noon on Oct. 31st, and was losing 2·3s daily.

14. On June 12th, A.M. at ship in lat. 38° 19' N., the obs. alt. of the Sun's L.L. was 27° 35'. Ht. of eye 18 ft. Time by chronometer was 04h 28m 11s. Chronometer was 5m 27s slow of G.M.T.

15. On Sept. 24th, P.M. at ship in lat. 53° 00' N., the obs. alt. of the Sun's L.L. was 21° 21'. Ht. of eye 23 ft. G.M.T. 16h 26m 51s.

16. On Oct. 9th, P.M. at ship in lat. 42° 12' N., the sext. alt. of the Sun's U.L. was 30° 00'. I.E.−2·4'. Ht. of eye 31 ft. Time by chronometer was 14h 29m 46s. Chronometer was correct at G.M. noon on Aug. 30th, and was losing 0·8s daily.

17. On Jan. 3rd, in est. lat. 2° 00' N., A.M. at ship, the obs. alt. of the Sun's L.L. was 26° 14'. Ht. of eye 27 ft. G.M.T. 03h 36m 29s.

18. On Dec. 22nd, P.M. at ship in lat. 26° 25' S., the sext. alt. of the Sun's L.L. was 42° 18'. I.E.+3'. Ht. of eye 32 ft. G.M.T. 11h 21m 53s.

19. On July 21st, A.M. at ship in lat. 49° 03' N., the obs. alt. of the Sun's L.L. was 37° 09'. Ht. of eye 20 ft. G.M.T. 08h 00m 00s.

20. On Oct. 8th, A.M. at ship in lat. 20° 51' N., the obs. alt. of the Sun's L.L. was 19° 22'. Ht. of eye 22 ft. A chronometer which was 27m 43s fast of G.M.T. read 12h 51m 37s.

LONGITUDE PROBLEM WITH RUN GIVEN.

In actual practice at sea, the position of a ship on passage is almost invariably entered in the ship's log-book at local noon, after the latitude by meridian altitude has been found.

The latitude used when finding the longitude by an A.M. or a P.M. observation of the Sun is an estimated or D.R. latitude, and the "longitude at sights" must be "brought up to noon" to get the ship's noon position. This additional process may be required in the examination room, Alternatively, the candidate is sometimes given the *noon* latitude in the problem, together with the necessary information regarding the ship's course and speed during the interval, leaving the candidate to find the "latitude at sights" himself. This is done by using the Traverse Tables.

In such a case, the candidate must read the question very carefully to find what information is given, and exactly what is required in the answer. Generally speaking, the different cases can be listed under four heads:—

1. A.M. observation with the *noon* latitude given, the candidate being required to find "Latitude at sights." In this case, only the D. Lat. between noon and sights is required, and the course given in the question *must be reversed*.

Example.—On June 16th, about 0830 L.M.T., an observation of the Sun was taken to determine the longitude. The ship's latitude was uncertain, but at noon a meridian observation put the ship in lat. 49° 37′ N. Between sights and noon the ship had run on a 166° T. course, 33 miles. Find the "latitude at sights."

Reverse the ship's course—346° T.=N. 14° W., 33 miles.

Lat. at noon	49°	37·0′ N.	
D. Lat.		32·0 N.	(from Traverse Table)
Lat. at sights	50	09·0 N.	

The longitude problem is then worked using latitude 50° 09′ N.

2. P.M. observation, with *noon* latitude given. In this case, the method to be used is the same as above, but the given course must NOT be reversed.

Example.—On June 16th, about 1540 L.M.T., an observation of the Sun was taken to determine the longitude. Latitude by meridian observation at noon was 38° 38′ N., and the ship had steered a course of 052° T. for 40 miles between noon and sights. Find the latitude at sights.

Lat. at noon	38°	38′ N.
D. Lat.		24·6 N. (from Traverse Table)
Lat. at sights	39	02·6′ N.

3. A.M. longitude observation with "lat. at sights" given, ship's A.M. position to be brought up to noon.

Using the ship's course and distance from sights to noon, find D. Lat. and Dep. from the Traverse Table. Apply D. Lat. direct to the latitude at sights to obtain the noon latitude. Then convert Dep. to D. Long. either "by inspection" or by using the formula. L. sec Mean lat.+Log Dep=Log D. Long. Apply D. Long. to the longitude at sights to obtain longitude at noon.

Example:—On July 23rd, A.M. at ship, using lat. 41° 13′ N., the longitude of the ship was found to be 19° 37′ W. Between sights and noon the ship steered 209° T., 36 miles. Find ship's noon position.

Lat. at sights	41° 13·0′ N.	
Co. S. 29° W., 36 miles. D. Lat.	31·5 S.	
Lat. at noon	40 41·5 N.	

Mean lat. 41°, Dep. 17·5′ gives D. Long. 23·2′.

Long. at sights	19°	37·0′ W.
D. Long.		23·2 W.
Long. at noon	20	00·2 W.

4. P.M. longitude observation, with latitude at sights given. It is required to bring the ship's P.M. position back to noon.

The method to be used is the same as is used in (3) above, with the exception that in this case, the ship's course between noon and the P.M. position must be reversed.

EXERCISE 28

1. On July 23rd, A.M. at ship, the obs. alt. of the Sun's L.L. was 36° 20′. Time by chronometer was 04h 26m 32s. Chronometer was 2m 10s slow of G.M. noon on June 25th, and was losing 2·8s daily. Lat. at noon by a meridian observation was 50° 19′ N. and the ship had steamed 41 miles on a true course of 070° between the A.M. observation and noon. Required the longitude at sights and also brought up to noon. Ht. of eye 22 ft.

2. On Oct. 9th, P.M. at ship, the obs. alt. of the Sun's L.L. was 27° 12′. Ht. of eye 18 ft. Time by chronometer was 17h 22m 33s. Chronometer was 8m 12s slow of G.M.T. Lat. by mer. alt. at noon was 30° 21′ N. Between noon and P.M. sights ship steamed 231° T., 37 miles. Required the longitude at sights, and also the ship's noon position.

3. On Oct. 9th, P.M. at ship in D.R. Lat. 37° 08′ N., the obs. alt. of the Sun's L.L. was 21° 18′. Ht. of eye 26 ft. Time by chronometer was 17h 50m 00s. Chronometer was 18m 18s fast of G.M. noon on August 2nd, and was 16m 03s. fast on September 5th. Required the longitude at sights and also the ship's noon position, the ship having run 037° T., 47 miles between noon and sights.

4. On June 12th, A.M. at ship in lat. 52° 07′ N., the obs. alt. of the Sun's L.L. was 29° 47′. Ht. of eye 25 ft. G.M.T. 12h 00m 00s. Required the longitude at sights, and also the ship's position at noon, the ship having run 158° T., 36 miles between sights and noon.

CHAPTER 23.

POSITION LINES—TERRESTRIAL POSITION LINES—CELESTIAL POSITION LINES—TRANSFERRING POSITION LINES—THE VALUE OF A SINGLE POSITION LINE—TO FIND SHIP'S TRUE NOON POSITION—TWO LONGITUDE OBSERVATIONS WITH RUN BETWEEN—PLOTTING POSITION LINES ON CHARTS.

A Position Line (P.L.) can be defined as a straight line plotted on a chart in a particular direction, on some unspecified part of which the observer's position lies.

Terrestrial Position Lines.—When an observer takes a compass bearing of a lighthouse or a point of land, and plots it on a chart as a true bearing, that line is a "position line." The vessel's position is at some latitude and longitude through which the position line passes. A single bearing cannot give him his exact position. He can only assume a position, but he does know that his ship is *somewhere* on that line.

When two such bearings of two different points or lighthouses are taken at the same time and plotted on a chart, the two position lines will intersect, or cross. Since the ship's position is *somewhere* on each line, it must necessarily be where the two bearings intersect. (See Chapter 10).

If two bearings are taken of the same light, or of two different lights, and the vessel has steamed a known course and distance in the period between the bearings, the position at the time of taking the second bearing is found in the following manner.

Lay off on the chart, from any point "A" on the first bearing, the direction and distance of the ship's run between the bearings. From the point thus found, "B", the estimated set and drift of the current, if any, during the same period is laid off—"C."—Through "C" draw a line parallel to the first bearing. Where this line—it is called a "transferred position line"—cuts the line of the second bearing is the ship's position. (See Chapter 11.)

Positions found by either of these methods are reliable, and are usually labelled on the chart "F" (Fix) or "OBS" (Observed).

Celestial Position Lines.—To find the ship's position using observations of celestial bodies in place of visual bearings of terrestrial objects, the same procedure can be followed.

278

The "geographical position" of the Sun, or of any heavenly body, is the latitude and longitude of that particular point on the Earth's surface where the star is momentarily right overhead.   If we know the Greenwich Mean Time, we can find from the *Nautical Almanac* the body's declination and its G.H.A. (East or West) at that time.   The star is then directly overhead at a terrestrial position whose latitude is the same as the star's declination, and whose longitude is the same as the G.H.A. of the star.

The true Zenith Distance of the star—this term includes the Sun, or any heavenly body—is found by correcting a sextant altitude, and subtracting it from 90°.

The observer's terrestrial position is then *somewhere* on the circumference of a circle whose centre is the star's geographical position, and whose radius is equal to the zenith distance.   The true bearing of the star at the same time indicates on which part of the circumference of the circle the observer's position lies.   (See Fig. 89).

A line drawn from the circumference to the centre of the circle, in the true direction of the star's azimuth, forms a radius of the circle of position, and, of course, meets the circumference at a right angle.

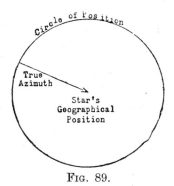

FIG. 89.

Although this circle is called a "small circle", it is in reality so large that no appreciable error is introduced into a calculation by assuming that the very small portion of the circumference with which we are concerned is a straight line.   Thus, in practice, a celestial position line is shown as a straight line drawn at a right angle to the true azimuth of the star.

The terrestrial position through which this P.L. is to be drawn is found by calculation.

Two methods of finding the position are in general use at sea, and each is discussed separately.   The methods are called respectively—

    1.   The Longitude Method.   (See Chapter 24.)
    2.   The Intercept Method   (See Chapter 28.)

The ultimate result is the same, or very nearly so, whichever method is used, and each method finds favour with numberless navigators.

While there is little to choose between them, it can be noted that in the Longitude Method observations are worked as ordinary "longitude by chronometer" problems, requiring no new rules or change of formula. Another point is that the Longitude Method requires only the D.R. latitude to be known, while in the Intercept Method both D.R. latitude and longitude are required.

The Best Time to take Longitude Observations.—It has been stated above that the P.L. on which the vessel lies is depicted as a line drawn at right angles to the true azimuth.

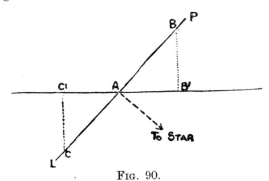

Fig. 90.

From Fig. 90, in which P.L. represents a position line, it can be seen that the longitude plotted at A is correct only if the D.R. latitude (C_1AB_1) is correct. If the true latitude is at B, the correct longitude is at B_1. If the true latitude is at C, the correct longitude is at C_1.

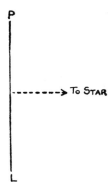

Fig. 91.

But if an observation for longitude is taken when the body bears true East or true West from the observer, as in Fig. 91, the P.L. lies in a true North-South direction. In fact, the P.L. itself is a meridian of longitude. Under these conditions an error in the D.R. latitude causes no error in the calculated longitude.

Thus the ideal time to take an observation for longitude is when the body bears East or West, or, as it is called, when the body is "on the prime vertical". Unfortunately, this is not always possible. To be able to take an altitude of a body on the prime vertical, the observer's latitude must be of the same name as the body's declination, and the latitude must be greater than the declination.

The Value of a Single Position Line.—Circumstances frequently arise when an observer has obtained only one position line, and owing to weather or other causes he finds it impossible to obtain another P.L. to fix the ship's position, Even under such conditions the single P.L. can make all the difference between a ship's safety or otherwise.

Suppose a vessel in foggy weather is shaping a course towards a lighthouse—Y in Fig. 92—where she has to alter her course to the northward.

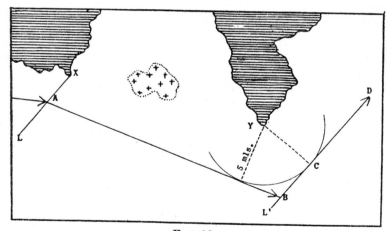

Fig. 92

Uncertain of her position, she has managed to get a visual bearing of lighthouse X. Her position at A is assumed only, but it is known she is somewhere on the P.L. represented by the bearing LAX The observer can hazard a guess as to the ship's distance off X, and if he is wise, his guess will put her well *inshore* of what he really thinks.

He can then alter his course to avoid any intervening danger, and at the same time can draw a transferred P.L. (L_1BCD) at a safe distance off lighthouse Y. Then, when he has run the distance AB—no matter where his actual position was on LAX.,—he can alter course in the direction of the transferred P.L., knowing he is fairly sure to be clear of danger.

Noon at sea is a very important time, and until comparatively recent years, the "astronomical day" was considered to begin at midday. At noon, too, a ship's latitude can be obtained by a very simple calculation. It is very usual, when a ship is on passage, whether coasting or out of sight of land, to fix her position daily at noon. A very ordinary method of doing so is worked as follows:—

Three or four hours before LOCAL APPARENT NOON, the ship's longitude is found from a sextant altitude of the Sun, using a D.R. latitude. At the same time the true bearing of the Sun is calculated, using for this purpose the L.H.A. found by observation. This serves a double purpose—the ship's P.L. is known, and, if the A.B.C. Tables have been used, the "C" correction is used to obtain a "longitude correction," necessary if the D.R. latitude was incorrect.

The D.R. latitude used at the a.m. observation and the longitude found by observation provide a definite position which is used as the point of departure, remembering that the "longitude at sights" is correct only if various conditions have been fulfilled.

From the point of departure the course and distance steamed by the ship is worked out to obtain a dead reckoning position at noon. Then, at noon, the actual latitude is found from a meridian observation of the Sun. The P.L. from this is, of course, always E.—W.

The difference between the observed latitude and the D.R. latitude is the "latitude correction". This correction, multiplied by the value of "C" obtained at the a.m. observation, is the correction to be applied to the noon D.R. longitude.

If the Sun's true bearing at the time of the A.M. observation was in a S.E'ly direction, the letters S.E. are written, with the opposite bearing —N.W.—written immediately below, thus:—

FIG. 93.

Then, if the D.R. latitude had been NORTH of the observed latitude, the latitude correction would be SOUTH. (See direction of arrow in Fig. 93.) The direction in which the correction has to be applied to the longitude is found by drawing a line *diagonally* from, in this case, SOUTH to WEST. Longitude correction is therefore West. Fig. 94 below shows the P.L. basis for the formula.

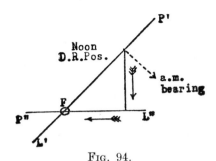

FIG. 94.

The noon assumed position is on P¹L¹, the transferred position line. P″ L″ is the position line drawn in an E.—W. direction through the noon observed latitude. Arrows indicate (1) the latitude correction to the southward; (2) the longitude correction to the westward.

Example 1.—An a.m. observation of the Sun when in a S.E'ly direction gave longitude 14° 37′ W., using a D.R. latitude 49° 40′ N. "C"=·216. Ship then steamed 33 miles on a true course of 342°, when a meridian observation gave latitude 50° 02′ N. Find the ship's true position at noon.

D.R. lat.	49° 40·0′ N.		Obs. long.	14° 37·0′ W.
D. Lat.	31·4 N.		D. long.	15·9 W.
Noon D.R. lat.	50 11·4 N.		D.R. long.	14 52·9 W.
Noon obs. lat.	50 02·0 N.		Long. corr.	2·0 W.
Lat. corr.	9·4 S.		Noon long.	14 54·9 W.

Long. corr.=9·4 × ·216=2·0′ W.

Example 2.—Using D.R. latitude 38° 51′ N., an a.m. observation of the Sun gave longitude 47° 54′ W. Sun's bearing S. 42° E. "C"=1·34. Ship then steamed 26 miles on a true course of 153°, when latitude by meridian altitude was 38° 34′ N. Find the ship's true position at noon.

| D.R. lat. | 38° 51·0′ N. | Obs. long. | 47° 54·0′ W. |
| D. Lat. | 23·2 S. | D. Long. | 15·1 E. |

| Noon D.R. lat. | 38 27·8 N. | D.R. long. | 47 38·9 W. |
| Noon obs. lat. | 38 34·0 N. | Long. corr. | 8·3 E. |

| Lat. corr. | 6·2 N. | Noon long. | 47 30·6 W. |

Long. corr.$= 6·2 \times 1·34 = 8·3'$ E.

S.   E.

N.   W.

True noon position—Lat. 38° 34′ N.   Long. 47° 30·6′ W.

EXERCISE 29

Given the following particulars, find ship's noon position in each case.

	D.R. Lat.	Obs. Long.	T. Bg.	"C"	Run to Noon	Noon Obs. Lat.
1.	51° 22′ N.	16° 28′ W.	S.E.	·622	107°, 27 mls.	51° 08′ N.
2.	40 40 N.	31 42 W.	S.E.	·805	198°, 35 ,,	39 59 N.
3.	18 21 N.	28 09 W.	N.E.	·228	260°, 42 ,,	18 22 N.
4.	39 55 N.	14 25 E.	S.E.	·412	038°, 29 ,,	40 25 N.
5.	47 20 N.	7 12 W.	S.E.	·776	328°, 21 ,,	47 44 N.
6.	28 37 S.	36 28 E.	N.E.	·518	287°, 25 ,,	28 40 S.
7.	52 06 N.	54 18 W.	S.E.	1·070	149°, 19 ,,	52 00 N.
8.	12 16 N.	61 23 W.	N.E.	·262	342°, 38 ,,	12 40 N.
9.	42 51 N.	29 51 W.	S.E.	·618	158°, 30 ,,	42 29 N.
10.	33 42 N.	17 42 W.	S.E.	·522	064°, 28 ,,	34 00 N.
11.	54 00 N.	28 00 W.	S.E.	1·240	316°, 17 ,,	54 03 N.
12.	5 37 N.	3 16 E.	N.E.	·312	254°, 22 ,,	5 39 N.
13.	15 40 S.	25 05 W.	N.E.	·543	015°, 36 ,,	15 12 S.
14.	25 25 N.	72 19 W.	S.E.	·493	216°, 31 ,,	24 51 N.
15.	47 29 N.	66 44 W.	S.E.	·609	118°,·39 ,,	47 00 N.
16.	35 12 N.	26 37 W.	S.E.	·580	337°, 42 ,,	36 06 N.
17.	27 25 N.	19 21 E.	N.E.	·181	133°, 18 ,,	27 25 N.
18.	49 52 N.	13 57 W.	S.E.	·629	301°, 25 ,,	49 55 N.
19.	53 31 N.	27 22 W.	S.E.	1·380	078°, 14 ,,	53 30 N.
20.	17 46 N.	41 25 W.	N.E.	·413	235°, 28 ,,	17 30 N.

Two Longitude Observations with Run Between.—It sometimes happens that after a satisfactory observation has been obtained in the forenoon, the Sun at noon is obscured. Under these circumstances, if suitable conditions arise in the afternoon, a p.m. observation for longitude can be taken. The course and distance run by the ship between observations is worked to provide a p.m. D.R. position.

The longitude found by the second observation is quite likely to differ by a few minutes from this D.R. longitude.

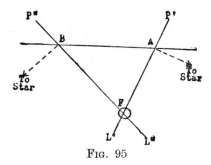

FIG. 95

In Fig. 95, such conditions are shown. *A* represents the p.m. D.R. position, P'L' being the position line transferred from the a.m. observation. *B* is the longitude found by observation at the p.m. sight, P"L" being the position line obtained from the Sun's true bearing at the same time.

The position *F*, where the two P.L.'s. meet, is the ship's true position.

Under actual sea conditions a chart of the area would be used. On this, the two longitudes would be plotted, and the two P.L.'s. laid off through their respective positions to find the position.

If a chart of the area is not available—as, for instance, in the examination room—the position is found by calculation.

In Fig. 95 above, it can be seen that as the a.m. and p.m. bearings of the Sun—and consequently the two P.L.'s.—lie in adjacent quadrants of the compass, a perpendicular line from *F* to the parallel of latitude will fall *inside* the triangle. If the two bearings are in the same, or opposite, quadrants, the perpendicular will fall *outside* the triangle. The procedure to be followed to find the latitude and longitude of *F* is simple.

The "C" correction from the A.B.C. Tables is noted at each observation. Then

1. If the two P.L.'s. are in adjacent quadrants, with the perpendicular falling *inside* the triangle, ADD the two "C" corrections. If the two P.L.'s. are in the same, or opposite, quadrants, subtract them.

2. The difference of longitude between *A* and *B* (in minutes of arc) is divided by the sum—or difference—of the "C" corrections. The result is the correction to be applied to the D.R. latitude to obtain the true latitude. A glance at a rough sketch shows whether this correction has to be applied to the northward or to the southward. In the case illustrated above, the correction is to the southward.

3. Longitude "A" is to the eastward of "F". Multiply the "C" correction found at the a.m. observation by the latitude correction which was found as described in (2) above. The result, applied in the same case above to the westward of longitude "A" gives the ship's true longitude. The "C" correction found at the p.m. observation, treated in the same way with longitude "B". and applied to the eastward, should yield the same answer.

Example 1.—An a.m. observation of the Sun bearing S. 40° E., gave latitude 35° 30′ N., longitude 24° 19′ W. when transferred. "C"=1·46. At the same time a p.m. observation of the Sun bearing S. 57° W. gave longitude 24° 10′ W. "C"=0·798. Find the ship's true position.

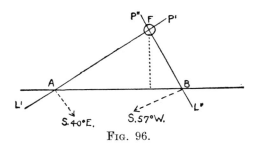

Fig. 96.

The bearings are in adjacent quadrants, and the perpendicular lies inside the triangle. The "C" corrections must be added. From the rough sketch above, latitude correction is to the northward, longitude *A* correction to the eastward, and longitude *B* correction (if required) is to the westward.

$$\text{Lat. corr.} = \frac{\text{D. Long. between "A" \& "B"}}{C' + C^2} = \frac{9}{2 \cdot 26} = 4'$$

Long. correction—

"A"—Lat. corr. × C′ = 4 × 1·46 = 5·84′ E.
"B"—Lat. corr. × C² = 4 × ·798 = 3·2 W.
D.R. Lat. 35° 30′ N.
Corr. 4 N.

True Lat. 35 34 N.

Long. *A*.	24°	19·0′ W.	Long. B.	24°	10·0′ W.
		5·8 E.			3·2 W.
True Long.	24	13·2 W.		24	13·2 W.

Example 2.—The D.R. position, transferred from an a.m. observation of the Sun when bearing S. 67° E. (*Y*) was 49° 10′ N., long. 7° 39′ W. At the same time a second observation of the Sun taken when it bore S. 25° E. gave long. 7° 33′ W. (*X*). "C" for *X*=3·28. "C" for *Y*=0·65. Find ship's true position.

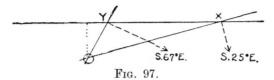

FIG. 97.

In this example the bearings of the Sun are in the same quadrant. "C" corrections must be subtracted when finding latitude correction. From the sketch, the latitude correction is to the southward, and both longitude corrections to the westward.

$$\text{Lat. Corr.} = \frac{\text{D. Long.}}{C^1 - C^2} = \frac{6}{2·63} = 2·3′$$

Long. corr.— X—Lat. corr.$\times C^2$=2·3$\times$3·28=7·5′ W.
$\qquad\qquad\quad Y$—Lat. corr.$\times C^1$=2·3$\times$0·65=1·5 W.

D.R. lat.	49° 10·0′ N.	Long. X 7° 33·0′ W.	Long. Y 7° 39·0′ W.
Corr.	2·3 S.	7·5 W.	1·5 W.
True lat.	49 07·7 N.	Long. 7 40·5 W.	7 40·5 W.

Example 3.—An a.m. observation of the Sun, using D.R. latitude 49° 14′ N., gave longitude 18° 42′ W. True bearing S. 61° E. "C"=·43. Ship then steered a course 062° T. for 50 miles, when a p.m. observation of the Sun gave longitude 17° 40′ W. True bearing S. 44° W. "C"=·76. Find the ship's position at the time of taking the second observation.

A.M. D.R. lat.	49° 14·0′ N.	Obs. long.	18° 42·0′ W.
D. Lat.	23·5 N.	D. Long.	1 08·0 E.	(Run 062°,
P.M. D.R. lat.	49 37·5 N.	D.R. long.	17 34·0 W.	50 miles). (A).

A.M. P.L. 029°—209°.   P.M. P.L. 134°—314°
D. Long. between results=6′. C^1+C^2=1·19

$$\text{Lat. corr.} = \frac{6}{1·2} = 5′ \text{ S.}$$ Long. corr. (A)=(5$\times$·43)=2·15′ W.

$\qquad\qquad\qquad\qquad\qquad\qquad (B)$=(5$\times$·76)=3·80 E.

D.R. lat.	49° 37·5′ N.	D.R. long. (A) 17° 34·0′ W.	(B) 17° 40·0′ W.
Corr'ns	5·0 S.	2·2 W.	3·8 E.
True lat.	49 32·5 N.	True long. 17 36·2 W.	17 36·2 W.

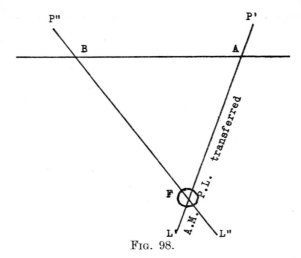

Fig. 98.

Example 4.—In D.R. latitude 32° 06′ N., an a.m. observation of the
Sun bearing 100° T. gave longitude 41° 23′ E. "C"=·68. Ship thereafter steamed 61 miles on a 213° T. course, when a p.m. observation of
the Sun bearing 228° T. gave longitude 40° 52′ E. "C"=·84. Find
ship's position at the time of taking the second observation.

A.M. D.R. lat.	32°	06·0′ N.	Obs. long.	41°	23·0′ E.		
D. Lat.		51·2 S.	D. Long.		39·0 W.	(Run 213°,	
						61 miles).	
P.M. D.R. lat.	31	14·8 N.	D.R. long.	40	44·0 E.	(A)	

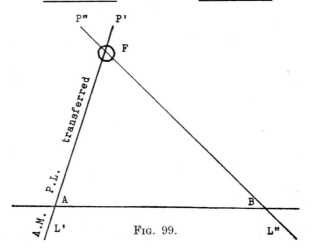

Fig. 99.

A.M. P.L. 010°—190°   P.M. P.L. 138°—318°

D. Long. between results=8'.   C¹+C²=1·52.

Lat. corr.$=\dfrac{8}{1\cdot5}$ $=5\cdot3$ N.   Long. corr. (A)=(5·3×·68)=3·6′ E.

(B)=(5·3×·84)=4·4 W.

D.R. lat. 31° 14·8′ N.   D.R. long. (A) 40° 44·0′ E.   (B) 40° 52·0′ E.

Corr'ns.   5·3 N.   3·6 E.   4·4 W.

True lat. 31 20·1 N.   True long.   40   47·6 E.   40   47·6 E.

EXERCISE 30.

Given the following particulars, find the ship's true position at the time of taking the second observation

	1st Observation					2nd Observation		
	D.R. Lat.	Obs. Long.	T. Bg	'C'	Run	Obs. Long.	T. Bg	'C'
1.	27° 45′ N.	45° 07′ W.	113°	·38	083°, 47 mls.	44° 07′ W.	205°	·74
2.	51 35 N.	9 48 E.	137	·46	163°, 51 ,,	10 00 E.	211	·68
3.	40 28 N.	33 24 W.	121	·32	307°, 63 ,,	34 36 W.	224	·55
4.	25 49 N.	12 57 W.	105	·29	049°, 57 ,,	12 00 W.	208	·59
5.	11 51 N.	24 00 E.	209	1·16	333°, 26 ,,	23 53 E.	250	·52
6.	47 02 S.	18 16 W.	066	·81	288°, 60 ,,	19 45 W.	313	·37
7.	31 11 N.	49 21 W.	214	·93	116°, 29 ,,	48 58 W.	262	·40
8.	55 02 N.	77 31 W.	129	·64	203°, 55 ,,	78 00 W.	217	·54
9.	14 18 S.	20 50 W.	072	·77	064°, 58 ,,	20 03 W.	329	·35
10.	49 57 N.	5 22 E.	119	·42	320°, 45 ,,	4 30 E.	240	·29
11.	36 23 S.	79 37 E.	081	·27	259°, 64 ,,	78 15 E.	306	·41
12.	44 13 N.	27 42 W.	214	·84	157°, 38 ,,	27 30 W.	252	·33

FORM EXN. 30c.

It has been said above that if a chart of the area is available, a ship's position can be found directly and expeditiously. A plotting chart has been produced by the Ministry of Transport—Form Exn. 30c. —especially for use in examinations for Fishing Certificates. Copies of the chart are available at most nautical schools, and they can also be obtained, at 4d. per copy, from H.M. Stationery Office. The chart covers an area from lat. 55° N. to 56° N., and from long. 10° W. to 12° W.

If the problems dealt with in this chapter—and in Chapter 24, 35 and 36—are given in an examination, and if the given positions lie within the limits of these latitudes and longitudes, candidates will be expected to find the ship's position by simple plotting.

The student should actually work each of the following examples step by step on a plotting chart to ensure that he obtains the correct answer to a reasonable degree of accuracy.

A.M. observation and run to noon.

Example 1.—In D.R. lat. 55° 03′ N., long. by observation was 11° 54′ W. The Sun was in the S.E. quadrant, and "C" was ·635. Ship then steamed on a course of 066° T. for 38 miles, when the latitude by meridian altitude of the Sun was 55° 24′ N. Find the ship's true position at noon.

Method of Plotting.—Lay off the given position on the chart, and find the true bearing of the Sun from Table C of the A.B.C. Tables. (S. 70° E.) P.L. is therefore 020°—200°.

From the original position, lay off the course and distance steamed between sights and noon—066° T., 38 miles. Through the position thus found, draw the transferred P.L. Through lat. 55° 24′ N., draw a line in an E.—W. direction, cutting the P.L. at *F*.

F is the ship's true position, found by chart reference to be Lat. 55° 24′ N., Long. 10° 49·4′ W.

Example 2.—An a.m. observation of the Sun in D.R. lat. 55° 40′ N. gave long. 10° 16′ W. "C" was 1·11, Sun in S.E. quadrant. The ship thereafter steamed 248° T. for 46 miles, when the latitude by meridian altitude of the Sun was found to be 55° 19′ N. Find the ship's true position at noon.

Method of Plotting.—"C" of 1·11 gives true bearing S. 58° E. in lat. 55° 40′ N. P.L.=032°—212°. From the position of departure, lay off the course and distance steamed to noon. Through this point draw the transferred P.L. Through lat. 55° 19′ N., draw an E.—W. line. Ship's position is where this line crosses the transferred P.L.

Lat. 55° 19′ N., long. 11° 35·2′ W.

A.M. observation, run, and P.M. observation.

Example 3.—In D.R. lat. 55° N., an a.m. observation of the Sun gave long. 11° 50′ W. Sun's true bearing 133°. Thereafter the ship steered a course of 039° T. for 52 miles, when a p.m. observation of the Sun bearing 231° T. gave a longitude of 11° 00′ W. Find the ship's true position at the time of taking the second observation.

Method of Plotting.—Lay off the ship's a.m. position as given. From this point lay off the course and distance steamed between observations—039° T., 52 miles. Through this point draw a parallel of latitude, mark the D.R. longitude, and call it *A*. Through *A*, draw the transferred P.L. (*P′ L′*). The a.m. bearing was 133°, so the P.L. is 043°—223°. On the same parallel, mark the longitude found at the second observation, calling it *B*. Through *B* draw P″ L″ in a direction 141°—321°. Where the two P.L.'s meet is the ship's true position—

Lat. 55° 37·7′ N., long. 10° 56·1′ W.

Note that it is unnecessary to draw a P.L. through the position of departure.

Example 4.—An observation of the Sun bearing 119° T. in D.R. lat. 55° 55′ N. gave long. 10° 16′ W. Thereafter the ship steamed 247° T. for 30 miles, when an observation of the Sun bearing 158° T. gave long. 11° 12′ W. Find the ship's position at the time of taking the second observation.

(Note that in this case both bearings are in the S.E. quadrant.)

The ship's position is found to be—Lat. 55° 45·0′ N. Long. 11° 03·0′ W.

ExERCISE 31.

PLOTTING EXERCISE.

1. In D.R. lat. 55° 56′ N., an a.m. observation of the Sun in the S.E. quadrant gave long. 11° 20′ W. "C"=1·45. Ship then steamed 157° T., 31 miles, when a mer. alt. of the Sun gave lat. 55° 31′ N. Find the ship's noon position.

2. In est. lat. 55° 15′ N., an observation of the Sun to the S.E'rd. gave long. 10° 07′ W. "C"=·856. Ship then steamed 288° T., 28 miles, when a meridian altitude of the Sun gave lat. 55° 19′ N. Find the ship's noon position.

3. In est. lat. 55° 28′ N., an observation of the Sun to the S.E'rd. gave long. 11° 35′ W. "C"=·526. Ship then steamed 043° T., 40 miles, when a meridian observation of the Sun gave lat. 55° 54′ N. Find the ship's noon position.

4. In D.R. lat. 55° 07′ N., an observation of the Sun to the S.E'rd. gave long. 11° 07′ W. "C"=·435. Ship then steamed 357° T., 36 miles, when a meridian observation of the Sun gave lat. 55° 47′ N. Find the ship's noon position.

5. In D.R. lat. 55° 44′ N., an observation of the Sun to the S.E'rd. gave long. 11° 36′ W. "C"=1·11. Ship then steamed 144° T., 33 miles, when a meridian observation of the Sun gave lat. 55° 13′ N. Find the ship's noon position.

6. In D.R. lat. 55° 58′ N., an observation of the Sun bearing 144° T., gave long. 10° 29′ W. Ship then steamed 255° T., 43 miles, when a second observation of the Sun bearing 220° T. gave long. 11° 30′ W. Find the ship's position at the time of taking the second observation.

7. In D.R. lat. 55° 41′ N., an observation of the Sun bearing 117° T. gave long. 11° 53′ W. Ship then steamed 128° T., 52 miles, when a p.m. observation of the Sun bearing 217° T. gave long. 10° 48′ W. Find ship's position at the time of taking the second observation.

8. An a.m. observation of the Sun bearing 078° T. gave long. 10° 43' W. in D.R. lat. 55° 08' N. Ship then steamed 316° T., 31 miles, when a second observation of the Sun bearing 153° T. gave long. 11° 11' W. Find ship's position at the time of taking the second observation.

9. In D.R. lat. 55° 52' N., an observation of the Sun bearing 213° T. gave long. 11° 17' W. Ship then steered a course 168° T. for 27 miles, when a second observation of the Sun bearing 252° T. gave long. 11° 17' W. Find ship's position at the time of taking the second observation.

10. A ship in D.R. lat. 55° 46' N. took an a.m. observation of the Sun on the prime vertical, which gave long. 10° 08' W. Ship then steamed 259° T. at 8 knots for 7 hours, when a second observation of the Sun bearing 215° T. gave long. 11° 54' W. Find the ship's position at the time of taking the second observation.

CHAPTER 24.

PRACTICAL POSITION LINE NAVIGATION
THE LONGITUDE METHOD

In M.O.T. examinations, questions on P.L. navigation may possibly follow the lines which have been explained in Chapter 23 and the examples given in Exercises 29, 30 and 31. It is, however, possible that candidates may be required to work out the actual calculations in full instead of having the results of the calculations given in the question.

Four examples of practical P.L. navigation are given below, with sextant observations of the Sun fully worked out by the Longitude Method. Two of these illustrate an a.m. observation for longitude; run to noon; and a meridian altitude observation. Each step is co-ordinated with the previous step, and the ship's noon position found. The third example illustrates in the same way an a.m. observation; run between sights; and a p.m. longitude observation. The last example is of two p.m. observations with a run between them.

Students are advised in the first place to work these four examples step-by-step. By this means they will not only make themselves familiar with the methods actually in use at sea of working and co-ordinating sights, but will also learn to adopt a straightforward, easy-to-understand form of lay-out for their work before proceeding to the examples given in Exercise 32.

It will be noted in these examples that the haversine method has been used when finding the longitude. Those who are accustomed to using the secant-cosecant method will find the resultant answers just the same as those given.

A.M. Longitude, Run to Noon, Noon Latitude.

Example 1.—On October 9th, a.m. at ship in D.R. latitude 41° 30' N., the obs. alt. of the Sun's L.L. was 22° 18'. Height of eye 26 feet. G.M.T. 12h 28m 49s. Ship then steered 255° T., 40 miles, when the obs. mer. alt. of the Sun's L.L. was 42° 25', South of observer. Height of eye 26 feet. G.M.T. 16h 00m 00s. Find the ship's true position at noon.

1. *Find "longitude at sights"*

G.M.T. 12h 28m 49s			Obs. alt.	22°	18·0′	Nat hav Z.D.		30906
G.H.A. Sun	3°	09·1′	Tot. corr.	+	9·0	Nat hav (L+D)		16339
Increment	7	12·3	True alt.	22	27·0	Nat hav		14567
	10	21·4	Z.D.	67	33·0	L. hav		9·16336

Decl.	6° 11·0′ S.	A	·679+	Lat. L. sec	0·12554
		B	·137+	Dec. L. sec	0·00253
(L+D)	47° 41·0′				
		C	·816+	L.H.A. L. hav	9·29143

True bearing S.E.

L.H.A. Sun 52° 30·1′ E.
G.H.A. Sun 10　21·4 W.

Longitude 62　51·5 W.

2. *Run to noon*

	Lat. sts.	41°	30·0′ N.	Long. sts.	62°	51·5′ W.
Run 255°, 40 mls.	D. Lat.		10·4 S.	D. Long.		51·4 W.
D.R. Lat. noon		41	19·6 N.	Long. noon 63		42·9 W.

3. *Find noon lat. and position.*

Obs. alt.	42°	25·5′ S.	D.R. Lat.	41°	19·6′ N.	S.　E.
Tot. corr.+		10·3	Obs. Lat.	41	09·9 N.	
True alt.	42	35·8 S.	Diff.		9·7′ S.	N.　W.

Z.D.	47	24·2 N.	
Decl.	6	14·3 S.	Longitude corr.=9·7 × ·816=7·9′ W.

Noon Lat. 41　09·9 N.　　Noon Long. 63° 42·9′ W.+7·9′ W.
　　　　　　　　　　　　　=63° 50·8′ W.

Example 2.—On July 22nd, a.m. at ship in D.R. latitude 51° 20′ N., the obs. alt. of the Sun's L.L. was 35° 42′. Height of eye 20 feet. G.M.T. 10h 38m 22s. Ship then steered 113° T., 44 miles, when the obs. mer. alt. of the Sun's L.L. was 58° 57′, bearing South. Height of eye 20 feet. Correct declination at noon 20° 18·4′ N. Find ship's noon position.

| G.M.T. 10h 38m 22s. | Obs. alt. | 35° 42·0′ | Nat hav Z.D. | 20700 |

| G.H.A. Sun 328° 25·0′ | Tot. corr. | + 10·4 | Nat hav (L—D) | 07140 |

| Increment | 9 | 35·5 | True alt. | 35 | 52·4 | Nat hav | 13560 |

| | 338 | 00·5 | Z.D. | 54 | 07·6 | L. hav | 9·13225 |

Decl.	20	20·3 N.	A ·796+		Lat. L. sec	0·20427
			B ·440—		Dec. L. sec	0·02796
(L—D)	30	59·7				
			C ·356+		L.H.A. L. hav	9·36448

L.H.A. Sun 302° 29·1′   Bearing   S.   E.
G.H.A. Sun 338   00·5

Longitude   35   31·4 W.   N.   W.

| | D.R. Lat. | 51° 20·0′ N. | Long. | 35° 31·4′ W. |
| Run—113°, 44 mls. | D. Lat. | 17·2 S. | D. Long. | 1 04·3 E. |

| Noon. D.R. Lat. | 51 02·8 N. | Long. | 34 27·1 W. |

| Obs. mer. alt. 58° 57·0′ S. | Lat. D.R. | 51° 02·8′ N. |
| Tot. corr. + 11·1 | Lat. obs. | 51 10·3 N. |

| True alt. | 59 08·1 S. | Lat. corr. | 7·5 | (Corr. N & E) |

| Z.D. | 30 51·9 N. | |
| Decl. | 20 18·4 N. | Long. corr.=7·5 × ·356=2·7′ E. |

| Latitude | 51 10·3 N. |

Noon latitude 51° 10·3′ N.   Longitude 34° 24·4′ W.

A.M. Longitude, Run Between Sights, P.M. Longitude.

Example 3.—On June 14th, a.m. at ship in D.R. lat. 49° 30′ N., the obs. alt. of the Sun's L.L. was 50° 20′. Height of eye 28 feet. G.M.T. 06h 36m 21s. Ship then steamed 55 miles on a course of 071° T., when an obs. alt, of the Sun's L.L., West of the meridian, was 46° 23′. Height of eye 28 feet. G.M.T. 12h 00m 00s. Required the ship's position at the time of taking the second observation.

First observation

G.M.T.	06h 36m 21s.		Obs. alt.	50° 20·0′
G.H.A. Sun	279° 05·3′		Tot. corr.	+ 10·1
Decl.	23° 14·5′ N.		True alt.	50 30·1
L.—D.	26° 15·5′		Z.D.	39 29·9

Nat hav Z.D.	11418		L.H.A.	322° 12·5′
Nat hav (L—D)	05160		G.H.A.	279 05·3
Nat hav	06258		Long.	43 07·2 E.
L. hav	8·79647		A	1·51+
Lat. L. sec	0·18746		B	·70—
Dec. L. sec	0·03676		C	0·81+
L.H.A. L. hav	9·02069		Bg.	S.E.

Run between Sights.

	Lat. left 49° 30·0′ N.		Long. left 43° 07·2′ E.
N. 71° E., 55 mls.	D. Lat. 17·9 N.		D. Long. 1 20·0 E.
	D.R. Lat. 49 47·9 N.		D.R. Long. 44 27·2 E.

Second Observation.

G.M.T.	12h 00m 00s.		Obs. alt.	46° 23·0′
G.H.A. Sun	359° 59·2′		Tot. corr.	+ 10·0
Decl.	23° 15·2′ N.		True alt.	46 33·0
(L—D)	26° 32·7′		Z.D.	43 27·0

Nat hav Z.D.	13701		L.H.A.	404° 17·8′
Nat hav (L—D)	05271		G.H.A.	359 59·2
Nat hav	08430		Long.	44 18·6 E.
L. hav	8·92580		A	1·21+
Lat. L. sec	0·19011		B	·62—
Dec. L. sec	0·03679		C	0·59+
L.H.A. L. hav	9·15270		Bg.	S.W.

To Find True Position

p.m. D.R. long. 44° 27·2′ E.
p.m. Obs. long. 44 18·6 E.

$$\text{Lat. corr.} = \frac{\text{D. Long.}}{C^1 + C^2} = \frac{8·6}{1·4} = 6·1' \text{ S.}$$

D. Long.   8·6

D.R. lat. 49° 47·9′ N.
Lat. corr. —   6·1 S.

Obs. lat. 49 41·8 N.

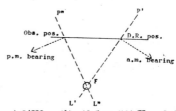

Long. correction (*a*) (6·1 × ·81) W.=4·9′W.   (*b*) (6·1 × ·59) E.=3·6′E.
D.R. long. (*a*) 44° 27·2′ E.   (*b*)   44° 18·6′ E.
Long. corr. —   4·9 W.   +   3·6 E.

Obs. long. 44 22·3 E.   44 22·2 E.

P.M. Longitude, Run Between Sights, P.M. Longitude.

Example 4.—On June 12th, p.m. at ship in D.R. lat. 52° 10′ N., the obs. alt. of the Sun's L.L. was 49° 05′. Height of eye 22 feet. G.M.T. 16h 21m 49s. Ship then steamed 28 miles on a 200° T. course, when a second obs. of the Sun's L.L. was 32° 02·5′. Height of eye 22 feet. G.M.T. 18h 20m 00s. Required the ship's position at the time of taking the second observation.

First Observation

G.M.T.	16h 21m 49s		obs. alt.	49° 05·0′
G.H.A. Sun	65° 32·3′		Tot. corr.	+ 10·7
Decl.	23° 08·9′ N.		True alt.	49 15·7
(L—D)	29° 01·1′		Z.D.	40 44·3
Nat hav Z.D.	12115		L.H.A.	37° 32·3′
Nat hav (L—D)	06277		G.H.A.	65 32·3
Nat hav	05838		Long.	28 00·0
L. hav	8·76626		A	1·68+
Lat. L. sec	0·21228		B	·70—
Dec. L. sec	0·03645		C	·98+
L.H.A. L. hav	9·01499		Bg.	S. W.

Run between sights

Lat. left	52° 10·0′ N.	Long. left	28° 00·0′ W.	
D. Lat.	26·3 S.	D. Long.	15·6 W.	(200° T.,
				28 miles.)
D.R. lat.	51 43·7 N.	Long.	28 15·6 W.	

Second Observation

G.M.T.	18h 20m 00s		Obs. alt.	32° 02·5′
G.H.A. Sun	95° 04·7′		Tot. corr.	+ 10·0
Decl.	23° 09·3′ N.		True alt.	32 12·5
(L—D)	28° 34·4′		Z.D.	57 47·5
Nat hav Z.D.	23350		L.H.A.	66° 48·5′
Nat hav (L—D)	06089		G.H.A.	95 04·7
Nat hav	17261		Long.	28 16·2 W.
L. hav	9·23707		A	·543+
Lat. L. sec	0·20803		B	·466—
Dec. L. sec	0·03648		C	·077+
L.H.A. L. hav	9·48158		Bg.	S. W.

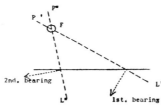

To find True Position

D.R. long. 28° 15·6′ W. $C^1—C^2 = 0.9$ Lat. corr. $= \dfrac{0·6}{0·9} = 0·7′$ N.

Obs. long. 28 16·2 W.

D. Long.	0·6	Long. corr.	(a) 0·7 × ·98 = 0·7′ W.
			(b) 0·7 × ·08 = 0
D.R. lat.	51° 43·7′ N.	D.R. long.	(a) 28° 15·6′ W.
Lat. corr.	0·7 N.	Long. corr.	0·7 W.
Obs. lat.	51 44·4 N.	Obs. long.	28 16·3 W.

EXERCISE 32.

To Find Ship's True Position.

1. On July 15th, a.m. at ship in D.R. latitude 49° 20' N., the obs. alt. of the Sun's L.L. was 27° 40'. Height of eye 25 feet. G.M.T. 11h 27m 36s. Ship then steered 328° T., 50 miles, when the obs. mer. alt. of the Sun's L.L. was 61° 21·5' S. Ht. of eye 25 feet. Noon decl. 21° 32·1' N. Required the ship's true position at noon.

2. On October 7th, a.m. at ship in D.R. latitude 40° 30' N., the obs. alt. of the Sun's L.L. was 19° 10'. Height of eye 22 feet. G.M.T. 09h 38m 21s. Ship then steered 153° T., for 4 hours at 9·5 knots, when the obs. mer. alt. of the Sun's L.L. was 44° 21' S. Ht. of eye 22 feet. Required the ship's position at noon.

3. On December 22nd, a.m. at ship in est. latitude 31° 17' N., the obs. alt. of the Sun's L.L. was 16° 22'. Height of eye 20 feet. G.M.T. 10h 27m 51s. Ship then steered 052° T., 33 miles, when the obs. mer. alt. of the Sun's L.L. was 34° 51' S. Ht. of eye 20 feet. Required ship's noon position.

4. On June 13th, a.m. at ship in D.R. latitude 52° 09' N., the obs. alt. of the Sun's L.L. was 20° 22'. Height of eye 25 feet. G.M.T. 09h 00m 00s. Ship then steered 219° T., 56 miles, when the obs. mer. alt. of the Sun's L.L. was 61° 41' S. Decl. 23° 12·3' N. Find true position of the ship at noon.

5. On July 23rd, a.m. at ship in D.R. latitude 48° 45' N., the obs. alt. of the Sun's L.L. was 24° 08'. Height of eye 25 feet. G.M.T. 09h 23m 41s. Ship then steered 031° T., 83 miles, when a p.m. observation of the Sun's L.L. gave obs. alt. 41° 20'. Ht. of eye 25 feet. G.M.T. 17h 37m 09s. Find the ship's position at the time of taking the second observation.

6. On October 8th, a.m. at ship in est. latitude 44° 25' N., the obs. alt. of the Sun's L.L. was 17° 22'. Height of eye 19 feet. G.M.T. 06h 29m 09s. Ship then steered 322° T., 62 miles, when a p.m. observation of the Sun's L.L. gave obs. alt. 25° 51·5'. Ht. of eye 19 feet. G.M.T. 13h 20m 13s. Required the ship's position at the time of taking the second observation.

7. On December 21st, a.m. at ship in D.R. latitude 38° 16' N., the obs. alt. of the Sun's L.L. was 12° 47'. Height of eye 20 feet. G.M.T. 11h 38m 16s. Ship then steered 071° T., for 55 miles, when a p.m. observation of the Sun's L.L. gave obs. alt. 13° 45'. Ht. 20 feet. G.M.T. 18h 00m 00s. Required the ship's true position at the time of taking the second observation.

8. On September 24th, a.m. at ship in D.R. latitude 49° 06′ N., the obs. alt. of the Sun's L.L. was 20° 23′. Height of eye 25 feet. G.M.T. 07h 22m 51s. Ship then steered 205° T. for 67 miles, when a p.m. observation of the Sun's L.L. gave obs. alt. 25° 39·5′. G.M.T. 14h 30m 02s. Required the ship's true position at the time of taking the second observation.

9. On January 2nd, a.m. at ship in est. latitude 30° N., the obs. alt. of the Sun's L.L. was 12° 47′. Height of eye 18 feet. G.M.T. 10h 39m 14s. Ship then steered 090° T. for 61 miles, when a p.m. observation of the Sun's L.L. gave obs. alt. 16° 21·5′. Ht. of eye 18 feet. G.M.T. 18h 00m 00s. Required the ship's position at the time of taking the second observation.

10. On October 9th, p.m. at ship in D.R. latitude 41° 57′ N., the obs. alt. of the Sun's L.L. was 37° 28′. Height of eye 23 feet. G.M.T. 16h 21m 19s. Ship then steered 341° T. for 22 miles, when a second observation of the Sun's L.L. gave obs. alt. 19° 23′. Ht. of eye 23 feet. G.M.T. 18h 37m 50s. Required the ship's position at the time of taking the second observation.

CHAPTER 25.

CROSSING A CELESTIAL POSITION LINE WITH A TERRESTRIAL POSITION LINE

In Chapters 10 and 11 (Chartwork), students were shown how a ship's position can be fixed by "crossing" visual bearings of shore objects. In Chapter 23, they were shown how a ship's position can be fixed by crossing position lines obtained from two observations of the Sun at different times.

A ship's position can also be fixed by crossing a P.L. obtained from an observation of a celestial body with a P.L. obtained from a visual bearing of a terrestrial object.

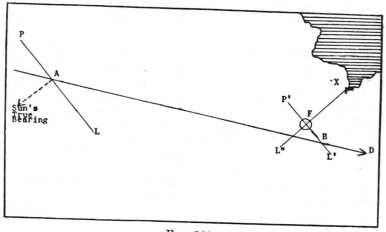

FIG. 100.

In Fig. 100, a p.m. observation of the Sun, using a D.R. latitude, gave position A on a position line PL.

The ship then steered in the direction AD for a certain known distance, represented on the sketch by AB. At that time, a corrected compass bearing of the light X was in the direction $P''L''$. The position line PL is transferred to $P'L'$, drawn through position B. Where the transferred position line meets $P''L''$ at F is the ship's position.

In an examination, the candidate may be furnished with the longitude found by observation of a celestial body "out of the meridian", or he may only be given the particulars of the observation, the actual longitude having to be found by calculation. The bearing of a shore

L   301

object is then given, after the ship is presumed to have steered a certain course for a specified distance. It is required to find the ship's true position at this time.

The correct answer can be found by using various methods. Three of these methods are discussed here:

    1. By Calculation;
    2. By Squared Paper;
    3. By Plotting on a Chart.

A Little Bit of Revision.—All triangles have three sides and three angles. To "solve" any triangle—that is, to be able to find the values of all six parts—the values of at least three parts must be known. If, however, the three known parts were all angles, the triangle could not be fully solved, as any number of triangles of different sizes can be formed using the same three angles.

The angles of a triangle are usually distinguished by capital letters, e.g., ABC; XYZ; PZX, etc., while the side opposite each angle is usually labelled with the small letter corresponding to the angle. (See page 24.)

Oblique-Angled Triangles.—In all previous problems which have involved the use of plane triangles, these have been "right-angled" triangles. That is, one of the angles has measured 90°.

Triangles in which none of the angles measure 90° are called Oblique-angled triangles, and the rules used for solving right-angled triangles cannot be used. Special formulae must be employed, depending on what particulars are known about the triangle.

It will be shown later in the chapter that in the problem now being discussed, the values of two angles are known, and also the length of the side opposite to one of these angles.

Of Two Angles and the Sides Opposite to Them in an Oblique-Angled Triangle, Given any Three to Find the Fourth.

The formula used in the problem is known as the Sine Formula, and it is particularly simple. Usually it is written in such a way as to cover all sides and angles of the triangle, thus:

$$\frac{a}{\sin A} = \frac{b}{\sin B} = \frac{c}{\sin C}$$

If angles A and B, and the length of side b are known, and it is required to find the length of side a, the formula would be written

$$\frac{a}{\sin A} = \frac{b}{\sin B}$$

In the equation, a (the unknown quantity) must appear on one side by itself, so $\sin A$ is transferred to the other side. A "dividing" factor in its original position, it must be made a "multiplying" factor when transferred, and the equation becomes

$$a = \frac{b \sin A}{\sin B}$$

To divide by a sine is the same as to multiply by its reciprocal, so, to facilitate the use of logarithms, the equation finally reads

$$a=b \sin A \cosec B$$

Example 1.—Given angle $A=23°$, side $a=17$ feet, and angle $B=61°$.

Find the length of side b.

$$\frac{b}{\sin B}=\frac{a}{\sin A} \quad \text{or} \quad b=a \sin B \cosec A$$

$$17 \times \sin 61° \times \cosec 23°$$

17	log	1·23045
61°	L. Sin	9·94182
23°	L. cosec	0·40812
	Log b	1·58039

Side $b=38·05$ feet.

Example 2.—Side $x=42·7$ feet; angle $X=38°$; and angle $Y=29°$. Find the length of side y.

$$\frac{y}{\sin Y}=\frac{x}{\sin X} \quad \text{or} \quad y=x \sin Y \cosec X$$

42·7	log	1·63043
29°	L. sin	9·68557
38°	L. cosec	0·21066
	log y	1·52666

Side $y=33·62$ feet.

Example 3.—The course and distance from B (ship's D.R. position) to lighthouse C is S. 34° W., 11 miles. A transferred P.L. through B is in the direction 170°—350° T. Bearing of C from ship is 265° T. Find the distance from B to ship's true position at F. (side c).

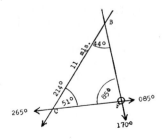

First draw a rough sketch, showing BC (side f)=214°, 11 miles;
$$FC \quad =265°;$$
$$BF \quad =170°.$$

F is the ship's true position.

Angle $C=51°$ (265°—214°)

Angle $B=44°$ (214°—170°)

Therefore angle $F=85°$ $\{180°-(51°+44°)\}$

$$\frac{c}{\sin C}=\frac{f}{\sin F} \quad \text{or} \quad c=f \sin C \; \text{cosec} \; F$$

11	log	1·04139
51°	L. sin	9·89050
85°	L. cosec	0·00166
	log c	0·93355

$$c=8\text{·}581 \text{ miles.}$$

Exercise on Sine Formula

1. Given angle A 31°, side a 47 feet, and angle B 46°, find the length of side b.

2. Given angle B 62°, side a 12·6 miles, and angle C 38°, find the length of side b.

3. Course and distance from ship's estimated position to a lighthouse bearing 252° T. is 287° T., 9·6 miles. (Side f). The transferred P.L. through B is 000°—180°. Find the distance from B to F (side c).

4. Course and distance from ship's estimated position to a lighthouse bearing 015° T. is 057° T., 8·2 miles. Transferred P.L. is 123°—303° T. Find the distance from ship's estimated position to the true position.

Answers.

1.   65·64 feet.   2.   Angle A=80°. b=11·3 miles.

3.   5·79 miles   4.   5·769 miles.

Working the Problem.—Whether the problem is solved by calculation, by using Squared Paper, or by Plotting, a certain order of work must be adhered to. While the method of using calculations throughout is fairly lengthy, the only new formula required is the sine formula, which has just been explained above.

Example 4.—In D.R. latitude 40° 40′ N., a p.m. observation of the Sun bearing 243° T. gave longitude 10° 21·5′ W. Thereafter the ship steered a course of 108° T. for 42 miles, when a light in latitude 40° 36′ N., longitude 9° 22′ W. was observed to bear 073° T. Find the ship's true position at this time.

1. The ship's D.R. position and the P.L. at the time of the celestial observation must be found.

   In this case, the D.R. position is given in the question, and the P.L., 90° from the true bearing of the Sun, is 153°—333°. (In the accompanying sketch, "A" is the D.R. position, and P.L. the position line.)

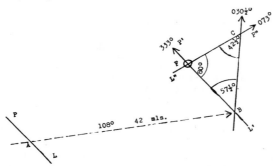

2. Using the course and distance run by the ship, (108° T., 42 miles) find the ship's D.R. position when the bearing of the light was taken. (Pos. "B". with P'L' the transferred position line in the sketch.)

Pos. "A" Lat.   40°   40·0′ N.   Long.   10°   21·5′ W.
    D. Lat.   13·0   S.   D. Long.   52·5   E.   (S. 72° E.,
                                                     42 miles.)
Pos. "B" Lat.   40   27·0   N.   Long.   9   29·0   W.

3. Using the Traverse Tables, find the direction and distance from "B" to the position of the shore light. (*BC* in the sketch.)
             "C"   40°   36·0′ N.   9°   22·0′ W.
             "B"   40   27·0   N.   9   29·0   W.

       D. Lat.   9·0   D. Long. 7·0   Dep. 5·3′

In lat. $40\frac{1}{2}°$, D. Long. 7·0′ gives Dep. 5·3′.
     D. Lat. 9·0 and Dep. 5·3′ gives
Co. and dist. from "B" to "C" (side *f* in sketch) $030\frac{1}{2}°$, 10·5 miles.

4. From the sketch, calculate angles *C* and *F*.
   Angle *C*   —   Diff. between the true bearing of the light (073°) and the direction of "C" from "B" ($030\frac{1}{2}°$) ($073—030\frac{1}{2}$)=$42\frac{1}{2}°$.
   Angle *B*   —   Diff. between P′L′ (333°) and the direction of "C" from "B" ($030\frac{1}{2}°$)=$57\frac{1}{2}°$.
   Angle *F*   — $\{180°-(42\frac{1}{2}°+57\frac{1}{2}°)\}$
                   =80°.

5.   Find the length of c (BF).

$$\frac{c}{\sin C} = \frac{f}{\sin F} \quad \text{or} \quad c = f \sin C \operatorname{cosec} F$$

10·5	log	1·02119
42·5°	L. sin	9·82968
80°	L. cosec	0·00665

Log c 0·85752

c=7·2 miles.

6.   Find ship's true position, N. 27° W., 7·2 miles from "B".

"B"	40° 27·0′ N.		9° 29·0′ W.
D. Lat.	6·4 N.	D. Long.	4·3 W.
Pos. "F" Lat.	40 33·4 N.		9 33·3 W. Long.

Example 5.—On July 23rd, A.M. at ship in est. lat. 41° 27′ N., long. 41° 10′ W., the true alt. of the Sun's L.L. was 25° 47·7′. G.M.T. 10h 00m 00s. The ship then steered a course of 216° T. for 47 miles, when a lighthouse in lat. 40° 54′ N., long. 42° 02′ W. bore 329° T. Find the ship's position at the time of taking the visual bearing.

(NOTE.—This example is fully worked out both by the "Longitude Method" and by the "Intercept Method*". Students who prefer the longitude Method should leave the other method alone, and *vice versa*.)

*See Chapters 26 *and* 27.

A.   BY LONGITUDE METHOD.

1.   G.M.T. July 23rd, 10h 00m 00s.
    Corr. Decl. 20° 08·6′ N.   P.D. 69° 51·4′.
    Corr. G.H.A. Sun 328° 24·4′.

Alt.	25°	47·7′			L.H.A. Sun	287°	07·4′
Lat.	41	27·0	Sec	0·12521	G.H.A. Sun	328	24·4
P.D.	69	51·4	Cosec	0·02741			
					Longitude	41	17·0 W.
Sum	137	06·1					
½S.	68	33·0	Cos	9·56311	A	·270+	
Rem.	42	45·3	Sin	9·83178	B	·383−	
	L. hav L.H.A.			9·54751	C	·113−	

Sun's True B'g. N. 85¼° E.

P.L.   175¼°—355¼°

2.

Lat. left	41°	27·0′ N.	Long. left	41°	17·0′ W.
D. Lat.		38·0 S.	D. Long.		36·6 W.

Co. S. 36° W., 47 miles.

Lat. "B"	40	49·0 N.	Long. "B"	41	53·6 W.

3.

Pos. "C"	40°	54·0′ N.	42°	02·0′ W.
Pos. "B"	40	49·0 N.	41	53·6 W.
D. Lat.		5·0 N.	D. Long.	8·4 W. Dep. 6·3′

Co. and dist. from "B" to "C" N. 52° W., 8·1 miles.

4.
Angle $C=21°$.
Angle $F=26\frac{1}{4}°$.

5.
$$c=8\cdot1\times\sin 21°\times \text{cosec } 26\frac{1}{4}°$$

8·1	log	0·90849
21°	L. sin	9·55433
26¼°	L. cosec	0·35429

Log c 0·81711 $c=6\cdot6$ miles.

From "B" to "F" is S. $4\frac{3}{4}°$ E., 6·6 miles.

6.

Pos. "B"	40°	49·0′ N.	41°	53·6′ W.
D. Lat.		6·6 S.	D. Long.	·7 E.

(S. 4¾° E., 6·6 miles.)

Pos. "F"	40	42·4 N.	41	52·9 W.

B. BY INTERCEPT METHOD.

(See Chapters 26 *and* 27)

1. G.M.T. July 23rd, 10h 00m 00s.
 True Alt. 25° 47·7'.   Z.D. 64° 12·3'.
 G.H.A. sun 328° 24·4'.   Est. L.H.A. Sun 287° 14·4'.
 Declination 20° 08·6' N.   (L—D) 21° 18·4'.

L.H.A. Sun	L. hav	9·54631		
Lat.	L. cos	9·87479		
Decl.	L. cos	9·97260		

 L. hav   9·39370   Nat. hav ·24757

 (L—D)   Nat hav ·03417

A ·275+
B ·384—

 C.Z.D. Nat. hav ·28174   C.Z.D. 64° 07·1'
                             T.Z.D. 64   12·3

C ·109—

 True B'g. N. 85¼° E.   Intercept away   5·2

 P.L. 175¼°—355¼°

Est. Pos.	41° 27·0' N.	41° 10·0' W.
Intercept	0·4 S.	6·9 W.
Pos. "A"	41 26·6 N.	41 16·9 W.

2. Pos. "A" 41° 26·6' N.   41° 16·9' W.
 D. Lat.   38·0 S.   36·6 W. S. 36° W., 47 miles.

 Pos. "B" 40 48·6 N.   41 53·5 W.

3. Pos. "C" 40° 54·0' N.   42° 02·0' W.
 Pos. "B" 40   48·6 N.   41 53·5 W.

 D. Lat.   5·4   D. Long.   8·5   Dep. 6·4

 D. Lat. 5·4' N., Dep. 6·4' W. gives
      Co. N. 50° W., 8·4 miles, from *B* to *C*.

4.   Angle C=19°
                      Angle F=26¼°

5.
$$c = 8 \cdot 4 \times \sin 19° \times \operatorname{cosec} 26\tfrac{1}{4}°$$

8·4	log	0·92128
19°	L. sin	9·51264
26¼°	L. cosec	0·35429

Log c 0·79121 $c = 6 \cdot 2'$

6. Pos. "B"   40° 48·6' N.   41° 53·5' W.
D. Lat.   6·2 S.   D. Long.   0·7 E.   S. 4¾° E.,
                                              6·2 miles
Pos. "F"   40   42·4 N.   41   52·8 W.

C. BY SQUARED PAPER.

After Parts 1, 2 and 3 of the calculation have been completed, the ship's position can then be found, if desired, by using squared paper instead of calculating the position by the sine formula.

It must be stressed, however, that difference of longitude cannot be used on squared paper. D. Long. must be converted to Departure, which is used instead.

As an example, if the above problem has been worked by the Longitude Method, any suitable point on the squared paper is chosen to represent position "B". From this point, using a protractor, lay off the course and distance to position "C", as found in Part 3— N. 52° W., 8·1 miles.

Through "B", draw also the transferred position line (175¼°), and through "C" draw the reversed bearing of the light from the ship (149° T.) to meet the transferred P.L. at "F".

By measurement it will be found that from "B" to "F", the difference of latitude is 6·6', and the departure 0·6'. The departure is converted to difference of longitude (0·7'), and this is applied to the longitude of "B".

D. BY PLOTTING ON A CHART.

If the latitude of the problem given in an examination lies within the limits of Plotting Chart Exn. 30c., the working of the problem can be greatly simplified. In actual practice at sea, this is the method which would be used to obtain a fix.

The ship's initial position is calculated in the usual way, either by the Longitude Method or by the Intercept Method, and marked on the chart. The ship's course is drawn through this position.

When a visual bearing of a terrestrial object has been taken, it is laid off on the chart in the normal way. At the same time, position "B" is marked on the course line, according to the distance steamed by the ship since the celestial observation was taken. The transferred P.L. is then drawn through "B", meeting the line of visual bearing at "F". This point is the ship's true position.

Celestial observation, run, and terrestrial bearing.

Example 6.—In estimated latitude 55° 40′ N., an observation of the Sun bearing 145° T. gave longitude 10° 20′ W. After steaming 40 miles on a course of 275° T., Exna Point bore 335° T. Find the ship's position at the time of taking this bearing.

Method of Plotting.—Lay off the latitude and longitude of the estimated point of departure. Call it "A".

From *A*, lay off the course and distance steamed, calling the position reached "B". Through *B* draw the transferred position line (*P′L′*) in the direction 055°—235°, 90° from the Sun's true bearing.

From Exna Point lay off the line of bearing 155°—335°. Where this bearing meets *P′L′*, at "F", is the ship's position:

Lat. 55° 40′ N., Long. 11° 37·8′ W.

Example 7.—In misty weather, a snap bearing—300° T.—was obtained of the lighthouse on Round Island. The ship then steamed 249° T., 50 miles, when an observation of the Sun bearing 110° T. gave longitude 11° 40′ W., using an estimated latitude of 55° N. Find the ship's position at the time of taking the observation of the Sun.

Method of Plotting.—Lay off the bearing of Round Island Lt. Ho. From *any point* on this line (the ship must be to the S.E'rd. of the island), lay off the course and distance steamed by the ship (249°, 50 miles). Call the D.R. position at that time "B". Through *B*, draw *P′L′*. Since the original bearing of the light was itself a position line, *P′L′* through *B* must also be in the direction 120°—300°. The observed longitude 11° 40′ W., was obtained using an estimated latitude of 55° N. Through this position draw *P″L″*, 90° from the Sun's true bearing. Where this *P″L″* cuts *P′L′* is the ship's actual position:

Lat. 55° 05·3′ N., Long. 11° 36·4′ W.

Exercise 33.

1. On September 24th, P.M. at ship in D.R. lat. 53° N., long 17° W., the obs. alt. of the Sun's L.L. was 21° 21′. Height of eye 23 feet. G.M.T. 16h 26m 51s. The ship then steamed 56 miles on a course 203° T., when a light in lat. 51° 59′ N., long. 17° 37·6′ W. bore 260° T. Find the ship's position at the time of taking the bearing.

2. On December 23rd, P.M. at ship in D.R. lat. 11° 52′ N., long. 45° W., the obs. alt. of the Sun's L.L. was 39° 15′. Height of eye 26 feet. G.M.T. 17h 27m 00s. Thereafter the ship steered 023° T. for 34 miles, when a light in lat. 12° 34′ N., long. 44° 32′ W., bore 102° T. Find the ship's position at the time of taking the bearing.

3. On July 16th, P.M. at ship in est. lat. 51° N., long. 42° 40′ W., the obs. alt. of the Sun's L.L. was 21° 11′. Height of eye

27 feet. G.M.T. 20h 25m 18s. The ship then steamed 31 miles on a course 017° T., when a light in lat. 51° 40' N., long. 42° 40' W. bore 350° T. Find the ship's position at the time the bearing was taken.

4. On June 14th, P.M. at ship in lat. by D.R. 50½° N., long. 14¼° E., the true alt. of the Sun was 38° 30·1'. G.M.T. 14h 51m 32s. Ship then steamed 40 miles on a course 127° T., when a light in lat. 50° N., long. 14° 30' E. bore 090° T. Find the ship's position at the time the bearing was taken.

5. On October 7th, A.M. at ship in D.R. lat. 32° 41' N., long. 8° 15' E., the true alt. of the Sun was 35° 41·5'. G.M.T. 08h 31m 14s. Thereafter the ship steered 326° T. for 25 miles, when a lt. ho. in lat. 32° 52' N., long. 8° 09' E., bore 013° T. Find the ship's position at the time of taking the bearing.

6. On October 9th, P.M. at ship in D.R. lat. 42° 20' N., long. 5¼° W., the corrected altitude of the Sun was 29° 30'. G.M.T. 14h 47m 25s. Ship then steered 218° T. for 39 miles, when a light in lat. 41° 40' N., long. 5° 50·5' W. bore 241° T. Find the ship's position when the bearing was taken.

(The remaining questions to be solved by plotting on Chart Exn. 30c)

7. In D.R. lat. 55° 20' N., an observation of the Sun bearing 246° T. gave long. 11° 07' W. Ship then steamed 310° T., 32 miles, when Exna Point was observed to bear 017° T. Find the ship's position when the bearing was taken.

8. In D.R. lat. 55° 55' N., an observation of the Sun bearing 280° T. gave long. 11° 22' W. Ship then steamed 34 miles on a course 150° T., when Round Island Light bore abeam to port. Find the ship's position at this time.

9. While steering a course of 074° T., Exna Point was observed abeam, but the ship's distance off the light was not obtained. After continuing on the same course for 6 hours at 8 knots, the longitude by observation was found to be 10° 12' W., using D.R. lat. 56° N. Sun's bearing was 144° T. Find the ship's position at the time of taking the observation.

10. Using est. lat. 56° N., an observation of the Sun bearing 265° T. gave long. 11° 16' W. Ship then steered 156·5° T. for 45 miles, when Round Is. Lt. bore 029° T. Find the ship's position at this time.

11. Steering 235° T., a bearing was taken of Round Is. Lt. when it was four points abaft the port beam. The ship continued on the same course for 36 miles, when an observation of the Sun bearing 116° T. gave long. 11° 40' W., using est. lat. 55° 15' N. Find the ship's position at the time of taking the solar position.

CHAPTER 26.

INTERCEPTS.

Geographical Position of Sun or Star.—The Geographical Position of the Sun or a star—sometimes also referred to as the "Sub-Solar" or "Sub-stellar" position—is the latitude and longitude of a terrestrial position which, at a chosen G.M.T., is immediately underneath the Sun or the particular star.

To find this position, say for the Sun, is a very simple matter. The latitude is the same as the Sun's corrected declination. The longitude is the same as the Sun's G.H.A. at that time. If the G.H.A. is less than 180°, the longitude of the position is West. If the G.H.A. is more than 180°, it is subtracted from 360° and the longitude is named East. For instance:

Decl. 22° N., G.H.A. 67° gives geographical position Lat. 22° N., Long. 67° W.

Decl. 15° S., G.H.A. 300° gives geographical position Lat. 15° S., Long. 60° E.

In Chapter 22, the method used to find a ship's longitude was by calculating the L.H.A. of the Sun, a D.R. latitude being used. The difference between the L.H.A. and the G.H.A. of the Sun at the same G.M.T. represents the longitude.

There is another modern method which is now very extensively used. The practical part remains the same as in the "longitude method". That is, a sextant altitude of the Sun is taken, corrected, and subtracted from 90° to obtain the Sun's true Zenith Distance at the observer's actual position. At the same time, the Greenwich Mean Time is noted.

For the calculation, the observer's *assumed* position, containing both latitude and longitude, is required. This position need not necessarily be the D.R. position, although naturally it should approximate the D.R. position fairly closely. Very often an assumed position can be used in which values are employed which render calculations somewhat easier.

The assumed latitude is used in the same way as if it were a D.R. latitude, and the longitude is used to provide an *assumed* L.H.A. of the Sun. (L.H.A.=G.H.A.± assumed longitude). When the calculation is worked, the result gives the value of the Sun's Zenith Distance AT THE OBSERVER'S ASSUMED POSITION. In most cases, this calculated

312

zenith distance (C.Z.D.) differs by some minutes of arc from the true zenith distance found by sextant observation (T.Z.D.) The difference between them is called AN INTERCEPT.

If the T.Z.D. is less in value than the C.Z.D., the observer's real position is closer to the body's geographical position by the value of the intercept, AND IN THE DIRECTION OF THE BODY'S TRUE BEARING. In this case the intercept would be labelled "T" (towards). If the conditions were reversed—T.Z.D. greater than C.Z.D.—the intercept would be labelled "A" (away).

As in the case of a position found by calculation of the longitude, the position found is correct only under the same conditions. What *has* been found is a position through which the P.L. can be drawn, at right angles to the body's true bearing.

Example.—In assumed latitude 49° N., longitude 16° E., the calculated zenith distance of a celestial body bearing 150° T. was 30°. The true zenith distance as found by sextant observation was 30° 10'.

This would be plotted as shown in Fig. 101.

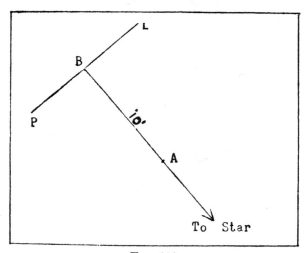

FIG. 101.

"A" is the assumed position, through which the intercept is drawn in a S. 30° E.—N. 30° W. direction, to represent the true bearing of the body.

C.Z.D.=30°. That is, the observer's assumed position is on the circumference of a circle whose centre is the body's geographical position, and whose radius is 30°.

T.Z.D.=30° 10'. That is, the observer's actual position is on the circumference of a circle 10' larger in radius than the first circle.

The intercept is therefore 10′ away, and the observer's actual position is *somewhere* on a P.L. passing through position "B". The P.L. is drawn through "B" at right angles to the true bearing.

Two Observations with Run Between.—As in the Longitude Method, a ship's position can be found by taking two observations of the same body—or of different bodies—at times separated by some hours, the ship continuing her course and speed between observations.

Example 1.—In assumed lat. 38° 30′ N., long. 11° 50′ W., an observation of the Sun bearing 100° T. gave an intercept of 2′ towards. Ship then steered 130° T. for 35 miles, when a second observation of the Sun bearing 220° T. gave an intercept of 3′ away. Find the ship's position at the time of taking the second observation.

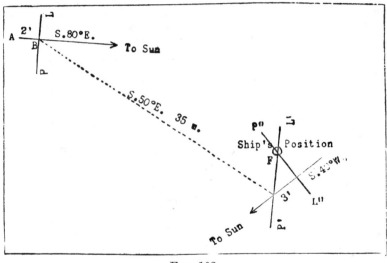

Fɪɢ. 102.

A is the vessel's assumed position, and *AB*, the intercept, is plotted in a true direction of 100° (S. 80° E.) 2 miles.

A P.L. is drawn through *B* at right angles to the bearing. Then from *B* the run—S. 50° E., 35 miles—is plotted. Through the point reached, *P′L′* is drawn, parallel to P.L.

Next the second intercept is drawn through the same point. As this intercept is "away", it is drawn in a N. 40° E. direction, for 3 miles. Through the latter point, *P″L″* is drawn at right angles to the intercept.

The point *F*, where the two position lines meet, represents the ship's position.

If a chart of the area is available, all plotting can be performed on it, and the ship's position read off without further ado. When, however, a chart is not available, the position can readily be found by means of the Traverse Tables.

Fig. 103 is an enlarged drawing of a portion of Fig. 102, position C being the point reached after applying the first intercept and the run between observations.

(1)   Find position C.   (See Fig. 103).

Assumed pos. (A)	38° 30·0' N.	11° 50·0' W.	
(*Traverse Table*)	0·3 S.	2·6 E.	Ist. intercept S. 80° E., 2'.
(B)	38 29·7 N.	11 47·4 W.	
	22·5 S.	34·2 E.	Run—S. 50° E., 35'.
(C)	38 07·2 N.	11 13·2 W.	

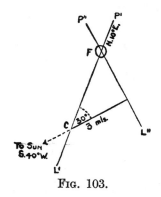

FIG. 103.

Position C has been found. Through it is drawn the transferred P.L. The second *intercept* also is drawn through C. As this is "away", it is drawn in a N. 40° E. direction.

It is now required to find the direction and distance from C to F, the ship's position.

(2)   Find position F.

P'L', the transferred P.L., lies in a direction 010°—190°. The second intercept lies in a direction 040°—220°. The angle at C is therefore 30°.

Using this angle as a Course in the Traverse Table, the D. Lat. is 3 miles. CF, for which the distance is required, is found in the corresponding Distance column.

When, as in the present example, small distances are involved, it is easier and yields more precise results when the figures are multiplied by 10, and the results divided by 10.

Course 30° D. Lat. 30·3 miles (nearest) gives in the Distance column 35 miles. Divided by 10, this gives the distance of C to F as 3·5 miles.

The ship's position is therefore in the direction of $P'L'$ (N. 10° E.), 3·5 miles from position C, which we already know.

(C)	38°	07·2′ N.	11°	13·2′ W.	
		3·5 N.		0·8 E.	CF—N. 10° E., 3·5 miles.
(F)	38	10·7 N.	11	12·4 W.	

Example 2.—Assumed position lat. 43° N., long. 6° W. An a.m. observation of the Sun when bearing 132° T. gave an intercept of 7′ away. Ship then steamed 51 miles on a 298° T. course, when a second observation of the Sun bearing 203° T. gave an intercept of 15′ away. Find the ship's position at the time of taking the second observation.

(A)	43°	00·0′ N.	6°	00·0′ W.	
		4·7 N.		7·1 W.	1st intercept N. 48° W., 7′.*
(B)	43	04·7 N.	6	07·1 W.	
		23·9 N.	1	02·0 W.	Run—N. 62° W., 51 miles.
(C)	43	28·6 N.	7	09·1 W.	
		11·8 N.		15·4 E.	CF—N. 42° E., 15·9′.**
(F)	43	40·4 N.	6	53·7 W.	

NOTES.— *N. 48° W., because intercept is away.

***P'L'* lies in a N. 42° E. direction. Second intercept is N. 23° E. (away), 15′. In the Tables, Course 19°, D. lat. 150′ gives Dist. 159′. *CF* is therefore N. 42° E., 15·9 miles. See Fig. 104.

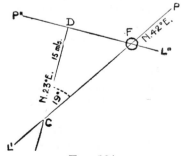

FIG. 104.

EXERCISE 34

From the following particulars, find the ship's position at the time of taking the second observation.

	Assumed position	First		Run	Second	
		Bearing	Intercept		Bearing	Intercept
1.	51° 00. N. 17 00 W.	149°	7′ towards	202° 45 mls.	202°	10′ away
2.	43 00 N. 00 00	248	9′ away	303 38 mls.	130	14′ away
3.	35 20 N. 8 30 E.	080	5′ away	270 49 mls.	145	12′ towards
4.	47 40 N. 12 10 W.	126	16′ towards	018 29 mls.	250	6′ towards
5.	29 15 N. 2 30 E.	287	8′ away	207 55 mls.	163	3′ towards
6.	52 50 N. 5 10 W.	118	11′ towards	163 41 mls.	232	12′ away
7.	42 07 S. 58 20 W.	047	6′ towards	041 50 mls.	295	8′ away
8.	15 30 N. 7 50 E.	082	11′ away	236 32 mls.	141	5′ away
9.	38 00 S. 18 00 W.	058	7′ towards	154 58 mls.	315	9′ towards
10.	28 45 N. 52 50 W.	146	10′ away	287 48 mls.	213	4′ towards
11.	48 30 N. 25 00 W.	113	7·5 towards	090 51 mls.	220	9·8 away
12.	9 20 N. 61 40 E.	077	12·3 away	258 43 mls.	150	8·4 towards

(*see overleaf for additional table.*)

(The following problems to be worked on Form Exn 30c..)

	Assumed position	First		Run	Second	
		Bearing	Intercept		Bearing	Intercept
13.	55 00 N. 10 00 W.	115	7′ away	280 53 mls.	235	4′ towards
14.	55 20 N. 11 50 W.	128	5′ away	064 46 mls.	244	6′ away
15.	55 05 N. 11 00 W.	134	4′ towards	354 54 mls.	258	6′ towards
16.	55 50 N. 10 15 W.	080	8′ towards	253 66 mls.	210	4·5 away
17.	55 34 N. 11 51 W.	239	8′ away	128 38 mls.	Round Id. Lt. bore 066° T.	
18.	Exna Pt. bore 027° T.,			083 59 mls.	095	3′ away

CHAPTER 27.

THE MARCQ ST. HILAIRE PROBLEM.

In Chapter 26 it was shown that if the Zenith Distance is calculated of a particular celestial object from an observer's assumed position, at the same instant as the True Zenith Distance of the same object is obtained by sextant observation, a definite position is found through which to draw a position line.

The means used to find the Calculated Z.D. remain to be explained. The method is generally called the "Marcq St. Hilaire" method, after the name of the navigator who evolved it.

It will be remembered that when finding the longitude by chronometer, the formula used was

$$\text{Hav L.H.A.} = \frac{\text{Hav Z.D.} - \text{Hav (Lat.} \pm \text{Decl.)}}{\text{Cos lat. Cos. decl.}}$$

The L.H.A. in this case is the "unknown quantity."

In the Marcq St. Hilaire problem, an assumed L.H.A. is used— (G.H.A. $\pm$ assumed longitude)—and the unknown quantity is the Z.D. Thus it is necessary to change the formula given above to bring Z.D. on one side of the equation by itself, with the other "arguments" on the other side.

First the denominator of the right-hand side (Cos lat. Cos decl.) is transferred to the left-hand side. A "divider" in its original position, it must be made a "multiplier" when transferred. This first change leaves the formula thus:

Hav L.H.A. Cos lat. Cos decl.=Hav Z.D.—Hav (lat.$\pm$ decl.)

The remaining argument to transfer to the left-hand side is Hav (lat$\pm$ decl.) Subtractive in its original position, it becomes additive when transferred, and the original formula, changed to meet the requirements of the calculation, becomes:

Hav L.H.A. Cos lat. Cos decl.$+$ Hav (lat$\pm$ decl.)=Hav Z.D.

Example 1.—On July 23rd, A.M. at ship in est. lat. 41° 27′ N., long. 41° 10′ W., the obs. alt. of the Sun's L.L. was 25° 38′. Height of eye 20 ft. G.M.T. 10h 00m 00s. Required the direction of the position line, and a position through which to draw it.

G.M.T. 10h 00m 00s   Obs. alt.   25° 38·0'   L.H.A. Log hav 9·54631

G.H.A. Sun 328° 24·4'   Tot. corr. +   9·7   Lat.   Log Cos 9·87479

Est. long. W–41 10·0   True alt.   25   47·7   Decl. Log Cos 9·97260

L.H.A. Sun 287 14·4   T.Z.D.   64   12·3   Log Hav 9·39370

Decl.   20° 08·6' N.   A=·275+   Nat Hav ·24757

(L—D)   21° 18·4'   B=·384—   (L—D) Nat Hav ·03417

C=·109—   C.Z.D. Nat Hav ·28174

True Bearing N. 85¼° E.   C.Z.D. 64° 07·1'

T.Z.D. 64 12·3

P.L.   175¼°—355¼°   Intercept   5·2 Away

Ship's est. pos.   Lat. 41° 27·0' N. Long. 41° 10·0'W.
Intercept (A) S. 85¼° W., 5·2'   D. Lat.   0·4 S. D. Long.   6·9 W.

P.L. 175¼°—355¼° through   Lat. 41 26·6 N. Long. 41 16·9 W.

Example 2.—On January 1st, P.M. at ship in estimated lat. 31° 14' N., long. 73° E., the obs. alt. of the Sun's U.L. was 19° 22'. Height of eye 25 ft. Time by chronometer was 10h 19m 37s. Chron. was 1m 12s slow of G.M. noon on Nov. 25th, 1957, and was losing 2·7 sec. daily. Find the position line and the position through which it should be drawn.

Chron. T., Jan. 1st 10h 19m 37s   *To find accum. rate* Nov. 5 days
Error slow   +   1 12   Dec. 31   ,,
                                                    Jan. 0·9 ,,
                   10 20 49
Acc. rate losing   +   1 40   36·9×
                                                    2·7 sec.
G.M.T.   10 22 29   =1m 40s accum. rate.

G.H.A. Sun

at 10h	329° 07·9′	Obs. alt.	19°	22·0′	L.H.A.	Log hav 9·21442
Increment	5 37·3	Tot. corr.	—	24·9	Lat.	Log cos 9·93200
					Decl.	Log cos 9·96394

Cor. G.H.A.	334 45·2	True alt.	18	57·1

Log hav 9·11036

Est. long. E.+73 00·0   Z.D.   71 02·9

L.H.A. Sun	47 45·2	A=·551+	Nat. hav ·12893
Decl.	23° 01·6′ S.	B=·574+	(L—D) Nat hav ·20794
(L—D)	54° 15·6′	C=1·125+	C.Z.D. Nat hav ·33687

True Bearing   S. 46·1° W.   C.Z.D.   70° 57·5′

P.L.   136·1°—316·1°   T.Z.D.   71 02·9

Intercept   5·4 Away

Ship's est. pos.	Lat.	31° 14·0′ N.	Long.	73° 00·0′ E.
Intercept (A) 046·1°, 5·4′.	D. Lat.	3·8 N.	D. Long.	4·5 E.
P.L. 136°—316° through	Lat.	31 17·8 N.	Long.	73 04·5 E.

EXERCISE 35.

Marcq St. Hilaire.

Given the following particulars, find the Position Line, and a position through which it passes.

1. On Jan. 2nd, A.M. at ship in est. lat. 7° 28′ N., long. 52° W., the sext. alt. of the Sun's L.L. was 22° 17′. I.E. 3′ to add. Ht. of eye 21 ft. Time by chronometer was 11h 19m 29s. Chron. was 5m 12s slow of G.M.T.

2. On Dec. 21st, A.M. at ship in est. lat. 11° N., long. 41° 10′ W., the sext. alt. of the Sun's L.L. was 19° 25′. I.E. 7′ to subtract. Ht. of eye 18 ft. Time by chronometer was 10h 32m 18s. Chron. was 2m 19s slow of G.M. noon on Oct. 13th, and was gaining 3·2 sec. daily.

3. On July 16th, P.M. at ship in est. lat. 51° 12′ N., long. 40° W., the obs. alt. of the Sun's L.L. was 19° 51′. Ht. of eye 23 ft. Time by chron. was 20h 16m 43s. Chron. was 2m 19s slow of G.M. noon on April 29th, and was 4m 35s slow on June 6th.

4. On Sept. 23rd, A.M. at ship in lat. 28° 20′ N., long. 17° W., the sext. alt. of the Sun's L.L. was 17° 25′. I.E. 7′ to add. Ht. of eye 22 ft. Time by chron. was 08h 15m 12s. Chron. was 2m 16s slow of G.M. noon on August 10th, and was losing 5·2 sec. daily.

5. On June 13th, P.M. at ship in est. lat. 40° 51′ N., long. 38° 25′ E., the sext. alt. of the Sun's L.L. was 23° 45′. I.E. 3·3′ to subtract. Ht. of eye 19 ft. Time by chron. was 14h 25m 37s. Chron. was 13m 05s slow of G.M. noon on April 27th, and was gaining 2·2 sec. daily.

6. On Sept. 23rd, A.M. at ship in D.R. lat. 33° 05′ N., long. 160° 30′ E., the obs. alt. of the Sun's L.L. was 38° 22′. Ht. of eye 24 ft. Time by chron. was Sept. 22nd, 22h 22m 22s. This was correct G.M.T.

7. On June 14th, P.M. at ship in est. lat. 50° 36′ N., long. 19° 19′ E., the obs. alt. of the Sun's L.L. was 40° 00′. Ht. of eye 20 ft. Time by chron. was 14h 16m 48s. Chron. was 5m 09s slow of G.M. noon on April 20th, and was gaining 1·6 sec. daily.

8. On Sept. 22nd, P.M. at ship in D.R. lat. 31° 26′ N., long. 162¼° W., the sext. alt. of the Sun's L.L. was 25° 53′. I.E. 2·7′ to add. Ht. of eye 22 ft. Time by chron. was Sept. 23rd, 02h 33m 19s. Chron. was correct G.M.T. at noon, July 6th, and was 2m 19s slow on August 5th.

9. On June 13th, A.M. at ship in est. long. 99¾° W. on the equator, the obs. alt. of the Sun's U.L. was 27° 15′. Ht. of eye 17 ft. Time by chron. was 14h 36m 39s. Chron. was 2m 41s slow of G.M. noon on April 30th, and was gaining 3·9 sec. daily.

10. On July 17th, P.M. at ship in est. lat. 49° 25′ N., long. 51¼° E., the obs. alt. of the Sun's L.L. was 41° 36′. Ht. of eye 28 ft. G.M.T. 12h 00m 00s.

11. On July 23rd, A.M. at ship in est. lat. 21° 08′ S., long. 22¼° W., the sext. alt. of the Sun's L.L. was 29° 14′. I.E. +4·5′. Ht. of eye 32 ft. Time by chron. was 10h 39m 51s. Chron. was 5m 22s fast of G.M.T.

12. On Oct. 7th, A.M. at ship in D.R. lat. 32° 41′ N., long. 8¼° E., the obs. alt. of the Sun's U.L. was 36° 05′. Ht. of eye 25 ft. G.M.T. 08h 31m 14s.

13. On Dec. 23rd, P.M. at ship in est. lat. 11° 52′ N., long. 45° W., the obs. alt. of the Sun's L.L. was 39° 15′. Ht. of eye 29 ft. Time by chron. was 17h 31m 20s. Chron. was 6m 22s fast of G.M. noon on Oct. 31st, and was losing 2·3 sec. daily.

14. On June 12th, A.M. at ship in lat. 38° 19′ N., long. 39° 30′ E., the obs. alt. of the Sun's L.L. was 27° 35′. Ht. of eye 18 ft. Time by chron. was 04h 28m 11s. Chron. was 5m 27s slow of G.M.T.

15. On Sept. 24th, P.M. at ship in lat. 53° N., long. 17° W., the obs. alt. of the Sun's L.L. was 21° 21'.   Ht. of eye 23 ft.   G.M.T. 16h 26m 51s.

16. On Oct. 9th, P.M. at ship in lat. 42° 12' N., long. 0° 50' W., the sext. alt. of the Sun's U.L. was 30° 00'.   I.E. −2·4'.   Ht. of eye 31 ft.   Time by chron. was 14h 29m 46s.   Chron. was correct at G.M. noon on August 30th, and was losing 0·8 sec. daily.

17. On Jan 3rd, A.M. at ship in est. lat. 2° N., long. 66⅔° E., the obs. alt. of the Sun's L.L. was 26° 14'.   Ht. of eye 27 ft.   G.M.T. 03h 36m 29s.

18. On Dec. 22nd, P.M. at ship in lat. 26° 25' S., long. 61° 40' E., the sext. alt. of the Sun's L.L. was 42° 18'.   I.E. +3'.   Ht. of eye 32 ft.   G.M.T. 11h 21m 53s.

CHAPTER 28.

PRACTICAL POSITION LINE NAVIGATION.
THE INTERCEPT METHOD.

Many students may prefer, for personal reasons, to find the ship's position using the Intercept (Marcq St. Hilaire) method. There is no need for students to learn both methods. It will be found more satisfactory to stick to one chosen method, disregarding the other.

The worked examples given below are the same as have been fully worked in Chapter 24 to illustrate the Longitude method. A comparison of final results will show that these are practically the same by either method. It will also be noted in the first two examples, that except for the method of finding a point of departure from the a.m. observation point, the method of correcting the longitude at noon is the same in each case.

A.M. Longitude, Run to Noon, Noon Latitude.

☞ *Example* 1.—On October 9th A.M. at ship in estimated lat. 41½° N., long. 63° W., the obs. alt. of the Sun's L.L. was 22° 18′. Height of eye 26 feet. G.M.T. 12h 28m 49s. Ship then steered 255° T., 40 mls., when the obs. mer. alt. of the Sun's L.L. was 42° 25·5′ S. Height of eye 26 ft. G.M.T. 16h 00m 00s. Find the ship's position at noon.

(*Formula*—Hav L.H.A. cos. lat. cos. decl.+Hav (L+D)=Hav C.Z.D.)

G.M.T. 12h 23m 49s.			Obs. alt.	22°	18·0′
G.H.A. Sun	3°	09·1′	Tot. corr.	+	9·0
Incr.	7	12·3	True alt.	22	27·0
	10	21·4	Z.D.	67	33·0
Long. W—	63	00 0			
L.H.A. Sun	307	21·4			
Decl.	6°	11·0′ S.			
(L+D)	47°	41·0′			

324

L.H.A.	L. hav	9·29361	C.Z.D.	67°	38·3′
Lat.	L. cos	9·87446	T.Z.D.	67	33·0

Dec.	L. cos	9·99747	Intcpt.	5·3 T.

	L. hav	9·16554	A	·675+

(L+D)	Nat hav	·14639	B	·137+

(L+D)	Nat hav	·16339	C	·812+

C.Z.D.	Nat. hav	·30978	T. Bg. S. 58·6° E.

Intercept S. 58·6° E., 5·3 mls. P.L. 031·4°—211·4°

Run to noon—

Pos (A)	Est. lat.	41° 30·0′ N.	long.	63° 00·0′ W.	
	D. lat.	2·8 S.	D. long.	6·0 E.	(S. 58½° E., 5·3 mls.)
(B)		41 27·2 N.		62 54·0 W.	
	Run	10·4 S.		51·3 W.	(S. 75° W., 40 mls.)
(C)		41 16·8 N.		63 45·3 W.	D.R. noon position

Meridian Observation—

Obs. mer. alt.	42° 25·5′ S.		Obs. lat.	41 09·9 N.
Tot. corr.	+ 10·3			
True alt.	42 35·8 S.		D.R. lat.	41° 16·8′ N.
Z.D.	47 24·2 N.		D. Lat.	6·9
Decl.	6 14·3 S.		Long. corr. 6·9 × ·812 = 5·6′ W.	
Obs. latitude	41 09·9 N.			

S E

N W

D.R. long.	63° 45·3′ W.
Long. corr.	5·6 W.
Obs. longitude	63 50·9 W.

NOTE.—The noon position could also have been found by use of the Traverse Table. Using as a course the angle between the transferred position line P′L′ (211·4°) and P″L″ (180°), and using also the D. lat. between the D.R. and obs. latitudes (6·9) as the Difference of Latitude, the distance found from the Traverse Table is 8·1 miles.

The ship's position is then S. $31\frac{1}{2}$° W., 8·1 miles from the D.R. noon position (C).

	Lat.	41°	16·8′ N.		Long.	63°	45·3′ W.
	D. Lat.		6·9 S.		D. Long.		5·6 W.
Noon Lat.	41	09·9 N.		Long.	63	50·9 W.	

Example 2.—On July 22nd, A.M. at ship in D.R. latitude 51° 20′ N., longitude $35\frac{1}{2}$° W., the obs. alt. of the Sun's L.L. was 35° 42′. Height of eye 20 feet. G.M.T. 10h 38m 22s. Ship then steered 113° T., 44 miles, when the obs. mer. alt. of the Sun's L.L. was 58° 57′, South of observer. Height of eye 20 feet. Corr. declination 20° 18·4′ N. Find the ship's position at noon.

First Observation—

G.M.T.	10h 38m 22s.			Obs. alt.	35°	42·0′
G.H.A. Sun	338°	00·5′		Tot. corr.	+	10·4
Long. W	− 35	30·0		True alt.	35	52·4
L.H.A. Sun	302	30·5		T.Z.D.	54	07·6
Decl.		20° 20·3′ N.				

L.H.A.	L. hav	9·36415		C.Z.D.	54°	06·6′
Lat.	L. cos	9·79573		T.Z.D.	54	07·6
Dec.	L. cos	9·97204		Intcpt.		1·0 A.
	L. hav	9·13192		A	·794+	
	Nat hav	13549		B	·440−	
(L—D)	Nat hav	07140		C	·354+	
C.Z.D.	Nat hav	20689		T. Bg. S. $77\frac{1}{2}$° E.		

Intercept N. 77° 30′ W. 1·0′.

Run to noon—

	(A)	Lat. left	51°	20·0′ N.		Lg. left	35°	30·0′ W.
Int. N. 77½° W., 1 ml.				0·2 N.				1·0 W.
	(B)		51	20·2 N.			35	31·0 W.
Run S. 67° E. 44 mls.				17·2 S.			1	04·3 E.
Noon D.R. position	(C)		51	03·0 N.			34	26·7 W.

Meridian Observation—

Obs. mer. alt.   58° 57·0′ S.   S   E   D.R. Lat. 51° 03·0′ N.

Tot. corr.   +   11·1   N   W   Obs. Lat. 51   10·3 N.

True alt.   59   08·1 S.   Difference   7·3 N.

Z.D.   30   51·9 N.
Decl.   20   18·4 N.   Long. corr=$(7·3 \times ·354)$ E.=2·5′ E.

Latitude   51   10·3 N.   D.R. long. 34° 26·7′ W.

Obs. long. 34   24·2 W.

A.M. Longitude, Run Between Sights, P.M. Longitude

Example 3.—On June 14th, AM at ship in lat. D.R. 49° 30′ N., long. 43 E., the obs. alt. of the Sun's L.L. was 50° 20′. Height of eye 28 feet. G.M.T. 06 36m 21s. Ship then steamed 55 miles on a course of 071° T., when an obs. alt. of the Sun's L.L., west of the meridian, was 46° 23′. Height of eye 28 feet. G.M.T. 12h 00m 00s. Find the ship's position at the time of taking the second observation.

First Observation—

G.M.T. 06h 36m 21s.			Obs. alt.	50°	20·0′
G.H.A. Sun	270°	00·0′	Tot. corr.	+	10·1
Increment	9	05·3	True alt.	50	30·1
	279	05·3	T.Z.D.	39	29·9
Long.	+	43			
L.H.A. Sun	322	05·3			
Decl.	23°	14·5′ N.			
(L—D)	26°	15·5′			

L.H.A.	L. hav	9·02334		C.Z.D.	39°	34·0′
Lat.	L. cos	9·81254		T.Z.D.	39	29·9
Dec.	L. cos	9·96324		Int.		4·1 T.
	L. hav	8·79912		A	1·50+	
	Nat hav	06296		B	·70−	
(L—D)	Nat hav	05160		C	·80+	
C.Z.D.	Nat hav	11456		T. Bg.	S. 62¼° E.	

PL 027¾°—207¾°

Run between sights—

D.R. lat. left	49° 30·0′ N.		Long. 43° 00·0′ E.	(A)
Intercept—S. 62¼° E. 4·1′	1·9 S.		5·6 E.	
	49 28·1 N.		43 05·6 E.	(B)
Run — N. 71° E. 55 mls.	17·9 N.		1 20·0 E.	
D.R. position	49 46·0 N.		44 25·6 E.	(C)

Second Observation—

G.M.T. 12h 00m 00s.   Obs. alt.   46° 23·0′

G.H.A. Sun	359° 59·2′		Tot. corr.	+ 10·0
Long.	+ 44 25·6		True alt.	46 33·0
L.H.A. Sun	44 24·8		Z.D.	43 27·0
Decl.	23° 15·2′ N.			
(L—D)	26° 30·8′			

L.H.A.	L. hav	9·15478		C.Z.D.	43°	30·3′
Lat.	L. cos	9·81017		T.Z.D.	43	27·0
Dec.	L. cos	9·96321		Int.		3·3 T.
	L. hav	8·92816		A	1·20+	
	Nat hav	08475		B	·61−	
(L—D)	Nat hav	05259		C	·59+	
C.Z.D.	Nat hav	13734		T. Bg. S. 69¼° W.		

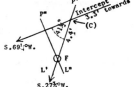

From sketch, ship's position is S. 27¾° W.,
4·4 mls. from D.R. pos. (C).

	Lat.	49°	46·0′ N.	Long.	44°	25·6′ E.
			4·0 S.			3·2 W. (S. 27¾° W.
						4·4 mls.)
Ship's pos.		49	42·0 N.		44	22·4 E.

P.M. Longitude, Run Between Sights, P.M. Longitude.

Example 4.—On June 12th, PM at ship in D.R. lat. 52° 10′ N.,
long. 27° 54′ W., the obs. alt. of the Sun's L.L. was 49° 05′. Height
of eye 22 feet. G.M.T. 16h 21m 49s. Ship then steamed 28 miles on a
course of 200° T., when an obs. alt. of the Sun's L.L. was 32° 02·5′.
Height of eye 22 feet. G.M.T. 18h 20m 00s. Find ship's position at
the time of taking the second observation.

First Observation—

G.M.T. 16h 21m 49s.   Obs. alt. 49° 05·0′

G.H.A. Sun 60° 05·0′   Tot. corr. + 10·7
Increment   5   27·3   True alt. 49   15·7

            65   32·3   T.Z.D. 40° 44·3
Long. W. −27   54·0
L.H.A. Sun 37° 38·3′

Decl.   23° 08·9′ N.

(L—D)   29° 01·1′

    L.H.A. L. hav 9·01729   C.Z.D. 40° 47·5′
    Lat.   L. cos 9·78772   T.Z.D. 40   44·3
    Dec.   L. cos 9·96355   Int.   3·2 T.

           L. hav 8·76856   A 1·67+

    Nat hav 05869   B   ·69−
(L—D) Nat hav 06277   C   ·98+

C.Z.D. Nat hav 12146   T. Bg. S. 58·7° W.

                              PL 148·7°—328·7°

Run between sights—

	Lat. left	52°	10·0′ N.	Long. 27°	54·0′ W.	(A)
Intercept S. 58·7° W. 3·2′			1·7 S.		4·4 W.	
		52	08·3 N.	27	58·4 W.	(B)
Run S. 20° W. 28 mls.			26·3 S.		15·6 W.	
	D.R. pos.	51	42·0 N.	28	14·0 W.	(C)

Second Observation—

G.M.T. 18h 20m 00s.	Obs. alt.	32° 02·5′
G.H.A. Sun 90° 04·7′	Tot. corr.	+ 10·0
Increment 5 00·0	True alt.	32 12·5
95 04·7	T.Z.D.	57 47·5
Long. W. −28 14·0		
L.H.A. Sun 66 50·7		
Decl. 23° 09·2′ N.		
(L—D) 28° 32·8′		

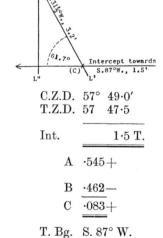

L.H.A.	L. hav	9·48200
Lat.	L. cos	9·79224
Dec.	L. cos	9·96353
	L. hav	9·23777
	Nat hav	17289
(L—D)	Nat hav	06079
C.Z.D.	Nat hav	23368

C.Z.D.	57° 49·0′
T.Z.D.	57 47·5
Int.	1·5 T.
A	·545+
B	·462−
C	·083+
T. Bg.	S. 87° W.

From sketch and Traverse Table, ship's position is N. 31⅓° W., 3·2 mls. from Pos. (C).

D.R. Lat.	51°	42·0′ N.	Long. 28°	14·0′ W.	(C)
		2·7 N.		2·7 W.	
Ship's position	51	44·7 N.	28	16·7 W.	

EXERCISE 36.

1. On July 15th, A.M. at ship in est. lat. 49° 20′ N., long. 62° 20′ W., the obs. alt. of the Sun's L.L. was 27° 40′. Height of eye 25 feet. G.M.T. 11h 27m 36s. Ship then steered 328° T., 50 miles, when the obs. mer. alt. of the Sun's L.L. was 61° 21·5′ S. Height of eye 25 feet. Noon decl. 21° 32·1′ N. Required the ship's position at noon.

2. On October 7th, A.M. at ship in est. lat. 40½° N., long. 26½° W., the obs. alt. of the Sun's L.L. was 19° 10′. Height of eye 22 ft. G.M.T. 09h 38m 21s. Ship then steered 153° T., for 4 hrs. at 9·5 knots, when the obs. mer. alt. of the Sun's L.L. was 44° 21·0′ S. Ht. of eye 22 ft. Required the ship's noon position.

3. On December 22nd, A.M. at ship in D.R. lat. 31° 17′ N., long. 28° 30′ W., the obs. alt. of the Sun's L.L. was 16° 22′. Ht. of eye 20 ft. G.M.T. 10h 27m 51s. Ship then steered 052° T., 33 mls., when the obs. mer. alt. of the Sun's L.L. was 34° 51′ S. Ht. of eye 20 ft. Required ship's noon position.

4. On June 13th, A.M. at ship in est. lat. 52° 09′ N., long. 41° W., the obs. alt. of the Sun's L.L. was 20° 22′. Ht. of eye 25 ft. G.M.T. 09h 00m 00s. Ship then steered 219° T., 56 mls., when the obs. mer. alt. of the Sun's L.L. was 61° 41′ S. Decl. 23° 12·3′ N. Required ship's noon position.

5. On July 23rd, A.M. at ship in est. pos. 48¾° N., 35° W., the obs. alt. of the Sun's L.L. was 24° 08′. Ht. of eye 25 ft. G.M.T. 09h 23m 41s. Ship then steered 031° T., 83 mls., when a P.M. observation of the Sun's L.L. gave obs. alt. 41° 20′. Ht. 25 ft. G.M.T. 17h 37m 09s. Find ship's position at the time of taking the second observation.

6. On October 8th, A.M. at ship in est. lat. 44ª 25′ N., long. 21° E., the obs. alt. of the Sun's L.L. was 17° 22′. Ht. of eye 19 ft. G.M.T. 06h 29m 09s. Ship then steered 322° T., 62 mls., when a P.M. observation of the Sun's L.L. gave obs. alt. 25° 51·5′. Ht. 19 ft. G.M.T. 13h 20m 13s. Find ship's position at the time of taking the second observation.

7. On December 21st, A.M. at ship in D.R. latitude 38° 16′ N., long. 44° 25′ W., the obs. alt. of the Sun's L.L. was 12° 47′. Height of eye 20 feet. G.M.T. 11h 38m 16s. Ship then steered 071° T., 55 mls., when a P.M. observation of the Sun's L.L. gave obs. alt. 13° 45′. Ht. of eye 20 feet. G.M.T. 18h 00m 00s. Find the ship's position at the time of taking the second observation.

8. On September 24th, A.M. at ship in est. lat. 49° 06′ N., long. 10° E., the obs. alt. of the Sun's L.L. was 20° 23′. Height of eye 25 feet. G.M.T. 07h 22m 51s. Ship then steered 205° T., 67 mls., when a P.M. observation of the Sun's L.L. gave obs. alt. 25°

39·5'. Ht. of eye 25 ft. G.M.T. 14h 30m 02s. Required the ship's position at the time of taking the second observation.

9. On January 2nd, A.M. at ship in D.R. lat. 30° 00' N., long. 37¼° W., the obs. alt. of the Sun's L.L. was 12° 47'. Height of eye 18 feet. G.M.T. 10h 39m 14s. Ship then steered 090° T., 61 mls., when a P.M. observation of the Sun's L.L. gave obs. alt. 16° 21·5'. Ht. of eye 18 ft. G.M.T. 18h 00m 00s. Required the ship's position at the time of taking the second observation.

10. On October 9th, P.M. at ship in D.R. lat. 41° 57' N., long. 46° W., the obs. alt. of the Sun's L.L. was 37° 28'. Height of eye 23 feet. G.M.T. 16h 21m 19s. Ship then steered 341° T., 22 mls., when a second obs. of the Sun's L.L. gave obs. alt. 19° 23·0'. G.M.T. 18h 37m 50s. Required the ship's position at the time of taking the second observation.

PART IV.

THE NAVIGATION PROBLEMS

FOR

MASTER HOME TRADE

AND

SKIPPER (FULL) EXAMINATIONS

CHAPTER 29.

STAR WORK—NAMING OF STARS—STAR MAGNITUDES—
DISTANCE OF STARS—APPARENT IMMOBILITY OF STARS—TO
IDENTIFY STARS—SIDEREAL TIME—LUNAR TIME—SIDEREAL
HOUR ANGLE—TO FIND STARS IN THE "NAUTICAL ALMANAC"
—GREENWICH HOUR ANGLE OF ARIES—GREENWICH HOUR
ANGLE OF A STAR—LOCAL HOUR ANGLE OF A STAR.

Although the Sun is the celestial body most often used for finding
ship's positions at sea, stars, planets and the Moon are also largely
used for the same purpose.

In clear weather during daylight hours the horizon is, of course,
plainly visible, so that from that particular viewpoint no time-limits
are imposed when using the Sun for observations. But, as a good
"hard" horizon is necessary when taking sextant altitudes, stars or
planets can only be used at morning and evening twilight, when there
is sufficient daylight to see the horizon plainly. Of these times, dawn
is naturally the better, since the observer should have been able to
note the position of various stars before daybreak, and to choose
beforehand such stars as are most suitable for his purpose.

In many details, navigation work by stars follows precisely the
same lines as does work by the Sun, and, where details differ, star
work is usually more simple than work by the Sun.

One big advantage in using stars for finding a ship's position lies in
the fact that very often several stars, some bearing Easterly and some
bearing Westerly, can be used for finding longitude, and in the same
way more than one star can often be used to find the latitude, all at
the same time. Thus a valuable check can be given to the observer's
calculations, and latitude and longitude are found at one time, provided
conditions are suitable.

On the other hand, when using the Sun for observations, the latitude
can only be found at or near noon, and the longitude can only be found
some hours before or after noon.

Azimuths of stars can be used to find the error and deviation of the
compass exactly as is done in the case of the Sun. The horizon is not
required for this operation, so that star azimuths can be taken at any
time during the night hours. It should be noted that stars are seldom
visible when their altitudes are less than 5° above the horizon. For
this reason it is impossible to observe the amplitude of stars.

334

Naming of Stars.—The naming of stars follows **much the** same idea as does the naming of families in the human race.

When, at the dawn of civilisation, astronomers first began to study stars, they used vivid imaginations, and likened certain groups of stars to animals or to mythological heroes. Hence the group which we know as "The Plough" was named by them "The Great Bear" (in Latin *Ursa Major*). Such a group is called a constellation.

But it is also necessary to differentiate between the individual stars in a group. In the Smith family, for instance, there are Tom Smith, James Smith, John Smith, and all the other members, the Christian names showing to which member of the family reference is being made. To differentiate between stars in a constellation, letters from the Greek alphabet are placed in front of the name of the constellation for easy recognition of individual stars, and thus the stars in the constellation *Ursa Major* are shown as—

> α Ursae Majoris,
> β Ursae Majoris,
> γ Ursae Majoris,

and so on.

It is not absolutely necessary for the student to learn the Greek alphabet, but it is given here, with the English equivalents, and a knowledge of it will make the picking out of stars easier, and will help the student to guard against taking the wrong star from the *Nautical Almanac.* When finding the star, particular note should be made as to the Greek letter in front of the required star.

α (alpha)	= a		ι (iota)	= i		ρ (rho)	= **r**
β (beta)	= b		ϰ (kappa)	= k		σ (sigma)	= **s**
γ (gamma)	= g		λ (lambda)	= l		τ (tau)	= **t**
δ (delta)	= d		μ (mu)	= m		υ (upsilon)	= u
ε (epsilon)	= e		ν (nu)	= n		φ (phi)	= ph
ζ (zeta)	= z		ξ (ksi)	= x		χ (khi)	= kh
η (aeta)	= e (long)		o (omicron)	= o		ψ (psi)	= ps
θ (theta)	= th		π (pi)	= p		ω (omega)	= o (long)

In addition to their distinguishing letters and the names of the constellations to which they belong, many of the larger stars possess special names, like Sirius, Antares, Alpheratz, etc. These are referred to as—

> α Canis Majoris (Sirius)
> α Scorpii (Antares)
> α Andromedae (Alpheratz), etc.

Star Magnitudes.—The magnitudes of stars (which are their comparative sizes as viewed from the Earth) are also noted specially in the *Nautical Almanac*, pp. 268-273. A star of the size that has been fixed as the standard for measurement is said to have a magnitude of 1·0. The smaller the star—or, more precisely, the less light emitted by a star—the larger the figure given for its magnitude. Thus α **Aurigae** (Capella), of mag. 0·2, is a much larger star than β Ursae Majoris, whose mag. is 2·4. Sirius (mag. —1·6) is the largest fixed star.

Distance of Stars.—Human minds can scarcely comprehend the enormous distances of stars from the Earth. When we consider these distances, the mile, our ordinary unit of measurement, becomes quite useless. Even the mean distance of the Earth from the Sun, 93 million miles, becomes too small to be used as a *unit* to measure the distances.

Various units have at various times been adopted when measuring stellar distances, and in turn have had to be scrapped in favour of others which are easier to handle. Astronomers previously used "light-years" as a standard unit. By careful experiment, it has been established that light travels at the rate of 186,000 miles per second, or approximately 11 million miles per minute. Thus, in a "light-year" light travels $(60 \times 11,000,000 \times 24 \times 365)$ miles, or roughly 6 billion miles.

As knowledge of space and the stars was extended, even this enormous distance was found to be too small as a unit for the measurement of stellar distances, and a new unit, the "parsec", was invented

As was explained in Chapter 21, Parallax is the angle at a heavenly body between the observer and the centre of the Earth. In the case of the Sun, with a normal altitude, parallax is about 6″, decreasing to zero as the altitude increases. A "parsec" (coined from the words "parallax" and "second") is the distance a star must be from the Earth to show a parallax of 1″ when the Earth's position, relative to the star, has shifted 93 million miles. This distance is equal to about 3·2 light-years, or, roughly, 19¼ billion miles. To try to imagine what a "parsec" means, try to imagine the angle between the top and the bottom of a halfpenny at a distance of four miles. An aeroplane travelling at a steady 200 miles per hour would take over 10 million years to traverse the distance of 1 parsec. Travelling for 50 million years at the same speed in any direction, the aeroplane would not encounter more than 30 of the countless thousands of stars that sprinkle the sky, so inconceivable is the distance between them.

The light from even the nearest star to the Earth (α Centauri) takes almost four years to reach us, while many of the stars now being studied through modern large telescopes are so distant that their light takes hundreds of thousands of years to reach us, and the conditions of these stars as seen by astronomers now are conditions ruling before our own Earth was inhabited. Astronomers feel that even the parsec is too small as a unit, and are talking in terms of "megaparsecs", or millions of parsecs.

Stars shine by their own light, and are Suns like our own Sun, though many of them are thousands of times larger than our Sun. The star Antares, for instance, is large enough to blot out our entire solar system.

Apparent Immobility of Stars.—Stars appear to us to preserve their positions in relation to each other because of their immense distance away from the Earth.

From our position on the Earth, we can only appreciate the "angular distance" apart of stars. Their real distance apart from each other cannot be judged casually, and two stars which to us seem quite close together may in actual fact be countless millions of miles apart. The "Plough", or "Great Bear", the best known of all the northern constellations, keeps its well-recognised shape year after year, as if the stars forming the constellation were absolutely fixed. Such movements as individual stars possess are so small compared with their distance from the Earth that they are unnoticeable, and the apparent circling motion of stars in the sky is, of course, caused solely by the rotation of the Earth on its axis.

To Identify Stars.—Books alone cannot supply the seaman with a real working knowledge of the stars. The first steps can certainly be gained from books, but the stars themselves must be studied on clear nights before the seaman can hope to identify stars easily. As in everything else, it is only by practice that one can become familiar with the stars required for observation.

At the beginning, the best plan for the student is to make himself able to recognise just a few of the brighter stars, singling them out from the rest by referring them to definite "guide-posts".

In the northern hemisphere, there are two such guide-posts from which the majority of northern navigational stars can be identified These are the well-known "Plough" or "Great Bear" (see Fig. 105) and the constellation of Orion (see Fig. 106), both of which are easy to find in the heavens, and, once found, easy to remember.

With these two constellations to help him, the seaman should then identify just one or two bright stars near these guides, and make himself thoroughly familiar with the method of finding them. Thereafter, he should add to the numbers only gradually, not trying to memorise even half-a-dozen at one time. By this method, he will be surprised how many stars can be identified with ease even in the period of a month.

One of the important jobs performed by the constellation of "Ursa Major" (the Great Bear), is to point to the Pole Star. An imaginary line drawn through the two westernmost stars (α and β) of the group passes quite close to the Pole Star. Because of this fact, these two stars are called "The Pointers".

Polaris (the Pole Star) is a very important star in the northern heavens, not by reason of its size, but by reason of its position.

It lies within $1\frac{1}{4}°$ of the true North point of the heavens, and its compass bearing *at any time* therefore gives an approximate error of the compass, since its true bearing is never more than $1\frac{1}{4}°$ East or West of true North.

A sextant altitude of the Pole Star can be taken at any time when conditions are suitable to obtain a latitude. (See Chapter 32.)

The constellation of *Cassiopeia* lies on the side of *Polaris* away from the Great Bear, so that when one constellation is above the Pole Star, the other is below it. Imaginary lines drawn from Polaris to

Cassiopeia, and from Polaris to the pointers of the Great Bear form the same angle as is formed by the hands of a clock at 1.30.

Dubhe (α Ursae Majoris).—The "pointer" of the Great Bear which lies nearer to the Pole Star is called Dubhe.

Arcturus (α Bootis).—Continue the curve of the tail of the Great Bear for about twice the length of the constellation. Arcturus is the first bright star that it passes.

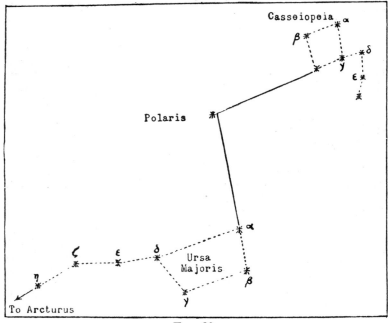

FIG. 89.

Spica (α Virginis).—Continue the curve of the tail of the Great Bear still further and it will come to Spica. The distance from the tail to Arcturus and the distance from Arcturus to Spica are about equal. Four lesser stars close to Spica are in the form of a vessel's square-sail. They are usually referred to as "Spica's spanker".

Denebola (β Leonis) forms an equilateral triangle with Arcturus and Spica. Denebola is the least bright of the three.

Regulus (α Leonis).—A line drawn through the pointers of the Great Bear away from the Pole Star, and produced about twice the length of the constellation passes between Denebola and Regulus. Regulus is the brighter star of these two. It can also be recognised as the brightest star in a group shaped like a reaping sickle, with Regulus placed at the end of the handle.

Capella (α Aurigae).—Draw a line through Polaris at right angles to the pointers, and in the direction of Cassiopeia. Produce this line well beyond Cassiopeia. Capella lies on the line. The star is easily recognised by a well-formed isosceles triangle of stars lying close to it.

Vega (α Lyrae).—From Capella draw a line passing midway between Polaris and Cassiopeia, and continuing well beyond it. This line passes close to the bright star Vega.

Altair (α Aquilae) lies to the southward of Vega. It is the middle— and brightest—star of a line of three.

Deneb (α Cygni) has a declination slightly North of Vega, and rises and sets about two hours later than that star.

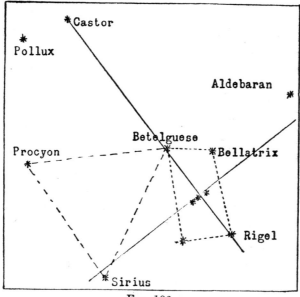

Fɪɢ. 106.

Fig. 106 shows the form of the constellation of Orion, one of the most outstanding constellations. The four main stars form the body of Orion, and the three smaller stars inside the quadrilateral represent his sword-belt. The corner stars α (*Betelgeuse*), β (*Rigel*), and γ (*Bellatrix*) are all valuable navigational stars.

Sirius (α Canis Majoris).—A line drawn through the "belt" of Orion passes close to Sirius. This is the brightest of all the fixed stars.

Procyon (α Canis Minoris) lies to the N. E'ward of Sirius. With Sirius and Betelgeuse, it forms a large equilateral triangle.

Castor and *Pollux* (Gemini, the Heavenly Twins).—A line drawn from Rigel, and passing just south of Betelgeuse, reaches close to Castor. Pollux lies a little to the E.S.E. of Castor.

Aldebaran (α Tauri) lies not very far distant from the N.W. corner of Orion. It is at the bottom left-hand corner of a cluster of stars (the *Hyades*) in a well-formed "V". Close by is another group of seven small stars, called the *Pleiades*, or the "Seven Sisters".

Many more stars, of course, can be used for navigational purposes. Detailed instructions for identifying other stars can be found in *Brown's Nautical Almanac* and other books.

Sidereal Time.—It has already been explained (Chapter 17) that terrestrial time is measured by the Sun for the obvious reason that the Sun is the most important heavenly body to the inhabitants of the Earth. The fact that the apparent motion of the Sun is subject to slight irregularity is countered by using MEAN TIME, as has been seen.

Owing to the immense distance away of even the nearest stars, the Earth makes one complete revolution on its axis, relative to the stars, in a space of time which never alters. If the time were to be noted when one particular star bore due South from an observer—which would mean that the star's longitude was momentarily the same as the observer's longitude—and the time was further noted when the same star again bore South, it would be found that the space of time between each "southing" was 23 hours 56 minutes 4 seconds, measured by an ordinary clock. Continued observations would show that each successive southing occurred after precisely the same lapse of time.

This interval of time is called a "sidereal day", or a day whose length is measured by the time-unit of stars, and its length compared with the 24 hours of a mean solar day gives the explanation why stars appear to rise and set about 4 minutes earlier each day.

Lunar Time.—The Moon is the heavenly body nearest to the Earth' and as its mean distance away is only about 236,000 miles, the irregularities in its motion are more easily noticeable than those of the Sun. The *mean* interval of time between successive southings of the Moon is approximately 24 hours 50 minutes. Thus the Moon appears to rise and set about 50 minutes later each day, although this period—called a "lunar day"—is subject to considerable fluctuations.

A "lunation" is the number of days between one new moon and the next, and is about 29½ days, though irregularities in the relative motions of the Earth and the Moon cause slight aberrations. But the Moon always makes one complete circuit of the Earth in 27½ days.

Sidereal Hour Angle.—The *First Point of Aries* has already been defined on page 199. In previous navigation problems, which have been concerned only with the sun and the G.H.A. of the Sun, the importance of the First Point of Aries has not been unduly stressed. When dealing with stars, however, Aries assumes a very considerable importance.

We have seen that two arguments are required to express terrestrial positions—latitude and longitude. In dealing with the Sun, it was shown that *Declination* corresponds to terrestrial latitude. This also holds good for any heavenly body.

We have now to consider the other argument, or "co-ordinate"— the co-ordinate which corresponds to terrestrial longitude.

The meridian through Greenwich Observatory was fixed as the "prime meridian" almost by accident, but the First Point of Aries, that point in the heavens where the Sun's centre crosses the equinoctial and brings spring to the northern part of the world, is a natural and almost predestined point from which to measure the celestial longitude of stars.

This second co-ordinate which finally fixes the position of a celestial body is measured from a celestial meridian which passes through the First Point of Aries. Instead of being called the body's longitude, it is called the star's "Sidereal Hour Angle". (S.H.A.) The longitude of Greenwich, the terrestrial "prime meridian", is expressed as 0°, and in the same way the First Point of Aries, the celestial prime meridian, can be expressed as a point on the equinoctial whose S.H.A. is 0°.

The angle at the pole between a meridian passing through Aries and a meridian passing through any particular star gives the value of the S.H.A. of the star. It is *invariably* measured to the westward.

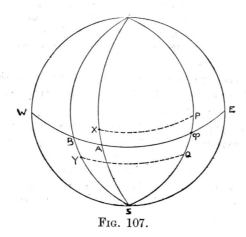

Fig. 107.

In Fig. 107, ♈ represents the First Point of Aries, and X and Y are two stars whose declinations are AX (North) and BY (South) respectively. The S.H.A. of star X is the angle ♈NX, or the arc PX. The S.H.A. of star Y is the angle ♈SY, or arc QY.

Note particularly that the Sidereal Hour Angle is ALWAYS measured to the westward, just as is the G.H.A. or the L.H.A. of the Sun.

It has been shown, earlier in this chapter, that because of their enormous distances from the Earth, all stars appear to us to be fixed, their apparent movement across the sky being actually due to the Earth's rotation on its axis from West to East. It has also been shown that Aries itself is a fixed point, with declination 0° and S.H.A. 0°. Thus the S.H.A. of every "fixed" star must also have a constant value. So, too, the declination of each star is constant, except, as with S.H.A., for very slight aberrations due to terrestrial causes. When using stars for navigational problems, no correction is necessary either for declination or S.H.A.

To Find Stars in the "Nautical Almanac".—A very full list of stars appears in pp. 268-273 of the (1958) *Nautical Almanac*. The stars listed on the even-numbered pages are the same stars that are listed on the odd-numbered pages. In the first case, some of the navigational stars are named according to their constellations, while in the latter case the same stars appear under the names by which they are more usually known. For instance, the second star listed on page 268 is named α Pegasi, while on page 269 it appears as Markab. The same method of naming is followed on the next four pages of the Almanac. On the left hand pages of this list, S.H.A. and declinations are given for the first six months of the year. S.H.A. and declinations from July to December are given on the right hand pages. These stars are listed in *ascending* order of S.H.A., the first star (γ Cephei) having a Sidereal Hour Angle of 5° 36′, and the last star (α Andromedae) having a Sidereal Hour Angle of 358° 26·7′.

It will be seen that some of the stars listed on these pages are followed by a number (44, 51, 57, etc.) The explanation of these numbers is given in the next paragraph.

In the daily pages of the *Nautical Almanac*, the final column of each left hand page consists of a list of 57 "navigational" stars, together with their S.H.A. and declinations for these dates. They are listed in alphabetical order. The numbers referred to in the previous paragraph call attention to the relative values of the S.H.A. of these stars in *descending* order from No. 1 (S.H.A. 358° 26′) to No. 57 (S.H.A. 5° 36′).

There is a further index to these 57 navigational stars given on page xxxiii, (near the back cover of the Almanac) the first column giving the stars in alphabetical order, the second in the numerical descending order of S.H.A.

The magnitudes of all stars are also given.

Greenwich Hour Angle of Aries (G.H.A. ♈)—When using an observation of any star to find a terrestrial longitude, or when finding a star's true bearing, all particulars must eventually be referred to the longitude of Greenwich. Thus the G.H.A. of the particular star being used for observation must be known.

To give in the *Nautical Almanac* the G.H.A. of every navigational star for every hour of every day would result in a book both unwieldy and expensive. Instead, the celestial position of Aries—from which point the S.H.A. of all stars are measured—has been fixed with mathematical precision, and Aries is used as if it were a fixed bright star. The G.H.A. ♈ is listed at each hour of G.M.T. in the first panel on the left hand pages of the *Nautical Almanac*.

It has already been pointed out that successive southings of fixed stars (in which we now include Aries) occur every 23 hours 56 minutes, 04 seconds. The hourly change of G.H.A.♈ is therefore 15° 02·46', and is due entirely to the rotation of the Earth on its axis.

To find the correct G.H.A.♈ for any specified time is a very simple operation, similar to finding the G.H.A. Sun. First find G.H.A.♈ for the required HOUR in the appropriate daily page of the *Nautical Almanac*. Next turn to the appropriate page of the Table of Increments and Corrections for the required *minutes*, and abreast of the given *seconds* take the correction from the second panel, headed ARIES. Add the two.

Example 1.—Find G.H.A.♈ at 07h 27m 52s G.M.T. on Jan. 2nd.

G.H.A.♈, Jan. 2nd, 07h=206° 24·8'
Increment, 27m 52s   =   6   59·1

Corrected G.H.A. ♈   =213   23·9

Example 2.—Find G.H.A. ♈ at 03h 29m 37s on July 16th.

G.H.A.♈, July 16th, 03h=338° 27·0'
Increment, 29m 37s   =   7   25·5

Corrected G.H.A.♈   =345   52·5

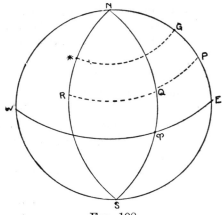

Fig. 108.

Greenwich Hour Angle of a Star (G.H.A.*)—Under preceding sub-headings, it has been shown

1. How to pick out the S.H.A. of any navigational star from the *Nautical Almanac*; and
2. How to find the G.H.A.♈ at any time.

In Fig. 108, the meridian $N G S$ represents the meridian of Greenwich projected into the sky; $N♈S$ represents a celestial meridian passing through Aries; and $N*S$ represents still another celestial meridian through a particular star. The arc PQ is G.H.A.♈, and the arc QR is the S.H.A.*. It can be seen that the sum of these two arcs is equal to the arc G *, which represents the Greenwich Hour Angle of the Star. Therefore

$$\text{G.H.A.*}=\text{G.H.A.♈}+\text{S.H.A.*}$$

Example 1.—On December 23rd, G.M.T. 16h 35m 12s., find the G.H.A. of the star Betelgeuse.

First find the G.H.A.♈ for the day and hour from the daily page. Correct this argument for odd minutes and seconds from the Table of Increments, as previously described. Next find the required star in the Star List on the same page, and add the S.H.A.* given there. This can all be performed in one operation.

G.H.A.♈, Dec. 23rd, 16h	=331°	41·2′
Increment, 35m 12s	= 8	49·4
S.H.A. Betelgeuse	=271	45·3
	612	15·9
	—360	
Correct G.H.A.*	252	15·9

(Note:—When the result exceeds 360°, subtract that amount from the result).

Example 2.—On June 12th, G.M.T. 08h 24m 45s., find the G.H.A. of the star Altair.

G.H.A.♈, June 12th, 08h	=20° 08·6'
Increment, 24m 45s	= 6 12·3
S.H.A. Altair	=62 48·3
Correct G.H.A.*	89 09·2

Example 3.—Find the G.H.A. of the star Alioth at 07h 38m 40s G.M.T. on September 22nd.

G.H.A.♈, Sept. 22nd, 07h	=105° 38·2
Increment, 38m 40s	= 9 41·6
S.H.A. Alioth	=166 57·4
Correct G.H.A.*	282 17·2

Local Hour Angle of a Star (L.H.A.*)—In Chapter 17, it was shown that—

L.H.A. Sun=G.H.A. Sun—West longitude,
+East longitude.

By the same reasoning, L.H.A.*=G.H.A.*+East longitude.
—West longitude.

It has just been shown that G.H.A.*=G.H.A.♈ + S.H.A.*, so that
L.H.A.*=G.H.A.♈ +S.H.A.*+East longitude
—West longitude.

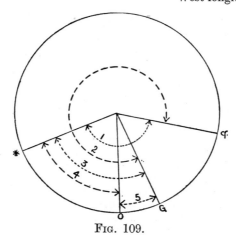

Fig. 109.

In Fig. 109, G.H.A.* (arc 3)=[G.H.A. ♈ (2)+S.H.A.* (1)]—360°

(arc 5)=West longitude.

Therefore L.H.A.* (arc 4)=(G.H.A. ♈ +S.H.A.*)—360°

—West longitude.

Example 1.—Find L.H.A. of star Vega at 05h 26m 26s G.M.T. on October 8th in long. 79° 04′ W.

G.H.A.♈, Oct. 8th, 05h	=91°	19·5′
Increment, 26m 26s	= 6	37·6
S.H.A. Vega	=81	06·9
G.H.A.*	179	04·0
Long. W.	—79	04·0
Correct L.H.A.*	100	00·0

Example 2.—Find the L.H.A. of star Deneb in long. 35° 24′ E. at 07h 28m 22s G.M.T. on June 13th.

G.H.A.♈, June 13th, 07h	= 6°	05·2′
Increment, 28m 22s	= 7	06·7
S.H.A. Deneb	=49	59·3
Long. East	+35	24·0
Correct L.H.A.*	98	35·2

Planets.—Planets are worlds which, like the Earth, circle ceaselessly round the Sun. Owing to this fact, they possess an apparent movement across the sky entirely different from the apparent motion of the stars. It is only necessary to remember that while the Sidereal Hour Angles of "fixed" stars are constant, the Sidereal Hour Angles of Planets, the Sun and the Moon are not constant, and must be corrected. The Earth's movements round the Sun, and the Moon's movements round the Earth, cause the changes in the Sidereal Hour Angles of those bodies. In a similar way, the motion of the Planets relative to the Earth, as they progress along their various orbits round the Sun, causes like changes.

Only four of the Planets which share the solar system with the Earth are used for purposes of navigation—Venus, Mars, Jupiter and Saturn. The G.H.A. and declinations of these bodies are listed on the left hand pages of the daily pages in the *Nautical Almanac*. Each planet is given a separate panel. At the foot of each panel the values of "*v*" and "*d*" are given. The "*d*" correction, as in the case of the Sun, is simply the mean *hourly* change in the body's declination. The method of using the correction was explained in Chapter 17, page 206.

In the Table of Increments and Corrections, an hourly variation of 15° is used in tabulating the G.H.A. of the Sun **and the Planets.** The "*v*" correction is the mean *hourly* amount on any particular day by which the ACTUAL hourly change of G.H.A. of each individual planet exceeds or is less than 15°. The "*v*" correction is used for correcting G.H.A. of a planet in exactly the same way as the "*d*" correction is used for correcting declination.

One important point to note is that the "*v*" correction of the planet Venus, and of that planet alone, is sometimes additive—the hourly change being more than 15°—and sometimes subtractive—the hourly change being less than 15°. In the latter case, a minus sign is placed in front of the figure.

Example 1.—On October 8th, find the G.H.A. and L.H.A. of the planet Venus at 03h 37m 18s., G.M.T., in long. 21° 19' W.

G.H.A. Oct. 8th, 03h	235°	36·3'
Increment, 37m 18s	9	19·5
	244	55·8
"*v*" correction	—	0·3
Correct G.H.A.	244	55·5
Long. W.	— 21	19·0
Correct L.H.A.	223	36·5

Decl.	0°	52·7' S.
Corr.	+	0·8
Corr. decl.	0	53·5 S.

Example 2.—Find the G.H.A. and L.H.A., and also the correct declination of the planet Mars at 20h 31m 21s on July 16th in long. 13° 47' E.

G.H.A. July 16th, 20h	208°	04·9'
Increment, 31m 21s	7	50·3
"*v*" corr.		0·5
Correct G.H.A.	215	55·7
Long. E.	+ 13	47·0
Correct L.H.A.	229	42·7

Decl.	8°	13·2' N.
Corr.	+	0·3
Corr. decl.	8	13·5 N.

EXERCISE 37.

(A)   Find G.H.A. ♈

1.	January 2nd,	at 10h 22m 09s G.M.T.			
2.	June 13th	at 02	28	37	,,
3.	July 16th	at 19	31	12	,,
4.	October 9th	at 16	19	25 L.M.T. in long. 11° 31' E.
5.	December 21st,	at 21	05	11	,, ,, ,, 5 18 W.

(B)　Find G.H.A.*

6.　Capella　　Sept. 22nd,　at 03h 25m 29s G.M.T.
7.　Procyon　　June 14th,　at 19　38　40　　,,
8.　Aldebaran　Jan. 1st,　　at 06　33　33　　,,
9.　Altair　　　Dec. 23rd　at 21　28　30　L.M.T. in long. 14° 26' E.
10.　Vega　　　July 21st,　at 02　15　51　　,,　　　,, ,,　　2 08 W.

(C)　Find L.H.A.*

11.　Sirius　　　Jan. 3rd,　　at 03h 38m 11s G.M.T. in long. 19° 51' W.
12.　Betelgeuse　June 14th　at 19　34　41　　,,　　,, ,,　　7 33 E.
13.　Canopus　　Oct. 7th　　at 06　28　48　　,,　　,, ,,　　1 39 E.
14.　Rigel　　　July 17th　at 22　16　40　L.M.T. ,,　,,　11 25 E.
15.　Denebola　Dec. 21st　at 05　15　14　　,,　　,, ,,　　4 19 W.

(D)　Find L.H.A. and declination of planets.

16.　Mars　　　July 22nd　at 04h 25m 51s G.M.T. in long. 12° 12' W.
17.　Saturn　　Sept. 24th,　at 17　37　00　　,,　　,, ,,　16 55 W.
18.　Venus　　July 15th　at 23　22　40　　,,　　,, ,,　　5 09 E.
19.　Jupiter　　Dec. 23rd,　at 06　15　21　L.M.T. ,,　,,　10 16 E.
20.　Venus　　Jan. 3rd　at 20　24　38　　,,　　,, ,,　12 33 E.

CHAPTER 30.

TIME AZIMUTH BY STAR OR PLANET.

The "arguments" required when calculating by Tables the true bearing of any celestial body—Sun, Moon, star or planet—are the same in every case, viz., latitude, declination, and hour angle or local apparent time.

When finding the true azimuth of a star, the observer's estimated latitude is known. The star's declination and its Sidereal Hour Angle, which require no correction, are found in the Star List in the appropriate daily page of the *Nautical Almanac*. The L.H.A. of the star is found by methods just described in the previous chapter. That is—

L.H.A.*=G.H.A.Ꮖ+S.H.A.*—West longitude.
+East longitude.

Thereafter, the problem is carried through precisely as in the case of finding the true bearing of the Sun. (Chapter 19).

It should be noted, however, that the time given in the problem gives no indication as to whether the star should be East or West of the observer's meridian. At 04 hrs., L.M.T. or G.M.T., the star may be either East or West.

Example 1.—On September 23rd, G.M.T. 01h 24m in lat. 56° 20′ N., long. 5° 18·7′ E., the star Betelgeuse was observed to bear 115° C. Var. 5° W. Required the deviation of the compass.

Sept. 23rd, G.H.A.Ꮖ at 01h	= 16°	22·6′
Increment for 24m	= 6	01·0
S.H.A. Betelgeuse	=271	45·8
Longitude East	= 5	18·7

Decl.
7° 24·0′ N.

L.H.A. Betelgeuse (W)   299   28·1
—360

L.H.A. Betelgeuse (E)   60   31·9   =   4h 02m 08s.

349

The L.H.A. is 299° 28·1'.
From Fig. 110 it can be seen
that W.H.A. 299° 28·1 (1)=
E.H.A. 60° 31·9' (2)

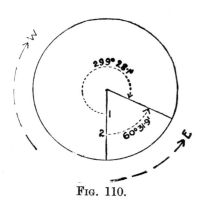

Fɪɢ. 110.

(a) *By Norie's A.B.C. Tables*
A gives ·85 S.
B gives ·15 N.

C   = ·70 S.

True Az. S. 68° 48' E.

(b) *By Burton's A.B.C. Tables*
A gives ·850+
B gives ·149−

C   = ·701+

True Az.   S. 68° 48' E.

(c) *By Alt-Azimuth Tables*

		Lat.	Decl.	Time
Lat. 56°	111° 48'	111° 48'	111° 48'	111° 48'
Decl. 7°				
H.A. 4h 00m	− 36	112 12	111 12	110 00
True Az. N. 111 12 E.		24	36	108
		× ·33	× ·4	× ·25
		+ 8	−14·4	− 27

True Az. S. 68° 48' E.
Obs. Az. S. 65   00 E.

Error   3 48 W.
Var.   5 00 W.

Dev.   1 12 E.

Example 2.—On January 1st, L.M.T. 04h 00m 50s., in lat. 49° 35' N., long. 7° 32·5' W., the obs. azimuth of the star Arcturus was S. 61° E. Var. 10° W. Required the true azimuth, error and deviation of the compass for the direction of the ship's head.

L.M.T. Jan 1st	04h 00m 50s		G.H.A. ♈ at 04h	160°	18·3′
Long. W.	+ 30 10		Increment 31m	7	46·3
			S.H.A.*	146	33·9
G.M.T. Jan. 1st	04 31 00				
			G.H.A.*	314	38·5
			Long. W.	— 7	32·5
Decl.	19° 23·9′ N.		W.L.H.A.*	307	06·0
			E.L.H.A.*	52	54·0
			=	3h 31m 36s.	

(a) *By Norie's A.B.C. Tables*   (b) *By Burton's A.B.C. Tables*

A gives	·89 S.		A gives	·885+
B gives	·44 N.		B gives	·441—
C	= ·45 S.		C	= ·444+

True Az. S. 73·8° E.   True Az. S. 73·9° E.

(Note that decimals have been used in this problem.)

(c) *By Alt-Azimuth Tables.*

		Lat.	*Dec.*	*Time*
Lat. 49°		106·9	106·9	106·9
Dec. 19°	106·9	106·9	106·9	106·9
H.A. 3h 28m	— ·8	107·6	106·0	105·1
True Az.	N. 106·1 E.	.7	·9	1·8
		× ·6	× ·4	× ·5
		+ ·42	— ·36	— ·9

	True Az.	S. 73·9° E.
	Obs. Az.	S. 61·0 E.
	Error	12·9 W.
	Var.	10·0 W.
	Dev.	2·9 W.

Azimuth by Planet.—When observing a planet instead of a star to determine compass error, only slight differences from the fore-going are found.

In the daily pages of the *Nautical Almanac* the Greenwich Hour
Angles of the four navigational planets are tabulated for each hour of
G.M.T., exactly as in the case of the Sun, the Moon, and Aries.   The
L.H.A. of these planets can therefore be found direct.

L.H.A. planet=G.H.A. planet—West longitude
+East longitude.

Thereafter, the planet's declination is corrected in the usual way,
and the true azimuth ascertained as shown above.

Example 3.—On September 24th, L.M.T. 18h 48m in lat. 39° 28' N.,
long. 6° E., the planet Jupiter bore 265° C.   Var. 8° W.   Required the
true azimuth, error and deviation of the compass.

L.M.T. Sept. 24th 18h 48m	G.H.A. Jupiter at 18h 61° 37·1'	
Long. East — 24	Increment, 24 min. 6 00·0	
	"*v*" correction 0·8	
G.M.T. Sept. 24th 18 24		
	Corr. G.H.A. Jupiter 67 37·9	
Decl. 11° 41·5' S.	Long. E. + 6 00·0	
	L.H.A. Jupiter (W) 73 37·9	

(a) *By Norie's Tables*		
A= ·24 S.	True Az. S. 70° 51' W.	
B= ·21 S.	Obs. Az. S. 85 00 W.	
C= ·45 S.	Error 14 09 W.	
	Var. 8 00 W.	
	Dev. 6 09 W.	

(b) *By Burton's Tables*		
A= ·241+	True Az. S. 70° 42' W.	
B= ·214+	Obs. Az. S. 85 00 W.	
C= ·455+	Error 14 18 W.	
	Var. 8 00 W.	
	Dev. 6 18 W.	

(c) By Alt-Azimuth Tables

			Dec.	*Time*	*Lat.*
Approx. True Az.	110°	00′	110° 00′	110° 00′	110° 00′
Correction	—	38			
True Az.	N. 109	22 W.	110 42	108 42	110 06
Obs. Az.	N. 95	00 W.	+ 42	−1 18	+ 6
Error	14	22 W.	× ·7	× ·9	× ·5
Var.	8	00 W.	+29·4	−70·2	+3·0
Dev.	6	22 W.			

EXERCISE 38.

Time Azimuth by Star and Planet.

(Answers at the end of the book have been worked from *Burton's Tables*)

1. On October 7th, at 23h 30m G.M.T. in lat. 17° 57′ S., long. 48° 28′ W., the star Rasalhague bore 307·5° C. Var. $14\frac{1}{2}°$ W. Required the true azimuth error and deviation of the compass for the direction of the ship's head.

2. On September 22nd, in lat. 50° 23′ N., long. 70° 07·5′ W., at L.M.T. 03h 19m 30s., the star Aldebaran bore 171° C. Var. 24° W. Required the deviation of the compass.

3. On December 23rd, at 07h 30m G.M.T. in lat. 58° 28′ N., long. 9° 49′ W., the star Arcturus bore 166° C. Var. $11\frac{1}{2}°$ W. Find the star's true bearing and the deviation of the compass.

4. On July 17th, in lat. 56° 41′ N., long. 5° 49′ W., G.M.T. 18h 24m., the star Regulus bore 260° C. Var. 9° W. Find the deviation of the compass.

5. On July 21st, L.M.T. 23h 38m, in lat. 37° 07′ N., long. 13° 15′ W., the star Deneb bore 062° C. Var. 6° W. Required the true azimuth, error and deviation of the compass for the direction of the ship's head.

6. On December 21st, in lat. 52° 25′ N., long. 32° 11′ W., G.M.T. 08h 27m., the star Alphecca bore 115° C. Var. 16° W. Required the true bearing of the star and the deviation of the compass.

7. On October 7th, L.M.T. 02h 51m in lat. 48° 53′ N., long. 7° 30′ W., the star Alpheratz bore N. $86\frac{3}{4}°$ W. by compass. Var. 8° W. Required the true azimuth, error and deviation of the compass.

8. On January 3rd, at 05h 27m G.M.T. in lat. 50° 33′ N., long. 14° 40′ W., the star Spica bore 163° C. Var. 12° 30′ W. Required the deviation of the compass.

9. On June 14th, in lat. 44° 16′ N., long. 11° 06′ W., L.M.T. 20h 36m 36s, the star Dubhe bore 320° C. Var. 5° W. Required the true azimuth, error and deviation of the compass.

10. On September 24th, L.M.T. 03h 00m in lat. 30° 55′ N., long. 30° E., the star Schedar bore 320° C. Var. 7° E. Required the deviation of the compass.

11. On December 23rd, in lat. 38° 12′ N., long. 55° 55′ W., L.M.T. 16h 49m 20s., the star Altair bore by compass West. Var. 26° W. Required the true azimuth and deviation of the compass.

12. On January 1st, G.M.T. 02h 38m in lat. 63° 26′ N., long. 23° 37′ E., the star Arcturus bore 109° C. Var. 15° 30′ E. Required the true azimuth, error and deviation of the compass.

13. On October 8th, G.M.T. 15h 39m in lat. 36° 36′ N., long. 52° 18′ E., the star Vega bore by compass West. Var. 12° E. Required the deviation of the compass.

14. On September 23rd, in lat. 41° 15′ N., long. 21° 26′ W., L.M.T. 21h 10m 16s, the star Markab bore S.E. by compass. Var. 9° W. Required the deviation of the compass.

15. On June 12th, G.M.T. 20h 34m in lat. 28° 47′ N., long. 34° 07′ E., the star Vega bore 060° C. Var. 4° E. Required the deviation of the compass.

Planets.

16. On January 2nd, L.M.T. 18h 17m in lat. 41° 19′ N., long. 47° 45′ W., the planet Venus bore 250° C. Var. 18° W. Required the true azimuth, error and deviation of the compass for the direction of the ship's head.

17. On June 12th, at G.M.T. June 13th, 01h 35m in lat. 36° 53′ N., long. 38° 33′ W., the planet Jupiter bore 245° C. Var. 15° 30′ W. Required the true azimuth, error and deviation of the compass.

18. On October 8th in lat. 53° 22′ N., long. 18° 06′ E., G.M.T. 00h 00m., the planet Mars bore 139° C. Var. 5° E. Required the true azimuth and deviation of the compass.

19. On July 21st, L.M.T. 01h 22m in lat. 25° 37' N., long. 31° W., the planet Saturn bore 252° C. Var. 14° W. Required the deviation of the compass.

20. On December 22nd, L.M.T. 00h 24m in lat. 49° 11' N., long. 11° 45' E., the planet Mars bore 250° C. Var. 5° W. Required the deviation of the compass.

CHAPTER 31.

LATITUDE BY MERIDIAN ALTITUDE OF A STAR.

When finding latitude by a meridian altitude observation of a star, the principle involved is the same as when using the Sun. The altitude of the star is observed when it is bearing true South or true North from the observer, and this altitude is corrected.

The distance of even the nearest star from the Earth is so great that the angle subtended at the star between an observer on the Earth's surface and the Earth's centre is immeasurably small. Therefore there is no Parallax to correct.

To an observer, stars are mere pinpoints of light. Hence no correction for semi-diameter is required. The declinations of fixed stars do not materially alter, so that no correction is required. The declination of the required star is found in the star list on the daily page of the *Nautical Almanac*, and is used as given. That being so, no Greenwich Time is required.

Thus, to find latitude by a meridian latitude of a star, first apply Index Error of the sextant, if any. Subtract Dip and Refraction in the same way as with the Sun. The result is the true altitude, which is subtracted from 90° to obtain the zenith distance. This is named opposite to the star's bearing.

Using the same rules as when finding latitude by the Sun, apply the declination to the Z.D. The result is the latitude.

Example 1.—On September 22nd, in long. 17° 18′ W., the sextant meridian altitude of the star Betelgeuse was 51° 27′, South of observer. Index error 3·3′ to add. Height of eye 18 feet. Required the latitude.

Sext. alt.	51° 27·0′	S.
Ind. err. +	3·3	
	51 30·3	
Dip. −	4·2	
	51 26·1	
Refr. −	0·8	
True alt.	51 25·3	S.
	90	
Z.D.	38 34·7	N.
Decl.	7 24·0	N.
Latitude	45 58·7	N.

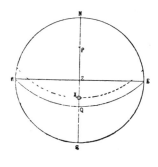

Example 2.—On October 9th, in long. 32° 17′ W., the obs. mer. alt. of the star Aldebaran was 33° 08′, South of observer.   Height of eye 15 feet.   Required the latitude.

Obs. alt.	33°	08·0′ S.
Dip.	—	3·8
	33	04·2
Refr.	—	1·5
True alt.	33	02·7 S.
	90	
Z.D.	56	57·3 N.
Decl.	16	25·6 N.
Latitude	73	22·9 N.

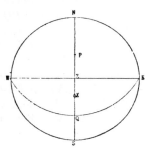

Meridian Altitude below the Pole.—Under certain conditions, stars which possess large declinations do not "set", but remain continuously above the observer's horizon throughout their daily journey.   This state of affairs occurs when the star's POLAR DISTANCE is smaller than the observer's latitude.

Such stars are visible when on the meridian in the ordinary way—"at the *upper* meridian passage"—and again when they are on the meridian at their *lower* passage—"below the pole".   In the northern hemisphere, the bearing of the star when on the meridian below the pole is always North, and the resultant latitude, of course, must always be North.

In Fig. 111, *X* indicates the position of the star on the meridian at its LOWER transit.   At its upper transit, its position would be at *Y*.

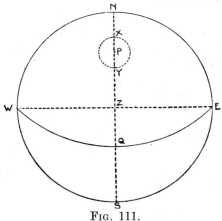

Fig. 111.

XN represents the true altitude below the pole;
PX represents the polar distance;
ZQ is the observer's latitude;
$NZ=90°$, and $PQ=90°$.
It will be seen from the sketch that
$NX+XP+PZ=90°$, and
$PZ+ZQ=90°$.
Since each is equal to 90°, each must be equal to the other.
$NX+XP+PZ=PZ+ZQ$
PZ, being included on each side of this equation, cancels out.   Then
$NX+XP=ZQ$, or
True alt.$+$Polar distance$=$Latitude.

Example 3.—On July 15th, in long. 2° 42′ E., the obs. mer. alt. of the star Dubhe below the pole was 21° 16′, North of observer.   Height of eye 22 feet.   Required the latitude.

Obs. alt.	21°	16·0′ N.			
Dip	—	4·6			
	21	11·4	Decl.	61°	58·7′ N.
Refr.	—	2·4		90	
True alt.	21	09·0	P.D.	28	01·3
P.D.	28	01·3			
Latitude	49	10·3 N.			

Example 4.—On June 14th, in long. 21° 18′ W., the obs. mer. alt. of the star Alioth below the pole was 27° 32′, North of observer.   Height of eye 26 feet.   Required the latitude.

Obs. alt.	27°	32·0′ N.			
Dip.	—	5·0			
	27	27·0	Decl.	56°	11·3′ N.
Refr.	—	1·8		90	
True alt.	27	25·2	P.D.	33	48·7
P.D.	33	48·7			
Latitude	61	13·9 N.			

Latitude By Meridian Altitude of a Planet.—The mechanical part of this problem is the same as is carried out when using a star, with the sole exception that when correcting altitudes of the planets Venus and Mars, an additional correction has to be applied. This correction, which varies according to the date, is found in the middle panel of corrections on the inside cover of the *Nautical Almanac*, and also on the card which accompanies the Almanac.

Since the navigational planets are relatively close to the Earth, their declinations alter. Greenwich Mean Time, approximately to the nearest minute at least, is therefore required when finding the planet's correct declination.

First the approximate time of the planet's meridian passage across the observer's longitude must be found—the time at which the body's L.H.A. is 360°

ONE time of meridian passage for each of the four planets is found at the foot of the left hand page in the "daily pages" of the *Nautical Almanac*. This time must be used with caution. It refers only to the time of meridian passage for the *middle day* on that page, and thus may be as much as 10 minutes of time in error for the required day. It is better to find the time by the following method.

Example 5.—Find the approximate L.M.T. and the G.M.T. of the meridian passage of the planet Jupiter in long. 11° W. on January 2nd. Find also its correct declination at this time.

In the appropriate panel, for January 2nd, G.H.A. of Jupiter is 359° 14·9′ at 07 hours. It is required to find the time when G.H.A. is 360°—that is when G.H.A. has increased by a further 0° 45·1′.

As explained in Chapter 28, increments to the G.H.A. of planets are included in the panel headed "SUN" in the Table of Increments and Corrections. These increments assume an hourly increase of 15°. At the foot of the panel of Jupiter in the daily page, the "*v*" correction is given as 2·2′, showing that the *real* hourly increase in Jupiter's G.H.A. is 15° 02·2′. While allowance for this has to be made in some navigational problems, it can be ignored for the purpose of correcting the planet's declination, as 2·2′ of arc=9 seconds of time only.

Look for an increment of 0° 45·1′ in the SUN panel in the Table of Increments. It is found to be 3 minutes exactly.

The G.M.T. of the meridian passage of Jupiter AT GREENWICH is therefore 07h 03m 00s. To within seconds, the time of the planet's meridian passage across the observer's longitude is also 07h 03m 00s, *L.M.T.*

Apply longitude in time to the L.M.T. in the usual way to obtain the G.M.T. of the planet's meridian passage across the required longitude. The declination is then corrected for the GREENWICH time thus found.

G.H.A. Jupiter, Jan. 2nd at 07h   =359° 14·9′
(360°—359° 14·9′=0° 45·1′)
Increment of 0° 45·1′ takes 3 mins.
Approx. L.M.T. of planet's mer. pass. 07h 03m 00s
Longitude West   +   44

G.M.T. of planet's mer. pass.   07   47   00

Correction for declination+0·1′
Correct declination of Jupiter=9° 52·3′ S.

Example 6.—On January 3rd in long. 14° E., the obs. mer. alt. of the planet Venus was 27° 05′, bearing South of observer. Height of eye 22 ft. Required the latitude.

G.H.A. Venus at 14hrs., Jan. 3rd=354° 45·6′
Reqd. increment 5° 14·4′ From Table, time=20m 57s,
                                    say 21 minutes.

L.M.T. of Mer. Pass.	14h	21m	Decl. at 13h	14°	46·4′ S.
Long. E.	—	56	Corr.	—	0·3
G.M.T. of Mer. Pass.	13	25	Corr. decl.	14	46·1 S.

Obs. alt.	27°	05·0′ S.
Dip.	—	4·6
	27	00·4
Refr.	—	1·9
	26	58·5
Addl. corr. +		0·7
True alt.	26	59·2 S.
	90	
Z.D.	63	00·8 N.
Decl.	14	46·1 S.
Latitude	48	14·7 N.

Example 7.—On June 13th in long. 27° 15′ W., the obs. mer. alt. of the planet Mars was 22° 43′, South of observer. Height of eye 20 ft. Required the latitude.

June 13th at 06h, G.H.A. Mars=346° 16·7'. Incr. reqd.=13° 43·3'.
Increase takes 54m 53s., say 55 minutes.

L.M.T. of Mer. Pass.	06h 55m	Decl. (G.M.T.) 08h 0°	15·7' S.
Longitude West	+ 1 49	Correction —	0·6
G.M.T. of Mer. Pass.	08 44	Corr. Decl.	0 15·1 S.

Obs. alt.	22°	43·0' S.
Dip	—	4·4
	22	38·6
Refr.	—	2·3
	22	36·3
Addl. Corr. +		0·1
True alt.	22	36·4 S.
	90	
Z.D.	67	23·6 N.
Decl.	0	15·1 S.
Latitude	67	08·5 N.

EXERCISE 39

LATITUDE BY MERIDIAN ALTITUDE OF STAR OR PLANET.

Given the following particulars, find the ship's latitude.

1. On January 2nd in long. 39° 23' W., the obs. mer. alt. of the star Capella was 68° 25', bearing North. Height of eye 17 feet.
2. On December 21st in long. 5° 41' W., the obs. mer. alt. of the star Sirius was 43° 19', bearing South. Height of eye 21 feet.
3. On December 21st in long. 20° 16' E., the obs. mer. alt. of the star Betelgeuse was 54° 42', bearing South. Height of eye 24 feet.
4. On July 21st, on the prime meridian, the obs. mer. alt. of the star Spica was 43° 18', South of observer. Height of eye 16 ft.
5. On July 15th the sextant mer. alt. of the star Deneb was 80° 15', bearing North. Height of eye 22 ft. Index error 1·2' to add.
6. On October 8th the obs. mer. alt. of the star Procyon was 53° 12', South of observer. Height of eye 18 ft.
7. On September 23rd, the obs. mer. alt. of the star Aldebaran was 76° 31', bearing North. Height of eye 26 ft.
8. On September 22nd, the sext. mer. alt. of the star Regulus was 49° 31', bearing South. Index error 2·5' to add. Height of eye 17 ft.

9. On October 7th in long. 15° W., the obs. mer. alt. of the star Rigel was 40° 40', South of observer. Height of eye 20 ft.

10. On June 14th the obs. mer. alt. of the star Alpheratz was 64° 18', bearing South. Height of eye 24 ft.

11. On January 1st the obs. mer. alt. of the star Vega was 62° 35', bearing North. Height of eye 27 ft.

12. On July 16th the obs. mer. alt. of the star Altair was 42° 37', bearing South. Height of eye 21 ft.

Meridian Altitude below the Pole.

13. On January 3rd the obs. mer. alt. of the star Alioth below the pole was 28° 32'. Height of eye 19 ft.

14. On December 23rd in long. 17° 43' W., the obs. mer. alt. of the star Kochab below the pole was 21° 16'. Height of eye 23 ft.

15. On September 24th the obs. mer. alt. of the star Alioth below the pole was 16° 35'. Height of eye 23 ft.

16. On July 23rd on the meridian of Greenwich the obs. mer. alt. of the star Mirfak below the pole was 21° 33'. Height of eye 23 ft.

Planets.

17. On June 13th on the prime meridian the obs. mer. alt. of the planet Mars was 27° 50', bearing South. Height of eye 29 ft.

18. On December 22nd in long. 15° 22' W., the obs. mer. alt. of the planet Jupiter was 38° 19', bearing South. Height of eye 25 ft.

19. On June 12th in long. 21° 19' W., the obs. mer. alt. of the planet Venus was 62° 13', bearing North. Height of eye 19 ft.

20. On October 9th, long. 7° 19' E., the obs. mer. alt. of the planet Mars was 46° 33', bearing South. Height of eye 27 ft.

CHAPTER 32.

TO FIND LATITUDE BY THE POLE STAR.

The Pole Star (*Polaris*) is situated within $1\frac{1}{4}°$ of the true North pole of the heavens, and circles round the celestial pole at that angular distance from it. Because it is so near the pole, Polaris appears to an observer to be practically motionless.

If the star were situated precisely at the celestial North pole, its true altitude would be equal to the observer's latitude. (See Fig. 112.)

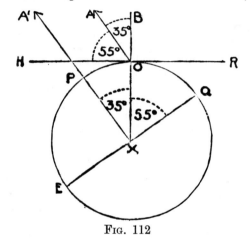

FIG. 112

In the sketch, EXQ represents the Earth's equator, P the geographical North pole, HOR the horizon, and O an observer in Lat. 55° N. The angle OXQ represents the latitude, 55°, so that the angle PXO measures 35°, being the complement of OXQ.

OA, a line drawn from the observer to the pole star, would represent true North if Polaris was situated at the celestial pole. The line XA^1, from the centre of the Earth to the pole star, is parallel to OA, since the distance from the Earth to the star is so infinitely great that the relatively small distance between the observer and the Earth's centre (O and X) is negligible.

Thus angle $AOB = 35° =$ angle PXO, and
angle AOH (alt.) $= 55° =$ angle OXQ (lat.)

363

Pole Star Corrections.—Owing to Polaris being about $1\frac{1}{4}°$ away from the celestial pole, various corrections have to be made to the true altitude to find the latitude. The values of these corrections depend primarily on the Local Hour Angle of the star.

It will be remembered that

$$\text{L.H.A.*}=\text{L.H.A.}\,\Upsilon+\text{S.H.A.*.,}$$

and since S.H.A. of the pole star is practically a constant, we need find only L.H.A. Υ, and from that, the corrections are adjusted.

The 1st correction, designated "a_0" in the Pole Star Tables, depends on the value of L.H.A. Υ alone.

The 2nd correction ("a_1" in the Tables) depends on L.H.A. Υ and latitude.

The 3rd correction ("a_2") depends on L.H.A. Υ and the date. Both the 2nd and the 3rd corrections are rather minor corrections.

Interpolation is required in the case of the 1st correction only, and can easily be performed mentally.

Pole Star Tables.—The three corrections mentioned in the preceding paragraph are tabulated in special Pole Star Tables—pp. 274-276 in the *Nautical Almanac*, and reproduced on pp. 483 to 485 of this book.

In order to ensure that the 2nd and 3rd corrections are always additive, each has had $0.6'$ added to it. The 1st correction has had $58.8'$ added. In all, $1°$ has been added to the three corrections, purely in order to make easier the mechanical part of the calculation. Therefore one full degree must always be subtracted from the true altitude.

The use of the Tables is extremely simple. Look for the L.H.A. Υ *to the nearest* $10°$ across the top of the page. From the left hand vertical column, find L.H.A. Υ to the nearest degree. Following across the page at that level to the original column required, find the 1st correction, interpolating mentally as necessary. Keep to the same column, and follow down the page, correcting first for latitude and finally for the month of the year. The lowermost table in the column gives the true bearing of the Pole Star.

    1.   Find L.H.A. Υ in the usual way;

    2.   Correct the observed altitude and subtract $1°$;

    3.   The "adjusted" altitude$+a_0+a_1+a_2=$latitude.

The result in every case gives NORTH latitude, as the Pole Star can never be seen by an observer in the southern hemisphere.

(NOTE:—When no D.R. latitude is given in the question, the latitude required for the 2nd correction can be taken to be the adjusted true altitude$+$corr. a_0.

Example 1.—On October 9th, L.M.T. 17h 19m 54s in long. $15°$ $46'$ W. the sext. alt. of Polaris was $43°$ $15'$. Height of eye 20 ft. I.E. $5'+$. Required the latitude.

L.M.T., Oct. 9th	17h	19m	54s	Long.	Sext. alt.	43°	15·0'
Long. W.	+ 1	03	04	15° 46'	Ind. Err. +		5·0

G.M.T., Oct. 9th	18	22	58	× 4	Obs. alt.	43	20·0
			60)63	04	Dip —		4·3
			1h 03m	04s		43	15·7

G.H.A. ♈ Oct. 9th, 18h	287°	50·7'	Ref. —		1·0
Incr. 22m 58s	5	45·4	T. alt.	43	14·7
	293	36·1		— 1	
Long. W.	— 15	46·0	Adj. alt.	42	14·7
L.H.A. ♈	277	50·1	a₀ (277° 50')	1	19·2

a_0 (277° 50')   1   19·2
a_1 (Lat. 43°)   0·5
a_2 (October)   0·9

Latitude   43   35·3 N.

Example 2.—On September 22nd at 05h 37m 22s G.M.T. in long. 6° 03' E., the obs. alt. of Polaris was 51° 09'. Height of eye 17 ft. Find the latitude.

G.H.A. ♈, Sept. 22nd, 05h	75°	33·3'	Obs. alt.	51°	09·0'
Increment, 37m 22s	9	22·0	Tot. corr. —		4·8
Long. E.	+ 6	03·0	True alt.	51	04·2
L.H.A. ♈	90	58·3		— 1	00·0

Adj. alt.   50   04·2
a_0 (90° 58·3')   33·2
a_1 (Lat. 50°)   0·6
a_2 (Sept.)   0·3

Latitude   50   38·3 N.

Exercise 40.
Latitude by Pole Star.

Given the following particulars, find the latitude.

1. On January 2nd, in long. 11° 17' W., at 16h 43m L.M.T., the sextant altitude of Polaris was 48° 22'. Index error 3·5' to add. Height of eye 17 ft.

N

2. On December 21st in long. 4° 35′ E., G.M.T. 07h 20m 15s., the obs. alt. of Polaris was 53° 17′. Height of eye 24 ft.

3. On October 7th in long. 00° 00′, L.M.T. 19h 24m., the obs. alt. of Polaris was 35° 21′. Height of eye 19 feet.

4. On June 12th on the prime meridian, G.M.T. 05h 00m 00s., the obs. alt. of Polaris was 43° 18′. Height of eye 21 ft.

5. On July 15th in long. 16° 35′ W., G.M.T. 19h 33m 45s, the sext alt. of Polaris was 29° 40′. Ind. err. 11′ to subtract. Height of eye 16 ft.

6. On July 16th in long. 12° 12′ E., L.M.T. 05h 15m, the obs. alt. of Polaris was 45° 00′. Height of eye 23 ft.

7. On September 24th in long. 21° W., L.M.T. 05h 13m 14s., the obs. alt. of Polaris was 49° 12′. Height of eye 15 ft.

8. On October 9th in long. 1° W., G.M.T. 18h 36m 33s., the obs. alt. of Polaris was 55° 49′. Height of eye 20 ft.

9. On September 22nd in long. 17° 58′ E., G.M.T. 04h 39m 17s., the obs. alt. of Polaris was 47° 47′. Height of eye 23 ft.

10. On December 22nd in long. 43° 19′ W., L.M.T. 05h 42m 30s., the obs. alt. of Polaris was 41° 27′. Height of eye 15 ft.

11. On October 8th in long. 3° 16′ W., L.M.T. 18h 20m 19s., the obs. alt. of Polaris was 55° 03′. Height of eye 19 ft.

12. On January 3rd in long. 50° W., G.M.T. 10h 21m 16s., the obs. alt. of Polaris was 46° 17′. Height of eye 26 ft.

Azimuth of Polaris.—It has already been stated in this chapter that the Pole Star appears to revolve round the North Pole of the heavens at an angular distance of about $1\frac{1}{4}°$ from it. Thus the true bearing of the star normally varies only between the limits of N. $1\frac{1}{4}°$ E. and N. $1\frac{1}{4}°$ W. Terrestrial causes sometimes make these bearings slightly larger, but generally speaking it can be said that any alterations to the normal maxima are small.

To find the star's true bearing, the arguments required are the L.H.A. ♈ to the nearest 10°, and the observer's latitude to the nearest 5° in high latitudes, but to the nearest 20° in low latitudes.

Example 1.—L.H.A. ♈ is 270°. Find the true bearing of the Pole Star in lat. 55° N.

The answer, taken direct from the Table, is 001·5°. (N. 1·5° E.)

Example 2.—L.H.A. ♈ is 73°. Find the true bearing of the Pole Star in lat. 62° N.

The answer, interpolating mentally from the Table is 358·5°. (N. 1·5° W.)

CHAPTER 33.

LONGITUDE BY STAR

By now, it will have been recognised that navigational problems involving stars or planets follow the same general procedure as is done when working the same problems, and using the Sun. It is only in details that star work differs from work where the Sun is the observed body.

In Chapter 22, students learned how to find the ship's longitude by a sextant observation of the Sun. The same methods are used to find the longitude by a sextant altitude of a star, and the mechanical part of the problem, when worked out, provides the Local Hour angle of the star. The difference between this and the Greenwich Hour Angle of the star is the observer's longitude.

In Chapter 29, it was shown that—

G.H.A.*=G.H.A. ♈ +S.H.A.*.

The G.H.A. ♈ is found to the nearest hour of G.M.T. in the "Aries" column in the daily pages of the *Nautical Almanac*, and is corrected for odd minutes and seconds of time from the "Aries" panel in the Interpolation Tables. The S.H.A.* is found directly, without correction, in the star list on the daily pages in the Almanac, together with the star's declination.

The information required in the problem is—
G.M.T.
True altitude and Z.D.
D.R. latitude.
Declination. (P.D. for Sec-Cosec Method).
(Lat.± Decl.)
G.H.A.*

In actual practice at sea, a compass bearing of the observed star shows whether it is East or West of the observer's meridian. In an examination, this information is usually provided. If not, the D.R. or estimated longitude must be stated.

It is important to remember that if the star's bearing is to the westward of the observer, its L.H.A. must be less than 180°. If the bearing is to the eastward, its L.H.A. must be more than 180° and less than 360°.

Example 1.—On September 23rd, in estimated latitude 54° 22′ N., the obs. alt. of the star Arcturus, West of the meridian, was 23° 27′. Height of eye 18 ft. Time by chronometer 20h 11m 17s. Chronometer was 14m 25s slow of G.M.T. Required the longitude.

Obs. alt.	23°	27·0′	Chr. Time	20h	11m	17s	G.H.A. ♈, 20h	302°	09·4′
Dip	—	4·1	Error slow +		14	25	Increment	6	26·6
	23	22·9	G.M.T.	20	25	42		308	36·0
Refr.	—	2·2					S.H.A.*	146	33·6
True alt.	23	20·7	Declination 19° 24·0′ N.					455	09·6
								−360	00·0
							G.H.A.*	95	09·6

Secant-Cosecant Method   *Haversine Method*

								Lat.	54°	22·0′ N.
Decl.	19°	24·0′ N.	T. alt.	23°	20·7′			Decl.	19	24·0 N.
	90			90						
P.D.	70	36·0	Z.D.	66	39·3			(L—D)	34	58·0
Alt.	23°	20·7′				Z.D.	66° 39·3′	Nat hav	·30187	
Lat.	54	22·0	Sec	0·23463		(L—D)	34 58·0	Nat hav	·09026	
P.D.	70	36·0	Cosec	0·02539				Nat hav	·21161	
Sum	148	18·7						Log hav	9·32553	
½ Sum	74	09·3	Cos	9·43621				Log sec	0·23463	
Rem.	50	48·6	Sin	9·88933		Lat. 54° 22·0′		Log sec	0·02539	
						Dec. 19 24·0				
	Log hav L.H.A.*			9·58556				Log hav L.H.A.*	9·58555	

L.H.A.*	76°	42·8′
G.H.A.*	95	09·6
Longitude	18	26·8 W.

Example 2.—On September 23rd in D.R. latitude 42° 19′ N., the obs. alt. of the star Procyon, East of the meridian, was 39° 30·5′. Height of eye 24 ft. Time by chronometer 03h 30m 21s. Chronometer was 8m 56s slow of G.M.T. Required the longitude.

Obs. alt.	39°	30·5′	Chr. Time	03h	30m	21s	G.H.A. ♈,	46°	27·5′
Dip	—	4·8	Error slow +		8	56	Increment	9	50·9
	39	25·7	G.M.T.	03	39	17	S.H.A.*	245	42·9
Refr.	—	1·2					G.H.A.*	302	01·3
True alt.	39	24·5	Declination 5° 19·9′ N.						

Secant-Cosecant Method | Haversine Method

Decl.	5° 19·9′ N.		T. alt.	39° 24·5′	Lat.	42° 19·0′ N.
	90			90	Dec.	5 19·9 N.
P.D.	84 40·1		Z.D.	50 35·5	(L—D)	36 59·1

Alt.	39° 24·5			Z.D.	50° 35·5′	Nat hav 0·18258 ⎫
Lat.	42 19·0	Sec	0·13110	(L—D)	36 59·1	Nat hav 0·10060 ⎬ —
P.D.	84 40·1	Cosec	0·00188			⎭
						Nat hav 0·08198
Sum	166 23·6					
½ Sum	83 11·8	Cos	9·07360			Log hav 8·91369
Rem.	43 47·3	Sin	9·84010	Lat.	42° 19·0′	Log sec 0·13110
				Dec.	5 19·9	Log sec 0·00188
Log. hav L.H.A.*			9·04668			
					Log hav L.H.A.*	9·04667

L.H.A.*	321° 00·8′
G.H.A.*	302 01·3
Longitude	18 59·5 E.

Exercise 41.

Longitude by Star.

Given the following particulars, find the longitude.

1. On January 2nd in D.R. latitude 31° 25′ N., the obs. alt. of the star Aldebaran, East of the meridian, was 30° 53′. Height of eye 20 ft. Time by chronometer 14h 18m 09s. Chronometer was 3m 11s slow of G.M.T.

2. On January 2nd in latitude 43° 21′ N., the obs. alt. of the star Regulus, West of the meridian, was 24° 47·5′. Height of eye 17 ft. G.M.T. 08h 21m 16s.

3. On January 3rd in latitude 25° 51′ N., the obs. alt. of the star Capella, West of the meridian, was 31° 05′. Height of eye 16 ft. Time by chron. January 2nd, 20h 06m 51s. Chron. was 6m 51s fast of G.M.T.

4. On January 1st in latitude 51° 17′ N., the obs. alt. of the star Pollux, East of the meridian, was 35° 11′. Height of eye 22 ft. Time by chronometer 23h 37m 00s. Chron. was correct G.M.T. at Greenwich noon on December 20th, 1957, and was gaining 2 sec. daily.

5. On September 22nd in latitude 49° 12′ N., the obs. alt. of the star Pollux, East of the meridian, was 48° 48′. Height of eye 20 ft. Time by chron. 04h 15m 41s, which was 4m 19s slow of G.M.T.

6. On September 23rd in lat. 51° 07′ N., the obs. alt. of the star Alphecca, West of the meridian, was 48° 41′. Ht. of eye 18 ft. G.M.T. 12h 38m 15s.

7. On January 3rd in lat. 51° 11′ N., the obs. alt. of the star Capella, East of the meridian, was 44° 23·5′. Ht. of eye 20 ft. Time by chron. was 20h 24m 25s. Chron. was 7m 28s slow of G.M.T.

8. On January 1st in lat. 49° 31′ N., the obs. alt. of the star Vega, East of the meridian, was 51° 02·5′. Ht. of eye 16 ft. G.M.T. 07h 22m 31s.

9. On October 8th in lat. 31° 43′ N., the obs. alt. of the star Antares, West of the meridian, was 19° 51·5′. Ht. of eye 22 ft. Time by chron. was October 9th, 00h 06m 07s. Chron. was 1m 02s slow of G.M. noon on July 11th, and was 1m 41s fast on August 14th.

10. On October 9th in lat. 25° 37′ N., the obs. alt. of the star Alphard, East of the meridian, was 24° 57′. Ht. of eye 17 ft. A chronometer which was 5m 53s fast of G.M.T. showed 01h 05m 53s.

11. On January 3rd in lat. 26° 18′ N., the obs. alt. of the star Antares, East of the meridian, was 23° 45′. Ht. of eye 18 ft. G.M.T. 10h 00m 00s.

12. On September 22nd in lat. 43° 25′ N., the obs. alt. of the star Markab, West of the meridian, was 48° 49′. Ht. of eye 18 ft. G.M.T. 01h 39m 42s.

13. On June 12th in lat. 42° 16′ N., the obs. alt. of the star Altair, East of the meridian, was 22° 16′. Ht. of eye 25 ft. G.M.T. 05h 29m 33s.

14. On October 9th in lat. 30¼° N., the obs. alt. of the star Rigel, West of the meridian, was 27° 13·5′. Ht. of eye 26 ft. G.M.T. 02h 39m 42s.

15. On September 23rd in lat. 20° S., the obs. alt. of the star Regulus, West of the meridian, was 23° 12′. Ht. of eye 23 ft. G.M.T. 18h 00m 00s.

16. On January 3rd in lat. D.R. 7° 10′ N., the obs. alt. of the star Sirius, East of the meridian, was 27° 52′. Ht. of eye 26 ft. G.M.T. 22h 20m 18s.

17. On October 8th in lat. 29° 16′ S., the obs. alt. of the star Regulus, East of the meridian, was 39° 47′. Ht. of eye 31 ft. G.M.T. 05h 40m 00s.

18. On October 7th in lat. 10° 21′ N., the obs. alt. of the star Alphard, East of the meridian, was 24° 33′. Ht. of eye 22 ft. G.M.T. 08h 22m 36s.

19. On December 22nd in lat. 43° 01·5′ N., G.M.T. 15h 23m 09s., the obs. alt. of the star Altair, West of the meridian, was 36° 08′. Ht. of eye 27 ft.

CHAPTER 34.

LATITUDE BY EX-MERIDIAN ALTITUDE—EX-MERIDIAN TABLES

In Chapters 21 and 31, the method of finding the observer's latitude by a "meridian altitude" of the Sun or a star was explained.

In actual experience at sea, the Sun is not always visible just at noon, though it may be visible shortly before or shortly after noon. When observing stars, none may actually be on the meridian just when conditions are most suitable, though one or more may be on the meridian just *before* the horizon is plain enough for observation, or just *after* the stars have disappeared in the growing daylight.

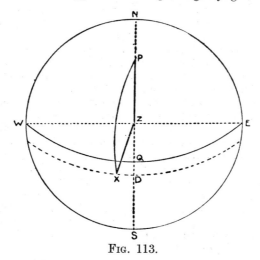

FIG. 113.

In Fig. 113, a star which was on the observer's meridian at D is supposed to have moved to X some minutes later. The triangle formed is similar to the spherical triangle formed when an observation is taken for longitude. But in this case the angle P (the hour angle) is very small.

From the sketch, it can be seen that if P is very small, PX and PD are very nearly equal. That being so, it can be assumed, within certain limits governing the size of P, that

$$(PZ-PX)=ZD=\text{Meridian Zenith Distance.}$$

It will be remembered that, in the meridian altitude problem

M.Z.D.$\pm$ Decl.=Latitude.

371

Since the triangle under discussion is of the same description as the triangle formed in the longitude problem, the same formula used when finding the longitude (haversine method), can also be used here, if it is changed round to meet our particular purpose.

$$\text{Hav } P = \frac{\text{Hav } ZX - \text{Hav } (PX - PZ)}{\text{Sin } PX \text{ sin } PZ}$$

If the estimated or D.R. latitude is known, then all the "arguments" in this formula are known, except $(PX-PZ)$, which we are assuming to be equal to the Meridian Zenith Distance. PZ, the co-latitude, is (90°—the estimated latitude).

The formula above was slightly altered for the purposes of simplicity. (See p. 269). It was given as

$$\text{Hav } P = \frac{\text{Hav } ZX - \text{Hav } (\text{Lat} \pm \text{Decl.})}{\cos \text{Lat} \cos \text{Decl.}} \qquad .. \qquad .. \qquad .. \qquad .. \quad (1)$$

By cross-multiplying this equation, we get—

Hav P cos Lat. cos Decl.$=$Hav ZX—Hav (Lat$\pm$ Decl.)　　.. 　(2)

By transposing as required from one side of the equation to the other, we get an "ex-meridian" formula:

Hav (Lat$\pm$ Decl.)$=$Hav ZX—Hav P cos Lat. cos Decl.　　.. 　(3)

The result obtained from this calculation gives a very close approximation of the meridian zenith distance, which, added to or subtracted from the declination—according to whether they have the same name or different names—gives the latitude *at the time of observation.*

Naturally, the space of time during which $(PZ-PX)$ can be assumed to be equal to M.Z.D. is limited to a short period either before or after noon in the case of the Sun, or before or after the time of the "meridian passage" in the case of a star or planet.

Generally speaking, the number of minutes of *time* in the Hour Angle should never exceed the number of degrees in—

(Lat.+Decl.), when these are of different names;

(Lat.—Decl.), when these are the same name. Or—which is the same thing—The number of degrees in the Hour Angle should never exceed one-quarter the number of degrees of the observed zenith distance.

NOTES: 　1. The smaller the H.A., the more exact the latitude.

　　　　　2. To obtain a good result, the estimated latitude must be fairly close to the actual latitude;

　　　　　3. G.M.T. is required in the problem to find G.H.A. Sun.

Example 1.—On January 3rd, G.M.T. 13h 26m 18s in estimated latitude $37\frac{1}{2}$° N., longitude 14° 36′ W., the obs. alt. of the Sun's L.L. near the meridian was 29° 09′, South of observer. Ht. of eye 22 feet. Required the latitude at the time of taking the observation.

Order of work: First find L.H.A. of the Sun

$$\left(\text{L.H.A.} = \text{G.H.A.} \begin{array}{l} +\text{East long.} \\ -\text{West long.} \end{array} \right)$$

Correct the declination and the observed altitude. Then work the problem using the ex-meridian formula.

G.H.A. Sun, 13h 13° 53·0'   Dec., 13 h 22° 50·4' S.   Obs. alt. 29° 09·0' S.
Incr., 26m 18s   6 34·5   Corr.   —   0·1   Tot. Cor. + 10·0

                 20 27·5   Corr. dec. 22 50·3 S.   True alt. 29 19·0

Long. West   −14 36·0

L.H.A. Sun   5 51·5   Z.D.   60 41·0 N.

    L.H.A. 5° 51·5' L. hav 7·41686 ⎫
    Lat.   37 30·0   L. cos 9·89947 ⎬ +
    Decl. 22 50·3   L. cos 8·96454 ⎭

              L. hav 7·28087   Nat hav 0·00191 ⎫ −
              Z.X.   60° 41·0'   Nat hav 0·25518 ⎭

              Nat hav Z.D. 0·25327

              Mer. Z.D. 60° 26·0' N.
              Decl.   22 50·3 S.

              Latitude   37 35·7 N.

Example 2.—On October 9th, G.M.T. 11h 39m 49s in D.R. lat. 32° N., long. 6° 22' W., the obs. alt. of the Sun's L.L. near the meridian was 50° 45', South of observer. Height of eye 20 feet. Required the latitude at the time of taking the observation.

G.H.A. Sun, 11h 348° 08·9'   Decl.   6° 09·5' S.   Obs. alt. 50° 45·0' S.
Incr., 39m 49s   9 57·3   Corr. +   0·6   Tot. cor. + 11·1

                358 06·2   6 10·1 S.   True alt. 50 56·1 S.

Long. West   − 6 22·0

L.H.A. Sun (W) 351 44·2 = 8° 15·8'E.   Z.D   39 03·9 N.

    L.H.A. Sun   8° 15·8' L. hav 7·71525 ⎫
    Latitude   32 00·0   L. cos 9·92842 ⎬ +
    Declination   6 10·1   L. cos 9·99748 ⎭

              L. hav 7·64115   Nat hav 0·00437 ⎫ −
              Z.D.   39° 03·9'   Nat hav 0·11178 ⎭

              Nat. hav M.Z.D. 0·10741

              M.Z.D. 38° 15·7' N.
              Decl.   6 10·1 S.

              Latitude 32 05·6 N.

Example 3.—On June 13th, D.R. lat. 53° 20' N., long. 14° 31' W., L.M.T. 11h 40m 45s, the obs. alt. of the Sun's L.L. near the meridian was 59° 40', S. of observer. Height of eye 27 feet. Required the latitude.

L.M.T. 13 June 11h 40m 45s	G.H.A. Sun 0° 02·4′	Obs. alt. 59° 40·0′ S.
Long. W. + 58 04	Increment 9 42·3	Tot. corr. + 10·4
G.M.T. 12 38 49	369 44·7	True alt. 59 50·4
Decl. 23° 12·0′ N.	Long. W.—14 31·0 Z.D.	30 09·6 N.
	L.H.A. Sun 355 13·7 = 4° 46·3′ E.	

```
L.H.A. Sun    4° 46·3′   L. hav  7·23877 ⎫
Latitude       53 20·0    L. cos  9·77609 ⎬ +
Declination    23 12·0    L. cos  9·96338 ⎭

              L. hav  6·97824   Nat hav  0·00095 ⎫
                                                 ⎬ —
              Z.D. 30° 09·6′    Nat hav  0·06769 ⎭

                        Nat hav M.Z.D.   0·06674

M.Z.D.    29° 56·6′ N.
Decl.      23  12·0  N.

Latitude   53  08·6  N.
```

Ex-Meridian Tables.—Latitude by an ex-meridian observation can be found with the minimum of trouble by the use of ex-meridian tables. In *Norie's*, they are given on pp. 140 to 156, while in *Burton's* they are on pp. 213 to 230. Although the methods of presenting these respective tables differ slightly, their use is identical.

There are three tables in all.

In Table I a factor is found—"A" in *Norie's*, "F" in *Burton's*. The arguments required are the latitude and the declination. Any interpolation that may be required can be performed mentally.

In Table II, the above factor is found in the first and last vertical columns on the various pages. Along the top of each page the L.H.A. of the body is given. In *Norie's* this is given in arc only, and to every 5′. In *Burton's* it is given in arc to every 5′, and also in time, to every 20 seconds. The required correction is found in the body of the table where the appropriate vertical and horizontal columns meet. Normally, this correction is added to the true altitude, which is then treated as a meridian altitude. If the ex-meridian observation is of a body AT THE LOWER TRANSIT, the correction is subtracted.

Table III contains a minor correction. It is not required unless the original correction from Table II exceeds 10′ or 20′, or unless the altitude is very high. When used, this correction is subtracted from the Table II correction.

Example 1.—In estimated latitude 40° N., Decl. 10° S., L.H.A. 14m 40s (3° 40′) find the correction to add to the true ex-meridian altitude of the Sun.

(a) By *Norie's.*

Table I, Lat. 40°, Decl. 10°, diff. names gives "A"=1·9.
Table II, H.A. 3° 40', "A" of 1' gives correction 3·6'
"A" of ·9' gives correction 3·23

Total correction to add   6·83'

(b) By *Burton's.*

Table I, Lat. 40°, Decl. 10°, diff. names, gives "F"=1·93.
Table II, H.A. 14m 40s, "F" of 1' gives correction   3·6'
"F" of ·9' gives correction   3·2
"F" of ·03' gives correction   ·1

Total correction to add   6·9

Example 2.—In estimated latitude 20° N., declination 18° S., true alt. 52°. L.H.A. 31m 20s (7° 50') find the correction to add to an ex-mer. alt. of a star.

	Norie's		*Burton's*	
Table I	"A"=2·9		"F"=2·85	
Table II	"A" of 2 gives	32·7	"F" of 2 gives	32·7
	"A" of ·9 gives	14·7	"F" of ·8 gives	13·1
		47·4	"F" of ·05 gives	·8
	Table III	— ·4		46·6
	True corr.	+47·0	Table III	— ·4
			True corr.	+46·2

Using *Burton's* ex-meridian tables to check the three fully-worked examples on pp. 372 to 374, these would appear as follows:—

Example 1.—

Lat. 37½° N., Decl. 22° 50' S., "F"=1·65
Table II, L.H.A. 5° 51·5', "F" of 1 gives   9·1
"F" of ·6 gives   5·5
"F" of ·05 gives   ·5

Total correction   15·1

True alt.	29°	19·0' S.
Ex-mer. corr. +		15·1
Mer. alt.	29	34·1
Z.D.	60	25·9 N.
Decl.	22	50·3 S.
Latitude	37	35·6 N.

Example 2.

Table I, Lat. 32° N., Decl. 6° 10′ S., gives "F" of 2·68.

Table II, L.H.A. 8° 16′, "F" of 2 gives   36·3′

                 "F" of ·6 gives   10·9

                 "F" of ·08 gives   1·5

                                48·7

           Table III   — ·4

           True correction   48·3

True alt.	50°	56·1′ S.
Corr.	+	48·3
Mer. alt.	51	44·4
Z.D.	38	15·6 N.
Decl.	6	10·1 S.
Latitude	32	05·5 N.

Example 3.

Table I, Lat. 53° 20′ N., Decl. 23° 12′ N., gives "F" of 2·15.

Table II, L.H.A. 4° 46′, "F" of 2 gives   12·0′

                 "F" of ·1 gives   ·6

                 "F" of ·05 gives   ·3

           Total correction   12·9

True alt.	59°	50·4′ S.
Corr.	+	12·9
Mer. alt.	60	03·3 S.
Z.D.	29	56·7 N.
Decl.	23	12·0 N.
Latitude	53	08·7 N.

The preceding examples have been worked using observations of the Sun in each. The same problem can be worked using observations of stars or planets. The working of problems is the same, the L.H.A. of star or planet being found by methods described in Chapter 27.

Example 4.—On June 13th at evening twilight in D.R. lat. 48° 30′ N., long. 7° 11′ W., the obs. altitude of the star Arcturus near the meridian was 59° 54′, bearing South. Height of eye 30 ft. G.M.T. 20h 37m 04s. Required the latitude at the time of taking the observation.

G.H.A. ♈ 201° 37·3′	Decl. 19° 24·0′ N.		Hav H.A.	7·85569
Increm. 9 17·5			Cos Lat.	9·82126
210 54·8	Obs. alt.	59° 54·0′	Cos Dec.	9·97461
S.H.A.* 146 33·2	Tot. corr. —	5·9	Log hav	7·65156
357 28·0	True alt.	59 48·1	Nat hav	0·00448
Long. W.—7 11·0	—90		Hav Z.D.	0·06785
L.H.A.* 350 17·0	Z.D.	30 11·9	Hav M.Z.D.	0·06337
E.H.A. 9 43·0				

M.Z.D.	29° 09·6′ N.
Decl.	19 24·0 N.
Latitude	48 33·6 N.

Check by *Burton's* ex-meridian tables.

Table I, Lat. 48½° N., Dec. 19½° N, "F"=2·53
Table II, L.H.A. 9° 43′, "F" of 2 gives 50·3′
  0·5 gives 12·6
  0·03 gives 0·8

  63·7
Table III — 1·1

True corr. 62·6′

True alt.	59° 48·1′ S.
Ex-mer corr.+	1 02·6
Mer. alt.	60 50·7
M.Z.D.	29 09·3 N.
Decl.	19 24·0 N.
Latitude	48 33·3 N.

Example 5.—On July 21st in D.R. lat. 46° 10· N., long. 34° 32′ W., G.M.T. 19h 20m 00s, the obs. alt. of the planet Jupiter near the meridian was 35° 39′, bearing South. Height of eye 25 ft. Required latitude by ex-mer. alt.

G.H.A., 19h 22° 01·7'	Decl. 7° 56·6' S.	Hav L.H.A. 7·63023

			Cos lat.	9·84046
Increment	5	00·0		
"v"		0·8	Obs. alt. 35° 39·0' S.	Cos dec. 9·99561

G.H.A. Jup. 27	02·5	Tot. cor. — 6·3	Log hav 7·46630

Long. W. —34	32·0	True alt. 35 32·7 S.	Nat hav 0·00292

L.H.A. Jup. 7	29·5 E.	Z.D. 54 27·3 N.	Nat hav 0·20932

Hav M.Z.D. 0·20640

M.Z.D.	54° 02·5' N.
Decl.	7 56·6 S.
Latitude	46 05·9 N.

Note that when correcting G.H.A. of planet, the Interpolation Table for the Sun was used, together with the "v" correction for the planet.

Check by *Burton's* Tables.
Table I, Lat. 46° N., Dec. 8° S., gives "F"=1·67

Table II.
H.A. 7° 30', "F" for 1 gives 15·0
　　　　　"F" for ·6 gives 9·0
　　　　　"F" for ·07 gives 1·0
　　　　　　　　　　　　　———
　　　　　　　　　　　　　25·0
Table III　　　　— 0·1
　　　　　　　　　———
True correction　24·9

True alt.	35°	32·7'
Ex-mer. Corr. +		24·9
Mer. alt.	35	57·6 S.
M.Z.D.	54	02·4 N.
Decl.	7	56·6 S.
Lat.	46	05·8 N.

EXERCISE 42.

To Find Latitude by Ex-Meridian Altitude.

In the following exercise, find the latitude at the time of taking the observation.

1. On July 16th in est. lat. 47° 35' N., long. 14° 33' W., G.M.T. 13h 27m 22s, the obs. alt. of the Sun's L.L. near the meridian was 63° 30', South of observer. Height of eye 24 ft.

2. On Oct. 9th in D.R. lat. 52° N., long. 14° 13' E., G.M.T. 11h 33m 47s, the obs. alt. of the Sun's L.L. after passing the meridian was 30° 53', bearing South. Height of eye 28 ft.

3. On January 2nd in D.R. lat. 51° 50' N., long. 47° 02' E., G.M.T. 08h 32m 17s, the obs. alt. of the Sun's L.L near the meridian was 15° 01', bearing South. Height of eye 37 ft.

4. On December 21st in latitude by account $11\frac{1}{2}°$ N., longitude 77° 17' W., G.M.T. 16h 37m 21s, the obs. alt. of the Sun's L.L. near the meridian was 54° 26', South of observer. Height of eye 36 ft.

5. On October 7th, D.R. lat. 40° N., long. 58° 23' E., G.M.T. 07h 24m 22s, the obs. alt. of the Sun's L.L. before passing the meridian was 43° 50', South of observer. Height of eye 30 ft.

6. On October 8th in est. lat. $48\frac{1}{2}°$ N., long. 39° W., G.M.T. 15h 00m 00s, the obs. alt. of the Sun's L.L. near the meridian was 34° 50', bearing South. Height of eye 25 ft.

7. On July 23rd, lat. $49\frac{3}{4}°$ N., long. 3° 02' E., G.M.T. 11h 23m 50s, the obs. alt. of the Sun's L.L. near the meridian was 59° 49', bearing South. Ht. 20 ft.

8. On January 3rd, est. lat. 37° 45' N., long. 25° 11' W., G.M.T. 14h 25m 44s, the obs. ex-mer. alt. of the Sun's L.L. was 28° 45', South of observer. Height of eye 27 ft.

9. On June 14th in D.R. lat. 55° N., long. 00°, G.M.T. 11h 37m 24s, the obs. alt. of the Sun's L.L. before reaching the meridian was 58° 00', South of observer. Height of eye 21 ft.

10. On September 23rd in D.R. lat. $47\frac{1}{2}°$ N., long. 19° 36' W., G.M.T. 12h 35m 24s, the obs. alt. of the Sun's L.L. near the meridian was 41° 41', bearing South. Height of eye 24 ft.

Stars.

11. On October 9th, D.R. lat. 40° N., long. 20° 13' E., G.M.T. 16h 38m 22s., the obs. alt. of the star Altair near the meridian was 57° 30', South of observer. Height of eye 27 ft.

12. On June 14th in est. lat. 42° 15' S., long. 70° 22' W., G.M.T. 23h 37m 26s, the obs. alt. of the star Denebola near the meridian was 32° 31', bearing North. Height of eye 41 ft.

13. On June 13th, D.R. lat. 50° 45' N., long. 16° 55' E., G.M.T. 19h 29m 46s, the obs. alt. of the star Spica near the meridian was 27° 43', bearing South. Height of eye 24 ft.

14. On September 22nd in lat. by account 44° 10' N., long. 51° 40' W., G.M.T. 20h 22m 40s, the obs. alt. of the star Antares near the meridian was 19° 22', South of observer. Height of eye 30 ft.

15. On December 21st in D.R. lat. 36° N., long. 27° 30' W., G.M.T. 19h 31m 22s, the obs. alt. of the star Markab near the meridian was 67° 25', South of observer. Height of eye 27 ft.

Planets.

16. On September 24th, lat. 23° N., long. 89° 48' E., G.M.T. 11h 39m 48s, the obs. alt. of the planet Saturn near the meridian was 44° 07', South. Ht. of eye 38 ft.

17.   On January 3rd, lat. by account 41° N., long. 120° 16′ W., L.M.T. 07h 30m 01s, the obs. alt. of planet Jupiter near the meridian was 38° 43′, South.   Ht. 38 ft.

18.   On July 15th, in lat. 21¼° N., long. 87¼° E., G.M.T. 12h 36m 21s, the obs. alt. of the planet Jupiter near the meridian was 60° 03′, South of observer.   Height of eye 40 ft.

CHAPTER 35.

TO FIND THE APPROXIMATE TIME OF A STAR'S MERIDIAN PASSAGE.

The space of time during which conditions are entirely suitable for stellar observations is limited, even in fine, cloudless weather. The horizon must be clear, and "hard" enough for the observation, so that a certain amount of twilight is necessary. But if there is too much light, the observer may not be able to sight the required star in the mirror of his sextant.

Thus a knowledge of the time at which a particular star will cross the observer's meridian is very valuable, as it can then be determined beforehand whether conditions for a meridian observation will be suitable.

To Find G.H.A. γ—From Fig. 114, it can be seen that at the precise time that a star is on the meridian of Greenwich

$$\text{G.H.A. } \gamma + \text{S.H.A.*} = 360°$$

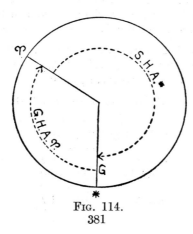

Fig. 114.
381

By transposing, this equation reads
$$360° - S.H.A.* = G.H.A. \Upsilon$$
In the same way, at the precise time that a particular star crosses the meridian of an observer in *any* longitude,
$$360° - S.H.A.* = L.H.A. \Upsilon$$

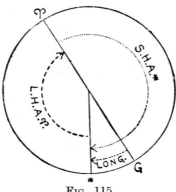

FIG. 115.

From Fig. 115, it will be seen that
$$G.H.A. \Upsilon = L.H.A. \Upsilon + \text{West longitude,} \quad \text{or}$$
$$- \text{East longitude.}$$

To Find L.M.T. of Star's Meridian Passage.—The value of the G.H.A. Υ is listed in the *Nautical Almanac* for every hour of G.M.T. throughout the year. The first step therefore is to find the value of the G.H.A. Υ, using the equation given above, and from that to find the G.M.T. of the star's meridian passage over the observer's meridian.

Example 1.—Find the G.M.T. at which the star Rigel will be on the meridian of an observer in long. 11° 16' E., on January 3rd. Find also the L.M.T. of the star's meridian passage.

Find the value of G.H.A. $\Upsilon = 360° - S.H.A.* - $ East longitude.

	360°	00·0'
S.H.A. Rigel	281	51·8
L.H.A. Υ	78	08·2
Long. East	11	16·0
G.H.A. Υ	66	52·2

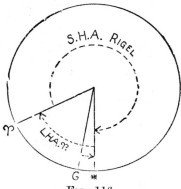

Fig. 116.

The S.H.A. Rigel is found in the Star List on the appropriate daily page in the *Nautical Almanac.* On the same page, for the date January 3rd, find the *next less* value of G.H.A. ♈ It is 57° 58·4′, at 21 hrs.

Reqd. G.H.A. ♈	66°	52·2
Next less	57	58·4
Difference	8	53·8

The difference between the required G.H.A. and the next less is 8° 53·8′. From the "Aries" column in the Table of Increments and Corrections, it is found that the minutes and seconds of time corresponding to 8° 53·8′ are 35m 29s. Therefore

G.M.T. of star's meridian passage in long. 11° 16′ E. is 21h 35m 29s.

The observer's longitude-in-time=45m 04s.

G.M.T. of star's mer. pass. =	21h	35m	29s
Long. in time East +		45	04
L.M.T. of star's mer. pass.	22	20	33

Right Ascension.—The "Right Ascension" of stars is not now given in the *Nautical Almanac*, having been dropped in favour of star's S.H.A.

Star's S.H.A.+Star's R.A. (in arc)=360°

or

Star's S.H.A. (in time)+Star's R.A.=24 hours.

The Right Ascension of a star is its Hour Angle EAST of the First Point of Aries, and calculated in terms of Time, whereas the Sidereal Hour Angle of a star is its Hour Angle WEST of the First Point of Aries, and calculated in terms of Arc.

Therefore   R.A. of the star Rigel $=(360°-281° 51\cdot8')$
                     $=78° 08\cdot2'$ in Arc,
                     $=$5h 12m 33s in Time.

From the above figures, it can be seen that, at the precise instant that a particular star is on the meridian of an observer in any longitude, L.H.A. ♈ $=$R.A. of the star in Arc.

Example 2.—Find the approximate L.M.T., and also the G.M.T. at which the star Vega will be on the meridian of an observer in long. 29° 10′ W. on September 23rd.

	360°	00·0′
S.H.A.*	81	06·8
L.H.A. ♈	278	53·2
Long. W.	29	10·0
G.H.A. ♈	308	03·2

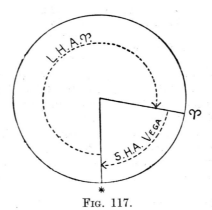

Fig. 117.

Required G.H.A. ♈	308°	03·2′	
Next less (20 hrs.)	302	09·4	
Difference	5	53·8	— From Table of Increments
			$=$23m 31sec.

G.M.T. of star's mer. pass. in long. 29° 10′ W.$=$20h 23m 31s
           Long. in Time W. $=$ 1   56   40

          L.M.T. of star's mer. pass. $=$18   26   51

EXERCISE 43.

Find the approximate L.M.T. and the G.M.T. at which the following stars will be on the observer's meridian.

	Date	Star	Longitude		
1.	September 24th	Aldebaran	13°	22′	E.
2.	January 3rd	Arcturus	27	11	W
3.	October 9th	Pollux	6	19	E.
4.	June 13th	Fomalhaut	18	42	W.
5.	January 1st	Canopus	21	07	E.
6.	July 16th	Alpheratz	13	51	W.
7.	December 21st	Elnath	22	18	E.
8.	June 12th	Betelgeuse	9	45	W.
9.	September 23rd	Diphda	14	08	W.
10.	July 22nd	Alnilam	6	55	E.
11.	October 9th	Altair	20	18	W.
12.	January 2nd	Rigel	5	23	E.
13.	December 23rd	Deneb	11	51	E.
14.	July 17th	Hamal	23	47	E.
15.	September 22nd	Deneb	2	09	W.
16.	October 7th	Alnilam	18	26	W.
17.	June 13th	Markab	10	14	E.
18.	January 2nd	Acrux	4	33	W.
19.	July 21st	Mirfak	25	41	W.
20.	October 7th	Alphard	17	20	E.

CHAPTER 36.

TO FIND SHIP'S POSITION BY SIMULTANEOUS ALTITUDES OF STARS—LONGITUDE METHOD—INTERCEPT METHOD.

In Chapters 23, 24, 27 and 28, methods have already been discussed by which the position of a ship can be found by co-ordinating two observations of a single heavenly body out of the meridian, the course and distance run by the ship between the observations being known. In these chapters, the heavenly body used was the Sun.

When observations of stars are used, a very obvious advantage lies in the fact that altitudes of two or even more stars can be obtained at practically the same time. If these stars are chosen so that their true bearings are well separated from each other, the ship's true position at that time can be found with the minimum of trouble. Either the "Longitude" Method or the "Intercept Method" can be used.

Both methods are discussed separately in this chapter, and the following introductory remarks should be especially noted.

At sea, when observations are taken, it is taken for granted that the navigator has available a chart of the area in which the ship is operating. If that is so, the ship's position is found by straightforward plotting on the chart, whichever method is used.

If the problem of finding the ship's position by simultaneous altitudes is given in an examination, and no chart of the area is available, the position can still be found very easily if the Longitude Method is used. But a candidate using the Intercept Method would require to use squared paper to find the position.

Candidates for Fishing Skippers' Certificates are advised to understand the method of laying off intercepts to find the position by plotting. (See Exercise 45.) It is possible they may be required to do this in an examination, though it is unlikely that they will be required to work the problem in its entirety.

The Longitude Method.

Example 1.—In D.R. latitude 48° 27′ N., an observation of a star bearing 148° T. (S. 32° E.) gave longitude 23° 36′ W. "C" correction was ·785. At the same time an observation of a second star bearing 221° T. (S. 41° W.) gave longitude 23° 42′ W. "C" correction ·542. Find the ship's position at this time.

386

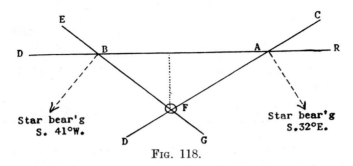

Fig. 118.

First make a rough sketch (Fig. 118) showing A and B (the first and second longitudes) in their correct *relative* positions on the D.R. parallel of latitude.

Through point A draw the true bearing of the first star, and a P.L. (CD) at right angles to it. Through B draw the true bearing of the second star, and a P.L. (EG) at right angles to it. Position F, where the two position lines meet, represents the position of the ship.

The calculations involved in finding this position are similar to those described in Chapter 23, page 278.

A perpendicular line drawn from the apex of the triangle which has been formed to its base falls *inside* the triangle, since the two P.L.'s. are in adjacent quadrants. To find the latitude correction, the two "C" corrections must be added.

$$C^1 + C^2 = \cdot785 + \cdot542 = 1\cdot327$$

$$\text{Latitude correction} = \frac{\text{D. Long. between results}}{C^1 + C^2}$$

$$= \frac{6'}{1\cdot327} = 4\cdot5'$$

From the sketch it can be seen that in this particular case the true latitude is to the southward of the D.R. latitude.

$$\begin{array}{ll} \text{D.R. latitude} & 48°\ 27\cdot0'\ \text{N.} \\ \text{Correction} & 4\cdot5\ \text{S.} \\ \hline \text{True latitude} & 48\quad 22\cdot5\ \text{N.} \end{array}$$

The longitude correction—

For star A = Lat. corr. × "C" for star A.

(To be applied, as seen from the sketch, to westward.)

For star B = Lat. corr. × "C" for star B.

(If required)   (To be applied, as seen from sketch, to eastward)

	Star A			*Star B*	
Corr.	(4·5 × ·785)W.		Corr.	(4·5 × ·542)E.	
	=3·5′ W.			=2·4′ E.	
Long A	23° 36·0′ W.		Long. B	23° 42·0′ W.	
Correction	3·5 W.		Correction	2·4 E.	
True long.	23 39·5 W.		True long.	23 39·6 W.	

Example 2.—In D.R. latitude 53° 45′ N., an observation of a star bearing S. 24° E. T., gave longitude 14° 54′ W. "C"=1·073. At the same time an observation of a star bearing S. 80° E. T., gave longitude 14° 46′ W. "C"=0·196. Find the ship's true position.

First draw a rough sketch.

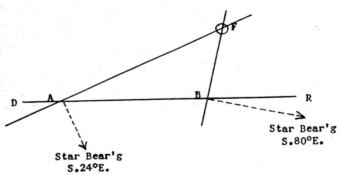

Star Bear'g
S.24°E.

Star Bear'g
S.80°E.

Fig. 119.

Both stars are in the S.E. quadrant, and a perpendicular from *F* to the base-line would fall outside the triangle. The "C" corrections must be subtracted to obtain the latitude correction.

D. Long. between results=8′ and $C^1-C^2=·877$.

$$\text{Latitude correction}=\frac{8}{·877}=9·1′ \text{ N.}$$

Longitude correction—Star *A*   9·1 × 1·073=9·8′ E.
                                    Star *B*   9·1 × ·196=1·8′ E.

D.R. lat.	53° 45·0′ N.	Long. *A*	14° 54·0′ W.	Long *B*	14° 46·0′ W.
Corr.	9·1 N.		9·8 E.		1·8 E.
Tr. lat.	53 54·1 N.	Tr. long.	14 44·2 W.		14 44·2 W.

Exercise 44 (A)

Given the following particulars, find the ship's true position.

	D.R. Lat.			Star A			Star B			
				Long.		T. Bg.	"C"	Long.		T. Bg.	"C"
1.	51°	27′	N.	15°	42′ W.	138°	·57	15°	48′ W.	194°	1·31
2.	35	08	N.	28	25 W.	101	·11	28	20 W.	142	·49
3.	47	15	N.	22	57 W.	216	·93	23	04 W.	174	1·87
4.	50	34	N.	18	43 W.	255	·18	18	47 W.	201	·92
5.	28	49	N.	37	31 W.	074	·26	37	24 W.	131	·64
6.	33	28	N.	41	09 W.	303	·74	41	00 W.	026	·86
7.	44	22	N.	25	46 W.	083	·08	25	42 W.	138	·62
8.	19	40	N.	11	11 W.	286	·13	11	15 W.	233	·41
9.	26	53	N.	19	37 W.	161	·97	19	30 W.	199	·89
10.	53	27	N.	30	24 W.	212	·60	30	21 W.	259	·15
11.	29	50	S.	59	13 E.	040	·55	59	05 E.	317	·56
12.	35	28	S.	27	52 W.	066	·39	27	46 W.	137	·48
13.	50	23	S.	84	05 E.	329	·67	83	58 E.	047	·55
14.	17	52	S.	96	39 E.	291	·28	96	42 E.	344	1·08
15.	25	09	S.	72	20 W.	078	·16	72	14 W.	026	·96

The haversine formula has been used for finding the longitudes in the following fully-worked example. The same result will be obtained if the secant—cosecant formula is used.

Example 3.—On June 14th, in D.R. latitude 41° 53′ N., at G.M.T. 06h 36m 36s, the obs. alt. of the star Diphda, East of the meridian, was 17° 25′. At the same time, the obs. alt. of the star Rasalhague, West of the meridian was 28° 42′. Height of eye 17 feet. Find the true position of the ship at this time.

Diphda						*Rasalhague*	
1°	12·4′	..	..	G.H.A. ♈	.. ..	1°	12·4′
349	37·5	..	..	S.H.A.*	.. ..	96	44·5
350	49·9	..	..	G.H.A.*	.. ..	97	56·9
17	25·0	..	..	Obs. alt.	.. ..	28	42·0
—	7·1	..	..	Tot. Corr.	.. ..	—	5·8
17	17·9	..	..	True alt.	.. ..	28	36·2
72	42·1	..	..	Z.D.	.. ..	61	23·8
41	53·0 N.	..	..	D.R. lat.	.. ..	41	53·0 N.
18	12·8 S.	..	..	Decl.	.. ..	12	35·4 N.
60	05·8	..	..	(L—D)	.. ..	29	17·6

·35132	. .	. .	Nat hav Z.D.	. .	. .	·26062
·25073	. .	. .	Nat hav (L—D)		. .	·06394
·10059	. .	. .	Nat hav	. .	. .	·19668
9·00258	. .	. .	Log hav	. .	. .	9·29375
0·12813	. .	. .	Log cos lat.	. .	. .	0·12813
0·02232	. .	. .	Log cos decl.	. .	. .	0·01057
9·15303	. .	. .	Log hav L.H.A.		. .	9·43245
315 41·1	. .	. .	L.H.A.*	. .	. .	62 42·0
350 49·9	. .	. .	G.H.A.*	. .	. .	97 56·9
35 08·8 W.	. .	. .	Longitude	. .	. .	35 14·9 W.
·921+	. .	. .	"A"	. .	. .	·466+
·471+	. .	. .	"B"	. .	. .	·252—
1·392+	. .	. .	"C"	. .	. .	·214+
S. 44° E.	. .	. .	True Bg.	. .	. .	S. 81° W.
046°—226°	. .	. .	P.L.	. .	. .	171°—351°

$$\text{Lat. corr.} = \frac{\text{D. Long.}}{C^1 + C^2} = \frac{6 \cdot 1}{1 \cdot 606} = 3 \cdot 8' \text{ S.}$$

Long. Corr. (A) = 3·8 × 1·392 = 5·3′ W.
            (B) = 3·8 × ·214 = 0·8 E.

D.R. Lat. 41° 53·0′ N.		Long. (A) 35° 08·8′ W.	(B) 35° 14·9′ W.		
Corr. 3·8 S.		5·3 W.	0·8 E.		
Lat. 41 49·2 N.		Long. 35 14·1 W.	35 14·1 W.		

Exercise 44 (B)

Given the following particulars, find the ship's true position.

1. On October 7th in D.R. lat. 40° 30′ N., G.M.T. 08h 21m 18s, the obs. alt. of the star HAMAL (W) was 27° 17·5′, and the obs. alt. of the star REGULUS (E) was 40° 11′.   Height of eye 26 feet.

2. On July 16th, in est. lat. 32° 17′ N., G.M.T. 23h 23m 55s, the obs. alt. of the star DENEBOLA (W) was 41° 49′, and the obs. alt. of the star RASALHAGUE (E) was 51° 06′.   Height of eye 21 feet.

3. On January 2nd in D.R. lat. 51° 11′ N., G.M.T. 06h 30m 40s, the obs. alt. of the star RASALHAGUE (E) was 36° 43′, and the obs. alt. of the star REGULUS (W) was 24° 32′. Height of eye 29 feet.

4. On December 23rd in D.R. lat. 38° 50′ N., G.M.T. 17h 33m 45s, the obs. alt. of the star HAMAL (E) was 35° 57′, and the obs. alt. of the star VEGA (W) was 51° 19′. Height of eye 29 feet.

5. On September 22nd in est. lat. 43° 11′ N., G.M.T. 06h 26m 28s, the obs. alt. of the star HAMAL (W) was 43° 17′. At G.M.T. 06h 27m 08s, the obs. alt. of the star ALPHARD (E) was 16° 24·5′. Height of eye 27 feet.

6. On July 21st in D.R. lat. 51° 50′ N., G.M.T. 03h 23m 57s, the obs. alt. of the star DENEB (W) was 59° 39·5′, and the obs. alt. of the star MIRFAK (E) was 56° 17′. Height of eye 24 feet.

7. On October 9th in lat. by account 31° 08′ N., G.M.T. 20h 27m 36s, the obs. alt. of the star ENIF (E) was 47° 32′, and the obs. alt. of the star ZUBEN'UBI (W) was 13° 05·5′. Height of eye 27 feet.

8. On December 21st in D.R. lat. 27° 19′ N., G.M.T. 11h 33m 20s, the obs. alt. of the star ANTARES (E) was 13° 19′, and the obs. alt. of the star ALPHARD (W) was 31° 16′. Height of eye 29 feet.

9. On September 24th in est. lat. 48° 56′ N., G.M.T. 17h 37m 49s, the obs. alt. of the star ENIF (E) was 33° 03·5′, and the obs. alt. of the star ARCTURUS (W) was 32° 41′. Height of eye 22 feet.

10. On January 3rd in D.R. lat. 54° 07′ N., G.M.T. 19h 23m 38s, the obs. alt. of the star HAMAL (E) was 44° 10′, and the obs. alt. of the star VEGA (W) was 43° 37′. Height of eye 27 feet.

The Intercept Method.

Example 1.—In assumed latitude 53° 30′ N., longitude 15° 00′ W., an observation of a star bearing 218° T. gave an intercept 6·2′ towards. At the same time an observation of a star bearing 158° T. gave an intercept 4·5′ towards. Find the ship's true position.

If a chart of the area is available, this problem is solved easily and readily by simple plotting.

The given assumed position is plotted on the chart ("A" in Fig. 120), and the two intercepts are drawn in their respective directions from this position. Since in this case both intercepts are "towards", they are drawn in the directions S. 38° W. for 6·2 miles, and S. 22° E. for 4·5 miles. (See points "B" and "C" in the sketch.) Position lines are then drawn through these points, at right angles to the intercepts.

The point "F", where the P.L's. cross, represents the ship's position, read in the usual way from the scales of latitude and longitude on the chart.

In cases where no chart is available, squared paper may be used. In that case it is very important to remember that while squares in a North-South direction represent differences of latitude, squares in an East-West direction represent DEPARTURE. This has to be converted to difference of longitude in the usual way, e.g.,

D. Long.=Dep.×Sec Mean Lat.

Point "A", the ship's assumed position, can be placed at any suitable spot on the squared paper. From this point, lay off the true bearings of the stars and the lengths of the respective intercepts— points "B" and "C". Through these points draw P.L's. at right angles to the bearings, as described above. (When the intercepts are "away", the true bearings of the stars are reversed.)

From Fig. 120, it can be seen that the D. Lat. is 5·8′ S., and the Dep. is 2·6′ W. With Mean Lat. 53° 27′, D. Long. is 4·4′ W.

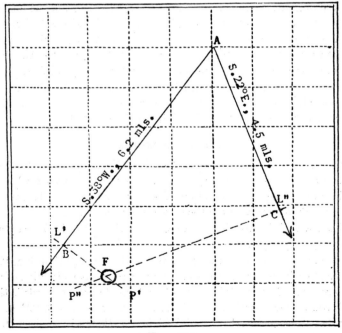

FIG. 120.

Assumed lat. 53°	30·0′ N.		Assumed long.	15°	00·0′ W.
D. Lat.	5·8 S.		D. Long.		4·4 W.
True lat.	53	24·2 N.	True long.	15	04·4 W.

Example 2.—In assumed latitude 39° 47′ N., longitude 32° 15′ W., an observation of the star Regulus bearing 118° T. gave an intercept 7·0′ towards. At the same time an observation of the star Aldebaran bearing 268° T. gave an intercept 5·0′ away. Find the ship's true position.

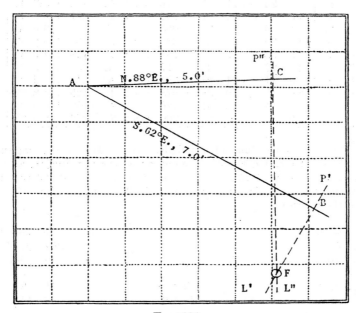

Fig. 121.

Using squared paper, D. Lat. is seen to be 5·3′ S., Dep. 5·1′ E., giving D. Long. 6·7′ E.

Assumed lat. 39°	47·0′ N.		Assumed long.	32°	15·0′ W.
D. lat.	5·3 S.		D. long.		6·7 E.
True lat.	39	41·7 N.	True long.	32	08·3 W.

The following exercise can be worked either on squared paper or on Form Exn. 30c. Answers are given for both methods. From these answers, it will be seen that differences are fractional only.

Exercise 45 (A)

Given the following particulars, find ship's true position.

	Lat. N.	Long. W.	Star A		Star B	
			Bg.	Intcpt.	Bg.	Intcpt.
1.	55° 28′	11° 22′	138°	7·6′ T.	194°	5·3′ T.
2.	55 37	11 12	101	5·8 A.	142	4·7 A.
3.	55 20	11 19	216	4·4 A.	174	5·8 T.
4.	55 18	10 47	255	6·2 T.	201	3·8 T.
5.	55 06	10 28	083	8·7 T.	138	6·6 A.
6.	55 29	11 33	286	3·8 A.	233	5·5 T.
7.	55 53	10 57	161	5·3 T.	199	4·9 T.
8.	55 22	11 05	212	4·0 A.	259	6·0 A.
9.	55 11	11 24	291	6·8 A.	243	7·5 A.
10.	55 47	10 38	078	7·2 T.	125	6·8 T.
11.	55 34	10 51	126	5·0 A.	197	6·0 A.
12.	55 25	11 29	200	8·2 T.	256	5·5 T.

Example 3.—On June 14th in D.R. latitude 41° 53′ N., longitude 35° W., at G.M.T. 06h 36m 36s, the obs. alt. of the star DIPHDA, East of the meridian was 17° 25′. At the same time the obs. alt. of the star RASALHAGUE, West of the meridian, was 28° 42′. Height of eye 17 feet. Find the position of the ship at this time.

Diphda							*Rasalhague*	
352°	01·9′						352°	01·9′
9	10·5						9	10·5
001	12·4	. .	. .	G.H.A. ♈	. .	. .	001	12·4
349	37·5	. .	. .	S.H.A.*	. .	. .	96	44·5
350	49·9	. .	. .	G.H.A.*	. .	. .	097	56·9
35	00·0	. .	. .	Long.	. .	. .	35	00·0
315	49·9	. .	. .	L.H.A.*	. .	. .	62	56·9
17	25·0	. .	. .	Obs. alt.	. .	. .	28	42·0
—	7·1	. .	. .	Tot. corr.	. .	. .	—	5·8
17	17·9	. .	. .	True alt.	. .	. .	28	36·2
72	42·1			T.Z.D.			61	23·8

41	53·0 N.	..	..	Lat.	..	..	41	53·0 N.
18	12·8 S.	..	..	Decl.	..	..	12	35·4 N.

60	05·8	..	..	(L±D)	..	..	29	17·6

9·15030	..	..	Hav L.H.A.	..	..	9·43553
9·87187	..	..	Cos lat.	..	..	9·87187
9·97768	..	..	Cos decl.	..	..	9·98943

8·99985	..	..	Log hav			9·29683

·09996	..	..	Nat hav	..	..	·19808
·25073	..	..	Nat hav (L±D)	..	..	·06394

·35069	..	..	Nat hav C.Z.D.	..	..	·26202

72	37·5	..	..	C.Z.D.	..	..	61	34·7
72	42·1	..	..	T.Z.D.	..	..	61	23·8

4·6 A.	..	..	Intcpt	..	..	10·9 T.

·926+			A	..	..	·459+
·472+	..	..	B	..	..	·251−

1·398+	..	..	C	..	..	·208+

136° (S. 44° E.)	..	..	True Bg.	..	261° (S. 81° W.)

	D.R. position—Lat.	41° 53·0′ N.	Long.	35° 00·0′ W.
	From squared paper—D. Lat.	3·5 S.	D. Long.	14·1 W.

	True position—Lat.	41 49·5 N.	Long.	35 14·1 W.

Exercise 45 (B)

Given the following particulars, find the ship's true position at the time of taking the observations.

1. On October 7th, in D.R. lat. 40° 30′ N., long. 36¼° W., at G.M.T. 08h 21m 18s, the obs. alt. of the star HAMAL, West of the meridian, was 27° 17·5′. At the same time the obs. alt. of the star REGULUS, East of the meridian was 40° 11′. Height of eye 26 feet.

2. On July 16th, at 23h 23m 55s G.M.T. in D.R. lat. 32¼° N., long. 59° W., the obs. alt. of the star DENEBOLA, West of the meridian, was 41° 49′, while at the same time the obs. alt. of the star RASALHAGUE, East of the meridian, was 51° 06′. Height of eye 21 feet.

3. On January 2nd, G.M.T. 06h 30m 40s in D.R. lat. 51° 11′ N., long. 18½° E., the obs. alt. of the star RASALHAGUE, East of the meridian, was 36° 43′. At the same time, the obs. alt. of the star REGULUS, West of the meridian, was 24° 32′. Height of eye 29 feet.

4. On December 23rd, G.M.T. 17h 33m 45s in est. lat. 38° 50′ N., long. 25¾° W., the obs. alt. of the star HAMAL, East of the meridian, was 35° 57′. At the same time the obs. alt. of the star VEGA, West of the meridian, was 51° 19′. Height of eye 29 feet.

5. On September 22nd, G.M.T. 06h 26m 28s, in D.R. lat. 43° 11′ N., long. 14¼° W., the obs. alt. of the star HAMAL, West of the meridian, was 43° 17′. At G.M.T. 06h 27m 08s, the obs. alt. of the star ALPHARD, East of the meridian, was 16° 24·5′. Height of eye 27 feet.

6. On July 21st, G.M.T. 03h 23m 57s in est. lat. 51° 50′ N., long. 6¼° E., the following simultaneous altitudes of stars were taken:— DENEB (W), 59° 39·5′; MIRFAK (E), 56° 17′. Height of eye 24 feet.

7. On October 9th, G.M.T. 20h 27m 36s in D.R. lat. 31° 08′ N., long. 39° 05′ W., the obs. alt. of the star ENIF (E), was 47° 32′. At the same time the obs. alt. of the star ZUBEN'UBI (W) was 13° 05·5′. Height of eye 27 feet.

8. On December 21st, in lat. by account 27° 20′ N., long. 73° 12′ W., the following simultaneous altitudes were taken:—ANTARES (E), 13° 19′; ALPHARD (W), 31° 16′. G.M.T. 11h 33m 20s. Height of eye 29 feet.

9. On September 24th in est. lat. 49° N., long. 8° 10′ E., G.M.T. 17h 37m 49s, the obs. alt. of the star ENIF (E) was 33° 03·5′, and the obs. alt. of the star ARCTURUS (W), was 32° 41′. Height of eye 22 feet.

10. On January 3rd, G.M.T. 19h 23m 38s in D.R. lat. 54° 07′ N., long. 48° 12′ W., the obs. alt. of the star HAMAL (E) was 44° 10′. At the same time, the obs. alt. of the star VEGA (W) was 43° 37′. Height of eye 27 feet.

PART V.

CHAPTER 37.

PRINCIPLES OF NAVIGATION—DEFINITIONS—PROJECTIONS

Sphere.—A sphere is a globe of any size, perfectly round. The Earth is not a perfect sphere, but for all practical purposes it can be, and is, considered to be a sphere. Spheres can be used to represent the Earth (Terrestrial), or to represent the bowl of the heavens (Celestial). This latter is also named the "celestial concave".

Great Circles.—Great Circles are circles drawn on a sphere in any direction, and in such a way that if a solid sphere were to be cut into two equal parts, the exposed "plane" surfaces would pass through the centre of the sphere.

Small Circles.—Small Circles are circles drawn on a sphere, whose planes do not pass through the centre of the sphere.

Meridians.—All meridians are great circles which pass through the true North and South poles of the earth, and cut the equator at right angles. (See Fig. 17, page 43.)

The Prime Meridian.—The Prime Meridian is a meridian which passes through the place from which terrestrial longitude is measured. The meridian of Greenwich is almost universally considered to be the Prime Meridian.

Equator.—The Equator is a great circle round the earth midway between the true poles. Terrestrial latitude is measured from the Equator, to North and South. (See Fig. 14, page 42.)

Parallels of Latitude.—Parallels of Latitude are small circles on a terrestrial sphere parallel to the equator, and either North or South of it. (See Fig. 16, page 43.)

Latitude.—The Latitude of a position or place is the arc of a meridian between the equator and a parallel through the place. See Fig. 122.

Latitude can also be defined as the angle subtended at the centre of the earth between the equator and the same parallel. In Fig. 122, WQE represents the equator, PLQ is a meridian. The arc QL, or the angle QCL represents the latitude of the place "L". Latitude extends to 90° North and South from 0° at the equator.

o   397

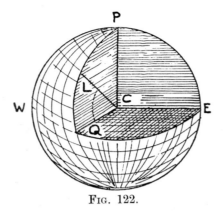

Fig. 122.

Longitude.—The Longitude of a position or place is the arc of the equator contained between the meridian of Greenwich and a meridian passing through the place. It can also be defined as the angle subtended at the centre of the earth between the same two meridians.

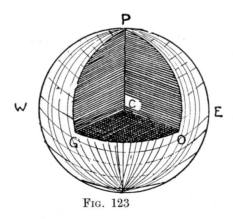

Fig. 123

In Fig. 123, *WGOE* represents the equator. *PG* represents the meridian of Greenwich (the Prime Meridian), and *PO* represents a meridian through the position of an observer. *C* is the centre of the earth. The arc *GO*, or the angle *GCO*, represents the Longitude. Longitude extends to 180° East or West from 0° at Greenwich.

Mean (or Clock) Time.—This is the time in general use for civil purposes. A day is considered to last exactly 24 hours. The "MEAN" Sun, used when measuring Mean Time, is an imaginary Sun.

Apparent Time.—The clock time which elapses between two successive crossings of the real (or apparent) Sun's centre over the meridian of a fixed observer alters slightly from day to day, owing to the earth's varying distance from the Sun, and to the earth's day-to-day progress on its orbit round the Sun. Time measured by reference to the real (or apparent) Sun is called Apparent Time.

Equation of Time.—This is the number of minutes and seconds of time that apparent time is ahead of or behind mean time. Equation of Time alters slowly from day to day. (See page 201.)

Mean Time=Apparent Time± Equation of Time.

Refraction.—Refraction is the apparent bending upward of a ray of light on its journey through the earth's atmosphere toward the surface of the earth. It is caused by the fact that the density of the atmosphere is greatest at the earth's surface, decreasing in density with height. Refraction is greatest (about 33′) when the altitude of the observed celestial object is near zero, and is zero when the object's altitude is 90°. (See Fig. 80, page 253.)

Semi-Diameter.—The semi-diameter of the Sun or Moon is half the angular measurement between the upper and lower limbs of these bodies, as read from a sextant observation. Semi-diameter is required when finding the true altitude of the Sun's (or Moon's) centre. The semi-diameter of the Sun is approximately 16′. (See Fig. 82, page 255.)

True Altitude.—This is the altitude of the centre of a heavenly body above an imaginary horizon. This horizon (the rational horizon) is assumed to cut through the earth's centre at an angle of 90° from the perpendicular. To find the True Altitude of a star, corrections are applied to the observed altitude to take into account the height of the observer's eye above the actual horizon, and for refraction. For the Sun and Moon, additional corrections are applied for semi-diameter and for "parallax".

Zenith Distance.—Zenith Distance is the angle between an observed heavenly body and a point in the heavens right above the observer's head, called the "Zenith". Zenith Distance=(90°—true alt.) See Fig. 83, page 257.

Declination.—Declination is the arc of a celestial meridian between the celestial equator and a small circle drawn parallel to the equator through the body. It corresponds to terrestrial latitude.

Polar Distance.—This is the arc of a celestial meridian between a small circle drawn through a heavenly body, and the pole of the hemisphere in which the observer is stationed. If the observer's latitude and the star's declination are both North or both South, Polar Distance=(90°—declination). If latitude and declination are of different names, Polar Distance=(90°+Declination). See Figs. 85 and 86, page 263.

Greenwich Hour Angle of the Sun.—is the angle contained between the Meridian of Greenwich and a meridian drawn through the geographical position of the Sun's centre at a specified instant of time. It is always measured to the westward from Greenwich. See Fig. 69, page 197.

Local Hour Angle of the Sun is the angle between a meridian drawn through the observer's position and a meridian drawn through the geographical position of the Sun's centre at a specified instant of time.

L.H.A. Sun=G.H.A. Sun—W. long;+E. long.   See Fig. 70, page 197.

Geographical Position of a heavenly body is the latitude and longitude of a position on the earth's surface immediately below the body at a specified instant of time. It is that point where a straight line drawn from the body to the earth's centre would meet the earth's surface. The latitude of the point equals the declination of the body, and the longitude equals the body's Greenwich Hour Angle at that time.

Position Line.—A Position Line is actually a small portion of an arc of a small circle whose centre is the geographical position of the Sun or a particular star at a specified time. The radius of the small circle is the same value as the zenith distance of the celestial body. The particular radius is drawn from the body's geographical position to the circumfereuce of the circle in the reverse direction to the body's true bearing. See Fig. 89, page 279.

The portion of the arc being used is so small that no appreciable error in position is caused by considering it to be a straight line, drawn at right angles to the body's true bearing.

A visual bearing of a shore light or a point of land is itself a Position Line, on some part of which the ship's position is situated.

Prime Vertical.—Every (imaginary) great circle drawn on the celestial concave is a vertical circle if it meets the horizon at right angles, and passes through the observer's zenith. The vertical circle which cuts the horizon at its true East and West points is called the Prime Vertical.

Azimuth.—The Azimuth of a celestial body is the angle at the observer's zenith between a celestial meridian drawn through the observer's position, and a vertical circle through the body's centre. See Fig. 74, page 219.

When the observer is in North latitude, the Azimuth is measured from North towards East or West. When the observer is in South latitude, it is measured from South. The Azimuth can never exceed 180°.

It should be noted that the Azimuth is not the same as the True Bearing. A body whose Azimuth is N. 100° W. has a true bearing 260°, or S. 80° W.

ADDITIONAL DEFINITIONS FOR FISHING SKIPPERS.

Rhumb Line.—The track followed by a ship which is pursuing a steady course is a Rhumb Line, which cuts each meridian at the same angle. On a Mercator Chart, a rhumb line appears as a straight line. On a sphere, it appears as a spiral gradually approaching the pole, which, theoretically, it never reaches.

First Point of Aries is that point in the heavens where the Sun's centre crosses the heavenly equator (or "equinoctial") on Spring Day each year, when the Sun changes from South to North declination. Like all stars, it is treated as a fixed point. The Sidereal Hour Angle, or celestial longitude, of all celestial bodies is measured from the First Point of Aries, in the same way as terrestrial longitude is measured from the meridian of Greenwich.

Sidereal Hour Angle of a Star is the angle contained between a meridian drawn through the First Point of Aries and a meridian drawn through the particular star. Like Greenwich Hour Angle, it is always measured to the westward from Aries. G.H.A. star=G.H.A. Aries+Sidereal H.A. of Star.

SUN'S MERIDIAN PASSAGE.

To obtain Clock (or Chronometer) Time of Sun's Meridian Passage.— At the foot of each right-hand page in the Daily Pages of the *Nautical Almanac*, a small panel contains information regarding the meridian passages of both the Sun and the Moon.

In the case of the Sun, the Equation of Time—with no plus or minus sign given—is quoted for 00h and 12h of each of the three days on that page. Alongside this is given the Mean Time of the Sun's meridian passage AT GREENWICH. This is given TO THE NEAREST MINUTE ONLY.

Since Equation of Time alters only a few seconds of time in any 24 hours, the quoted time of Meridian Passage is also the Local Mean Time of the Sun's meridian passage *at the observer's longitude*. To find the Greenwich Mean Time—required for correcting the Sun's declination—apply the "longitude in time" in the usual way; that is, long. W+; long. E—.

Example 1.—Find the G.M.T. of the Sun's meridian passage on September 24th, 1958, in long. 60° 30′ W.

L.M.T. Mer. Pass.   11h 52m
Long. in time (W) + 4   2

G.M.T. Mer. Pass.   15   54   in long. 60° 30′ W.

Example 2.—Find the G.M.T. of the Sun's meridian passage on September 22nd, 1958, in long. 5° 45′ E.

$$\begin{array}{lll} \text{L.M.T. Mer. Pass.} & \text{11h 53m} \\ \text{Long. in time (E)} & - & 23 \\ \hline \text{G.M.T. Mer. Pass.} & \underline{11 \quad 30} & \text{in long. 5° 45′ E.} \end{array}$$

As stated above, the G.M.T. of the Sun's meridian passage in any specified longitude is required only for the purpose of correcting the Sun's declination. Time is thus required to the nearest minute only, and odd seconds can usually be disregarded.

The Pelorus.—A Pelorus is a "dumb" compass card, or compass card without magnetic needles. Various models are on the market, and while different models require different handling, the principles involved remain the same in all cases.

The Pelorus can be moved to various parts of a ship's bridge, so that by its use, bearings of objects which may temporarily be invisible from the ship's compass can be obtained. The "ship's head" point of the Pelorus, when the instrument is being used, must always be parallel to the ship's fore-and-aft line.

To obtain Compass Bearings using the Pelorus.—Clamp the moveable compass card of the instrument so that the course the ship is steering is opposite to the "ship's head" point. Sight the terrestrial object carefully through the movable sight-vanes, making sure that the ship is right on her course, and then read the compass bearing direct.

To Put a Ship on a Pre-determined True Course.—Suppose you wish to steer a certain TRUE course from a position which is known to be correct. From the chart, find the TRUE bearing of a conspicuous shore object. Clamp the compass card of the Pelorus with the pre-determined true course opposite the "ship's head" point. Turn the sight vanes to the true bearing of the object. Alter the ship's course till the object is fairly in the sight vane. The ship's heading by compass at that time is the COMPASS course to be steered to make the required TRUE course.

PROJECTIONS.

Map projections represent endeavours to reproduce parts of a sphere on a flat surface. In these endeavours, many different varieties of projections are used. Much depends on the particular purpose for which the projection is required.

Reference has already been made to maps, or charts, drawn on Mercator's projection. (See page 110.) These charts are used to reproduce portions of the earth's surface for navigational purposes.

Projections are also used to represent the "celestial concave", and are in common use for this purpose at sea, and also very largely in nautical text-books. Two projections are very widely used—one drawn on "the plane of the rational horizon", the other on "the plane of the observer's meridian".

Projections on the Plane of the Rational Horizon.—This projection is used extensively, and is straightforward and easily constructed.

The rational horizon is a great circle on the celestial concave, every point of which is 90° from the zenith of the observer. The figure should therefore be drawn on a "9-part" scale, and very usually the radius of the circle is made 9/10 of an inch. This scale simplifies measurements, as 1/10″ measures 10°.

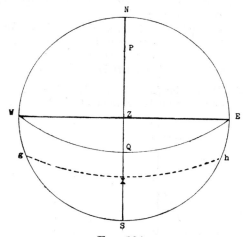

Fig. 124.

In the sketch the centre of the circle, the point "Z", represents the observer's zenith. Every point of the circumference of the circle, which represents the rational horizon, is 90° from the centre. The North-South line and the East-West line are both vertical circles, which are shown as straight lines. All vertical circles, which pass through the observer's zenith, are drawn as straight lines. Assume that the sketch is to represent an observer in latitude 30° N., with a heavenly body of declination 20° S. on the meridian.

First draw the celestial equator, WQE. The observer is in lat. 30° N., therefore point Q is 30° South of him. (3/10″ on the scale.) The distance between "P", the elevated pole, and the equator is 90°, so that P is placed 3/10″ South of N, or alternatively, 6/10″ North of Z.

The centre of the circle of which WQE is an arc lies somewhere on the line ZN, produced if necessary, and is found by trial, using a pair of compasses.

The small circle representing the body's declination, 20° S. in this case, is usually shown pecked—*gXh* in the sketch. The point *X* is marked 20° South of *Q*. Before the points "g" and "h" can be plotted, the Amplitude of the body must be known. The Amplitude is the arc of the horizon between the true East point and an object when rising, or between the true West point and an object when setting. *Burton's* Amplitude Table is No. 28, while *Norie's* is on pp. 534-535. With lat. 30° and decl. 20°, the Amplitude is found from the Tables to be 23·3°.

With a protractor centred at *Z*, and its zero points passing through *E* and *W*, mark an angle of 23·3° at "g" and "h" respectively. These points must be to the southward of *E* and *W*, the body's declination being South. By trial, find the centre of the small circle which passes through "g", "X" and "h". As before, this centre lies somewhere on the line *ZN*, produced if necessary.

In the figure, *XS* represents the true altitude of the body; (South);

$$ZX \quad ,, \quad \text{the zenith distance of body} \quad \text{(North)};$$
$$QX \quad ,, \quad \text{the declination of body,} \quad \text{(South)};$$

Therefore *ZX*—*QX*=*ZQ* latitude of the observer.

To Project the *PZX* Triangle.—Assume the observer's latitude to be 40° N., the body's declination 15° N., and the body's hour angle 30°.

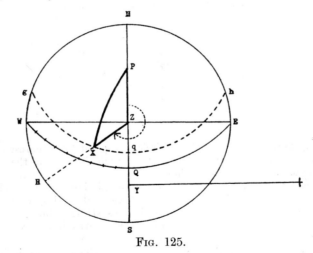

Fig. 125.

Using 9/10″ as radius, draw the circle, and mark the zenith and the *N-S* and *E-W* vertical circles. At 4/10″ from the point *N*, plot *P* the elevated pole, and at the same distance South of *Z*, plot *Q*, On the meridian *ZN*, produced if necessary, find the centre of the arc *WQE*, and draw the celestial equator. Plot *q*, the declination of the body, 15° North of *Q*. In the Amplitude Table, with lat. 40° and decl. 15°, find the Amplitude (19·7°). The declination being North, points g and h must be plotted to the north-ward of W and E respectively. On ZN produced, find the centre of the circle whose arc passes through g, q and h, and draw the pecked line to represent the body's declination.

Hour angles are now commonly measured in arc, and not in time. By eye, divide the arc QW into 9 equal parts, each part representing 10° of hour angle.

On the meridian ZS, find by trial, using compasses, the centre of a circle which would pass through the points W, P and E. Call this centre Y. (It is not necessary actually to draw the circle.) Through the point Y draw a line at right angles to ZS.

This line is called a "locus", and the centres of all "hour circles" lie somewhere on the locus.

By trial, find the centre of the circle which passes through P, the elevated pole, and through the 30° Hour Angle on WQ, and draw PX, the great circle from the elevated pole to the body. Join ZX, and produce the line to meet the circumference of the circle at H. Then—

PX represents the body's Polar Distance;
PZ ,, the observer's co-latitude;
ZQ ,, the observer's latitude;
ZX ,, the body's zenith distance;
HX ,, the body's true altitude;
Angle P ,, the body's Hour Angle;
Angle Z ,, the body's Azimuth.

The angle from N through E and S to X represents the true bearing of the body.

Projections on the Plane of the Observer's Meridian.—The observer's meridian is the imaginary celestial meridian which passes through the zenith of an observer who is situated on the surface of the earth. Fig. 126 is a projection on this plane, showing the same particulars as are shown in Fig. 124, which is a projection on the plane of the rational horizon. Frequent comparison should be made between the two figures.

In the sketch, the observer's position is at the point E, which is really *the centre of a sphere*. The circumference of the circle represents the observer's meridian. Only the upper semi-circle is visible to him. The lower semi-circle is below his horizon, and is invisible. SEN represents the rational horizon, and Z is the observer's zenith. The sketch shows the observer in latitude 30° N., with a celestial body of declination 20° S. on his meridian at the point X.

With centre at E, and radius 9/10″, describe a circle, and draw the vertical circles ZEZ' and SEN. The observer's latitude is 30° N. Using a protractor, at the point E measure the angle $PEN=30°$. Draw PEP'. The point P represents the elevated pole of the heavens, and P' is the depressed pole.

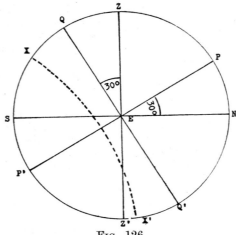

Fig. 126.

The celestial equator is 90° from *P*. *QEQ'*, a vertical circle through the observer's position at right angles to *PEP'*, therefore represents the celestial equator, and the angle *QEZ* measures 30°.

From *E*, measure 20° (2/10″) towards *P'*. The arcs *QX* and *Q'X'* represent the amplitude bearing of *X*, and measure 23·3°. By trial, find on the vertical circle *EP'*, produced if necessary, the centre of a circle which passes through these three points, and draw a pecked line to represent the orbit of the body.

In the figure—*XS* represents the meridian altitude of the body;
        ZX   ,,   the zenith distance of the body.

ZX is North, and the body's declination is South, and it can be seen from the sketch that

$$ZX - QX = ZQ = \text{observer's North latitude.}$$

When a projection on the plane of the observer's meridian is being used to illustrate a celestial body *on the meridian*, the *N* point of the projection may be placed either on the right of the sketch, as in Fig. 126, or on the left side. Fig. 127 shows the projection with the *N* point on the left side, the particulars being unchanged. It will be noted that when *N* is on the right side, the centre of the circle represents the East point (*E*). When *N* is on the left side, the centre of the circle represents the West point (*W*).

One Important Point.—When the celestial body is NOT on the meridian of the observer, the North point MUST be placed to the left if the L.H.A. of the body is less than 180°, or less than 12 hours.

L ess, North to
  eft.

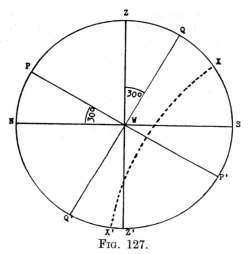

FIG. 127.

The explanation is simple. When the body's L.H.A. is less than 180°, the azimuth is to the westward, and, since the figure represents a sphere, and not simply a circle, the westerly side of the sphere must be shown.

If the L.H.A. is over 180°, the azimuth is to the eastward, and the easterly side of the sphere must be shown. In this case, therefore, the North point (N) must be placed to the right.

This rule holds good whether the observer's latitude is North or South.

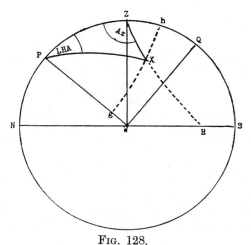

FIG. 128.

To Project the *PZX* **Triangle.**—Draw a figure on the plane of the observer's meridian to illustrate an observer in lat. 40° N. The body's declination is 15° N., and L.H.A. 30°. (These are the same particulars as are illustrated on the plane of the rational horizon in Fig. 125, to which frequent reference should be made for purposes of comparison.)

The L.H.A. being less than 180°, the point N is put on the left side of the circle. The angle NWP is 40°, and WQ is drawn at right angles to PW. The point g on the vertical circle PW is marked about 3/20″ from W, and the angle QWh measures 19·7°, the body's amplitude bearing. The centre of the pecked line is somewhere on the line WP, produced if necessary. The angle ZPX (the body's L.H.A.), is judged by eye to be 30°, and the arcs PX and ZX are drawn by hand. In the figure—

PX represents the body's polar distance;
ZX　　,,　　,,　　,, zenith distance;
XH　　,,　　,,　　,, altitude;
Angle PZX　,,　　,,　　,, azimuth;
Angle ZPX　,,　　,,　　,, local hour angle.

For the sake of clarity, the lower (non-visible) semi-circle has been left untouched.

Gnomonic Projections.—Terrestrial charts can be constructed in such a way that great circles on them are represented by straight lines. Such charts are said to be constructed on a Gnomonic Projection.

Since a great circle drawn between two points on a sphere represents the shortest distance between these points, gnomonic charts are of great use when a ship is required to make the shortest possible voyage between two ports.

Gnomonic charts can be constructed to cover any desired area, and their simplest form is illustrated by the well-known polar gnomonic charts. Near the earth's poles, the difference between a rhumb line course and a great circle course is most noticeable, and what is known as "great circle sailing" becomes most important. Even in the northern hemisphere, where there are great land masses in the polar regions, great saving of time and fuel can result by following a great circle track. In the southern hemisphere, where the polar regions are much more clear of land masses, time and fuel can be saved to a much greater extent.

In a polar gnomonic chart, the pole appears as the centre of a circle. Meridians radiating from the pole, being great circles, appear as straight lines, exactly like spokes of a wheel. Parallels of latitude, being small circles, appear as concentric circles, each with the pole as centre, and each circle the same distance away from the next. (See Fig. 129.)

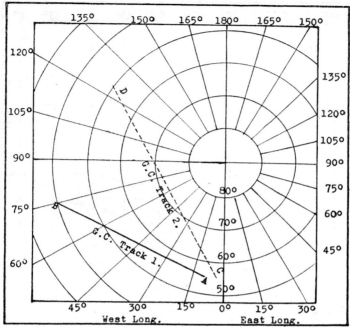

FIG. 129.

The sketch is a gnomonic projection of the North polar regions. The centre is the terrestrial North Pole; the concentric circles represent parallels of latitude for every 10°, and the straight lines radiating from the centre represent meridians of longitude for every 15°.

In the sketch, Track 1 represents a great circle track from a position in the vicinity of Tory Island, (Lat. 55° N., Long. 8° W.), to Philadelphia, (Lat. 40° N., Long. 75° W.). Following along the line of the great circle track, it will be seen that in long. 15° W., the track reaches lat. 56° N. Thereafter it crosses the various meridians, 15° apart, in lats. 57°, 55°, 50°, and finally 40° N.

Track 2, shown as a pecked line, represents the great circle track which would be taken by an aeroplane flying non-stop from Prestwick, (Lat. 55° N., Long. 4° W.), to Vancouver, (Lat. 50° N., Long. 125° W.). The saving of time and distance by this track is very spectacular, and it will be seen that, in proceeding from Lat. 55° N. to Lat. 50° N. by this track, the plane would reach as far as Lat. 72° N.

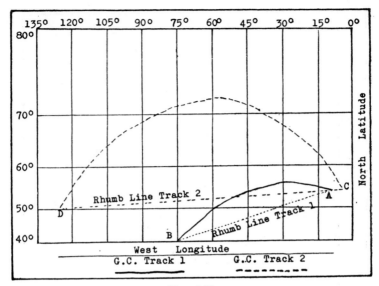

F𝐼𝐺. 130.

Fig. 130 represents a chart covering the same areas on the Mercator projection. In this sketch, the rhumb line tracks are shown as straight lines, while the curved lines show roughly the respective great circle tracks. On the Mercator chart, the great circle tracks are *apparently* very much longer than the rhumb line tracks, although in reality this is not so.

When using a great circle track, it is usual to plot on a Mercator chart the different latitudes at which the track crosses meridians about 5° apart, these latitudes being read from a gnomonic chart. The ship steers a straight course from one point to the next, thus keeping as close as possible to an actual great circle.

SPECIMEN QUESTIONS ON PRINCIPLES OF NAVIGATION, WITH ANSWERS.

1. *Why does the observed altitude of a heavenly body require to be corrected before being used in calculations?*

The altitude required in calculations is the altitude of the body— in the case of the Sun and the Moon, the body's centre—above an imaginary horizon drawn through the earth's centre at right angles to a perpendicular dropped from the observer at the earth's surface. A correction is made to offset the height of the observer's eye above sea level, and another to correct "refraction", which causes the observed altitude to appear too high. The Sun also requires corrections for "parallax" and "semi-diameter". Stars are too far away to require correction for parallax, and appear too small to require correction for semi-diameter.

2. *Explain why "height of eye" must be known when taking an observation of the Sun. From where is the height measured?*

The Sun's altitude, as stated above, is required above an imaginary horizon—the "Rational Horizon"—drawn through the earth's centre. This is parallel to another imaginary horizon—the "sensible Horizon"—drawn through the observer's eye at right angles to the perpendicular. Because the observer is usually above sea level, the "Visible Horizon" lies below the level of the Sensible Horizon. The angle between them—the "Dip of the Sea Horizon"—is therefore subtracted from the observed altitude. Height is taken above sea level. See Figs. 79 and 81, pages 253 and 254.

3. *What is the best time to observe the Sun to obtain a longitude?*

The best time to observe the Sun for longitude is when it bears true East or true West from the observer. At that time, a position line would be in a North-South direction, and the observation would yield the correct longitude even if the D.R. latitude was in error. The Sun can bear East or West only if its declination is of the same name as the observer's latitude, and less in value than the latitude. If these conditions cannot be obtained the observation should be taken about 3 or 4 hours before or after noon. See Fig. 91, page 280.

4. *You took an observation of the Sun when it was bearing E.S.E., and later you obtained a latitude by meridian altitude. How would you plot the position lines to obtain a fix?*

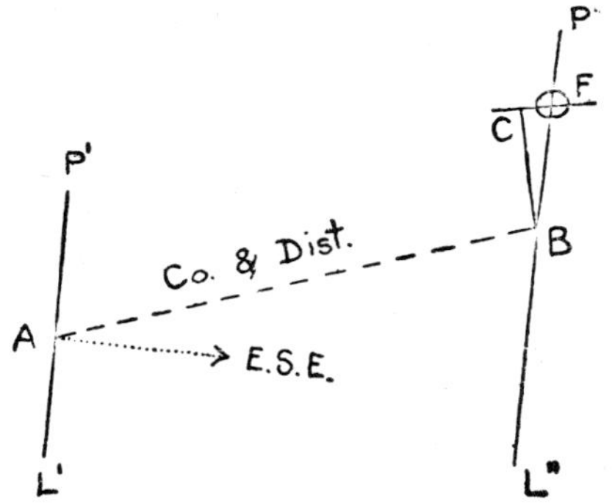

Fig. 131.

First plot position *A*—the assumed latitude and the observed longitude. Through *A* draw a line (*P'L'*) at right angles to the Sun's bearing. From *A* lay off *AB*, the course and distance made good between observations. *B* is the assumed (D.R.) noon position. Through *B*, draw *P"L"* parallel to *P'L'*.

After obtaining the true latitude by meridian altitude observation (*C*), draw *BC* in a North—South direction. Through *C* draw a position line at right angles to *BC*, meeting *P"L"* at *F*. *F* is the ship's true position.

5. *How would you obtain the latitude and longitude of a fix after plotting two position lines?*

In Fig. 131, the position *F* could be found by direct reference to the scales of latitude and longitude if the plotting is done on a Mercator chart. If plotted to scale on squared paper, *BC* would represent difference of latitude in units of minutes of arc, and *CF* in the same units would represent DEPARTURE, which would require to be converted to difference of longitude in the usual way.

ADDITIONAL QUESTIONS FOR SKIPPERS ONLY.

6. *How would you determine the best time to take stellar observations?*

These must be taken at morning or evening twilight, when the horizon can be seen easily. From the daily page of the *Nautical Almanac* find L.M.T. of sunrise or sunset, and also L.M.T. of twilight. Observations should be taken between these times, preferably as near as possible to the quoted time of observation.

7. *A star has been observed to the westward. What method would you use to reduce this observation to obtain a position line?*

Using a D.R. latitude, calculate the longitude from the observation. Using the L.H.A. obtained in the calculation, find the star's true bearing. A position line at right angles to the true bearing can then be drawn through the longitude found by calculation at the position of the D.R. latitude.

8. *A single light is visible to the westward. In which direction would you look for a suitable star to observe, to obtain a position line to cross with the visual bearing of the light?*

The visual bearing constitutes a position line in an East-West direction. I would look for a suitable star to the eastward, or, if no land appeared on the horizon, to the westward. The position line obtained from an observation of such star would lie in an approximate North-South direction, and would give a good cross with the visual bearing.

CHAPTER 38.

THE HYPERBOLA—LATTICE CHARTS—CONSOL—HOW TO OBTAIN A COUNT—DECCA—FIXED AND VARIABLE ERRORS—RADAR—ITS LIMITATIONS AND WEAKNESSES—ECHO SOUNDERS.

During the Second World War the science of Electronics produced many instruments, invented and developed for purely military purposes. These instruments included equipment for position-finding at sea or in the air under conditions of bad visibility, for detecting enemy submarines, etc., etc.

After the war, many of these inventions were subjected to further intensive research work and were released from war-time secrecy, so that systems evolved through war-time needs have now become valuable additions to the safety equipment of merchant vessels. There are very few ships indeed which do not include one or more of these "aids" as integral parts of the ship's safety equipment.

Special attention has been given to systems which allow vessels to pinpoint their positions at any time under weather conditions which permit neither visual nor celestial observations. Roughly, these systems can be divided into two classes—those which use "hyperbolic" aids to navigation, and those which use visual (electronic) aids.

The Hyperbola.—In Fig. 132, A and B are two fixed points, 6 miles apart. In the sketch, circles are drawn at distances apart representing 1 mile, using A and B as the centres of the circles.

Point a is 9 miles from A, and 4 miles from B. The difference between the two distances $(9-4)=5$.

Similarly

Point b is 8 miles from A and 3 miles from B. Diff. $(8-3)=5$.

,, c ,, 7	,, ,, ,, ,, 2	,, ,, ,, ,,	$(7-2)=5$.
,, d ,, 6	,, ,, ,, ,, 1	,, ,, ,, ,,	$(6-1)=5$.
,, e ,, $5\frac{1}{2}$	,, ,, ,, ,, $\frac{1}{2}$	,, ,, ,, ,,	$(5\frac{1}{2}-\frac{1}{2})=5$.

and so on.

The *distance* of each point from the two fixed points is different in every case, but the *difference between the distances* is always the same.

The curved line CD drawn through these points, and through other points whose difference of distances also measures 5 miles, is called a HYPERBOLA.

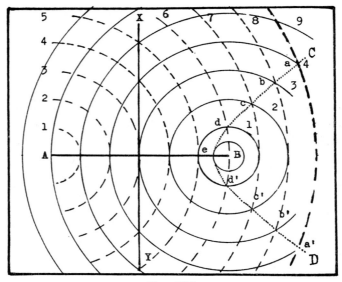

Fig. 132.

When a moving point is kept on such a path that the difference of its distances from two fixed points remains constant, that path is a Hyperbola.

AB, the line joining the two fixed points, is called a "base line." XY, the line at right angles to the base line midway between the two fixed points, is called the "centre line". It will be noticed that XY is drawn through the intersecting points of circles of equal radius, the "difference of distances" being zero. XY is therefore also a hyperbola, but with a difference of zero, it forms a straight line.

From the sketch it can also be seen that the curvature of a hyperbola is greatest in the vicinity of the base line, and that the curvature of a hyperbola nearer to the centre line is less than that of hyperbolae farther away from the centre line.

The farther any hyperbola is extended away from the base line, the more nearly it approaches being a straight line. At distances of over 12 times the length of the base line, all hyperbolae can be reckoned as straight lines, radiating from the middle point of the base line.

Lattice Charts.—Hyperbolae can be printed on navigational charts, the differences of distances being recorded not only in terms of distance but in terms of time, expressed to an accuracy of millionth parts of a second, or, using electrical terms, as differences of phase.

Each hyperbola is therefore a single "Position Line", the vessel's position being *somewhere* on one particular hyperbola. In order to fix the position accurately, it is necessary to add a second position line. When one of the position lines is a hyperbola, the other could be a second hyperbola, or a visual bearing, or a P.L. obtained by celestial observation. Most usually a second hyperbola is used, both hyperbolae being keyed to the same system.

Various well-known systems of "radiolocation" have special navigational charts, on which the hyperbolae used in the particular system are over-printed. From the appearance of these charts they are called "lattice charts".

At least three different systems—Loran, Decca and Consol—provide full coverage round the British Isles and adjacent seas. Each system employs its own shore stations from which radio signals are transmitted. Each system requires its own lattice charts, and, with the sole exception of Consol, each requires its own special receiving equipment on board.

Loran—from LOng RAnge Navigation—is an American system, and is less widely used on board British ships than Decca or Consol. The hyperbolae are based on time differences between radio signals received from two stations—a Master and a Slave. In some cases, owing to geographical difficulties, a Master station may be used with two separate Slave stations. In these cases, the Master sends characteristic signals to each Slave, and the three stations operate as two different entities. In Loran, the Master and Slave stations may be from 200 to 400 miles apart. Each pair of stations produces its own hyperbolae, and to obtain a "fix", at least two pairs of stations are required. The signals transmitted from them are received on board an observing ship visually on a radar-like screen, the two separate signals requiring to be brought into coincidence. Loran can be used to fix a vessel's position under open sea conditions, or when making a landfall.

The Decca System depends on phase differences, and each "chain" of stations consists of a Master station and three Slave stations. Thus there are three different sets of hyperbolae overprinted on the Decca lattice-charts. For purposes of differentiation and recognition, one of these sets is coloured red, one green, and the third purple, while the appropriate Slave stations are known respectively as the Red, Green and Purple stations. It is usually only necessary to take readings of two sets of hyperbolae in order to obtain a good fix.

Decca provides information for obtaining a fix under conditions of open sea navigation, when making a landfall, and also in narrow waters when making harbour. The Decca Navigator, required in addition to Decca lattice charts, is totally different from the equipment required for Loran. (See p. 420).

Consol.—While the Consol system also comes under the heading of hyperbolic aids to navigation, the lattice charts are very different in appearance from either Decca or Loran charts. Owing to the fact that the total base line used at Consol stations is very short, Consol should not be used within 25 miles of the particular station. Outside of that distance the hyperbolae become straight lines, radiating from the position of the Master station like so many spokes of a wheel. (See below.) In addition, as each Consol station provides a definite bearing, stations are usually referred to as Consol beacons.

Consol is useful for obtaining a ship's position under conditions of open sea navigation, but it is not advisable to use the system for other conditions if alternative methods are available.

CONSOL.

Consol requires no equipment on board ship beyond a radio receiver capable of receiving C.W. signals on medium frequencies. The frequencies used differ from station to station, but all lie within the range 255-325 kc/s. Consol charts are, of course, desirable, but even when none are on board, special tables are available, so that Consol bearings can be plotted direct on navigational charts. It should be remembered that half-convergency corrections must be applied when circumstances call for them.

Five sets of transmitters in the system cover all seas adjacent to the entire European coastline from Norway and Sweden—including the Baltic Sea—to Italy in the Mediterranean. All ocean areas round Britain, Ireland and Iceland are also covered.

Each "station" consists of a central transmitter and two outer transmitters. The base line measures only about 6 kilometres, and signals are radiated in every direction. The circle through which signals are transmitted is divided into sectors. The number of sectors depends on the individual station, but salient features are common to them all. The sectors in any one circle differ in extent, the broadest sectors being those which are adjacent to the extension of the base line, and on each side of it. The narrowest sectors are those adjacent to the centre line, the line through the main transmitting station at right angles to the base line.

The signals transmitted consist of dashes and dots. Every second sector is a "dash" sector; that is, the signals commence with dashes. The other sectors are "dot" sectors, in which the signals commence with dots.

An important exception to this is found in the broadest sectors, which lie next to each other, one on each side of the extension of the base line. Both adjacent sectors are either dash sectors or dot sectors.

Because of this double disadvantage—the breadth of the sectors and the ambiguity of the signals—these sectors MUST NOT BE USED WHEN FIXING A SHIP'S POSITION. Taking the Stavanger station as an example, the base line lies in a direction 157°—337°, and the station should not be used when it lies between the bearings of $307\frac{1}{2}°$ through $360°$ to $006\frac{1}{2}°$, or between $127\frac{1}{2}°$ and $186\frac{1}{2}°$.

To Identify the Sector.—As every alternate sector is a "dot" sector, a ship can identify the particular sector by using her D.R. position, or, alternatively, by taking D/F bearings of the station during the periods when it is transmitting its identification signal. (See below).

Transmission.—The complete cycle of transmission consists of the station's identification signal, followed by the dot-dash signal. The time occupied for the full cycle may be 40 seconds or 120 seconds, according to the station. The cycle of the Stavanger station occupies 120 seconds. During the first minute the central aerial alone transmits the station's identity signal—a long dash, followed by the station's signal letters, followed by a long dash. During the second minute, 60 dots and 60 dashes are transmitted by each outer station respectively, so timed that the dots are transmitted from one station in the intervals between the dashes transmitted by the other station.

If the observer's ship is in one of the dot sectors, dots will be heard first; if in a dash sector, dashes will be heard first. During the 60-second period of transmission, a total of 60 dots and dashes should be received by the observing ship. In this time, the phase of current received by one of the outer aerials from the centre station is gradually advanced by 180°, while the phase in the other outer aerial is retarded by 180°, so that the pattern of signals rotates. (See Fig. 133.) In those sectors which lie on one side of the base-line extension, the pattern rotates clockwise, and on the other side of the base line, it rotates in an anti-clockwise direction.

At the commencement of each "dot-dash" transmission, an observer stationed on any of the lines OA, OB, OC, OD, etc.,—which represent the limits of various sectors—would hear both the dots and the dashes. As the dots are transmitted during the intervals between the dashes, the resultant would be a continuous note, called the "equi-signal".

Due to the rotation of the signal, the equi-signal line revolves from OA towards OB, reaching this latter point at the end of the transmitting period. The sector AOB would then have become a "dash" sector. Transmission then ceases from the outer aerials for 60 seconds, during which time the identification signal is transmitted from the middle station. Rotation, however, still continues, so that when the next "dot-dash" transmission commences, sector AOB has again become a "dot" sector. The same changes take place in all sectors.

In Fig. 133, the sector BOC is a "dash" sector. If the angle BOC measures 24°, and the observer's ship—X—is in such a position that angle BOX measures 18°, the signal received by the ship will be 45 dashes followed by 15 dots.

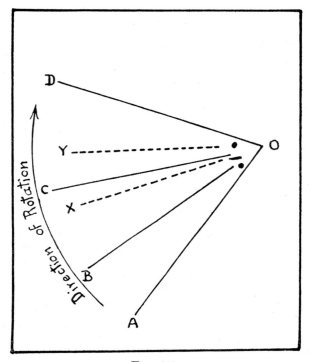

Fig. 133.

If sector *COD*—which is a "dot" sector—measures 30°, and the ship *Y* is in such a position that angle *COY* measures 10°, that ship will receive a signal of 20 dots followed by 40 dashes.

To Obtain a Count.—In the sector *BOC*, the equi-signal at *OB* traces a vector to *OC* during each period of transmission. Therefore an observer within the sector must hear the equi-signal at some time during that period.

It will be remembered that dots are transmitted during the intervals between "dash" signals, giving a continuous note, so that when the equi-signal approaches the line of a ship's position, a certain number of "counts" is inevitably lost. It is usually considered that equal numbers of dots and dashes have been lost.

The total "count" should be 60. Suppose the actual "count" received was 32 dots and 22 dashes.

$$(32+22)=54$$

The number of dots and dashes lost was therefore 6. Add half of this number to the dots and half to the dashes. The correct count would then be 35 dots and 25 dashes.

The same loss of count is experienced in all sectors of the pattern, and as a check for accuracy, it is best to take two or three counts during an observation.

A count received from a single station provides one Position Line only, and to obtain a fix, a count must also be obtained at the same time from a second station working in conjunction with the first.

DECCA.

The Decca system of radiolocation requires special equipment on board the receiving vessel, in addition to Decca lattice charts. The equipment is in two main parts—the receiving apparatus, and the "decometers".

In Northern Europe there are 6 Decca "chains", each chain covering a specific area, so that all the seas round Britain and the adjacent coasts are effectively covered. Each "chain" consists of a Master station and three Slave stations. For purposes of differentiation and identification, the Slave stations in each chain are named Red, Green and Purple slaves respectively. On the lattice charts, hyperbolae which depend on signals from the Master station and the Red slave are coloured red; those which depend on signals from the Master and the Green slave are coloured green; and similarly with the signals from the Purple slave.

Slave stations in a chain are spaced about 200 miles apart in the shape of an equilateral triangle, the Master station being placed at the centre of gravity of the triangle. The Master station of the "English chain" is situated some distance north of London; that of the S.W. chain in Devon, and that of the N.W. chain in the south-west part of Scotland. In addition there are Danish, German and French chains.

The hyperbolae used in the Decca system measure "phase differences". The Master station transmits its signal, which is picked up by the slave station. The receiver of this station is so connected to its own transmitter that the transmitting aerials of both Master and Slave send out their signals accurately in phase.

Each of the four stations in a chain transmits its signal on a different frequency. Each frequency is a simple multiple of the same unit— $14 \cdot 167$ kc/s per second. Thus the Master transmits on a frequency of $(14 \cdot 167 \times 6)$ kc/s, while, for example, the green slave transmits on a frequency of $(14 \cdot 167 \times 9)$ kc/s. Being on different frequencies, these signals are received separately by the ship's aerial, and are amplified. The frequency of the signal from the Master station is then automatically increased by three times, and that of the green slave by two times, so that the frequency of each becomes the same—$(14 \cdot 167 \times 18)$ kc/s. The "phase difference" between the signals can now be measured by the "discriminator", and this difference is passed to the appropriate (green) decometer, where its value is shown visually. All this happens in a space of time measured in millionth-parts of a second.

A separate instrument panel—the Decca Navigator—carries three circular "phase meters", one for each slave station. They are marked "RED", "GREEN" and "PURPLE" respectively. Each station covers 10 Zones, which are named from A to J. This letter appears in a small window in the lower part of each meter. The limits of zones are indicated on lattice charts by hyperbolae printed more heavily than the others.

The number "18" quoted above when dealing with signals from the green slave station determines the number of "lanes" in each green zone.

The frequencies of signals received from the Master and the Red slave station are each increased in a similar manner, in this case to $(14\cdot167\times24)$ kc/s. Thus there are 24 lanes in each of the Red zones. The frequencies of the Master and the Purple slave signals are increased to $(14\cdot167\times30)$ kc/s., and there are 30 lanes in each of the Purple zones.

Each phase-meter carries two pointers, very similar to the hands of a clock. In all cases, the smaller of the two movable pointers—the "fraction-pointer"—refers to the marks on the inner of two circles. These marks are numbered from zero to 100, and give the vessel's position on a particular lane to an accuracy of one-hundredth part of the lane. The longer pointer—the "lane-pointer"—indicates the number of the particular lane in which the vessel is presently situated, the zone being shown by its letter in the small window to which reference has already been made. The "lane" numbers appear on the outer of the two circles on each decometer.

To prevent ambiguity, the Red lanes are numbered from 1 to 24; Green lanes are numbered from 30 to 48, and Purple lanes from 50 to 80.

Lane Identification.—The instrument panel described above is the "Mark IV" Decca Navigator. This type is perfectly satisfactory on board ships which normally voyage within an area covered by one of the chains only.

In ships which perform voyages during which they pass from one chain to another, the "Mark V" instrument provides extra identification. On the Mark V panel there is a fourth dial, known as the "lane identification meter". In addition to providing a check when new Decca positions are required when the ship changes from one chain to another, the meter also guards against any error which might arise through what is technically known as "lane-slipping". Although this contingency arises very infrequently indeed, it *can* happen, the main causes being through interference to the Decca receiver from the ship's own W/T transmitter; when one of the ship's dynamos is switched off and another switched on; or by a sudden load being put on the ship's electric power.

During the first part of every minute of G.M.T., lane identification takes place as follows:—

For the RED lane   ..   ..   from 00 sec. to 05 sec.
For the GREEN lane   ..   from 15 sec. to 20 sec.
For the PURPLE lane   ..   from 30 sec. to 35 sec.

During each period of 5 seconds while lane identification is being carried out, normal transmission from all stations of the chain ceases, and the ship's receiver automatically cuts out.   During the 5-second period, the Master station and the slave station being identified operate on a much lower frequency.   As soon as identification of that station ceases, normal transmission recommences.

The lane identification meter consists of a circular dial, round the outer edge of which are three rings, the outermost the Purple lane ring, the middle one the Red lane ring, and the innermost one the Green lane ring.   The scales are of a transparent substance, and a light shows temporarily only in the ring of that lane for which identification is being carried out.

On the meter, six thin pointers—"vernier pointers"—are pivoted on a central revolving pin, the angle between each pair of pointers being 60°.   A second pointer—the "sector pointer"—consists of two thin rods the outer ends of which are joined by a thin rod of the same metal, the fitting being in the shape of a sector of a circle.   This pointer operates separately from the vernier pointers.   The two arms subtend an angle of 60° at the central pivot, and in the middle of the joining arm there is a small notch or mark.

During Red lane identification the red ring lights up, and vernier pointers and the sector pointer swing to their proper positions, when the centre mark of the sector pointer will coincide with one of the vernier pointers.   The lane number which is indicated by this pointer is then read from the Red scale.   This is compared with the lane number actually indicated on the Red decometer.   The identification of the Green and Purple lanes follows, *always in that order.*

Decometer readings should not differ by more than half a lane from the readings given by the identification meter, and three successive readings of each lane should be taken as a check.   Should a difference occur of more than half a lane in any of the identifications, the lane pointer of the affected decometer should be turned to the correct lane number by using the "RESET" knob on that decometer.

Owing to "indirect radiation", the identification system may be untrustworthy during night hours at distances over 150 miles from the station.   During daylight hours it is trustworthy up to distances of about 250 miles from the station.

To Use the Decca Navigator.—To obtain accurate results from the equipment, certain rules must be adhered to.   Failure to do so can result in the meters providing wrong information, with consequent potentially disastrous effects.

The receiver should be switched on well in advance of the ship's sailing time.   Half an hour is the very minimum time to allow the set to warm up to a temperature which will remain more or less constant.

If the Navigator had been in use up to the time of the vessel's last arrival in harbour, and the meters had not been altered in any way, they should register the correct Decca co-ordinates for the ship's position.

If, however, the set had not been in use on arrival, or if the meters had been altered, it will be necessary to put the correct co-ordinates on the meters.   This should not be done till the set has been warmed up.

On each decometer there is a knob marked "RESET".   Working on one meter at a time, this knob is pressed inward and turned till the dial registers the correct zone and lane.   As soon as the knob is released, the lane fraction-pointer turns automatically to register the correct fraction.   It is important to realise that this pointer always moves to its position *by the shortest way*.   If the pointer was near zero, and turned anti-clockwise through zero to, say 65 on the dial, it would carry the lane-pointer backwards with it, in the same way as the minute hand of a clock turns the hour-hand when turned backwards. The lane-pointer would then register one lane in error.   This should be carefully checked when the Reset knob is released.

The same operation is then carried out on the other meters, and all should then be registering correctly.

"Test"—There is a second knob on the Red decometer, marked "TEST".   This is used after the set has warmed up to ensure that transmitters and receiver are working properly.   When the knob is pressed inwards, the fraction-pointers on *all* meters should simultaneously turn from 10 to 20 divisions in a clockwise direction.   Failure on the part of one or more of the meters to do so indicates that either a transmitter or the receiver is not functioning properly.

Drift.—Alterations in the temperature in the set can cause a slight change in "phase-difference".   This is called "Drift", and the most likely time for it to occur is within two hours of the set being switched on.   Drift causes the fraction-pointer to give an incorrect reading.

To check against drift, press the knob marked "REF" (Reference) found on the Green decometer,   This causes an oscillator in the sets to send signals such that the phase difference registered on *all* meters is zero, and all fraction-pointers should turn to zero on their respective dials.   Should any pointer not register zero, the "ZERO" knob on the appropriate meter must be turned till the pointer registers correctly. The "REF" knob is kept depressed during this operation.

When the "Ref" knob is released, the fraction-pointers immediately turn to register the correct fraction, and again, they take the shortest route to do so.   If any pointer moves in an anti-clockwise direction, through zero, the lane number must be rechecked, and probably reset.

The sector pointer and one of the six pointers on the lane identification meter should also point to zero during the operation. If either does not do so, it is corrected by turning the appropriate reset knob just below the lane-identification meter.

Indirect Radiation.—Correct results are obtained only from signals received direct from the transmitters. When indirect radiation signals are received, the phase differences registered on the meters will be incorrect.

Indirect radiation occurs most frequently during the hours of darkness, especially when the receiving ship is a long way from the transmitters. It is also rather frequent during daylight hours in winter. It effects are always greatest at dawn and dusk. It is caused by signals from a transmitter being radiated upwards and reflected back to earth from the ionosphere.

The actual amount of error cannot be predicted, but sometimes the possible effects of indirect radiation can be estimated approximately. The Decca Company supplies data-sheets which list the most likely areas of error round the coasts of the British Isles. If any doubt should arise regarding the accuracy of the information, a series of observations should be used as a check. If possible, the ship's D.R. position, or celestial observations, or—best of all—visual checks by bearings of terrestrial points should also be used.

Fixed Errors.—Certain known areas of land possess more than ordinarily poor conductive qualities. When signals are transmitted across such land, the actual phase-differences registered on the Navigator will not agree with the smooth hyperbolic curves on the Decca lattice-chart of the area. Until charts which show these "distortions" are published, information regarding the areas can be obtained from pamphlets supplied by Decca. The information includes the corrections which should be made to meter readings in the areas.

The information supplied by the Decca Navigator should therefore never be used in a careless or slipshod manner. During passages, readings should be taken regularly, and as regularly "logged". The Decca co-ordinates of important points *en route* should be especially noted in writing, so that at these places the correct functioning of the set can be checked instantly. Checking should also be carried out under conditions of good visibility so that confidence in the set and in the observer's proper understanding of its controls can be thoroughly established.

RADAR.

It is beyond the scope of this chapter to deal with technical descriptions of Radar equipment. Candidates for Certificates as Home Trade Mate and Fishing Second Hand must possess Radar Observers' Certificates before being issued with the respective M.O.T. Certificates, and will therefore have undergone a Radar Observer's Course.

Shipborne radar constitutes one of the most important of modern aids to navigation. It possesses one outstanding feature lacking in other electronic systems of radiolocation by providing *visual* evidence of the presence of other vessels and floating objects in the ship's vicinity, as well as visual evidence of the proximity of land. But it must be emphasised that radar is only an AID to navigation, that there are weaknesses inherent in the system, and that there are limitations to its use.

By recognising these weaknesses and limitations, an observer can do much to minimise their effects. Every opportunity should be taken by masters and watchkeeping officers to understand the particular set on board, and to familiarise themselves with the various controls which are fitted, so that the best possible results can be obtained. The set should be used freely during periods of good visibility, and the picture presented on the screen compared with a navigational chart of the area, and with the scene actually visible to the observer. A chart provides a bird's-eye plan of an area, whereas the radar screen—the P.P.I.—presents a picture seen from the height of the scanner only. Thus features which appear on a chart may be temporarily unseen on a radar screen, masked, in all probability, by higher land between these features and the scanner. Very often the picture "painted" on the P.P.I. may show little likeness to the land represented on the chart. Continual practice on the set under conditions of good visibility is essential if these differences are to be noted, and if the same place is to be confidently recognised on the P.P.I. under conditions of poor visibility.

A ship's funnel, the cross-trees of a mast, ventilators, or other parts of the ship's superstructure, if placed higher than the scanner, will cause either "shadow" or "blind" arcs on the screen. Targets within these arcs will not be visible on the screen. Accurate bearings of any such blind arcs should be taken, relative to the ship's head, and a permanent notice of them should be posted near the set for reference. During fog, when searching for possible targets, the ship's course should be altered from time to time, sufficiently to ensure that these blind areas are uncovered. This operation is usually referred to as "snaking".

A vertical cliff returns a strong echo, whereas a low sloping beach may return no echo at all. Thus it is important to have an intelligent appreciation of a coastline as delineated on a chart. A range of hills well inshore of a low sandy beach could give an erroneous picture on the P.P.I., whereby an unwary observer could be lulled into a false sense of security.

Sea Clutter.—The surface of a rough sea reflects echoes back to the scanner. These echoes do not produce such a strong picture on the P.P.I. as do echoes reflected from solid bodies, but they can be very worrying to an observer. Echoes naturally are strongest when reflected from wave surfaces which most nearly approach the vertical. If a ship is steaming into a rough head sea, the effects of "clutter" will be more noticeable on the screen ahead of the ship. Similarly, in a beam sea, echoes from clutter will be stronger to windward than to leeward.

These echoes can be reduced by operating the "clutter-control", but this must be done with discretion. If control is reduced too far, small targets near the ship could be missed. Practice under conditions of good visibility, especially with small targets actually in sight, gives an observer experience which enables him to produce the best results. In fog, when a search for targets is being carried out, the clutter control-knob should be operated throughout the search, care being taken not to set the "receiver gain" control too low.

Abnormal Propagation.—The beam transmitted from the scanner normally tends to follow the curvature of the earth, to some extent at least. Certain meteorological conditions, however, cause abnormal propagation of the beam, when its downward tendency is decreased. Under these conditions targets which may actually be seen from the bridge can be missed by the scanner. This condition is known as "sub-refraction". Other conditions may cause the beam to be bent still more towards the curvature of the earth. This condition is known as "super refraction", when targets which are normally well outside the range of the scanner receive pulses from the transmitter, and return echoes to the ship.

Sub-refraction can occur when the amount of water-vapour in the air is small at sea level, increasing with height. The condition is particularly noticeable in cold areas, when the wind, super-cooled after blowing over ice-fields or snow-covered land, blows across relatively warm sea. If the ship is near icebergs, there is a danger that the presence of these may not be noted on the P.P.I.

Super-refraction occurs under conditions opposite to the above; i.e., when a warm wind is blowing over relatively cold water. This is especially so if the wind is coming from the direction of an extensive land mass. Generally speaking, super-refraction usually occurs with a high barometer, with light breezes and a cloudless sky.

Cloud echoes, reflected from the raindrops in the clouds, present characteristic pictures on a radar screen, and practice in the recognition of these characteristics during clear weather allows an observer to separate cloud echoes from land echoes under conditions of poor visibility.

Side Lobe Echoes.—By far the greater part of the energy sent out by the radar transmitter goes out in a narrow beam, called the "main lobe". This beam measures about 2° horizontally, and 12° vertically. Some energy, however, does escape to the sides of the main lobe, but the amount is generally small compared with the energy in the main lobe.

Even this small amount can produce noticeable echoes on the screen, especially if the "receiver gain" control is set high, and if the target is at a comparatively short range. These echoes appear on the P.P.I. at the same range as the true target, but on different bearings on each side of the true target. Usually, they appear as an "arc" of echoes, the echo from the true target being in the middle of the arc. Less usually, and generally when a large target is very close, with the observing ship's receiver gain very high, the side-lobe echoes may be of nearly the same intensity as the main-lobe echo. On the P.P.I., this appears as a distinctive arc of light. Receiver gain should be reduced till only the echo of the true target remains on the screen.

False Echoes.—Parts of the ship's fittings are capable of reflecting echoes from a target back to the scanner. As an instance, an echo from a target somewhere ahead can be reflected from the ship's funnel, to be received by the scanner when it has turned to face the funnel. Similarly, an echo from a target somewhere aft can be reflected by a mast or cross-trees, and be received by the scanner when it is facing the mast. On the radar screen, this will appear on practically the correct range of the true target, but on the bearing of the object from which it has been reflected.

Especially in the case of an echo reflected from the funnel, the bearing of the false echo on the P.P.I. will be on a bearing which is normally a "blind area". If this fact is appreciated, the observer can recognise the echo as being false.

When a large target is at short range near the observing vessel's beam, echoes may be repeatedly reflected backwards and forwards between the scanner and the target. On the radar screen this will be shown as several echoes all on the same bearing, but at different ranges. The echo nearest to the observing ship represents the position of the true target.

THE ECHO SOUNDER.

Because of its usefulness, because of the speed at which successive soundings can be taken, and because a visual record of depths is obtainable over relatively long periods of time, the Echo Sounder has practically ousted all other depth-finding instruments at sea.

The principle used in echo-sounding is the known fact that sound in sea water of a normal density of 1·025 travels at a constant speed of about 4900 feet per second.

The equipment on board ship consists of (a) the Recording Unit. An electric motor in this unit triggers off an electric impulse to (b) the Transmitter Unit. This impulse is sent at very high frequency (supersonic) to (c) the Transmitter Oscillator, fitted to the ship's hull close to the keel on one side of the vessel. The sound wave sent out by the transmitter is channelled into a comparatively narrow beam, and "beamed" to the sea-bed. From there it is reflected back, and the echo is received by (d) the Receiving Oscillator, which also is fitted to the hull of the vessel on the other side of the keel from the Transmitting Oscillator. The mechanical vibration received by (d) is re-converted to an electrical oscillation and passed to (e) the Amplifier, which magnifies the echo by over a million times before passing it back to the Recording Unit.

The speed at which the individual impulses are sent out depends on the depth of water at the time. Usually a second pulse is not transmitted until the echo of the first has been received in the recording unit. As this space of time is very short indeed in shallow water, as many as 300 pulses per minute may be sent out under these conditions. In deep water there may be no more than 20 pulses transmitted per minute, because of the extra time taken for the echo to be returned to the recording unit.

In the recording unit, a pen (called a Stylus) revolves from left to right at a constant speed. This speed is conditioned to the depth of water. When the revolving stylus arrives at the position which can be termed the starting-point of a revolution, an electric contact is made. This creates a current which causes the pulse to be transmitted at the same instant. Current is also supplied to the stylus at the same time, and flows to a metal plate behind the stylus.

A slow-moving sheet of specially prepared paper moves slowly on rollers at a constant speed between the stylus and the metal plate. As a result of momentary current through the stylus, a dot appears on the left-hand side of the paper. The stylus continues its revolution at a steady speed, and when the echo of the electric pulse is received in the recording unit, current again flows through the stylus, which prints another dot on the paper at the point the stylus has reached. Thus the length of time which has elapsed between the transmission of the impulse and the reception of the echo is shown on the paper, transformed into terms of depth—in metres, fathoms, or feet, as required.

The paper continues to move slowly under the stylus, and, as the stylus may be recording as many as 300 echoes in the space of a minute, the dots on the left-hand side of the paper record a straight line, while the dots on the right-hand side trace a line which is a contour plan of the sea bed. Thus a picture of the bottom of the sea immediately under the ship is gradually built up on the recording paper, together with the actual depth of water. Any sudden shallowing of the water is shown instantaneously, giving immediate warning to the observer.

Vibrations are caused by the movement of the ship's propeller, by the ship itself moving through the water, etc., but these are not nearly of the same supersonic frequency as the electric impulses transmitted by the instrument. The Amplifier is so constructed that only vibrations closely allied to the frequency of the transmitted pulse can be received by it, so that no false information can be given by these other vibrations.

Reflected Echoes.—In shallow water, especially with a rocky bottom, echoes may be reflected back and forth from the sea bed to the ship two or three times. On the recording paper, this appears as a double or a treble recording of the contour plan of the sea bed. It is usually safe under these circumstances to accept the first recording, which shows the least depth.

False Echoes.—False echoes and loss of delineation can be caused when the vessel alters course. "Feathery" echoes can also be the effect of particles of sand, etc., being in a state of suspension in water, especially noticeable where the tidal streams are fairly strong. Because of the vagueness of the recorded contours, these false echoes are easily recognised.

When a vessel's engines are put astern when she is moving ahead, a great deal of "aeration" is caused in the water by the churning of the propeller. These air bubbles can reflect impulses from the transmitter, the echoes appearing in the recording paper as a maze of irregular dots.

Fish Echoes.—A shoal of fish reflects an echo in the same way as echoes are reflected from the sea bed. Many fishing vessels use echo sounders for the special purpose of detecting such shoals. Various differences in the appearance of these echoes denote different varieties of fish in the shoals, and experienced fishermen become quite expert in interpreting the different characteristic echoes.

Care must be taken to ensure that the correct reading is used when the sounder is being used in very deep water. If the maximum scale reading is 600 fathoms, and the depth of water expected is over 600 fathoms, a reading on the paper should, of course, be read as 640 fathoms, as the stylus will have completed one revolution, and have started on a second revolution before the echo is recorded on the paper.

EXAMINATION PAPERS

EXAMINATION PAPERS.

MATE (HOME TRADE).

(Time allowed 3 hours, excluding Tide Problem.)

Paper 1.

1. On January 3rd, in D.R. lat. 43° N., long. 22° W., G.M.T. 10h 22m, the Sun bore 158° C. Var. 20° W. Required the True Azimuth, Error and Deviation of the compass for the direction of the ship's head.

2. On July 23rd, in long. 37° 30′ W., the sextant meridian altitude of the Sun's L.L. was 48° 33′, bearing South. I.E. 4′ to add. Height of eye 15 feet. Required the latitude and P.L.

3. On July 23rd, in D.R. lat. 58° N., long. 30° W., G.M.T. 14h 28m 37s, the obs. alt. of the Sun's L.L. after passing the meridian was 51° 37′, bearing South. Height of eye 25 feet. Required the latitude and P.L.

4. On July 16th, A.M. at ship in lat. 56° 48′ N., the sext. alt. of the Sun's L.L. was 36° 26′. I.E. 4′ on the arc. Height of eye 18 ft. Time by chronometer was 08h 25m 00s. The chron. was 1m 43s fast of G.M.T. Required the longitude by chronometer and the P.L.

5. On May 16th, off Immingham, at 2250 Standard Time, find the depth of water over a shoal marked 2½ fm. on the chart.

Paper 2.

1. On Oct. 7th, in lat. 47° 10′ N., long. 22° 50′ W., L.M.T. 17h 27m, the Sun was observed to set bearing 278° C. Var. 17° 45′ W. Required the True Amplitude, Error and Deviation of the compass for the direction of the ship's head.

2. On Oct. 8th, in long. 54° 36′ E., the sext. mer. alt. of the Sun's L.L. was 40° 59′, bearing South. I.E. 2′ off the arc. Height of eye 19 ft. Required the latitude and P.L.

3. On July 15th, in D.R. lat. 52½° N., long. 13° 09′ W., the obs. alt. of the Sun's L.L. near the meridian was 58° 51′ S. Height of eye 21 ft. G.M.T. 12h 29m 00s. Required the latitude and P.L.

431

4. On July 22nd, A.M. at ship in lat. 52° 41′ N., the sext. alt. of the Sun's L.L. was 26° 53′. I.E. 5′ to add. Height of eye 21 ft. Time by chronometer was 10h 24m 26s. Chron. was 10m 19s slow of G.M.T. Required the Position Line and a position through which it should be drawn.

5. On May 26th, find the height of the tide off Immingham at noon, G.M.T.

Paper 3.

1. On Oct. 9th, in lat. 38° 35′ N., long. 44° 41′ W., L.M.T. 09h 24m 20s, the Sun bore by compass S.E· by S. Var. 7° W. Required the True Azimuth, Error and Deviation of the compass for the direction of the ship's head.

2. On Sept. 22nd, in long. 67° 14′ W., the sext. mer. alt. of the Sun's L.L. was 78° 35′, bearing South. I.E. 5′ off the arc. Height of eye 17 ft. Required the latitude and P.L.

3. On Jan. 3rd, in D.R. lat. 34¼° N., long. 14° 30′ W., G.M.T. 13h 39m 33s, the obs. alt. of the Sun's L.L. near the meridian was 32° 16′ S. Ht. of eye 27 ft. Required the latitude and P.L.

4. On July 23rd, A.M. at ship in lat. 42° 47′ N., the sext. alt. of the Sun's L.L. was 36° 27′. I.E. 7′ to add. Height of eye 22 ft. G.M.T. 15h 27m 21s. Required the P.L. and a position through which it should be drawn.

5. On May 29th, find the Standard Time at which the A.M. tide at Immingham will have risen 2·6 feet.

Paper 4.

1. On Sept. 23rd, in lat. 31° 47 ′N., long. 40° 16 W., L.M.T. 05h 48m, the Sun rose bearing 106° C. Var. 18° W. Required the True Amplitude, Error and Deviation of the compass for the direction of the ship's head.

2. On Sept. 23rd, in D.R. lat. 32° N., long. 7° 32′ E., the sext. mer. alt. of the Sun's U.L. was 58° 24·5′ S. I.E. 5′ off the arc. Height of eye 24 ft. Required the latitude and P.L.

3. On June 13th in D.R. lat. 57° N., long. 26° 05′ W., G.M.T. 14h 20m 00s, the obs. alt. of the Sun's L.L. near the meridian was 55° 37′. Height of eye 27 ft. Required the latitude by ex-meridian observation, also the P.L.

4. On Jan. 3rd, A.M. at ship in lat. 51° 20′ S., the obs. alt. of the Sun's L.L. was 35° 21′. Height of eye 22 ft. Time by chronometer was 08h 21m 33s. Chron. was 1m 30s slow of G.M.T. Required the longitude by chronometer and the P.L.

5. On May 9th, at 1620 Standard Time, being off Immingham, took a cast. Required the correction to be applied to the leadline before comparing it with the depth marked on the chart.

Paper 5.

1. On Dec. 21st, in lat. 41° 46′ N., long. 49° 50′ W., G.M.T. 18h 39m 20s, the Sun was observed to bear 239° C. Var. 17° W. Required the True Azimuth, Error and Deviation of the compass for the direction of the ship's head.
2. On Dec. 21st, in long. 27° 34′ W., the sext. mer. alt. of the Sun's U.L. was 33° 43′ S. I.E. 4·5′ to subtract. Height of eye 18 ft. Required the latitude by meridian altitude and the P.L.
3. On July 21st, in lat. by account 55° 10′ N., long. 17° W., L.M.T. 12h 30m 08s., the obs. alt. of the Sun's L.L. near the meridian was 54° 48′, South of observer. Height of eye 25 ft. Required the latitude and P.L.
4. On Jan. 3rd, p.m. at ship in lat. 45° 22′ N., G.M.T. 16h 37m 08s, the obs. alt. of the Sun's L.L. was 12° 34′. Height of eye 22 ft. Required the Position Line and a position through which it should be drawn.
5. On May 22nd, off Immingham at 2200 hrs. G.M.T., what would be the clearance for a ship of 15′ 6″ draft at a place where the chart shows 2½ fm.?

Paper 6.

1. On Oct. 7th in lat. 50° N., long. 95° W., the Sun rose bearing 125° C. Var. 21° W. Required the True Amplitude, Error and Deviation of the compass for the direction of the ship's head.
2. On June 12th, in long. 9° 43′ W., the obs. mer. alt. of the Sun's L.L. was 40° 37·3′ N. Height of eye 24 ft. Required the latitude and P.L.
3. On Oct. 9th, in D.R. lat. 41° N., long. 35° W., G.M.T. 14h 32m 12s, the obs. alt. of the Sun's L.L. near the meridian was 42° 30′, bearing South. Height of eye 25 ft. Required the latitude and P.L.
4. On July 23rd, p.m. at ship in lat. 34° 49′ N., the obs. alt. of the Sun's L.L. was 41° 40′. Height of eye 16 ft. Time by chronometer 21h 25m 35s. Chron. was 3m 06s fast of G.M. noon on June 20th, and was losing 3·6s. daily. Required the P.L. and a position through which it should be drawn.
5. Required the Standard Time when the p.m. rising tide at Immingham on May 24th will be 3 feet below the height of H.W.

MASTER (HOME TRADE.)
(Time allowed 2 hours, excluding Tide Problem).

Paper 1.

1. On July 21st, in lat. 41° 14′ N., long. 14° W., L.M.T. 0250, the star ALTAIR was observed to bear 245° C. Var. 8° W. Required the True Azimuth, Error and Deviation of the compass for the direction of the ship's head. (Correct G.H.A. Aries 354° 54·6′.)

2. On Oct. 8th, the obs. mer. alt. of the star BETELGEUSE was 49°
    45', bearing South of the observer. Height of eye 19 ft. Required
    the latitude and P.L.

3. On Oct. 7th, in D.R. lat. 53° N., long. 14° 14' E., G.M.T. 11h 33m
    36s, the obs. alt. of the Sun's L.L. near the meridian was 30° 53'.
    Height of eye 28 ft. Required the latitude and Position Line.

4. On Sept. 24th, in D.R. lat. 54° 10' N., G.M.T. 07h 32m 32s., the
    star HAMAL (W) had an obs. alt. 41° 04'. Height of eye 21 ft.
    Required the Position Line and a position through which it
    should be drawn.

5. Describe how you would recognise the star DUBHE by reference to
    adjacent constellations.

6. Find the depth of water over a 3 fm. shoal off Immingham at
    2 hours before A.M. L.W. on May 10th.

Paper 2.

1. On Sept. 24th, in lat. 50° 30' N., long. 65° 06' W., G.M.T. 07h 38m
    24s, the star RIGEL was observed to bear 175° C. Var. 20° W.
    Required the True Azimuth, Error and Deviation of the compass
    for the direction of the ship's head.

2. On Sept. 23rd, in long. 11° 40' E., required the L.M.T. and G.M.T.
    of the meridian passage of the star RASALHAGUE.

3. On July 17th, in D.R. lat. 47° N., long. 14° 30' W., G.M.T. 13h
    26m 41s, the obs. alt. of the Sun's L.L. near the meridian was
    63° 25', S. of obs. Height of eye 24 ft. Required the latitude
    and P.L.

4. On Dec. 21st, in lat. 49° 33' N., G.M.T. 15h 34m 44s, the obs. alt.
    of the star VEGA, West of the meridian was 49° 36'. Ht. of eye
    20 ft. Required the longitude by chronometer and the P.L.

5. Explain how you would recognise the star SIRIUS by reference to
    other constellations.

6. Find the depth of water under the keel of a ship drawing 15' 6" at
    1530 G.M.T., May 24th, at a place off Immingham where the
    chart shows 2 fm.

Paper 3.

1. On June 14th, in lat. 45° 16' N., long. 11° 28' W., L.M.T. 2140,
    the star REGULUS bore 271° C. Var. 5° W. Required the True
    Azimuth, Error and Deviation of the compass for the direction of
    the ship's head.

2. On Jan. 3rd, in D.R. lat. 39½° N., 22° 09' W., the obs. alt. of
    POLARIS was 38° 36'. Ht. of eye 27 ft. Required the latitude
    and P.L. G.M.T. 08h 38m 36s.

3. On Dec. 22nd, in D.R. lat. 51½° N., long. 13° 46′ W., G.M.T. 08h 33m 18s, the obs. alt. of the star ARCTURUS near the meridian was 57° 12′. Height of eye 23 ft. Required the latitude and P.L.

4. On June 14th, in lat. 33° 25′ N., G.M.T. 20h 20m 24s, the obs. alt. of the star SABIK (E) was 10° 08′. Height of eye 22 ft. Required the Position Line, and a position through which it should be drawn.

5. Describe how you would recognise the star ARCTURUS by reference to nearby constellations.

6. A ship went ashore off Immingham at 1620 S.T., May 3rd. She pumped out ballast estimated to raise the ship 8 inches. At what time should she refloat?

Paper 4.

1. On Jan. 3rd, in lat. 59° 42′ N., long. 21° 12′ E., G.M.T. 0339, the star ALPHECCA bore 090° C. Var. 15° E. Required the True Azimuth, Error and Deviation of the compass for the direction of the ship's head.

2. On Dec. 22nd, the obs. mer. alt. of the star SIRIUS was 34° 04′, bearing South of observer. Height of eye 20 ft. Required the latitude and P.L.

3. On July 15th, in D.R. lat. 47° 12′ N., long. 21° 18′ W., G.M.T. 05h 35m 27s, the obs. alt. of the star MARKAB near the meridian was 56° 46′, bearing South. Height of eye 26 ft. Required the latitude and P.L.

4. On Oct. 8th, in lat. 47° 51′ N., G.M.T. 06h 26m 56s, the obs. alt. of the star DUBHE, East of the meridian, was 53° 44·5′. Height of eye 27 ft. Required the Position Line and a position through which to draw it.

5. Describe how you would recognise the star REGULUS by reference to nearby constellations.

6. A fully-loaded ship, freeboard 5′ 8″, ran aground off Immingham at 1700 G.M.T. on May 19th. What was her freeboard at L.W.?

Paper 5.

1. On July 22nd, in lat. 25° 41′ N., long. 32° 00′ W., L.M.T. 0130, the planet SATURN bore 252° C. Var. 14° W. Required the True Azimuth, Error and Deviation of the compass for the direction of the ship's head.

2. On July 16th, in D.R. lat. 49½° N., long. 36° 19′ W., the obs. alt. of the Pole Star was 50° 16′. Height of eye 23 ft. Required the latitude. L.M.T. 04h 00m 00s.

3. On June 12th, in D.R. lat. 53¼° N., long. 14° 30′ W., G.M.T. 12h 38m 45s, the obs. alt. of the Sun's L.L. near the meridian, was 59° 36′, bearing South. Height of eye 21 ft. Required the latitude and P.L.

4. On July 15th, in lat. 55° 09′ N., G.M.T. 20h 34m 36s, the obs. alt. of the star SPICA, west of the meridian, was 13° 04′. Height of eye 18 ft. Required the Position Line and a position through which to draw it.

5. Describe how you would recognise the Pole Star by reference to nearby constellations.

6. To what draft could a vessel load so as to have a minimum of 6 inches below her keel when crossing a 1 fm. shoal off Immingham at 2200, May 24th.

Paper 6.

1. On Oct. 9th, in lat. 53° 30′ N., long. 18° 00′ E., G.M.T. 00h 00m., the planet MARS bore 139° C. Var. 5° E. Required the True Azimuth, Error and Deviation of the compass for the direction of the ship's head.

2. On June 12th, find the L.M.T. and G.M.T. of the meridian passage of the star ENIF in long. 17° 30′ W.

3. On Jan. 3rd, D.R. lat. 34° 50′ N., long. 35° 10′ W., G.M.T. 19h 27m 40s, the obs. alt. of the star DIPHDA near the meridian was 36° 13′, bearing South. Height of eye 27 ft. Required the latitude and P.L.

4. On Jan. 3rd, in lat. 45° 12′ N., G.M.T. 09h 23m 12s, the obs. alt. of the star VEGA, East of the meridian, was 41° 43′. Height of eye 18 ft. Required the Position Line and a position through which it should be drawn.

5. Describe how you would recognise the star PROCYON by reference to nearby constellations.

6. The A.M. H.W. at Immingham was at 0642, May 9th. When would the tide next reach the same height?

FISHING SECOND HAND (FULL.)

Paper 1.

Nav. I.   (2 hours.)

1. Departure was taken from a position with a point of land (Lat. 33° 25′ N., Long. 23° 50′ W.) bearing 137° C., distant 13 miles. Ship's head was on 1st course by compass. Variation and deviation as per log.

Time	Comp. Co.	Speed	Wind	Lee	Dev.	Var.
Noon - 6 p.m.	067°	12 kts.	North	2°	5° E.	16° W.
6 p.m. - midnt.	070	12 ,,	,,	2	6 E.	16 W.
Midnt. - 6 a.m.	052	11 ,,	,,	1	1 E.	15 W.
6 a.m. - noon	058	11 ,,	,,	1	2 E.	15 W.

Find the ship's position at the end of 24 hours, also the course and distance made good from noon to noon.

2. On Dec. 21st, in lat. 41° 46′ N., long. 49° 50′ W., G.M.T. 18h 39m 20s, the Sun was observed to bear 239° C. Var. 17° W. Required the True Azimuth, Error and Deviation of the compass for the direction of the ship's head.

Nav. II. (3 hours)

1. On Sept. 22nd, in long. 67° 14′ W., the sextant mer. alt. of the Sun's L.L. was 78° 35′, bearing South. I.E. 5′ to add. Height of eye 17 ft. Required the latitude and P.L.

2. On Jan. 3rd, A.M. at ship in lat. 51° 20′ S., G.M.T. 08h 23m 03s, the obs. alt. of the Sun's L.L. was 35° 21′. Height of eye 22 ft. Ship then steamed 50 miles on a course 306° T., when the latitude by meridian altitude was found to be 50° 40′ S. Find the ship's noon position.

Principles of Navigation. (2 hours)

1. Define (a) Local Hour Angle of the Sun; (b) Azimuth.

2. An A.M. observation of the Sun bearing 117° T. gave long. 11° 08′ W., using D.R. lat. 55° 28′ N. Ship then steamed 38 miles on a course 063° T., when an observation of the Sun on the meridian gave lat. 55° 39′ N. Find the ship's noon position. (Use Chart Exn. 30c.)

3. Find the L.M.T. and G.M.T. of the Sun's Meridian Passage on Oct. 9th in long. 19° 44′ W. For what purpose is G.M.T. required?

4. Draw a projection of the celestial sphere either on the plane of the rational horizon or the observer's meridian, showing (a) Lat. 40° N.; (b) Dec. 10° N.; (c) Sun's W.H.A. 60°.

Paper 2
Nav I.

1. Departure was taken from a position with a point of land in lat. 43° 51′ N., long. 2° 16′ W., bearing 270° C., distant 11 miles. Ship's head on 1st compass course. Variation and deviation as per log.

Time	Comp. Co.	Speed	Wind	Lee	Dev.	Var.
Noon - 4 p.m.	020°	12·0 kts.	S.E.	3°	12° W.	13· W.
4 p.m. - 8 p.m.	000	12·5 ,,	,,	3	14 W.	13 W.
8 p.m. - midnt.	356	12·0 ,,	,,	1	15 W.	13 W.
Midnt. - 6 a.m.	344	12·0 ,,	S.W.	0	15 W.	12 W.
6 a.m. - noon	341	11·5 ,,	,,	0	16 W.	12 W.

Find the ship's position at the end of the run, also the course and distance made good from noon to noon.

2. On Jan. 3rd, in lat. 43° N., long. 22° W., G.M.T. 10h 22m 00s, the Sun bore 158° C. Var. 20° W. Required the True Azimuth, Error and Deviation of the compass for the direction of the ship's head.

Nav. II.

1. On Sept. 23rd, in long. 7° 32′ E., the sext. mer. alt. of the Sun's U.L. was 58° 24·5′, bearing South of observer. I.E. 5′ to add. Required the latitude and P.L. Height of eye 24 ft.
2. On July 15th, A.M. at ship in D.R. lat. 54° 33′ N., G.M.T. 10h 26m 14s, the obs. alt. of the Sun's L.L. was 21° 36′. Height of eye 22 ft. Ship then steamed 72 miles on a course 311° T., when a P.M. obs. of the Sun's L.L. gave alt. 45° 45·5′. Height of eye 22 ft. G.M.T. 18h 33m 42s. Required the ship's true position at the time of taking the second observation.

Principles of Navigation.

1. Define (a) Geographical position of the Sun; (b) G.H.A. of Sun.
2. Describe how a single position line (e.g., a snap bearing of a lighthouse) can be used with advantage when on passage.
3. A vessel took her departure from lat. 51° 16′ N., and steered a course of 063° T. for 316 miles. What was her latitude then?
4. Draw a projection on the plane of the rational horizon or the observer's meridian, showing the following particulars:—(a) Lat. 30° N.; (b) Sun's decl. 10° S.; (c) Sun's L.H.A. 50°; (d) Sun's True Azimuth.

Paper 3.
Nav. I.

1. Departure was taken from a position with an island in lat. 49° 37′ N., long. 22° 16′ W., bearing 045° C., distant 12 miles. Ship's head was 217° C. Variation and Deviation as per log.

Time	Comp. Co.	Speed	Wind	Lee	Dev.	Var.
Noon - 6 p.m.	217°	10·0 kts.	N.W.	2°	6° E.	10° W.
6 p.m. - midnt.	199	9·5　,,	,,	2	4 E.	10 W.
Midnt. - 4 a.m.	186	9·5　,,	West	1	3 E.	9 W.
4 a.m. - 8 a.m.	180	9·5　,,	,,	1	Nil	8 W.
8 a.m. - Noon	165	9·0　,,	,,	2	2 W.	8 W.

Find the ship's position at the end of 24 hours, also the course and distance made good from noon to noon. Allow for current setting 047° T., 2 knots throughout.

2. On Oct. 9th, in lat. 38° 35′ N., long. 44° 41′ W., L.M.T. 09h 24m., the Sun was observed to bear 146¼°. Var. 7° W. Required the True Azimuth, Error and Deviation of the compass for the direction of the ship's head.

Nav. II.

1. On June 12th, in long. 9° 43' W., the obs. mer. alt. of the Sun's L.L. was 40° 37·3', bearing North. Height of eye 24 ft. Required the latitude and P.L.
2. On July 22nd, A.M. at ship in lat. D.R. 52° 41' N., the obs. alt. of the Sun's L.L. was 26° 58'. Height of eye 21 ft. G.M.T. 10h 34m 45s. Required the longitude by chronometer and the P.L.
3. (Use Chart Exn. 30c.) In D.R. lat. 55° 34' N., an A.M. obs. of the Sun bearing 150° T. gave long. 10° 26' W. Ship then steered a course 286° T. and picked up the lighthouse on Exna Point 18° to starboard, when the patent log showed 46½ miles. Find the ship's true position then.

Principles of Navigation.

1. Define (a) Prime Vertical; (b) Azimuth.
2. Describe how you would use a Pelorus to find the compass course to steer to a fixed destination from a known position.
3. Find the L.M.T. and G.M.T. of the Sun's meridian passage in long. 27° 27' W., on December 22nd.
4. Find the course to steer and the distance to steam from lat. 41° 10' N., long. 5° 22' W., to lat. 52° 40' N., long. 12° 06' W.

Paper 4.
Nav. I.

1. Departure was taken from a position in lat. 42° 18' N., long. 5° 22' W.

Time	Comp. Co.	Speed	Dev.	Var.
Noon - 4 p.m.	127°	9·0 kts.	Nil.	21° W.
4 p.m. - 8 p.m.	120	9·0 ,,	2 E.	21 W.
8 p.m. - 4 a.m.	114	9·5 ,,	4 E.	20 W.
4 a.m. - 8 a.m.	086	9·5 ,,	5 E.	20 W.
8 a.m. -Noon	080	9·0 ,,	7 E.	20 W.
Current set 112° T., 1¼ kts., throughout the day.				

Find the ship's position at noon, also the course and distance made good from noon to noon.

2. On Oct. 9th, in lat. 52° 16' N., long. 17° 39' W., G.M.T. 16h 23m 16s, the Sun was observed to bear 252° C. Var. 13° W. Required the True Azimuth, Error and Deviation of the compass for the direction of the ship's head.

Nav. II.

1. On July 23rd in D.R. long. 37° 30' W., the sext. mer. alt. of the Sun's L.L. was 48° 33', bearing South. I.E. 4' off the arc. Height of eye 15 ft. Required the latitude and P.L.

2. On July 16th, A.M. at ship in D.R. lat. 56° 48′ N., G.M.T. 08h 23m 17s, the obs. alt. of the Sun's L.L. was 36° 22′. Height of eye 18 ft. Ship then steamed 57 miles on a course 251° T., when an obs. alt. of the Sun's L.L. was 38° 32′. Height of eye 18 ft. G.M.T. 15h 37m 03s. Required the ship's position at the time of taking the second observation.

Principles of Navigation.

1. Define (a) Celestial meridian; (b) Geographical position of the Sun.
2. A vessel steered 128° T. from lat. 21° 52′ N. till she had altered her longitude 13° 20′. What distance had she steamed?
3. Find the G.M.T. of the Sun's meridian passage in long. 12° 32′ E. on September 24th.
4. Draw a projection on the plane of the rational horizon showing (a) Lat. 35° N.; (b) Sun's Decl. 10° S.; (c) L.H.A. Sun (E) 65°; (d) Zenith Distance; (e) True altitude.

Paper 5.
Nav. I.

1. At noon, departure was taken from a position with a point of land in lat. 46° 35′ N., long. 22° 16′ E., bearing 270° C., dist. 14 miles. Ship's head on 1st course by compass.

Time	Comp. Co.	Speed	Wind	Lee	Dev.	Var.
Noon - 6 p.m.	105°	10·0 kts.	N.E.	Nil	6° E.	10° W.
6 p.m. - midnt.	147	10·5 ,,	,,	2°	1 E.	10 W.
Midnt. - noon	180	10·5 ,,	,,	1	3 W.	9 W.

During first 12 hrs., current set 105° T., 1½ kts., and for the remainder of run, 074° T., 1 knot.

Find ship's position at the end of the run, and the course and distance made good from noon to noon.

2. On July 23rd in lat. 59° 05′ N., long. 9° 32′ W., G.M.T. 08h 28m 08s, the Sun was observed to bear 106° C. Var. 8½° W. Required the True Azimuth, Error and Deviation of the compass for the the direction of the ship's head.

Nav. II.

1. On Oct. 8th, in long. 11° 40′ E., the sext. mer. alt. of the Sun's L.L. was 40° 50′, bearing South. I.E. 5′ on the arc. Height of eye 19 ft. Required the latitude and P.L.
2. On Jan. 3rd, P.M. at ship in lat. by account 45° 22′ N., the obs. alt. of the Sun's L.L. was 12° 34′. Height of eye 22 ft. G.M.T. 16h 37m 08s. Required the longitude by chronometer and the P.L.

3. In D.R. lat. 28° 37·5′ N., an A.M. obs. of the Sun bearing 118° T. gave long. 11° 32·6′ W. "C"=0·612. Ship then steamed 78 mls. on a course 027° T., when a second obs. of the Sun bearing 204° T. gave long. 11° 04′ W., "C"=2·58. Find the ship's true position at the time of taking the second observation.

Principles of Navigation.

1. Using D.R. lat. 55° 27′ N., an A.M. obs. of the Sun bearing 119° T. gave long. 11° 42′ W. Ship then steered 064° T. for 38 mls., when the corrected meridian altitude of the Sun was 53° 15′, bearing South. Correct declination was 18° 52′ N. Using Chart Exn. 30c, find the ship's position at noon.
2. A vessel steamed 503 miles on a course of 216° T., when the latitude by meridian altitude was 38° 41′ N. What was the latitude of her departure?
3. Define a Pelorus, and describe its uses on board ship.
4. Draw a projection on the plane of the rational horizon or the observer's meridian, showing Lat. 45° N., Long. 20° W., Sun's decl. 20° N., L.H.A. Sun (W) 70°. Show also the True Azimuth and the G.H.A. Sun.

Paper 6.
Nav. I.

1. At noon, an island in lat. 50° 19′ N., long. 3° 33′ W., bore 131° C., distant 12 miles. Ship's head on 1st course by compass. Var. and dev. as per log.

Time	Comp. Co.	Speed	Dev.	Var.
Noon - 6 p.m.	097°	11·5 kts.	3° W.	18° W.
6 p.m. - 9 p.m.	090	11·5 ,,	3 W.	18 W.
9 p.m. - midnt.	088	11·5 ,,	3 W.	18 W.
Midnt. - 4 a.m.	080	11·0 ,,	2 W.	17 W.
4 a.m. - noon	040	11·0 ,,	1 E.	17 W.
Current set 330° T., 2 knots, throughout day.				

Find the ship's position at the end of the run, also the course and distance made good from noon to noon.
2. On Jan. 1st, in lat. 55° 54′ N., long. 21° 16′ W., G.M.T. 11h 25m 04s, the Sun bore 173·5° C. Var. 16° W. Required the True Azimuth, Error and Deviation of the compass for the direction of the ship's head.

Nav. II.

1. On June 12th, in long. 28° 19′ W., the obs. mer. alt. of the Sun's U.L. was 68° 12′, bearing South. Height of eye 20 ft. Required the latitude and P.L.

2. On Sept. 23rd, A.M. at ship in D.R. lat. 48° 26′ N., G.M.T. 10h 24m 36s, the obs. alt. of the Sun's L.L. was 22° 37′. Height of eye 24 ft. Required the longitude by chronometer and the P.L.

3. In D.R. lat. 47° 01′ N., an obs. of the Sun bearing 071° T. gave long. 14° 11·3′ W. "C"=0·515. Ship then steered N. 38° W., T. for 66 mls., when a second observation of the Sun bearing 204° T. gave long. 15° 24′ W. "C"=3·36. Find the ship's position at the time of taking the second observation.

Principles of Navigation.

1. Describe clearly why a P.L. from a first observation is transferred to the D.R. position when taking a second observation to obtain a fix.

2. A ship steered a course of 216° T., and made departure 190′, D. Long. 6°. Between what latitudes had she sailed and what distance had she steamed?

3. Define (a) Prime Vertical; (b) Celestial Meridian.

4. Find L.M.T. and G.M.T. of the Sun's meridian passage on Oct. 8th in long. 43° 16′ W.

FISHING SKIPPER (FULL.)
Paper 1.
Nav. I. (3 hours.)

1. On July 16th in D.R. lat. 49½° N., long. 36° 19′ W., the obs. alt. of the Pole Star was 50° 16·0′. Height of eye 23 ft. L.M.T. 04h 00m 00s. Required the latitude and the True Azimuth of the Pole Star.

2. On June 14th in lat. 33° 25′ N., G.M.T. 20h 20m 24s, the obs. alt. of the star SABIK, East of the meridian, was 10° 08′. Height of eye 22 ft. Required the longitude and P.L.

3. On Oct. 8th in D.R. lat. 55° 11′ N., long. 11° 15′ W., G.M.T. 18h 30m 32s, the obs. alt. of the star MARKAB (E) was 27° 55·5′, and of the star ALPHECCA (W) was 44° 21′. Height of eye 22 ft. Using calculation or Chart Exn. 30c., find the ship's true position.

Nav. II. (2 hours excluding tide.)

1. On Jan. 3rd in lat. 59° 42′ N., long. 21° 12′ E., G.M.T. 0339, the star ALPHECCA bore 090° C. Var. 15° E. Required the True Azimuth, Error and Deviation of the compass for the direction of the ship's head.

2. On Star Chart 1, mark the following stars:—DUBHE, MARKAB, POLARIS.

3. Define (a) Sidereal Hour Angle; (b) Great Circle.

4. At Immingham on May 9th, the A.M. High Water occurred at 0642. When would the tide next reach the same height?

Paper 2.
Nav. I.

1. On Jan. 3rd in D.R. lat. $39\frac{1}{2}°$ N., long. 22° 09' W., the obs. alt. of the Pole Star was 38° 36'. Height of eye 27 ft. G.M.T. 08h 38m 36s. Required the latitude, and also the true bearing of the Pole Star.
2. On Jan. 3rd in lat. 45° 12' N., G.M.T. 9h 23m 12s., the obs. alt. of the star VEGA, East of the meridian, was 41° 43'. Height of eye 18 ft. Required the longitude and P.L.
3. On Jan. 3rd in D.R. lat. 55° 49' N., G.M.T. 08h 37m 41s, the star REGULUS (W) had an obs. alt. of 21° 24'. Height of eye 25 ft. Ship then steered 268° T. for 35 mls., when Exna Pt. Lt. Ho. bore 284° T. Find the ship's position when the bearing was taken.

Nav. II.

1. On July 21st in lat. 41° 14' N., long. 14° W., L.M.T. 0250, the star ALTAIR bore 245° C. Var. 8° W. Required the True Azimuth, Error and Deviation of the compass for the direction of the ship's head.
2. On the Star Chart, mark the following stars:—SIRIUS, PROCYON, BELLATRIX.
3. Define (a) Rhumb Line; (b) First Point of Aries.
4. Find the depth of water over a 3-fm. shoal 2 hours before A.M. Low Water at Immingham on May 10th.

Paper 3.
Nav. I.

1. On Dec. 21st in D.R. lat. 50° 40' N., long. 19° 05' W., G.M.T. 17h 32m 20s, the obs. alt. of the Pole Star was 51° 22'. Height of eye 21 ft. Required the latitude, also the true bearing of the Pole Star.
2. On Sept. 24th in D.R. lat. 54° 10' N., G.M.T. 07h 32m 32s, the obs. alt. of the star HAMAL, West of the meridian, was 41° 04'. Height of eye 21 ft. Required the longitude and P.L.
3. On July 17th in D.R. lat. 46° 15' N., long. 34° 19' W., G.M.T. 06h 22m 41s, the following simultaneous altitudes were observed:— ALTAIR (W) 27° 45'; MENKAR (E) 30° 10'. Height of eye 18 ft. Required the ship's position at this time.

Nav. II.

1. On June 14th, in lat. 45° 16' N., long. 11° 28' W., L.M.T. 2140, the star REGULUS was observed to bear 271° C. Var. 5° W. Required the True Azimuth, Error and Deviation of the compass for the direction of the ship's head.
2. On May 29th, off Immingham, find the Standard Time when the A.M. tide will have risen 2·6 feet.

Paper 4.
Nav. I.

1. On June 13th in D.R. lat. 34° 20′ N., 4° 27′ E., G.M.T. 04h 27m 12s, the obs. alt. of POLARIS was 33° 51′. Height of eye 24 ft. Required the latitude, also the true bearing of Polaris.

2. On Oct. 8th in lat. 47° 51′ N., G.M.T. 06h 26m 56s, the obs. alt. of the star DUBHE, East of the meridian, was 53° 44·5′. Height of eye 27 ft. Required the longitude and P.L.

3. On Sept. 22nd in D.R. lat. 52° 52′ N., G.M.T. 08h 30m 23s, the obs. alt. of the star HAMAL, West of the meridian, was 42° 37′. Height of eye 27 ft. Ship then steamed 27 mls. on a course of 153° T., when the obs. alt. of the Sun's L.L. was 20° 34·5′. Height of eye 27 ft. G.M.T. 11h 21m 44s. Required the ship's position at the time of taking the second observation.

Nav. II.

1. On Sept. 24th in lat. 50° 30′ N., long. 65° 06′ W., G.M.T. 07h 38m 24s, the star RIGEL was observed to bear 175° C. Var. 20° W. Required the True Azimuth, Error and Deviation of the compass for the direction of the ship's head.

2. On May 9th, at 1620 St. Time, being off Immingham, took a cast. Required the correction to apply to the leadline before comparing it with the depth marked on the chart.

Paper 5.
Nav. I.

1. On Jan. 3rd in D.R. lat. 41½° N., long. 24° 17′ W., G.M.T. 08h 37m 08s, the obs. alt. of POLARIS was 41° 11′. Height of eye 16 ft. Required the latitude by observation, and the true bearing of Polaris.

2. On Dec. 21st in lat. 49° 33′ N., G.M.T. 15h 34m 44s, the obs. alt. of the star VEGA, West of the meridian, was 49° 36′. Height of eye 20 ft. Required the longitude and P.L.

3. On July 22nd, P.M. at ship in D.R. lat. 51° 05′ N., G.M.T. 17h 36m 09s, the obs. alt. of the Sun's L.L. was 38° 22′. Height of eye 27 ft. Ship then steered 107° T. for 48 mls., when a lighthouse in lat. 51° 00′ N., long. 27° 54′ W. bore 066° T. By calculation or by squared paper, find the ship's position at the time of taking the bearing of the lighthouse.

Nav. II.

1. On July 17th in lat. 47° 26′ N., long. 9° 13′ E., G.M.T. 21h 34m, the star ALKAID bore 295° C. Var. 3° W. Required the True Azimuth, Error and Deviation of the compass for the direction of the ship's head.

2. Find the depth of water under the keel of a ship drawing 15' 6" at 1530 Standard Time off Immingham on May 24th, at a place where the chart shows 2 fathoms.

Paper 6.
Nav. I.

1. On Oct. 8th in D.R. lat. 57° N., long. 32° W., G.M.T. 19h 38m 00s, the obs. alt. of POLARIS was 56° 51'. Height of eye 27 ft. Required the latitude of the ship and the true bearing of Polaris.
2. On July 15th in D.R. lat. 55° 09' N., G.M.T. 20h 34m 36s, the obs. alt. of the star SPICA, West of the meridian, was 13° 04'. Height of eye 18 feet. Required the longitude and P.L.
3. On Oct. 9th, P.M. at ship in D.R. lat. 35° 56' N., G.M.T. 14h 23m 24s, the obs. alt. of the Sun's L.L. was 21° 01'. Height of eye 21 ft. Ship then steamed 21 mls. on a course of 309° T., when the obs. alt. of the star MARKAB, East of the meridian, was 32° 32'. Height of eye 21 ft. G.M.T. 16h 33m 54s. Required the ship's position at the time of taking the second observation.

Nav. II.

1. On Sept. 22nd in lat. 54° 19' N., long. 16° 41' W., G.M.T. 21h 36m, the star ALPHERATZ was observed to bear 119° C. Var. 11° W. Required the True Azimuth, Error and Deviation of the compass for the direction of the ship's head.
2. A ship went ashore off Immingham at 1620 G.M.T., May 3rd. Water was pumped out to lift the vessel 8". At what time would she refloat?

YACHTMASTER (COASTAL.)
Paper 1. (2 hours.)

1. On Sept. 23rd in lat. 31° 47' N., long. 40° 16' W., L.M.T. 05h 48m, the Sun was observed to rise bearing 106° C. Var. 18° W. Required the True Amplitude and the Deviation for the direction of the ship's head.
2. Explain the difference between Mean Time and Apparent Time. What is meant by Zone Time?
3. On May 22nd at 2200 hrs. off Immingham, what would be the clearance of a ship drawing 15' 6" at a place where the chart shows 2½ fathoms?
4. How often should a 2-day chronometer be wound?

Paper 2.

1. On Dec. 21st in lat. 41° 46' N., long. 49° 50' W., G.M.T. 18h 39m 20s, the Sun bore 239° C. Var. 17° W. Required the True Azimuth and the Deviation of the compass for the direction of the ship's head.

2. Find the L.M.T. and G.M.T. of sunrise and sunset in lat. 45° N., long. 11° 15′ W., on July 16th.

3. On May 9th, being off Immingham, took a cast at 1620 Standard Time. Required the correction to be applied to the leadline before comparing it with the depth marked on the chart.

4. Under what circumstances would it be necessary to correct radio bearings from a Consol Station before laying off these bearings on a Mercator chart?

Paper 3.

1. On Jan. 3rd in lat. 43° N., long. 22° W., G.M.T. 10h 22m, the Sun bore 158° C. Var. 20° W. Required the true azimuth and the deviation of the compass for the direction of the ship's head.

2. A ship obtains a Consol count of 30 dashes and 24 dots from Bushmills Consol Station. What is the true count.?

3. On May 16th, at 2250 G.M.T. off Immingham, what is the depth of water over a $2\frac{1}{2}$ fathom shoal?

4. Find the L.M.T. of moonrise and moonset in lat. 37° 30′ N., Sept. 23rd.

Paper 4.

1. On Oct. 7th, in lat. 50° N., long. 95° W., the Sun rose bearing 125° C. Var. 21° W. Required the true amplitude and the deviation of the compass for the direction of the ship's head.

2. Explain clearly how you would "rate" a chronometer by the use of radio time signals.

3. On May 24th, off Immingham, find the time when the rising P.M. tide will be 3 feet below High Water.

4. What precautions should be used when choosing objects suitable for obtaining a fix from horizontal sextant angles?

Paper 5.

1. On Oct. 7th in lat. 47° 10′ N., long. 22° 50′ W., L.M.T. 17h 27m, the Sun was observed to set bearing 278° C. Var. 17° 45′ W. Required the true amplitude, also the deviation of the compass for the direction of the ship's head.

2. If you obtained a Consol count of 26 dots and 28 dashes, what is the true count?

3. Find the height of the tide off Immingham at noon, G.M.T. on May 26th.

4. How is a chronometer kept at a steady temperature at sea?

Paper 6.

1. On Oct. 9th in lat. 38° 55' N., long. 44° 41' W., L.M.T. 09h 24m, the Sun was observed to bear S.E. by S. Var. 7° W. Required the true azimuth, error and deviation of the compass for the direction of the ship's head.

2. Find the G.M.T. of moonrise and moonset on June 12th in lat. 51° N., long. 11° 30' E.

3. On May 29th, at what time will the A.M. tide have risen 2·6 feet off Immingham?

4. Your chronometer on board has stopped. How would you re-start it, and when?

ANSWERS.

Exercise 1.

Addition, Subtraction, Multiplication, and Division by Decimals.

1.	2284·14	2.	24899·921	3.	564·830
4.	495·680	5.	13·64	6.	1152·868
7.	1792·753	8.	10·931	9.	102·196
10.	1291·82475	11.	3766·422	12.	252·1818
13.	41·139	14.	3·556	15.	4·830
16.	5·002	17.	0·64	18.	0·331
19.	0·035	20.	0·15009		

Exercise 2.

Converting Minutes, etc., to Decimal Fractions and Vice Versa.

1.	23·3°	13.	17° 42′
2.	75·7°	14.	25° 18′
3.	12·6°	15.	42° 54′
4.	16·5°	16.	38′ 36″
5.	38·4′	17.	51′ 24″
6.	5·1′	18.	22′ 12″
7.	29·58′	19.	1 hr. 30 min.
8.	2·28 hr.	20.	3 hr. 06 min.
9.	5·67 hr.	21.	11 hr. 38 min. 24 sec.
10.	3·4 hr.	22.	9 hr. 28 min. 48 sec.
11.	18·88 min.	23.	6 min. 19·2 sec.
12.	48·37 min.	24.	54 min. 55·8 sec.

Exercise 3.

Logarithms (Stage 1.)

1.	3·23980	13.	730·4
2.	3·41179	14.	54·68
3.	5·18667	15.	8·648
4.	2·13767	16.	20750
5.	1·81431	17.	5040000
6.	0·19285	18.	211·8
7.	1·10517	19.	14860
8.	0·60206	20.	277·4
9.	0·90331	21.	50·68
10.	2·81551	22.	75550
11.	1·75136	23.	35·63
12.	3·88264	24.	2280

449

Exercise 4.
Logarithms (Stage 2.)

	Norie's	Burton's			Norie's	Burton's
1.	1·87291	1·87291		17.	984·1	984·1
2.	2·11992	2·11992		18.	2578	2578
3.	0·58422	0·58422		19.	1·767	1·767
4.	0·75289	0·75289		20.	1446	1446
5.	3·94221	3·94221		21.	25645·3	25645
6.	2·64140	2·64139		22.	390563·63	390560
7.	2·52455	2·52455		23.	51·755	51·755
8.	3·52528	3·52527		24.	736·55	736·55
9.	1·08472	1·08471		25.	4486·6	4486·6
10.	4·74446	4·74447		26.	32767·7	32767·5
11.	2·70757	2·70758		27.	3865455·56	3865400
12.	4·87491	4·87491		28.	1·59122	1·5912
13.	3·50736	3·50736		29.	2253·42	2253·4
14.	3·09380	3·09380		30.	29171·333	29171·5
15.	2·63625	2·63625		31.	399·7273	399·73
16.	2·94624	2·94624		32.	50118·889	50119

Exercise 5.
Use of Logarithms.

	Norie's	Burton's			Norie's	Burton's
1.	290513·3	290515		10.	2·289	2·289
2.	36·314	36·314		11.	3·82586	3·826
3.	10768·75	10768·5		12.	11·617	11·617
4.	45035	45035		13.	13·617	13·617
5.	6·196	6·1961		14.	0·408004	0·40801
6.	8·102	8·102		15.	1·6303	1·6303
7.	0·24946	0·24945		16.	114007·89	114010·0
8.	1·1268	1·1268		17.	1·5787	1·5787
9.	1·8166	1·8166				

Exercise 6.
Log Functions of Angles and Vice Versa.

(Users of *Burton's Tables* may obtain a few seconds difference in the angles.)

1.	9·59690	9.	8·66168	17.	30°	47′	30″	
2.	10·13542	10.	8·66168	18.	38	07	30	
3.	9·82277	11.	10·02766	19.	67	17	00	
4.	10·19325	12.	10·00000	20.	26	10	30	
5.	10·65287	13.	10·01105	21.	65	34	26	
6.	10·22875	14.	9·04745	22.	13	19	58	
7.	9·05814	15.	9·78664	23.	36	40	37	
8.	10·56931	16.	8·89864	24.	46	28	28	
				25.	4	40	55	
				26.	5	09	33	
				27.	12	54	36	
				28.	10	18	55	

Exercise 7.

1. Angle   6° 27′
2. Height   185·77 ft.
3. Distance   10·95 miles.
4. Angle   19° 11′   Length of stays 23·6 feet.
5. Angle   83° 06′   Dist. astern 2975 feet.
6. Angle of depression 23° 26′.   Height of mast 37·15 feet.
7. Angle   20° 34′   Length of shrouds 42·7 feet.

EXERCISE 8.

Finding True Courses.

1.	N. 35° E.		9.	S. 84° W.	
2.	S. 56° E.		10.	N. 74° E.	
3.	S. 13° E.		11.	S 84° E.	(096°)
4.	N. 23° W.		12.	N. 87° E.	(087°)
5.	S 22° E.		13.	N. 7° E.	(007°)
6.	S 35° E.		14.	North	(000°)
7.	N. 35° W.		15.	S. 27° W.	(207°)
8.	S. 3° W.		16.	N. 81° E.	(081°)

EXERCISE 9.

The Day's Work.

1.

Courses	
S. 88° W.	38 miles
N. 77° W.	36 ,,
N. 77° W.	36 ,,
S. 65° W.	51 ,,
S 30° W.	54 ,,
S. 30° E.	18 ,,
D. Lat.	69·1′ S.
Dep.	172·4′ W.
D. Long.	234·2′ W.
Lat.	42° 01·9′ N.
Long.	3° 29·2′ W.
Course	S. 68° W.
Distance	186 miles

2.

Courses	
S. 74° W.	44 miles
N. 51° W.	42 ,,
N. 38° W.	88 ,,
N. 22° W.	88 ,,
S. 74° E.	24 ,,
D. Lat.	158·6′ N.
Dep.	139·0′ W.
D. Long.	220·5′ W.
Lat.	52° 15·6′ N.
Long.	16° 30·5′ W.
Course	N. 41½° W.
Distance	211½ miles

3.

Courses	
N. 52° E.	45 miles
N. 88° E.	57 ,,
S. 79° E.	81 ,,
S. 49° E.	40 ,,
South	12 ,,
D. Lat.	24·0′ S.
Dep.	202·2′ E.
D. Long.	272·6′ E.
Lat.	41° 55·0′ N.
Long.	3° 20·6′ E.
Course	S. 83¼° E.
Distance	203½ miles

4.

Courses	
S. 22° W.	110 miles
S. 6° W.	55 ,,
S. 16° W.	99 ,,
S. 10° E.	24 ,,
D. Lat.	275·5′ S.
Dep.	70·0′ W.
D. Long.	131·1′ W.
Lat.	55° 25·0′ N.
Long.	3° 11·9′ E.
Course	S. 14¼° W.
Distance	284½ miles

5.

Courses	
S. 19¾° W.	52 miles
S. 8¼° E.	34 ,,
S. 42° E.	84 ,,
S. 19½° E.	35 ,,
D. Lat.	178·1′ S.
Dep.	55·2′ E.
D. Long.	72·2′ E.
Lat.	38° 42·9′ N.
Long.	2° 09·4′ E.
Course	S. 17¼° E.
Distance	186¼ miles

6.

Courses	
034°	19 miles
052°	43 ,,
354°	37 ,,
336°	66 ,,
357°	35 ,,
234°	19 ,,
D. Lat.	163·2′ N.
Dep.	3·4′ W.
D. Long.	4·2′ W.
Lat.	36° 30·2′ N.
Long.	10° 59·2′ W·
Course	N. 1½° W.
Distance	163½ miles

The Day's Work.—*Continued.*

7.　　Courses
104°	42 miles
137°	65 ,,
080°	73 ,,
089°	53 ,,
293°	36 ,,

D. Lat.	30·0′ S.
Dep.	176·9′ E.
D. Long.	235·3′ E.

Lat.	41° 01·0′ N.
Long.	14° 37·7′ W.
Course	S. 80½° E.
Distance	179 miles

8.

Dep. Position		Courses			D. Lat.	11·5′ S.
					Dep.	194·4′ E.
Lat.	42° 47·9′ N.	N. 66° E.	30 mls.		D. Long.	264·5′ E.
Long.	18° 14·9′ E.	N. 89° E.	70 ,,			
D. Lat.	10·9′ N.	S. 86° E.	38 ,,		Lat.	42° 36·4′ N.
Dep.	11·7′ E.	S. 57° E.	95 ,,		Long.	22° 39·4′ E.
D. Long.	15·9′ E.	N. 35° W.	36 ,,		Course	S. 86½° E.
					Distance	196 miles

9.

Dep. Position		Courses			D. Lat.	173·6′ N.
					Dep.	87·6′ W.
Lat.	41° 00·1′ N.	301°	45 miles		D. Long.	118·7′ W.
Long.	7° 03·8′ W.	335°	63 ,,			
D. Lat.	9·1′ N.	005°	68 ,,		Lat.	43° 53·7′ N.
Dep.	6·2′ E.	010°	36 ,,		Long.	9° 02·5′ W.
D. Long.	8·2′ E.	254°	36 ,,		Course	N. 26¾° W.
					Distance	194 miles

10.

Dep. Position		Courses			D. Lat.	164·0′ N.
					Dep.	69·5′ W.
Lat.	51° 12·0′ N.	N. 3° E.	70 miles		D. Long.	114·3′ W.
Long.	0° 31·5′ E.	N. 1° W.	38 ,,			
D. Lat.	Nil	N. 8° W.	45 ,,		Lat.	53° 56·0′ N.
Dep.	11·0′ E.	N. 71° W.	72 ,,		Long.	1° 22·7′ W.
D. Long.	17·5′ E.	S. 9° E.	12 ,,		Course	N. 23° W.
					Distance	178 miles

11.

Dep. Position		Courses			D. Lat.	79·1′ S.
					Dep.	227·4′ W.
Lat.	5° 05′ N.	221°	66 miles		D. Long.	228·0′ W.
Long.	74° 15·3′ E.	234°	66 ,,			
D. Lat.	7·0′ S.	270°	80½ ,,		Lat.	3° 45·9′ N.
Dep.	0·7 W.	279°	69 ,,		Long.	70° 27·3′ E.
D. Long.	0·7′ W.	094°	18 ,,		Course	S. 71° W.
					Distance	241 miles

The Day's Work.—*Continued.*

12.

Dep. Position			Courses			D. Lat.		1·1' N.
						Dep.		271·1' E.
Lat.	37°	47·1' N.	S. 58° E.		56 miles	D. Long.		343·1' E.
Long.	5°	14·2' W.	S. 76° E.		64 ,,			
D. Lat.		2·9' S.	N. 74° E.		168 ,,	Lat.	37°	48·2' N.
Dep.		8·5' E.	Current			Long.	0°	28·9' E.
D. Long.		10·8' E.	Set		N. 27° E.	Course		East
			Drift		10 miles	Distance		271 miles

13.

Courses			D. Lat.		227·1' S.
			Dep.		39·0' E.
South		120 miles	D. Long.		40·9' E.
S. 20° E.		114 ,,			
			Lat.	15°	37·9' N.
Current			Long.	0°	40·9' E.
Set	N. 34° W.		Course	S.	10° E.
Drift	15¾ miles		Distance		230½ miles

14.

Courses			D. Lat.		51·1' N.
			Dep.		120·5' W.
N. 5½ E.		55 miles	D. Long.		151·8' W.
N. 31° W.		65 ,,			
S. 70½° W.		132 ,,	Lat.	37°	53·1' N.
East		24 ,,	Long.	22°	12·8' W.
South		12 ,,	Course	N.	67° W.
S. 67½° E.		9 ,,	Distance		131 miles

15.

Dep. Position			Courses			D. Lat.		16·1' S.
						Dep.		41·9' W.
Lat.	55°	59·0' N.	310°		31 miles	D. Long.		74·6' W.
Long.	3°	43·4' W.	254°		17 ,,			
D. Lat.		1·0' S.	200°		22 ,,	Lat.	55°	42·9' N.
Dep.		12·0' W.	152°		12 ,,	Long.	4°	58·0' W.
						Course	S.	68° W.
						Distance		45 miles

16.

Dep. Position			Courses			D. Lat.		213·8' S.
						Dep.		36·3' E.
Lat.	56°	38·6' N.	S. 22° W.		52 miles	D. Long.		63·0' E.
Long.	4°	38·1' W.	S. 11° E.		65 ,,			
D. Lat.		3·4' N.	S. 7° E.		40 ,,	Lat.	53°	04·6' N.
Dep.		8·3' W.	S. 30° E.		80 ,,	Long.	3°	35·1' W.
D. Long.		15·1' W.	N. 65° E.		10 ,,	Course	S.	10° E.
			N. 74° W.		11 ,,	Distance		217 miles

17.

Dep· Position			Courses			D. Lat.		159·7' S.
						Dep.		50·1' E.
Lat.	0°	35·8' N.	180°		53 miles	D. Long.		50·1' E.
Long.	18°	36·0' W.	196°		48 ,,			
D. Lat.		0·8' N.	140°		98 ,,	Lat.	2°	03·9' S.
Dep.		9·0' W.	320°		8 ,,	Long.	17°	45·9' W.
D. Long.		9·0' W.	033°		10 ,,	Course	S.	18° E.
						Distance		163 miles

Exercise 10.

1.	012° or N. 12° E.	6.	355° or N. 5° W.
2.	089° or N. 89° E.	7.	000° or North
3.	107° or S. 73° E.	8.	195° or S. 15° W.
4.	352° or N. 8° W.	9.	139° or S. 41° E.
5.	010° or N. 10° E.	10.	352° or N. 8° W.

Exercise 11.

	Comp. Course		Dev.		Comp. Course		Dev.
1.	N. 28° E.	(028°)	7° E.	19.	N. 74° E.	(074°)	16° E.
2.	N. 39° E.	(039°)	9° E.	20.	N. 71° W.	(289°)	19° W.
3.	N. 51° E.	(051°)	11° E.	21.	N. 80° W.	(280°)	20° W.
4.	N. 62° E.	(062°)	13° E.	22.	S. 1° W.	(181°)	2° E.
5.	N. 72° E.	(072°)	16° E.	23.	North	(000°)	2° E.
6.	N. 19° W.	(341°)	5° W.	24.	N. 2° W.	(358°)	2° E.
7.	N. 28° W.	(332°)	7° W.	25.	S. 5° E.	(175°)	3° E.
8.	N. 40½ W.	(319½°)	10½° W.	26.	S. 2½° E.	(177½°)	2½° E.
9.	N. 50° W.	(310°)	14° W.	27.	133·6		10·4° E.
10.	N. 60° W.	(300°)	17° W.	28.	223·8		6·2° E.
11.	N. 65° W.	(295°)	18° W.	29.	304·3		5·3° W.
12.	S. 28° W.	(208°)	8° W.	30.	017·5		8·5 W.
13.	S. 50½° W.	(230½°)	12½° W.	31.	073·0		Nil
14.	S. 88½° W.	(268½°)	21½° W.	32.	076·2		0·8° E.
15.	S. 28° E.	(152°)	8° E.	33.	267·5		0·5° E.
16.	S. 57° E.	(123°)	14° E.	34.	333·8		10·8° W.
17.	S. 74° E.	(106°)	18° E.	35.	004·2		11·2° W.
18.	N. 81° E.	(081°)	19° E.	36.	008·3		10·3° W.

Exercise 12.

	True	Dev.	Comp.	Dist.
1.	S. 89¾° E.	20° E.	N. 85¼° E.	95 miles
2.	S. 45¾ E.	12 E.	S. 43¾ E.	60 ,,
3.	S. 39¾ W.	16½ W.	S. 70¾ W.	68½ ,,
4.	S. 87½ E.	20 E.	N. 84½ E.	126¼ ,,
5.	N. 28½ E.	8 E.	N. 33½ E.	118½ ,,
6.	N. 77 E.	16 E.	N. 73 E.	211 ,,
7.	N. 75½ E.	15½ E.	N. 72 E.	117 ,,
8.	East	20½ E.	N. 85½ E.	58½ ,,
9.	S. 62¾ W.	20½ W.	N. 81¼ W.	113½ ,,
10.	N. 71½ W.	13¼ W.	N. 48¼ W.	77 ,,

Exercise 13.

1\. (*a*) True Co. S. 79° W. Dev. 18½° W. Comp. Co. N. 70½° W.

(*b*)	True Bearings	Position	Set and Drift
(1)	N. 65½° W.	50° 29′ 30″ N.	182°
	N. 49½ E.	0 3 15 W.	5 miles
(2)	N. 58½ W.	50° 28 00 N.	259°
	N. 54½ E.	1 00 00 W.	3¼ miles
(3)	N. 70½ W.	50 25 00 N.	000°
	N. 45½ E.	2 00 00 W.	4½ miles
(4)	North	50 19 00 N.	057°
	N. 47 E.	2 27 00 W.	6 miles
(5)	West	50 12 30 N.	113°
	N. 60½ E.	3 17 00 W.	5 miles

2. (a) True Co. N. 29° E. Dev. 8° E. Comp. Co. N. 35° E.
   (b) True Bearings Position Set and Drift
   (1) S. 40° E. 50° 13′ 00″ N. Nil
       N. 60½ E. 5 56 30 W. Nil
   (2) South 50 29 00 N. 057°
       N. 80 E. 5 39 00 W. 4½ miles
   (3) S. 25 E. 50 51 00 N. 150°
       N. 67 E. 5 14 00 W. 6 miles
   (4) S. 70 E. 51 18 00 N. 327°
       N. 13 E. 5 05 00 W. 3½ miles
   (5) North 51 23 00 N. 089°
       N. 45 W. 4 41 00 W. 8½ miles

EXERCISE 14.

	Comp. Error	True Co.	True Bearings		Ship's Position						
					Lat.			Long.			
			°	°	°	′	″	°	′	″	
1	—	East	N. 50 E.	N. 40 W.	50	22	30 N.	1	01	15 W.	
2	—	N. 70° E.	N. 43 E.	N. 50 W.	50	29	00 N.	0	25	00 W.	
3	1° E.	N. 68½ E.	N 28 E.	N. 54 W.	49	50	30 N.	4	56	30 W.	
4	34 W.	S. 56 W.	South	S. 70 E.	49	49	00 N.	2	51	00 W.	
5	30½ W.	S. 82 W.	N. 57½ W.	N. 20½ E.	49	55	30 N.	3	50	00 W.	
6	6 W.	N. 28 E.	N. 62 E.	S. 62 E.	51	49	30 N.	5	58	30 W.	
7	—	East	North	N. 30 W.	49	42	00 N.	4	54	00 W.	
8	26 W.	S. 30 W.	S. 34 E.	N. 87 E.	49	25	00 N.	3	07	00 W.	
9	4 W.	S. 38 E.	S. 81 E.	N. 52 E.	49	43	30 N.	6	46	30 W.	
10	1½ W.	N. 66 E.	N. 9 E.	N. 52 W.	51	26	00 N.	8	10	15 W.	

EXERCISE 15.

	True Co.	Comp. Co.	Deviation	Dist.	Time
1	S. 83° W.	N. 66½° W.	17½° W.	24¼ miles	——
2	S. 45 E.	S. 44 E.	12 E.	44 ,,	——
3	S. 44 W.	S. 73 W.	17 W.	18 ,,	——
4	N. 30 W.	N. 14¾ W.	3¼ W.	32 ,,	——
5	S. 16 W.	S. 36½ W.	9½ W.	29½ ,,	——
6	N. 10 W.	N. 1¾ E.	2¼ E.	——	7 hr. 07 min.
7	S. 38 W.	S. 68 W.	16 W.	——	9 00
8	S. 56 E.	S. 56 E.	14 E.	——	5 07
9	N. 32 W.	N. 15½ W.	3½ W.	——	8 00
10	N. 42 W.	N. 24½ W.	6½ W.	——	8 24

EXERCISE 16.

	Lat.	Long.
1.	51° 12′ 00″ N.	8° 54′ 00″ W.
2.	51 46 15 N.	7 04 00 W.
3.	52 04 30 N.	5 39 00 W.
4.	49 42 30 N.	4 20 00 W.
5.	50 14 00 N.	1 45 00 W.
6.	49 55 00 N.	1 56 00 W.

EXERCISE 17.

CHART EXAMINATION PAPERS.

Paper 1.

1. True Course S. 83° W.   Dev. 18° W.   Comp. Course N. 68° W.   Dist. 103 miles.
2. Lat. 50° 25' 30" N.   Long. 00° 58' 00" W.   Set. 140°.   Drift 3 miles.
3. Lat. 50° 22' 00" N.   Long. 1° 52' 00" W.   Dist. 13½ miles.
4. True Co. N. 87° W.   Dev. 16½° W. Comp. Co. N. 59½° W. Dist. 13½ miles.
5. Lat. 50° 20' 00" N.   Long. 1° 10' 00" W.

Paper 2.

1. True Co. N. 56° E.   Dev. 12° E.   Comp. Co. N. 56° E.   Dist. 125 miles.
   True Co. S. 89° E.   Dev. 19½° E.   Comp. Co. N. 83½° E.   Dist 103½ mls.
2. Lat. 48° 56' 00" N.   Long. 4° 28' 00" W.   Set 181°.   Drift 4 miles.
3. Lat. 49° 50' 30" N.   Long. 1° 08' 00" W.   Dist, 10 miles.
4. True Co. S. 86° E.   Dev. 20½° E.   Comp. Co. N. 85½° E.   Time 5 hr. 17 min.
5. Lat. 49° 50' 00" N.   Long. 2° 24' 00" W.

Paper 3.

1. True Co. S. 56° W.   Dev. 21½° W.   Comp. Co. N. 86½° W.   Dist. 60 miles.
   True Co. S. 85° W.   Dev. 17° W.   Comp. Co. N. 61° W.   Dist. 168 miles.
2. Lat. 49° 53' 45" N.   Long. 1° 45' 00" W.   Set 116°.   Drift 5½ miles.
3. Lat. 49° 44' 00" N.   Long. 5° 15' 30" W.   Dist. 15 miles.
4. True Co. N. 82° W.   Dev. 15½° W.   Comp. Co. N. 54° W.   Time 7 hr.
5. Lat. 49° 35' 00" N.   Long. 5° 58' 30" W.

Paper 4.

1. True Co. S. 60° E.   Dev. 15° E.   Comp. Co. S. 61° E.   Dist. 42 miles.
   True Co. S. 38° W.   Dev. 16° W.   Comp. Co. S. 68° W.   Dist. 72 miles.
   True Co. S. 00° W.   Dev. 6° W.   Comp. Co. S. 20° W.   Dist. 60 miles.
2. Lat. 50° 33' 00" N.   Long. 5° 25' 00" W.   Set North.   Drift 2¾ miles.
3. Lat. 50° 17' 30" N.   Long. 5° 46' 00" W.   Dist. 14 miles.
4. True Co. S. 19° W.   Dev. 11° W.   Comp. Co. S. 44° W.   Time 1 hr. 45 min.
5. Lat. 50° 25' 00" N.   Long. 5° 44' 30" W.

Paper 5.

1. True Co. S. 26° W.   Dev. 13° W.   Comp. Co. S. 52½° W.   Dist. 30 miles.
   True Co. S. 68° E.   Dev. 17¼° E.   Comp. Co. S. 71¾° E.   Dist. 49 miles.
   True Co. N. 74° E.   Dev. 15½ E.   Comp. Co. N. 72° E.   Dist. 31 miles.
2. Lat. 51° 54' 00" N.   Long. 5° 50' 00" W.   Set. 026°.   Drift 3 miles.
3. Lat. 51° 23' 00" N.   Long. 5° 11' 00" W.   Dist. 22 miles.
4. True Co. N. 57° E.   Dev. 12½° E.   Comp. Co. N. 58° E.   Dist. 17 miles.
5. Lat. 51° 22' 00" N.   Long. 4° 09' 00" W.

Paper 6.

1. True Co. N. 83° E.   Dev. 18° E.   Comp. Co. N. 80° E.   Dist. 146 miles.
2. Lat. 51° 28' 15" N.   Long. 8° 04' 00" W.   Set 163°.   Drift 3 miles.
3. Lat. 51° 57' 30" N.   Long. 6° 43' 00" W.   Dist. 13 miles.
4. True Co. S. 56° W.   Dev. 21½° W. Comp. Co. N. 87½° W.   Dist. 29½ mls. Time 4 hr. 30 min.
5. Lat. 51° 43' 45" N.   Long. 7° 34' 30" W.

Paper 7.

1. True Co. N. 20° W.   Dev. 1¼° W.   Comp. Co. N. 8¾° W.   Dist. 79 miles.
   True Co. North.   Dev. 3¼° E.   Comp. Co. N. 6¾° E.   Dist. 23¾ miles.
   True Co. N. 41° E.   Dev. 10° E.   Comp. Co. N. 45° E.   Dist. 93½ miles.
2. Lat. 50° 24′ 00″ N.   Long. 5° 41′ 00″ W.   Set 249°.   Drift 5 miles.
3. Lat. 50° 57′ 00″ N.   Long. 5° 01′ 00″ W.   Dist. 18½ miles.
4. True Co. N. 42° E.   Dev. 10° E.   Comp. Co. N. 46° E.   Dist. 32½ miles.
5. Lat. 49° 42′ 00″ N.   Long. 5° 42′ 00″ W.

Paper 8.

1. Lat. 49° 40′ 00″ N.   Long. 6° 41′ 00″ W.
2. True Co. N. 89° E.   Dev. 19¼ E.   Comp. Co. N. 82¾° E.   Dist. 164 miles.
3. Lat. 49° 46′ 00″ N.   Long. 5° 30′ 00″ W.   Set. 018°.   Drift 5 miles.
4. True Co. N. 13° E.   Dev. 6° E.   Comp. Co. N. 23° E.   Time 4 hr.
   51 min.

EXERCISE 18.

Reduction to Soundings.

	Duration	Range	
1.	6 hr. 07 min.	18·2 ft.	Corr. 6·0 ft. to subtract.
2.	6 ,, 23 ,,	13·8 ,,	Corr. 4·3 ft. to subtract.
3.	6 ,, 01 ,,	11·6 ,,	Time 05 hrs. 06 min.
4.	6 ,, 05 ,,	17·7 ,,	Time 14 hrs. 39 min.
5.	6 ,, 13 ,,	18·1 ,,	
	6 ,, 08 ,,	17·5 ,,	Refloat at 15 hrs. 49 min.
6.	6 ,, 05 ,,	17·4 ,,	Interval 41 minutes
7.	6 ,, 20 ,,	15·2 ,,	Addl. Freeboard 11·0 feet.
8.	6 ,, 05 ,,	15·4 ,,	Time 14 hrs. 40 min.
9.	6 ,, 17 ,,	10·2 ,,	Draught 17·4 feet.
10.	6 ,, 03 ,,	13·6 ,,	Height 15·6 feet.

EXERCISE 19.

Converting Time to Arc and Vice Versa.

	h	m	s		°	′	″
1.	2	52	48·5	9.	83	11	00
2.	1	15	07·5	10.	151	53	45
3.	0	30	29·8	11.	117	21	15
4.	8	26	50·5	12.	6	42	45
5.	3	29	26·8	13.	33	48	30
6.	2	29	13·6	14.	103	22	15
7.	0	56	27·7	15.	16	06	00
8.	3	57	30·3	16.	66	25	15

EXERCISE 20.

To Find Greenwich Mean Time.

		h	m	s				h	m	s
1.	2nd Jan.,	13	13	27	11.	3rd Jan.,	11	13	41
2.	13th June,	13	25	19	12.	14th June,	08	48	53
3.	16th July,	15	14	08	13.	15th July,	18	39	47
4.	23rd July,	10	11	18	14.	22nd Dec.,	03	16	21
5.	23rd Sept.	06	52	35	15.	23rd Sept.,	15	56	59
6.	12th June,	15	41	41	16.	21st July,	20	34	06
7.	9th Oct.,	07	36	43	17.	1st Jan.	16	07	07
8.	21st Dec.,	14	43	58	18.	7th Oct.,	09	51	15
9.	12th June,	14	04	35	19.	13th June,	18	08	13
10.	24th Sept.,	09	11	29	20.	21st Dec.,	09	49	28

EXERCISE 21.

To Find Declination and G.H.A. Sun.

		G.M.T.			Decl.		G.H.A.	
		h	m	s	°	′	°	′
1.	2nd Jan.,	13	21	32	22	55·9 S.	19	23·0
2.	12th June,	13	24	04	23	08·5 N.	21	06·4
3.	22nd July,	15	27	24	20	17·9 N.	50	15·8
4.	15th July,	16	28	00	21	32·2 N.	65	32·6
5.	8th Oct.,	23	31	28	5	58·6 S.	175	58·9
6.	21st Dec.,	05	31	48	23	26·2 S.	263	29·4
7.	24th Sept.,	02	22	46	0	12·9 S.	217	37·0
8.	17th July,	07	38	47	21	16·3 N.	293	12·0
9.	7th Oct.,	21	39	00	5	33·9 S.	147	47·3
10.	14th June,	09	34	10	23	14·9 N.	323	32·1
11.	23rd July,	16	37	28	20	05·2 N.	67	46·3
12.	3rd Jan.,	03	32	52	22	52·7 S.	232	08·9
13.	23rd Dec.,	20	35	01	23	26·0 S.	128	58·1
14.	9th Oct.,	03	27	00	6	02·4 S.	234	52·6
15.	16th July,	20	31	45	21	20·9 N.	126	27·1
16.	1st Jan.,	15	34	14	23	00·5 S.	52	39·9

EXERCISE 22.

Amplitudes.

		G.M.T.			Decl.		True Amp.		Dev.
		h	m	s	° ′		° ′		° ′
1.	1st Jan.,	09	32	26	23 01·8 S.	E.	30 49·1 S.		3 49·1 E.
2.	8th Oct.,	06	37	36	5 42·5 S.	E.	7 51·8 S.		2 08·2 W.
3.	16th July	19	38	09	21 21·3 N.	W.	38 29·0 N.		3 30·0 E.
4.	21st Dec.,	14	28	48	23 26·4 S.	W.	24 38·0 S.		2 22·0 E.
5.	13th June,	10	00	00	23 11·6 N.	E.	26 40·5 N.		4 40·5 W.
6.	23rd July,	06	23	12	20 10·4 N.	E.	23 54·8 N.		4 35·2 E.
7.	24th Sept.	16	37	56	0 26·7 S.	W.	0 28·2 S.		5 01·8 E.
8.	3rd Jan.,	21	23	00	22 48·3 S.	W.	22 55·1 S.		9 04·9 E.
9.	23rd Dec.,	07	24	00	23 26·3 S.	E.	30 32·4 S.		6 32·4 E.
10.	16th July,	04	38	00	21 27·3 N.	E.	36 45·0 N.		0 15·0 W.
11.	17th July	07	38	19	21 16·4 N.	E.	25 14·5 N.		5 14·5 W.
12.	23rd Sept.,	06	00	00	0 07·0 N.	E.	0 10·0 N.		2 40·0 W.
13.	9th Oct.,	09	21	54	6 08·0 S.	E.	7 21·2 S.		0 21·2 E.
14.	21st Dec.,	03	39	00	23 26·2 S.	E.	28 50·6 S.		4 20·6 E.
15.	14th June,	21	23	16	23 16·3 N.	W.	40 17·0 N.		5 17·0 E.
16.	3rd Jan.,	17	05	28	22 49·4 S.	W.	40 26·0 S.		4 26·0 W.
17.	22nd July,	02	25	00	20 24·3 N.	E.	27 08·3 N.		8 51·7 E.
18.	23rd Sept.,	04	59	00	0 08·0 N.	E.	0 14·5 N.		8 45·5 E.
19.	1st Jan.,	09	27	00	23 01·8 S.	E.	32 25·7 S.		5 04·3 W.
20.	15th July,	12	34	00	21 33·8 N.	W.	21 33·8 N.		6 16·2 W.

EXERCISE 23.

To Find the True Azimuth.

	° ′	° ′		° ′	° ′
1.	N. 124 18 E.	or S. 55 42 E.	8.	N. 149 15 W.	or S. 30 45 W.
2.	N. 142 00 E.	or S. .38 00 E.	9.	N. 148 20 E.	or S. 31 40 E.
3.	N. 168 18 W.	or S. 11 42 W.	10.	N. 123 19 W.	or S. 56 41 W.
4.	N. 128 30 W.	or S. 51 30 W.	11.	N. 137 23 W.	or S. 42 37 W.
5.	N. 103 00 W.	or S. 77 00 W.	12.	N. 128 35 E.	or S. 51 25 E.
6.	N. 119 18 E.	or S. 60 42 E.	13.	N. 119 24 W.	or S. 60 36 W.
7.	N. 148 48 E.	or S. 31 12 E.	14.	N. 130 02 E.	or S. 49 58 E.

Exercise 24.

(A) Deviation by Time Azimuth of Sun.

	L.A.T.	L.H.A.		Decl.		True Az.		Dev.	
	h m s	° ′		° ′		°	′	°	′
1.	09 44 00			22	56·6 S.	N. 55	00 E.	8	00 E.
2.	12 46 00			23	26·3 S.	N. 21	13 W.	4	13 W.
3.	14 50 00			22	49·7 S.	N. 64	04 W.	3	04 W.
4.	10 46 49			6	11·5 S.	S. 20	54 E.	6	06 E.
5.	14 25 33			23	12·2 N.	S. 57	20 W.	4	40 W.
6.	10 32 47			21	33·7 N.	S. 37	14 E.	3	14 W.
7.	13 18 57			21	23·9 N.	S. 33	56 W.	1	56 E.
8.	11 18 22			20	09·9 N.	S. 23	21 E.	0	21 W.
9.	9 26 34			22	50·7 S.	N. 59	18 E.	7	18 E.
10.	10 49 58			23	26·2 S.	N. 29	28 E.	3	28 E.
11.	08 43 00	310	45·2	22	51·1 S.	S. 44	54 E.	5	06 E.
12.	15 10 00	47	30·1	6	11·4 S.	S. 51	42 W.	3	42 E.
13.	07 05 00	286	15·0	0	12·5 S.	S. 80	04 E.	3	04 W.
14.		61	34·4	20	28·2 N.	S. 74	30 W.	1	30 W.
15.		337	32·5	23	15·0 N.	S. 36	00 E.	3	00 E.
16.		59	17·4	21	31·4 N.	S. 81	12 W.	4	12 E.
17.		293	49·9	5	25·6 S.	N. 79	36 E.	2	24 W.
18.		351	15·6	0	31·3 N.	S. 15	12 E.	6	42 W.
19.		82	40·5	6	18·5 S.	S. 80	36 W.	4	36 E.
20.		43	14·3	23	26·4 S.	S. 38	54 W.	1	54 E.

(B) Deviation by Supplementary Methods.

21.	12 W.	26.	5 W.	31.	4 E.	36.	4·7 W.
22.	6 E.	27.	4 E.	32.	3 W.	37.	4 E.
23.	5 E.	28.	2 E.	33.	4 E.	38	5·9 E.
24.	3 E.	29.	5 W.	34.	5 E.	39.	2 E.
25.	3 W.	30.	2 W.	35.	6 E.	40.	3 E.

Exercise 25.

Correcting Chronometer Times.

	Daily Rate		Accum. Rate		G.M.T.			
	Days	Rate	Days	Rate				
		s		m s		h	m	s
1.		3·5 L.	56·0	3 16	9th Sept.	11	17	48
2.		2·9 G.	77·5	3 45	19th June,	00	19	25
3.		5·5 L.	66·1	6 04	8th May,	14	00	08
4.		2·8 G.	77·8	3 38	19th Oct.,	06	55	51
5.	52	3·5 G.	46·3	2 42	10th June,	18	55	41
6.	63	2·5 G.	40·9	1 42	14th Dec.,	10	45	43
7.	32	4·3 L.	35·7	2 34	19th April,	05	17	04
8.	51	4·4 L.	31·6	2 19	1st Oct.,	02	11	19
9.	35	3·8 L.	34·4	2 11	3rd Nov.,	22	34	21

Exercise 26.
Latitude by Meridian Altitude of the Sun.
(Altitude Corrections have been taken from the Tables in the *Nautical Almanac.*)

	G.M.T. of Mer. Pass.	Decl.	True Alt.	Latitude
	h m	° ′	° ′	° ′
1.	23rd Sept., 15 36	0 02·4 S.	23 32·7	66 24·9 N.
2.	7th Oct., 18 05	5 30·5 S.	43 07·4	52 23·1 S.
3.	12th June, 08 40	23 07·7 N.	75 07·3	8 15·0 N.
4.	16th July, 13 38	21 23·8 N.	45 30·7	23 05·5 S.
5.	9th Oct., 17 28	6 15·7 S.	63 25·3	20 19·0 N.
6.	21st Dec., 07 21	23 26·3 S.	81 42·0	31 44·3 S.
7.	2nd Jan., 18 33	22 54·7 S.	41 48·5	25 16·8 N.
8.	13th June, 11 34	23 11·9 N.	47 55·2	65 16·7 N.
9.	22nd Sept., 12 30	0 24·0 N.	69 42·8	19 53·2 S.
10.	22nd July, 07 37	20 21·8 N.	67 17·6	43 04·2 N.
11.	8th Oct., 13 40	5 49·3 S.	32 22·7	51 48·0 N.
12.	23rd Dec., 11 59	23 26·2 S.	66 55·7	0 21·9 S.
13.	1st Jan., 15 39	23 00·5 S.	68 19·0	44 41·5 S.
14.	14th June, 04 32	23 14·2 N.	74 20·1	38 54·1 N.
15.	9th Oct., 10 35	6 09·2 S.	40 48·7	43 02·1 N.
16.	17th July, 16 32	21 12·6 N.	58 13·2	52 59·4 N.
17.	22nd Sept., 06 28	0 29·8 N.	68 32·0	21 57·8 N.
18.	21st Dec., 13 20	23 26·4 S.	29 01·0	37 32·6 N.

Exercise 27.
Longitude by Sun.

	G.M.T.	True Alt.	Decl.	Hav. L.H.A.	Longitude
	h m s	° ′	° ′		° ′
1.	2nd Jan., 11 24 41	22 29·5	22 56·3 S.	9·41964	51 51·7 W.
2.	21st Dec., 10 30 57	19 27·4	23 26·3 S.	9·43607	41 14·7 W.
3.	16th July 20 23 43	19 59·7	21 20·9 N.	9·65333	40 10·1 W.
4.	23rd Sept. 08 21 16	17 40·5	0 04·7 N.	9·51575	17 02·5 W.
5.	13th June, 14 36 58	23 51·3	23 12·3 N.	9·59604	38 32·5 E.
6.	22nd Sept., 22 22 22	38 32·0	0 14·4 N.	9·11263	160 23·1 E.
7.	14th June, 14 20 29	40 10·6	23 15·4 N.	9·31903	19 13·7 E.
8.	22nd Sept., 02 39 22	26 05·2	0 10·2 N.	9·38602	162 34·7 W.
9.	13th June, 14 36 28	26 52·1	23 12·3 N.	9·40510	99 42·0 W.
10.	17th July, 12 00 00	41 45·8	21 14·5 N.	9·24957	51 21·5 E.
11.	23rd July, 10 34 29	29 27·3	20 08·3 N.	9·17134	22 20·3 W.
12.	7th Oct., 08 31 14	35 41·5	5 21·3 S.	9·08573	8 20·1 E.
13.	23rd Dec., 17 27 00	39 24·9	23 26·1 S.	9·00385	44 56·4 W.
14.	12th June, 04 33 38	27 45·1	23 07·0 N.	9·53909	39 25·2 E.
15.	24th Sept., 16 26 51	21 29·9	0 26·5 S.	9·27966	16 56·8 W.
16.	9th Oct., 14 30 18	29 33·3	6 12·9 S.	9·06343	0 57·3 W.
17.	3rd Jan., 03 36 29	26 23·3	22 52·6 S.	9·40015	66 46·6 E.
18.	22nd Dec., 11 21 53	42 30·7	23 26·5 S.	9·29337	61 46·3 E.
19.	21st July, 08 00 00	37 19·4	20 33·2 N.	9·34643	5 20·7 E.
20.	8th Oct., 12 23 54	19 31·0	5 48·0 S.	9·47855	75 36·2 W.

Q

Exercise 28.
Longitude with Run.

	G.M.T.	T.Alt	Decl.	Latitude		Longitude	
				Sights	Noon	Sights	Noon
	h m s	° ′	° ′	° ′	° ′	° ′	° ′
1.	04 30 00	36 30·2	20 11·4 N.	50 05·0 N.	50 19·0 N.	57 20·2 E.	58 20·4 E.
2.	17 30 45	27 22·1	6 15·7 S.	29 57·7 N.	30 21·0 N.	32 30·8 W.	31 57·4 W.
3.	17 36 14	21 26·9	6 15·7 S.	37 08·0 N.	36 30·5 N.	30 12·8 W.	30 48·2 W.
4.	12 00 00	29 56·4	23 08·2 N.	52 07·0 N.	51 33·6 N.	70 32·7 W.	70 10·8 W.

Exercise 29.
Longitude and Run to Noon.

	Noon D.R. Lat.	Noon D.R. Long.	Long. Corrn.	True Noon Long.
	° ′	° ′	′	° ′
1.	51 14·1 N.	15 46·7 W.	3·8 W.	15 50·5 W.
2.	40 06·7 N.	31 56·2 W.	6·2 W.	32 02·4 W.
3.	18 13·7 N.	28 52·6 W.	1·8 W.	28 54·4 W.
4.	40 17·9 N.	14 48·4 E.	2·9 E.	14 51·3 E.
5.	47 37·8 N.	7 28·4 W.	4·8 E.	7 23·6 W.
6.	28 29·7 S.	36 00·8 E.	5·3 E.	36 06·1 E.
7.	51 49·7 N.	54 02·1 W.	11·0 E.	53 51·1 W.
8.	12 52·1 N.	61 35·0 W.	3·2 E.	61 31·8 W.
9.	42 23·2 N.	29 35·7 W.	3·6 E.	29 32·1 W.
10.	33 54·3 N.	17 11·7 W.	3·0 E.	17 08·7 W.
11.	54 12·2 N.	28 20·0 W.	11·4 W.	28 31·4 W.
12.	5 30·9 N.	2 54·8 E.	2·5 W.	2 52·3 E.
13.	15 05·2 S.	24 55·4 W.	3·7 E.	24 51·7 W.
14.	24 59·9 N.	72 39·1 W.	4·4 W.	72 43·5 W.
15.	47 10·7 N.	65 53·2 W.	6·5 W.	65 59·7 W.
16.	35 50·7 N.	26 57·2 W.	8·9 E.	26 48·3 W.
17.	27 12·7 N.	19 35·8 E.	2·2 W.	19 33·6 E.
18.	50 04·9 N.	14 24·9 W.	6·2 W.	14 31·1 W.
19.	53 33·9 N.	26 59·0 W.	5·4 W.	27 04·4 W.
20.	17 29·9 N.	41 49·0 W.	Nil	41 49·0 W.

Exercise 30.
Two Longitude Observations with Run Between.

	D.R. Lat.	D.R. Long.	Lat. Corrn.	Long. Corrn.		Observed Position	
				A	B	Lat.	Long.
	° ′	° ′	′	′	′	° ′	° ′
1.	27 50·7 N.	44 14·3 W.	6·5 N.	2·5 E.	4·8 W.	27 57·2 N.	44 11·8 W.
2.	50 46·2 N.	10 11·8 E.	10·3 S.	4·6 W.	6·9 E.	50 35·9 N.	10 07·0 E.
3.	41 05·9 N.	34 30·4 W.	6·4 S.	2·0 W.	3·5 E.	40 59·5 N.	34 32·4 W.
4.	26 26·4 N.	12 09·1 W.	10·3 N.	3·0 E.	6·1 W.	26 36·7 N.	12 06·1 W.
5.	12 14·2 N.	23 47·9 E.	8·0 S.	9·3 E.	4·2 E.	12 06·2 N.	23 57·2 E.
6.	46 43·5 S.	19 39·7 W.	4·5 N.	3·6 W.	1·7 E.	46 39·0 S.	19 43·3 W.
7.	30 58·3 N.	48 50·6 W.	14·0 N.	13·0 W.	5·6 W.	31 12·3 N.	49 03·6 W.
8.	54 11·4 N.	78 08·0 W.	6·8 N.	4·3 E.	3·7 W.	54 18·2 N.	78 03·7 W.
9.	13 52·6 S.	19 56·3 W.	6·0 N.	4·6 W.	2·1 E.	13 46·6 S.	20 00·9 W.
10.	50 31·5 N.	4 36·8 E.	9·6 S.	4·0 W.	2·8 E.	50 21·9 N.	4 32·8 E.
11.	36 35·2 S.	78 18·9 E.	5·8 N.	1·6 W.	2·4 E.	36 29·4 S.	78 17·3 E.
12.	43 38·0 N.	27 21·4 W.	16·9 N.	14·2 W.	5·6 W.	43 54·9 N.	27 35·6 W.

EXERCISE 31.

To Find Ship's Position by Plotting.

	Latitude N.	Longitude W.
	° ′	° ′
1.	55 31·0	10 53·0
2.	55 19·0	10 58·0
3.	55 54·0	10 52·0
4.	55 47·0	11 08·0
5.	55 13·0	11 06·5
6.	55 49·0	11 35·4
7.	55 07·0	10 42·3
8.	55 27·5	11 20·2
9.	55 30·0	11 19·8
10.	55 31·3	11 44·8

EXERCISE 32.

P.L. Navigation—Longitude Method.

	Long. "A"	"C"	Noon D.R. position		Noon Obs. position	
			Lat. N.	Long.	Lat. N.	Long.
	° ′		° ′	° ′	° ′	° ′
1.	62 23·1 W.	·039—	50 02·4	63 04·1 W.	50 00·1	63 04·0 W.
2.	26 26·6 W.	·620+	39 56·1	26 03·9 W.	40 02·0	26 00·2 W.
3.	28 36·1 W.	1·044+	31 37·3	28 05·6 W.	31 31·9	28 11·2 W.
4.	41 02·6 W.	·340—	51 25·5	41 59·4 W.	51 20·8	41 57·8 W.

	Long. "A"	"C"	Transferred position		Long. "B"	"C"
5.	35 05·3 W.	·087—	49 56·1	33 59·6 W.	34 00·3 W.	·564+
	Ship's position		49 42·1 N.	33 58·4 W.		
6.	21 04·3 E.	·720+	45 13·9	20 10·4. E.	20 03·6 E.	1·220+
	Ship's position		45 10·4 N.	20 07·9 E.		
7.	44 21·8 W.	1·153+	38 33·9	43 15·3 W.	43 19·8 W.	1·336+
	Ship's position		38 32·1 N.	43 17·4 W.		
8.	10 07·6 E.	·746+	48 05·3	9 24·9 E.	9 14·2 E.	·983+
	Ship's position		47 59·1 N.	9 20·3 E.		
9.	37 1 0·9W.	·852+	30 00·0	36 00·4 W.	35 57·7 W.	·967+
	Ship's position		30 04·8 N.	35 56·3 W.		
10.	46 03·5 W.	2·456+	42 17·8	46 13·2 W.	46 19·4 W.	·739+
	Ship's position		42 21·4 N.	46 22·0 W.		

EXERCISE 33.
Crossing Celestial and Terrestrial P.L.'s.
(Problems worked by Longitude Method).

	Pos. "A"	Pos. "B"	B.C. (f)	B.F. (c)	Pos. "F"
	° ′	° ′	°	°	° ′
1.	53 00·0 N. 16 56·8 W.	52 08·5 N. 17 32·8 W.	S. 18 W. 10 mls.	S. 32½ E. 9·6 mls.	52 00·4 N. 17 24·4 W·
2.	11 52·0 N. 44 56·4 W.	12 22·0 N. 44 40·0 W.	N. 33 E. 14·3 mls.	N. 44½ W. 24·2 mls·	12 39·3 N· 44 57·4 W.
3.	51 00·0 N. 42 45·3 W.	51 29·6 N. 42 30·7 W.	N. 29 W. 11·9 mls.	S. 8 W. 12·5 mls.	51 17·2 N. 42 33·5 W.
4.	50 30·0 N. 14 11·1 E.	50 05·9 N. 14 16·1 E.	S. 56 E. 10·7 mls.	S. 10 E. 8·9 mls.	49 57·1 N. 14 18·6 E
5.	32 41·0 N. 8 20·2 E.	33 07·7 N. 8 03·5 E.	S. 25½ E. 10·8 mls.	N. 36¾ E. 15·5 mls.	33 14·1 N. 8 14·6 E.
6.	42 20·0 N. 5 18·2 W.	41 49·3 N. 5 50·5 W.	South 9·3 mls.	S. 43 E. 8·4 mls.	41 43·2 N. 5 42·8 W.

Plotting.

		° ′		° ′
7.	Lat.	55 45·3 N.	Long	11 53·5 W.
8.	,,	55 19·3 N.	,,	10 53·3 W.
9.	,,	55 55·8 N.	,,	10 22·0 W.
10.	,,	55 12·2 N.	,,	10 43·5 W.
11.	,,	55 09·6 N.	,,	11 44·7 W.

EXERCISE 34.
Intercepts.

	"C.F."	Latitude	Longitude
		° ′	° ′
1.	12·5 miles	50 18·7 N.	17 04·1 W.
2.	15·9 ,,	43 38·8 N.	00 40·6 W.
3.	13·2 ,,	35 06·1 N.	7 26·9 E.
4.	7·2 ,,	47 52·4 N.	11 44·0 W.
5.	3·6 ,,	28 20·3 N.	2 09·1 E.
6.	13·1 ,,	52 17·2 N.	4 24·3 W.
7.	8·6 ,,	41 31·5 S.	57 22·4 W.
8.	5·8 ,,	15 16·3 N.	7 02·8 E.
9.	9·2 ,,	38 40·6 S.	17 26·4 W.
10.	4·3 ,,	29 04·9 N.	53 52·9 W.
11.	10·3 ,,	48 36·6 N.	23 30·2 W.
12.	8·8 ,,	8 59·7 N.	60 47·3 E.
		Plotting	
13.		55 07·8 N.	11 47·0 W.
14.		55 48·4 N.	10 37·2 W.
15.		55 50·8 N.	11 14·0 W.
16.		55 36·5 N.	11 54·0 W.
17.		55 21·9 N.	10 52·9 W.
18.		55 45·6 N.	10 19·9 W.

EXERCISE 35.
The Intercept Problem (Marcq St. Hilaire).

	G.M.T.	L.H.A.	T.Z.D.	T. Bg.	Intcpt.	P.L. through	
						Lat.	Long.
	h m s	° '	° '	°	° '	° '	° '
1.	11 24 41	298 10·9	67 30·5	118·7	7·2 T.	7 24·5 N.	51 53·6 W.
2.	10 30 57	297 05·2	70 32·6	120·0	4·0 A.	11 02·0 N.	41 13·6 W.
3.	20 23 43	84 26·6	70 00·3	280·0	6·2 T.	51 13·1 N.	40 09·8 W.
4.	08 21 16	290 10·5	72 19·5	099·8	2·2 A.	28 20·4 N.	17 02·5 W.
5.	14 36 58	77 41·6	66 08·7	280·3	5·5 A.	40 50·0 N.	38 32·2 E.
6.	22 22 22	317 54·8	51 28·0	121·0	5·0 A.	33 07·6 N.	160 24·9 E.
7.	14 20 29	54 25·3	49 49·4	258·0	3·3 T.	50 35·3 N.	19 14·0 E.
8.	02 39 22	59 10·7	63 54·8	252·8	3·8 T.	31 24·9 N.	162 34·2 W.
9.	14 36 28	299 24·1	63 07·9	063·8	2·8 T.	00 01·2 N.	99 42·5 W.
10.	12 00 00	49 44·9	48 14·2	252·7	4·1 A.	49 26·2 N.	51 21·0 E.
11.	10 34 29	314 46·7	60 32·7	050·3	3·7 A.	21 10·4 S.	22 18·1 W.
12.	08 31 14	319 03·5	54 18·5	126·5	3·5 T.	32 38·9 N.	8 18·3 E.
13.	17 27 00	36 58·8	50 35·1	225·6	2·4 A.	11 53·7 N.	44 58·2 W.
14.	04 33 38	288 10·0	62 14·9	081·1	3·7 A.	38 18·4 N.	39 25·4 E.
15.	16 26 51	51 41·3	68 30·1	237·5	1·6 A.	53 00·9 N.	16 57·8 W.
16.	14 30 18	39 53·9	60 26·7	227·1	4·0 A.	42 14·7 N.	00 46·1 W.
17.	03 36 29	299 43·2	63 36·7	117·0	6·0 T.	1 57·3 N.	66 45·3 E.
18.	11 21 53	52 31·4	47 29·3	261·5	5·5 A.	26 24·2 S.	61 46·0 E.

EXERCISE 36.
P.L. Navigation—Intercept Method.

	C.Z.D.	Intcpt.	"C"	Noon D.R. position	C.Z.D.	Intcpt.	"C"	Noon Obs. position
	° '	'		° '	° '	'		° '
1.	62 08·5	2·2 A.	·039 −	50 02·3 N. / 63 04·4 W.				50 00·1 N. / 63 04·3 W.
2.	70 43·3	2·4 T	·618 +	39 55·1 N. / 26 04·5 W.				40 02·0 N. / 26 00·2 W.
3.	73 25·5	3·8 A.	1·048 +	31 39·8 N. / 28 02·8 W.				31 31·9 N. / 28 11·1 W.
4.	69 27·9	1·6 A.	·340 −	51 25·2 N. / 41 59·6 W.				51 20·8 N. / 41 58·1 W.
				Transfrd position				Final position
5.	65 39·6	3·4 A.	·085 −	49 55·9 N. / 33 59·5 W.	48 34·0	4·0 T.	·562 +	49 42·2 N. / 33 58·5 W.
6.	72 31·7	2·7 T.	·713 +	45 12·7 N. / 20 09·4 E.	64 00·6	2·2 T.	1·218 +	45 10·6 N. / 20 07·9 E.
7.	77 06·9	1·7 T.	1·248 +	38 32·7 N. / 43 17·0 W.	76 07·6	0·7 T.	1·330 +	38 32·2 N. / 43 17·6 W.
8.	69 32·8	4·3 T.	·745 +	48 03·4 N. / 9 23·2 E.	64 15·3	3·9 T.	·981 +	47 59·3 N. / 9 20·2 E.
9.	77 08·0	3·0 T.	·852 +	29 58·2 N. / 36 01·7 W.	73 25·6	4·0 T.	·967 +	30 04·7 N. / 35 56·1 W.
10.	52 23·0	1·3 T.	2·456 +	42 16·7 N. / 46 10·6 W.	70 33·3	5·1 T.	·732 +	42 21·3 N. / 46 21·9 W.

Exercise 37.

G.H.A. and L.H.A. of Aries, Stars and Planets.

	G.M.T.			G.H.A.γ			G.M.T.			L.H.A.*	
	h	m	s	°	'		h	m	s	°	'
1.				257	05·4	11.				36	07·5
2.				298	03·3	12.				115	35·0
3.				226	55·7	13.				18	29·3
4.	15	33	21	251	04·9	14.	21	31	00	191	13·8
5.	21	26	23	51	32·0	15.	05	32	30	351	21·0

	G.M.T.			G.H.A.*			G.M.T.			L.H.A.		Decl.	
	h	m	s	°	'		h	m	s	°	'	°	'
6.				333	26·9	16.				324	22·9	9	24·5 N.
7.				82	58·8	17.				351	16·3	21	55·0 S.
8.				130	24·7	18.				207	11·3	22	06·7 N.
9.	20	30	46	102	22·3	19.	05	34	17	314	56·7	17	26·9 S.
10.	02	24	23	55	33·5	20.	19	34	26	91	07·3	14	42·1 S.

Exercise 38.

Time Azimuth of Stars, etc.

	G.M.T			L.H.A.*		Decl.		T. Az	Dev.
	h	m	s	°	'	°	'	°	
1.	23	30	00	56	52·7	12	35·6 N.	294·5°	1·5 E.
2.	08	00	00	342	09·7	16	25·6 N.	150·7	3·7 E.
3.	07	30	00	340	34·5	19	23·7 N.	151·8	2·7 W.
4.	18	24	00	53	42·8	12	10·2 N.	244·9	6·1 W.
5.	00	31	00	343	44·8	45	08·0 N.	052·0	4·0 W.
6.	08	27	00	310	44·3	26	51·1 N.	105·2	6·2 E.
7.	03	21	00	56	27·0	28	52·0 N.	266·4	1·2 E.
8.	05	27	00	328	40·3	10	56·6 S.	146·4	4·1 W.
9.	21	21	00	46	31·3	61	58·7 N.	320·0	5·0 E.
10.	01	00	00	37	48·6	56	18·7 N.	325·2	1·8 W.
11.	20	33	00	47	00·9	8	45·7 N.	247·6	3·6 E.
12.	02	38	00	309	55·8	19	23·9 N.	118·7	5·8 W.
13.	15	39	00	24	55·7	38	45·1 N.	284·0	2·0 E.
14.	22	36	00	334	08·8	14	59·2 N.	132·1	6·1 E.
15.	20	34	00	324	23·0	38	44·7 N.	061·8	2·2 W.
16.	21	28	00	58	25·0	14	56·7 S.	237·2	5·2 E.
17.	01	35	00	45	23·4	7	14·0 S.	233·7	4·2 E.
18.	00	00	00	333	29·6	19	13·4 N.	138·9	5·1 W.
19.	03	26	00	59	41·1	21	43·4 S.	236·2	1·8 W.
20.	23	37	00	52	24·9	18	26·7 N.	252·8	7·8 E.

EXERCISE 39.
Latitude by Meridian Altitude of Star or Planet.

A. Star Above the Pole

	True Alt.	Latitude		True Alt.	Latitude
	° ′	° ′		° ′	° ′
1.	68 20·6	24 18·0 N.	7.	76 25·9	2 51·5 N.
2.	43 13·6	30 06·7 N.	8.	49 28·7	52 41·5 N.
3.	54 36·5	42 47·4 N.	9.	40 34·6	41 10·6 N.
4.	43 13·1	35 50·2 N.	10.	64 12·7	54 38·8 N.
5.	80 11·5	35 19·5 N.	11.	62 29·5	11 14·2 N.
6.	53 07·2	42 12·7 N.	12.	42 31·5	56 14·2 N.

B. Star Below the Pole.

	True Alt.	Latitude		True Alt.	Latitude
13.	28 26·0	62 15·1 N.	15.	16 27·1	50 16·0 N.
14.	21 08·7	36 49·5 N.	16.	21 25·8	61 43·1 N.

C. Planets.

	True Alt.	Decl.	Latitude
	° ′	° ′	° ′
17.	27 43·1	0 16·5 S.	62 00·4 N.
18.	38 12·9	17 24·4 S.	34 22·7 N.
19.	62 08·3	13 44·7 N.	14 07·0 S.
20.	46 27·3	19 15·9 N.	62 48·6 N.

EXERCISE 40.
Latitude by Altitude of Pole Star.

	G.M.T.	L.HA.γ	True Alt.	a₀	a₁	a₂	Lat. North
	h m s	° ′	° ′	° ′	′	′	° ′
1.	17 28 08	352 35·6	48 20·6	0 14·0	0·6	0·7	47 35·9
2.	07 20 15	204 00·3	53 11·5	1 54·3	0·6	0·3	54 06·7
3.	19 24 00	306 55·9	35 15·4	51·4	0·4	0·9	35 08·1
4.	05 00 00	335 01·2	43 12·6	26·3	0·5	0·2	42 39·6
5·	19 33 45	209 59·9	29 23·4	1 54·5	0·6	1·0	30 19·5
6.	04 26 12	12 15·5	44 54·3	5·5	0·6	0·2	44 00·6
7.	06 37 14	80 54·0	49 07·4	25·0	0·6	0·3	48 33·3
8.	18 36 33	296 00·5	55 44·0	1 02·1	0·7	0·9	55 47·7
9.	04 39 17	88 19·7	47 41·4	31·0	0·6	0·3	47 13·3
10.	08 35 46	176 01·3	41 22·1	45·8	0·5	0·2	42 08·6
11.	18 33 23	291 57·6	54 58·1	1 06·0	0·7	0·9	55 05·7
12.	10 21 16	207 51·2	46 11·2	1 54·5	0·6	0·5	47 06·8

EXERCISE 41.

Longitude by Star.

	G.M.T.	Z.X.	G.H.A.*	L. Hav.	L.H.A.*	Longitude
	h m s	° ′	° ′		° ′	° ′
1.	14 21 20	59 12·9′	248 39·8	9·44309	296 26·3	47 46·5 E.
2.	08 21 16	65 18·6	75 14·7	9·48849	67 24·8	7 49·9 W.
3.	20 00 00	59 00·5	324 31·5	9·53016	71 12·7	106 41·2 E.
4.	23 36 35	54 54·9	339 33·6	9·49470	292 02·2	47 31·4 W.
5.	04 20 00	41 17·2	309 49·8	9·19771	313 12·7	3 22·9 E.
6.	12 38 15	41 24·0	318 11·1	9·15917	44 38·7	86 27·6 E.
7.	20 31 53	45 41·8	332 31·1	9·53302	288 31·0	44 00·1 W.
8.	07 22 31	39 02·2	292 11·9	9·30762	306 25·6	14 14·1 E.
9.	00 00 00	70 15·7	130 23·3	9·09862	41 29·7	88 53·6 W.
10.	01 00 00	65 09·1	250 45·5	9·35921	302 51·9	52 06·4 E.
11.	10 00 00	66 21·3	5 49·0	9·10744	318 03·7	47 45·3 W.
12.	01 39 42	41 16·0	39 39·6	8·95925	35 07·4	4 32·2 W.
13.	05 29 33	67 51·3	45 14·0	9·49459	292 02·8	113 11·2 W.
14.	02 39 42	62 53·3	338 59·9	9·28148	51 51·5	72 51·6 E.
15.	18 00 00	66 55·0	120 32·1	9·39329	59 38·8	60 53·3 W.
16.	22 20 18	62 14·7	337 16·3	9·37330	301 50·5	35 25·8 W.
17.	05 40 00	50 19·6	309 48·6	8·81451	330 24·2	20 35·6 E.
18.	08 22 36	65 33·6	359 44·4	9·43737	296 54·2	62 50·2 W.
19.	15 23 09	53 58·3	24 16·3	9·21715	47 54·8	23 38·5 E.

EXERCISE 42.

Latitude by Ex-Meridian Altitude.

	L.H.A.	Decl.	True Alt.	Latitude
BY SUN	° ′	° ′	° ′	° ′
1.	5 48·7 W.	21 23·8 N.	63 40·7	47 17·8 N.
2.	10 48·7 W.	6 10·0 S.	31 02·6	52 03·8 N.
3.	5 52·3 E.	22 57·0 S.	15 07·8	51 44·6 N.
4.	7 27·7 E.	23 26·4 S.	54 35·7	11 12·2 N.
5.	7 31·7 E.	5 20·3 S.	43 59·9	40 08·2 N.
6.	9 05·5 W.	5 50·5 S.	35 00·0	48 34·6 N.
7.	7 36·1 E.	20 07·9 N.	60 00·1	49 30·9 N.
8.	10 07·7 W.	22 50·1 S.	28 54·5	37 30·6 N.
9.	5 39·6 E.	23 15·1 N.	58 11·0	54 47·3 N.
10.	8 52·6 E.	0 00·5 N.	41 51·1	47 31·9 N.
BY STAR				
11.	9 35·8 E.	8 45·8 N.	57 24·4	40 12·7 N.
12.	10 00·6 E.	14 48·3 N.	32 23·3	42 03·8 S.
13.	10 12·2 W.	10 56·8 S.	27 36·4	50 48·5 N.
14.	8 28·1 W.	26 20·4 S.	19 13·9	44 00·1 N.
15.	9 31·3 W.	14 59·2 N.	67 19·6	35 59·9 N.
BY PLANET				
16.	8 27·5 W.	21 55·0 S.	44 00·0	23 20·3 N.
17.	7 55·7 W.	9 55·5 S.	38 35·8	40 57·3 N.
18.	7 40.3 W.	7 43·6 S.	59 56·3	21 22·5 N.

EXERCISE 43.
Approximate Time of Star's Meridian Passage.

	G.H.A.γ	G.M.T.	L.M.T.		G.H.A.γ	G.M.T.	L.M.T.
	° ′	h m s	h m s		° ′	h m s	h m s
1.	55 01·5	03 30 14	04 23 42	11.	317 29·7	19 58 17	18 37 05
2.	240 37·1	09 12 31	07 23 47	12.	72 45·2	22 02 53	22 24 25
3.	109 22·9	06 08 06	06 33 22	13.	298 09·3	13 46 14	14 33 38
4.	2 32·5	06 45 51	05 31 03	14.	7 25·6	04 51 39	06 26 47
5.	74 38·9	22 14 23	23 38 51	15.	312 09·8	20 43 51	20 35 15
6.	15 24·9	05 27 27	04 32 03	16.	101 58·0	05 46 23	04 32 39
7.	58 37·9	21 54 42	23 23 54	17.	335 26·5	04 57 45	05 38 41
8.	97 58·6	13 10 29	12 31 29	18.	190 37·3	05 57 00	05 38 48
9.	24 31·2	01 32 29	00 35 57	19.	76 01·4	09 09 34	07 26 50
10.	76 36·5	09 07 59	09 35 39	20.	124 03·3	07 14 30	08 23 50

EXERCISE 44 (A)
Position by Simultaneous Altitudes of Stars, Longitude Method.

	Lat. Corr.	Long Corrns. A	Long Corrns. B	Latitude	Longitude
	′	′	′	° ′	° ′
1.	3·2 S.	1·8 W.	4·2 E.	51 23·8 N.	15 43·8 W.
2.	13·1 S.	1·4 W.	6·4 W.	34 54·9 N.	28 26·4 W.
3.	2·5 N.	2·3 W.	4·7 E.	47 17·5 N.	22 59·3 W.
4.	5·4 S.	1·0 E.	5·0 E.	50 28·6 N.	18 42·0 W.
5.	7·8 S.	2·0 E.	5·0 W.	28 41·2 N.	37 29·0 W.
6.	5·6 N.	4·1 E.	4·8 W.	33 33·6 N.	41 04·8 W.
7.	5·5 S.	0·5 E.	3·5 W.	44 16·3 N.	25 45·5 W.
8.	7·4 S.	1·0 W.	3·0 E.	19 32·6 N.	11 12·0 W.
9.	3·7 N.	3·6 E.	3·3 W.	26 56·7 N.	19 33·3 W.
10.	6·7 S.	4·0 E.	1·0 E.	53 20·3 N.	30 20·0 W.
11.	7·2 N.	4·0 E.	4·0 W.	29 42·8 S.	59 09·0 E.
12.	7·0 S.	2·7 E.	3·3 W.	35 35·0 S.	27 49·3 W.
13.	5·7 S.	3·9 W.	3·1 E.	50 28·7 S.	84 01·1 E.
14.	3·8 S.	1·1 W.	4·1 W.	17 55·8 S.	96 37·9 E.
15.	7·5 N.	1·2 W.	7·2 W.	25 01·5 S.	72 21·2 W.

Exercise 44 (B)

Position by Simultaneous Altitudes of Stars, Longitude Method.

	Star	Z.X.	L.H.A.	"C"	Long.	Lat. Corr.	Ship's Position
		° ′	° ′		° ′	′	° ′
1.	HAMAL	62 49·3	73 20·7	·196	36 14·4 W.		40 33·0 N.
	REGULUS	49 55·1	313 00·4	·502	36 15·3 W.	3·0 N.	36 13·8 W.
2.	DENEBOLA	48 16·5	49 39·6	·190	58 52·2 W.		32 09·5 N.
	RASALHAGUE	38 59·2	323 13·2	·475	58 47·2 W.	7·5 S.	58 50·8 W.
3.	RASALHAGUE	53 23·5	314 12·0	·900	18 23·0 E.		51 16·7 N.
	REGULUS	65 35·3	66 01·1	·317	18 29·9 E.	5·7 N.	18 28·1 E.
4.	HAMAL	54 09·5	298 10·0	·057	25 48·0 W.		39 01·1 N.
	VEGA	38 47·0	50 25·5	·376	25 52·8 W.	11·1 N.	25 48·6 W.
5.	HAMAL	46 49·0	51 49·6	·194	14 11·2 W.		43 06·5 N.
	ALPHARD	73 43·8	301 53·7	·763	14 06·9 W.	4·5 S.	14 10·3 W.
6.	DENEB	30 25·9	45 36·1	·140	6 14·1 E.		51 56·2 N.
	MIRFAK	33 48·4	305 20·8	·540	6 18·3 E.	6·2 N.	6 15·1 E.
7.	ENIF	42 33·9	320 20·0	·461	38 58·0 W.		31 04·0 N.
	ZUBEN'UBI	77 03·6	63 39·7	·617	39 02·3 W.	4·0 S.	38 59·8 W.
8.	ANTARES	76 50·2	302 48·0	·922	73 20·9 W.		27 24·4 N.
	ALPHARD	58 50·8	48 15·7	·661	73 12·4 W.	5·4 N.	73 16·0 W.
9.	ENIF	57 02·5	310 06·1	·742	8 08·8 E.		49 01·5 N.
	ARCTURUS	57 25·0	62 17·6	·209	8 14·0 E.	5·5 N.	8 12·9 E.
10.	HAMAL	45 56·0	314 12·5	·743	48 24·1 W.		54 15·6 N.
	VEGA	46 29·0	66 36·5	·279	48 20·1 W.	8·6 N.	48 17·7 W.

Exercise 45 (A).

Position by Simultaneous Altitudes of Stars, Intercept Method.

	D. Lat.	Dep.	D. Long.	Squared Paper		Plotting	
				Lat. N.	Long. W.	Lat. N.	Long. W.
	′	′	′	° ′	° ′	′ ′	° ′
1.	6·5 N.	4·0 E.	7·0 E.	55 21·5	11 15·0	55 21·0	11 15·0
2.	1·6 N.	5·5 W.	9·7 W.	55 38·6	11 21·7	55 38·6	11 22·0
3.	4·5 S.	13·3 E.	23·4 E.	55 15·5	10 55·5	55 15·7	10 55·0
4.	2·0 S.	6·0 W.	10·5 W.	55 16·0	10 57·5	55 15·9	10 57 8
5.	15·0 N.	6·6 E.	11·6 E.	55 21·0	10 16·4	55 20·7	10 16·3
6.	10·3 S.	0·9 E.	1·6 E.	55 18·7	11 31·4	55 18·4	11 31·5
7.	5·5 S.	0·8 E.	1·4 E.	55 47·5	10 55·6	55 47·8	10 55·9
8.	1·2 N.	5·9 E.	10·4 E.	55 23·2	10 54·6	55 22·9	10 54·4
9.	1·3 N.	7·7 E.	13·5 E.	55 12·3	11 10·5	55 12·2	11 10·2
10.	1·0 S.	7·7 E.	13·7 E.	55 46·0	10 24·3	55 46·2	10 24·3
11.	6·7 N.	1·3 W.	2·3 W.	55 40·7	10 53·3	55 40·5	10 53·5
12.	7·4 S.	4·0 W.	7·0 W.	55 17·6	11 36·0	55 17·8	11 36·3

Exercise 45 (B)
Position by Simultaneous Altitudes of Stars, Intercept Method.

	Star	T.Z.X.	C.Z.X.	Bg.	D. Lt.	Dep.	D. Lg.	Lat.	Long.
		° ′	° ′	°	′	′	′	° ′	° ′
1.	HAMAL	62 49·3	62 48·9	278½					
	REGULUS	49 55·1	49 54·7	111	3·4 N.	0·9 E.	1·2 E.	40 33·4 N.	36 13·8 W.
2.	DENEBOLA	48 16·5	48 09·7	260¾					
	RASALHAGUE	38 59·2	39 08·5	111½	5·3 S.	7·8 E.	9·2 E.	32 09·7 N.	58 50·8 W.
3.	RASALHAGUE	53 23·5	53 19·7	119¼					
	REGULUS	65 35·3	65 35·3	259¼	5·7 N.	1·2 W.	1·6 W.	51 16·7 N.	18 28·4 E.
4.	HAMAL	54 09·5	54 07·2	087¾					
	VEGA	38 47·0	38 52·7	286	10·8 N.	2·7 W.	3·5 W.	39 00·8 N.	25 48·5 W.
5.	HAMAL	46 49·0	46 46·3	262					
	ALPHARD	73 43·8	73 49·0	119	4·5 S.	3·4 E.	4·7 E.	43 06·5 N.	14 10·3 W.
6.	DENEB	30 25·9	30 26·2	275					
	MIRFAK	33 48·4	33 50·5	072	6·3 N.	0·2 E.	0·3 E.	51 56·3 N.	6 15·3 E.
7.	ENIF	42 33·9	42 39·3	111					
	ZUBENUBI	77 03·6	77 01·6	242	3·8 S.	4·3 E.	5·0 E.	31 04·2 N.	39 00·0 W.
8.	ANTARES	76 50·2	76 44·8	129					
	ALPHARD	58 50·8	58 51·6	239	4·2 N.	3·5 W.	4·0 W.	27 24·2 N.	73 16·0 W.
9.	ENIF	57 02·5	57 03·7	116					
	ARCTURUS	57 25·0	57 22·8	261½	1·4 N.	2·0 E.	3·1 E.	49 01·4 N.	8 13·1 E.
10.	HAMAL	45 56·0	45 49·4	113¾					
	VEGA	46 29·0	46 33·7	279¼	8·4 N.	3·4 W.	5·8 W.	54 15·4 N.	48 17·8 W.

EXAMINATION PAPERS.
MATE (HOME TRADE.)
Paper 1.

1. G.H.A. 334° 23·9'. Dec. 22° 51' S. A 0·851. B 0·573. True Az. 136°. Dev. 2° W.
2. G.M.T. 14h 36m. Dec. 20° 06·3' N. Alt. 48° 48·3'. Lat. 61° 18·0' N.
3. L.H.A. 5° 33·6'. Dec. 20° 06'4' N. Z.X. 38° 12·7'. Lat. 58° 06·1' N. A 16·6. B 3·8. P.L. 098·4°−278·4°.
4. G.H.A. 304° 20·8'. Z.X. 53° 27·4'. Dec. 21° 25·8' N. Long. 00° 17·4' E. A 1·05. B 0·478. P.L. 017·5°−197·5°.
5. Dur. rise 6h 38m. Angle 138°. Depth 30·2 ft.

Paper 2.

1. G.M.T. 18h 58m 20s. Dec. 5° 31·3' S. True Amp. W. 8° 08·2' S. Dev. 1° 36·8' E.
2. G.M.T. 08h 09m 36s. Dec. 5° 44' S. Z.X. 48° 48·1' N. Lat. 43° 04·1' N.
3. L.H.A. 352° 38·8'. Dec. 21° 33·8' N. Z.X. 30° 58'. Lat. 52° 00·5' N. A 9·91. B 3·07. P.L. 076·7°−256·7°.
4. G.H.A. 337° 06·3'. Z.X. 62° 52·3'. Dec. 20° 20·3' N. Long. 48° 41·3' W. A 0·436. B 0·395. P.L. 001·5°−181·5°.
5. Dur. fall 6h 21m. Angle 104°. Height 8·75 ft.

Paper 3.

1. G.M.T. 12h 23m 04s. L.H.A. 324° 14·1'. Dec. 6° 10·9' S. A 1·11. B 0·185. True Az. 135·3°. Dev. 3·9° W.
2. G.M.T. 16h 22m. Dec. 0° 20·2' N. Z.X. 11° 08·3'. Lat. 11° 28·5' N.
3. L.H.A. 9° 16·3'. Dec. 22° 50·3' S. Z.X. 57° 34·3' N. Lat. 34° 03·2' N. A 4·14. B 2·64. P.L. 100°−280°.
4. G.H.A. 50° 14·6'. Dec. 20° 05·8' N. Z.X. 53° 15·8'. Long. 108° 17·5' W. A 0·578. B 0·429. P.L. 006·2°−186·2°.
5. Dur. 6h 11m. Angle 52½°. Time 06h 23m.

Paper 4.

1. G.M.T. 08h 29m. Dec. 0° 04·5' N. True Amp. 089·9°. Dev. 1·9° E.
2. G.M.T. 11h 23m. Dec. 0° 01·7' N. Z.X. 31° 52·9'. Lat. 31° 54·6' N.
3. L.H.A. 8° 57·1'. Dec. 23° 12·2' N. Z.X. 34° 12·7' N. Lat. 56° 47·3' N. A 9·63. B 2·74. P.L. 104·7°−284·7°.
4. G.H.A. 304° 40·3. Dec. 22° 51·5' S. Long. 5° 49·6' W. A 0·687. B 0·475. P.L. 172·5°−352·5°.
5. Dur. 6h 07m. Time from H.W. 2h 39m. Angle 78°. Corr. 12·9 ft.

Paper 5.

1. L.H.A. 50° 28·4'. Dec. 23° 26·4' S. A 0·735. B 0·561. True Az. 225·9°. Dev. 3·9° E.
2. Dec. 23° 26·4' S. Z.X. 56° 44·3'. Lat. 33° 17·9' N.
3. G.M.T. 13h 38m 08s. Dec. 20° 30·5' N. L.H.A. 5° 57·6'. Z.X. 35° 01·6' N. Lat. 55° 14·7' N. P.L. 099·7°−279·7°.
4. G.H.A. 68° 09·2'. Dec. 22° 49·5' S. Z.X. 77° 18·5'. L.H.A. 40° 02·4'. Long. 28° 06·8' W. A 1·20. B 0·65. P.L. 127·5°−307·5°.
5. Dur. 6h 21m. Angle from H.W. 122·3°. Clearance 4·7 ft.

473

Paper 6.

1. Dec. 5° 25·1′ S. True Amp. 098° 27′. Dev. 5° 33′ W.
2. Dec. 23° 08·3′ N. Z.X. 49° 12·6′. Lat. 26° 04·3′ S.
3. L.H.A. 6° 12·4′. Z.X. 47° 19·7′. Dec. 6° 12·9′ S. Lat. 40° 46·2′ N.
   A 7·94. B 0·98. P.L. 098·5°−278·5°.
4. G.M.T. 21h 24m 29s. G.H.A. 139° 31·5′. Dec. 20° 02·8′ N. Z.X.
   48° 09′. Long. 87° 12·5′ W. A 0·537. B 0·460. P.L. 176·3°−
   356·3°.
5. Dur. 6h 10m. Angle 43°. Time 17h 52m.

MASTER (HOME TRADE.)

Paper 1.

1. L.H.A. 43° 42·7′. A 0·916. B 0·222. True Az. 242·5°. Dev. 5·5° E.
2. Z.X. 40° 20·0′ N. Lat. 47° 44·0′ N.
3. L.H.A. 10° 38·5′. Z.X. 58° 57·4′. Lat. 52° 51·7′ N. A 7·08. B 0·513.
   P.L. 102·3°−282·3°.
4. G.H.A. 84° 32·7′. Z.X. 49° 01·5′. Long. 33° 07·9′ W. P.L. 162·2°−
   342·2°.
6. 24·6 feet.

Paper 2.

1. L.H.A. 334° 05·7′. A 2·50. B 0·331. True Az. 151°. Dev. 4° W.
2. L.H.A. Aries 263° 15·3′. L.M.T. 17h 24m 49s. G.M.T. 16h 38m 09s.
3. L.H.A. 5° 40·1′. Z.X. 26° 24·3′. M.Z.X. 26° 00·2′. Lat. 47° 14·1′ N.
   A 10·7. B 3·88. P.L. 102·2°−282·2°.
4. G.H.A. 44° 29·9′. Z.X. 40° 29·1′. Long. 11° 19·1′ E. P.L. 006′5°−
   186·5°.
6. 3·4 feet.

Paper 3.

1. L.H.A. 76° 12·0′. A 0·247. B 0·222. True Az. 269°. Dev. 3·0° E.
2. True Alt. 38° 29·8′. Lat. 39° 25·4′ N. True Bearing N. 0·1° E.
3. L.H.A. 351° 30·5′. Z.X. 32° 53·3′. M.Z.X. 32° 12·2′. Lat. 51°
   35·9′ N. A 8·44. B 2·38. P.L. 075°−255°.
4. G.H.A. 310° 42·8′. Z.X. 79° 57·3′. Long. 17° 00·1′ W. P.L. 026·4°−
   206·4°.
9. Refloat 1h 56m a.m., 4th May.

Paper 4.

1. L.H.A. 304° 59·2′. A 1·20. B 0·617. True Az. 106·4°. Dev. 1·4° E.
2. Z.X. 56° 01·7′ N. Lat. 39° 22·0′ N.
3. L.H.A. 9° 27·2′. Z.X. 33° 19·5′. M.Z.X. 32° 23·0′. Lat. 47° 22·0′ N.
   A 6·49. B 1·62. P.L. 106·9°−286·9°.
4. G.H.A. 307° 49·8′. Z.X. 36° 21·2′. Long. 9° 13·8′ W. P.L. 134·2°−
   314·2°.
6. Freeboard 21 ft. 2 in.

Paper 5.

1. L.H.A. 62° 44·0′. A 0·248. B 0·448. True Az. 237·9°. Dev. 0·1° W.
2. True Alt. 50° 10·5′. Lat. 49° 24·8′ N. True Bearing N. 0·8° E.
3. L.H.A. 355° 16·8′. Z.X. 30° 13·0′. M.Z.X. 30° 00·5′. Lat. 53° 08·8′ N.
   A 16·1. B 5·16. P.L. 081·3°−261·3°.
4. G.H.A. 41° 04·9′. Z.X. 77° 04·2′. Long. 6° 20·5′ E. P.L. 138·0°−
   318°.
6. Draught 19·3 feet.

Paper 6.

1. L.H.A. 334° 21·4′. A 2·80. B 0·804. True Az. 139·9°. Dev. 4·1° W.
2. L.H.A. Aries 325° 32·5′. L.M.T. 04h 22m 12s. G.M.T. 05h 32m 12s.
3. L.H.A. 349° 17·3′. Z.X. 53° 53·3′. M.Z.X. 52° 55·0′. Lat. 34° 41·9′ N.
   A 3·65. B 1·77. P.L. 077·3°—257·3°.
4. G.H.A. 324° 25·5′. Z.X. 48° 22·2′. Long. 30° 48·0′ W. P.L. 164·0°—
   344·0°.
6. On May 20th, 15h 19m.

SECOND HAND (FULL.)

Paper 1.

NAV. I.

1. Dep. pos.—Lat. 33° 32·6′ N., Long. 24° 02·6′ W. D. Lat. 169·1′ N.
   Dep. 213·7′ E.   D. Long. 260·7′ E.   Lat. in 36° 21·7′ N.   Long. in
   19° 41·9′ W.   Course 051½°.   Dist. 273 mls.
2. L.H.A. 50° 28·4′. Dec. 23° 26·4′ S. A 0·735. B 0·561. True Az.
   225·9°. Dev. 3·9° E.

NAV. II.

1. G.M.T. 16h 22m. Dec. 0° 20·2′ N. Z.X. 11° 08·3′. Lat. 11° 28·5′ N.
2. 1st obs.—G.H.A. 304° 40·3′. Dec. 22° 51·5′ S. Long. 5° 49·6′ W.
   P.L. 172·5°—352·5°. Noon pos.—Lat. 50° 40·0′ S. Long. 6° 56·1′ W.

Principles.

2. Lat. 55° 39·0′ N. Long. 10° 13·5′ W.
3. L.M.T. 11h 47m. G.M.T. 13h 06m.

Paper 2.

NAV. I.

1. Dep. pos.—Lat. 43° 55·6′ N. Long. 2° 02·1′ W. D. Lat. 230·9′ N.
   Dep. 157·4′ W.   D. Long. 226·0′ W.   Lat. in 47° 46·5′ N.   Long. in
   5° 48·1′ W.   Course 325¾°.   Dist. 279½ miles.
2. G.H.A. 334° 23·9′. Dec. 22° 51·0′ S. A 0·851. B 0·573. True Az. 136°.
   Dev. 2° W.

NAV. II.

1. G.M.T. 11h 23m. Dec. 0° 01·7′ N. Z.X. 31° 52·9′. Lat. 31° 54·6′ N.
2. 1st long.—57° 32·3′ W. C 0·214. D. Lat. 47·2′ N. D. Long. 1° 34·7′ W.
   2nd long.—58° 56·0′ W. C 1·21. Pos.—Lat. 55° 30·8′ N. Long.
   59° 09·3′ W.

Principles.

3. Latitude 53° 39·5′ N.

Paper 3.

NAV. I.

1. Dep. pos.—Lat. 49° 27·9′ N. Long. 22° 28·2′ W. D. Lat. 182·3′ S.
   Dep. 16·2′ E.   D. Long. 24·2′ E.   Lat. in 46° 25·6′ N.   Long. in 22°
   04·0′ W.   Course 175°.   Dist. 183 miles.
2. G.M.T. 12h 23m 04s. L.H.A. 324° 14·1′. Dec. 6° 10·9′ S. A 1·11.
   B 0·185. True Az. 135·3°. Dev. 3·9° W.

NAV. II.

1. Dec. 23° 08·3′ N.　Z.X. 49° 12·6′.　Lat. 26° 04·3′ S.
2. G.H.A.　337°　06·3′.　Z.X.　62°　52·3′.　Dec.　20°　20·3′　N.　Long.　48°
   41·3′ W.　A 0·436.　B 0. 395.　P.L. 001·5°−181·5°.
3. Lat. 55° 49·3′ N.　Long. 11° 37·0′ W.

Principles.

3. L.M.T. 11h 58m.　G.M.T. 13h 48m.
4. D.M.P. 1012·5′.　Course N. 21° 45·2′ W.　Dist. 742·9 miles.

Paper 4.
NAV. I.

1. D. Lat. 12·1′ S.　Dep. 242·0′ E.　D. Long. 326·7′ E.　Lat. in 42° 05·9′ N.
   Long. in 00° 04·7′ E.　Course 093°.　Dist. 242 miles.
2. Dec. 6° 14·7′ S.　L.H.A. 51° 19′.　A 1·04.　B 0·14.　Dev. 4·8° W.

NAV. II.

1. G.M.T. 14h 36m.　Dec. 20° 06·3′ N.　Z.X. 41° 11·7′.　Lat. 61° 18·0′ N.
2. 1st obs.−G.H.A. 304° 20·8′.　Z.X. 53° 27·4′.　Dec. 21° 25·8′.　Long.
   00° 17·4′ E.　A 1·05.　B 0·478.　P.L. 017½°−197½°.　D. Lat. 18·6′ S.
   D. Long. 1° 38·0′ W.　2nd obs.−G.H.A. 52° 46·9′.　Z.X. 51° 17·3′.
   A 1·21.　B 0·50.　Lat. corr. 6·3′ S.　Lat. in 56° 23·1′ N.　Long. in
   1° 24·2′ W.

Principles.

2. D.M.P. 625·0′.　D. Lat. 10° 01′.　Distance 976·2 miles.
4. L.M.T. 11h 52m.　G.M.T. 11h 02m.

Paper 5.
NAV. I.

1. Dep. pos−Lat. 46° 36·0′ N.　Long. 22° 36·4′ E.　D. Lat. 184·8′ S.
   Dep. 152·3′ E.　D. Long. 215·6′ E.　Lat. in 43° 31·2′ N.　Long. in
   26° 12·0′ E.　Course 140·5°.　Dist. 239½ miles.
2. L.H.A. 295° 54·4′.　Dec. 20° 09·4′ N.　A 0·812.　B 0·409.　Dev. 4·2° E.

NAV. II.

1. Dec. 5° 46·6′ S.　Z.X. 49° 04·1′.　Lat. 43° 17·5′ N.
2. G.H.A. 68° 09·2′.　Dec. 22° 49·5′ S.　Z.X. 77° 18·5′.　Long. 28° 06·8′ W.
   A 1·20.　B 0·65.　P.L. 127·5°−307·5°.
3. Lat. corr. 3·76′ S.　Long. corr. (A) 2·3′ W.　(B) 9·7′ E.　Lat. 29° 43·3′ N.
   Long. 10° 54·4′ W.

Principles.

1. Lat. 55° 37·0′ N.　Long. 10° 48·0′ W.
2. Dep. latitude 45° 27·9′ N.

Paper 6.
NAV. I.

1. Dep. pos.−Lat. 50° 23·1′ N.　Long. 3° 50·7′ W.　D. Lat. 185·8′ N.
   Dep. 181·3′ E.　D. Long. 294·0′ E.　Lat. in 53° 28·9′ N.　Long. in
   1° 03·3′ E.　Course 044·5°.　Dist. 260 miles.
2. L.H.A. 329° 07·6′.　Dec. 23° 01·4′ S.　A 2·48.　B 0·824.　Dev. 6·0° W.

NAV. II.

1. Dec. 23° 08·6′ N.   Z.X. 22° 09·7′.   Lat. 45° 18·3′ N.
2. G.H.A. 338° 01·0′.   Z.X. 67° 14·1′.   Long. 32° 24·0′ W.   A 0·806.
   B Nil.   P.L. 028°—208°.
3. Lat. corr. 4·5′ S.   Long. corr. (A) 2·3′ E.   (B) 15·1′ E.   Lat. in 47°
   48·5′ N.   Long. 15° 08·7′ W.

Principles.

2. Mean Lat. 58° 08·5′.   Latitudes—60° 19·2′ and 55° 57·8′.   Dist.
   323·2 miles.
4. L.M.T. 11h 48m.   G.M.T. 14h 41m.

SKIPPER (FULL).

Paper 1.

NAV. I.

1. T. Alt. 50° 10·5′.   Corrns.—13·4′; 0·6′; 0·3′.   Lat. 49° 24·8′ N.   Bearing
   N. 0·8° E.
2. G.H.A. 310° 42·8′.   Z.X. 79° 57·3′.   L.H.A. 293° 42·7′.   Long. 17°
   00·1′ W.   P.L. 026·4°—206·4°.
3. *Long. method*—G.H.A. (a) 308° 49·8′; (b) 61° 16·9′.   Long. (a) 11° 23·4′ W.;
   (b) 11° 13·4′ W.   "C" (a) 0·447; (b) 0·550.   True Bg., (a) 104·3°;
   (b) 252·6°.   *Intercept method*—(a) 4·7′ away; (b) 1·0′ away.   Lat. 55°
   21·0′ N.   Long. 11° 18·9′ W.

NAV. II.

1. L.H.A. 304° 59·2′.   A 1·20.   B 0·617.   Dev. 1·4° E.
4. 1519 hrs., May 20th.

Paper 2.

NAV. I.

1. Alt. 38° 29·8′.   Corrns. 1° 54·5′; 0·6′; 0·5′.   Lat. 39° 25·4′ N.   True
   bearing N. 0·1° E.
2. G.H.A. 324° 25·5′.   Z.X. 48° 22·2′.   L.H.A. 293° 37·5′.   Long. 30°
   48′ W.   P.L. 164°—344°.
3. G.H.A. 80° 20·8′.   Z.X. 68° 43·4′.   Long. 10° 25·1′ W.   A 0·536.
   B, 0·230.   P.L. 170·2°—350·2°.   2nd D.R. pos.   Lat. 55° 47·8′ N.
   Long. 11° 27·4′ W.   True pos. Lat. 55° 51·0′ N.   Long. 11° 28·7′ W.

NAV. II.

1. L.H.A. 43° 42·7′.   A, 0·916.   B, 0·222.   True Az. 242·5°.   Dev. 5·5° E.
4. Depth 24·6 feet.

Paper 3.

NAV. I.

1. L.H.A. 333° 46·7′.   Alt. 51° 16·8′.   Lat. 50° 45·7′ N.   Bg. N. 1·2° E.
2. G.H.A. 84° 32·7′.   Z.X. 49° 01·5′.   L.H.A. 51° 24·8′.   Long. 33°
   07·9′ W.   P.L. 162·2°—342·2°.
3. *Long. method*—G.H.A. (a) 93° 02·8′; (b) 345° 13·1′.   Long. (a) 34°
   14·8′ W.; (b) 34° 20·1′ W.   "C" (a) 0·453; (b) 0·815.   Bearing (a)
   252·6°; (b) 119·4°.   *Intercepts*—(a) 2·7′ away; (b) 0·6′ away.   Lat.
   46° 19·2′ N.   Long. 34° 16·7′ W.

NAV. II.

1. L.H.A. 76° 12·0'.　A, 0·247.　B, 0·222.　True Az. 269°.　Dev. 3·0° E.
2. Dur. 6h 11m.　Angle 52½°.　Time 0623.

Paper 4.

NAV. I.

1. L.H.A. 332° 13·9'.　Alt. 33° 44·8'.　Lat. 33° 13·9' N.　Bg. N. 1·0° E.
2. G.H.A. 307° 49·8'.　Z.X. 36° 21·2'.　L.H.A. 298° 36·0'.　Long. 9° 13·8' W.　P.L. 134·2°−314·2°.
3. HAMAL—G.H.A. 97° 04·6'.　Z.X. 47° 29·1'.　Long. 47° 40·1' W.　A, 1·13. B, 0·565.　P.L. 161·2°−341·2°.　D.R. pos.−52° 27·9' N. 47° 19·8' W.　SUN—G.H.A. 352° 12·9'.　Z.X. 69° 17·0'.　A, 0·906. B, 0·005.　P.L. 028·8°−208·8°.　Lat. corr. 2·3' N.　Lat. 52° 30·2' N. Long. 47° 21·1' W.

NAV. II.

1. L.H.A. 334° 05·7'.　A, 2·50.　B, 0·331.　True Az. 151°.　Dev. 4° W.
2. Dur. 6h 07m.　Time from H.W. 2h 39m.　Angle 78°.　Corrn. 12·9 ft.

Paper 5.

NAV. I.

1. L.H.A. 207° 27·9'.　Alt. 41° 06·0'.　Lat. 42° 01·6' N.　Bg. N. 0·1° W.
2. G.H.A. 44° 29·9'.　Z.X. 40° 29·1.　L.H.A. 55° 49·0'.　Long. 11° 19·1' E. P.L. 006·5°−186·5°.
3. G.H.A. 82° 27·1'.　Z.X. 51° 28·2'.　Long. 29° 17·1' W.　A, 0·925. B, 0·461.　P.L. 163·7°−343·7°.　D.R. Lat. 50° 51·0' N.　Long. 28° 04·1' W.　C.F. 343·7°, 5·7 mls.　Lat. 50° 56·5' N.　Long. 28° 06·6' W.

NAV. II.

1. L.H.A. 61° 26·3'.　A, 0·590.　B, 1·335.　True Az. 296·7°.　Dev. 4·7°E.
2. Depth under keel 3·4 feet.

Paper 6.

NAV. I.

1. L.H.A. 279° 25·6'.　Alt. 56° 45·4'.　Lat. 57° 04·8' N.　Bg. N. 1·6° E.
2. G.H.A. 41° 04·9'.　Z.X. 77° 04·2.　L.H.A. 47° 25·4'.　Long. 6° 20·5' E. P.L. 138°−318°.
3. 1st obs.—Z.X. 68° 49·6'.　Long. 19° 09·0' E.　A, 0·450.　B, 0·128. P.L. 155°−335°.　D.R. pos.−Lat. 36° 09·2' N.　Long. 18° 48·8' E. 2nd obs.—G.H.A. 280° 34·7'.　Z.X. 57° 33·9'.　Long. 18° 53·8' E. A, 0·411.　B, 0·307.　P.L. 004·8°−184·8°.　Lat. corr. 7·2' S.　Lat. 36° 02·0' N.　Long. 18° 53·0' E.

NAV. II.

1. L.H.A. 306° 58·9'.　A, 1·043.　B, 0·691.　True Az. 258·4°.　Dev. 6·4° W.
2. Refloat May 4th, 0156.

COASTAL YACHTMASTER

Paper 1.

1. G.M.T. 08h 29m. Dec. 0° 04·5′ N. True Amp. 089·9°. Dev. 1·9° E.
3. Dur. 6h 21m. Angle from H.W. 122·3°. Clearance 4·7 feet.

Paper 2.

1. L.H.A. 50° 28·4′. Dec. 23° 26·4′ S. A, 0·735. B, 0·561. True Az. 225·9°. Dev. 3·9° E.
4. Dur. 6h 07m. Time from H.W. 2h 39m. Angle 78°. Corr. 12·9 ft.

Paper 3.

1. G.H.A. 334° 23·9′. Dec. 22° 51′ S. A, 0·851. B, 0·573. True Az. 136°. Dev. 2° W.
2. True Count—33 dashes, 27 dots.
3. Dur. rise 6h 38m. Angle 138°. Depth 30·2 ft.
4. Moonrise 1525; moonset 0134.

Paper 4.

1. Dec. 5° 25·1′ S. True Amp. 098° 27′. Dev. 5° 33′ W.
3. Dur. 6h 10m. Angle 43°. Time 17h 52m.

Paper 5.

1. G.M.T. 18h 58m 20s. Dec. 5° 31·3′ S. True Amp. W. 8° 08·2′ S. Dev. 1° 36·8′ E.
2. True Count—29 dots, 31 dashes.
3. Dur. 6h 21m. Angle 104°. Height 8·75 ft.

Paper 6.

1. G.M.T. 12h 23m 04s. L.H.A. 324° 14·1′. Dec. 6° 10·9′ S. A, 1·11. B, 0·185. True Az. 135·3°. Dev. 3·9° W.
2. Moonrise—0025. Moonset—1407.
3. Dur. 6h 11m. Angle 52½°. Time 06h 23m.

EXTRACT FROM ADMIRALTY TIDE TABLES.
ENGLAND, EAST COAST—IMMINGHAM.
Lat. 53°38′N.   Long. 0°11′W.

TIMES AND HEIGHTS OF HIGH AND LOW WATER.

TIME ZONE: Greenwich.   YEAR: 1959.

Month Day	Week Day	MAY				Month Day	Week Day	MAY			
		HIGH WATER		LOW WATER				HIGH WATER		LOW WATER	
		Time H. M.	Ht. F.	Time H. M.	Ht. F.			Time H. M.	Ht. F.	Time H. M.	Ht. F.
1	F	00 24	16·8	06 17	6·7	16	S	11 14	17·3	05 02	6·1
		12 34	16·9	19 11	5·2			—	—	17 45	5·1
2	S	01 45	16·8	07 43	6·7	17	S	00 23	16·7	06 17	6·2
		13 54	17·0	20 29	4·6			12 29	17·5	19 07	4·7
3	S	02 51	17·5	08 52	5·9	18	M	01 39	17·4	07 38	5·6
		14 59	17·7	21 28	3·9			13 48	18·1	20 23	3·6
4	M	03 44	18·5	09 45	4·8	19	Tu	02 45	18·8	08 50	4·4
		15 51	18·6	22 15	3·2			14 56	19·5	21 27	2·4
5	Tu	04 26	19·2	10 29	3·9	20	W	03 41	20·2	09 50	2·9
		16 34	19·3	22 54	2·8			15 55	21·0	22 22	1·1
6	W	05 04	19·9	11 08	3·1	21	Th	04 32	21·6	10 44	1·5
		17 12	19·8	23 29	2·5			16 49	22·0	23 14	0·3
7	Th	05 38	20·3	11 44	2·6	22	F	05 20	22·5	11 34	0·5
		17 49	20·0	—	—			17 41	22·5	—	—
8	F	06 10	20·5	00 03	2·3	23	S	06 07	22·9	00 02	−0·1
		18 24	20·1	12 19	2·4			18 31	22·5	12 23	0·0
9	S	06 42	20·5	00 35	2·4	24	S	06 52	22·7	00 48	0·0
		18 59	20·0	12 52	2·2			19 20	22·2	13 10	−0·1
10	S	07 13	20·3	01 07	2·4	25	M	07 36	22·3	01 32	0·6
		19 34	19·7	13 26	2·2			20 09	21·4	13 56	0·3
11	M	07 44	20·0	01 39	2·7	26	Tu	08 20	21·5	02 16	1·5
		20 09	19·2	13 59	2·5			20 58	20·5	14 41	1·0
12	Tu	08 15	19·5	02 12	3·2	27	W	09 04	20·6	02 59	2·8
		20 45	18·5	14 32	3·0			21 48	19·3	15 27	2·0
13	W	08 48	18·8	02 45	3·9	28	Th	09 52	19·6	03 44	4·1
		21 24	17·9	15 08	3·6			22 43	18·1	16 17	3·2
14	Th	09 25	18·2	03 22	4·6	29	F	10 46	18·5	04 35	5·4
		22 11	17·2	15 48	4·4			23 46	17·2	17 15	4·3
15	F	10 13	17·6	04 06	5·5	30	S	11 50	17·5	05 37	6·4
		23 10	16·7	16 38	4·9			—	—	18 25	5·0
						31	S	00 58	16·9	06 50	6·6
								13 02	17·1	19 37	5·0

ELEMENTS

FROM THE

ABRIDGED NAUTICAL ALMANAC

FOR THE YEAR

1958